This unusual photograph shows the interior of a low-intensity nuclear reactor in operation. The vertical rods that you see within the outer structure are the boron-steel rods which control the rate of nuclear reaction. This subject was photographed by its own light, "radiation light," which is a weird diffused blue.

Union Carbide and Carbon Corporation
operators Oak Ridge National Laboratory.

The Authors

WALTER G. MARBURGER brings to Physics for Our Times unusual experience in physics teaching and scientific research. High school and college teaching of physics and general physical science, training physics teachers, and electronics research in industry are all a part of his background. He has served as Physicist with the Naval Ordnance Laboratory in Washington, D.C., and the Argonne National Laboratory, Lemont, Illinois. Walter G. Marburger is Professor of Physics at Western Michigan College of Education, Kalamazoo.

CHARLES W. HOFFMAN is Physicist, Rocket Branch, Ballistic Research Laboratories, Aberdeen Proving Ground, Maryland, and Special Lecturer in Physics, University of Delaware. His experience includes high school physics teaching and research in the fields of plastics, rubber, and ultrasonics.

Drawings by HAROLD K. FAYE

Rockets of this type carry equipment which obtains and reports important scientific information in flights high above the earth's surface.
(U.S. Army Photograph)

Physics
for Our Times

Walter G. Marburger

& Charles W. Hoffman

McGRAW-HILL BOOK COMPANY, INC.
NEW YORK   TORONTO   LONDON

Acknowledgments

While taking full responsibility for this book, the authors wish to express appreciation for advice and guidance from many colleagues and friends. The following are among those who have been of special assistance: W. H. Crouse, Charlottesville, Virginia; Joseph E. Dickinson, Watervliet, Michigan, High School; Warren J. McGonnagle, Argonne National Laboratories; M. B. Messinger, Abington, Pennsylvania, Senior High School; Gerald Osborn, Western Michigan College of Education; Harold S. Spielman, The City College of New York; and Elbert C. Weaver, Phillips Andover Academy.

Contents

Tables

Physics and You

The chapters of this book are guides for a series of explorations into the field of physics. As you join in these explorations, you will find opportunities to learn about familiar things and events in our everyday world, such as the action of pulleys, the freezing of water, the production of an echo, and the formation of a rainbow. You will also find opportunities to explore effects such as those that occur in electricity and magnetism and in the tiny cores of atoms.

The Language of Physics

Science has a language of its own, which you will need to learn in order to understand its ideas. If you have studied biology or chemistry, you may recall some of the new words and expressions you had to learn before you could read your textbook easily and express your ideas readily in class discussions. The language of physics also contains new terms and expressions, some of which you will meet as you study this book. Moreover, words with which you may already be familiar, such as force, work, and power, are used in physics with special meanings that you will need to know.

Events, Principles, and Laws

Rain falls, water freezes, sugar dissolves, a rainbow appears in the sky; each of these is an event in nature.

Science is founded on the belief that there is a definite *cause* for every natural event. Thus we might say, for example, that rain is *caused* by sufficient cooling of a body of moist air or that rainfall is an *effect* (result) produced by cooling moist air. Scientists spend much time and effort seeking *causes* of the *effects* they observe and observing *effects* produced by *causes* they set up and control.

Some effects are more complicated than others; in fact, a natural event may actually consist of several effects acting together. In such a case, the event may be called a *physical process* or a *natural process*. The freezing of water into ice is often called a physical process.

Snowflakes fall toward the earth, water in streams and rivers runs downhill, a batted baseball falls into the glove of an alert outfielder; in these actions snowflakes, water, and baseball move closer to the center of the earth. As a general statement covering these and other cases that we have observed, we can say that all bodies near the surface of the earth tend to fall toward the center of the earth. Such a general statement is often called a *physical principle* because it applies not only to the motion of snowflakes, water in streams, and baseballs, but to all other falling bodies as well. This principle can then be used to predict what will happen when any object is free to fall.

1

A physical principle that has a very broad application is often called a *physical law* or a *natural law*. For example, a general principle that will explain not only the falling of bodies toward the earth, but the motion of the earth and moon in fixed paths and many other effects as well, is, "Every particle of matter in the universe attracts every other particle. . . ." This general principle is part of the law of universal gravitation. Study about this law in Chapter 4.

Certain ideas, principles, and laws form the foundation on which other ideas, principles, and laws of a science are constructed. The former are called *basic* or *fundamental* ideas, principles, and laws. The law of universal gravitation is one of the *fundamental laws* of our physical universe.

Natural laws differ from civil laws to which we are accustomed. Civil laws are designed to regulate society and make it possible for people to live together peaceably. Civil laws prescribe what people shall do and what they shall not do; they are made for us to obey. Natural laws, on the other hand, are general statements based on experience of how natural effects or processes actually do happen; they do not fix or prescribe what *must* happen. Events in the physical universe do not *obey* natural laws in the sense that we obey civil laws. Natural laws cannot be amended or repealed by popular vote or by the action of any court or legislature, as civil laws sometimes can. You will find a number of natural laws in the chapters that follow.

Characteristics and Properties

Scientists frequently have to identify objects, materials, or effects that they observe. To do this they study the *distinguishing characteristics* or *properties* of these objects, materials, or effects.

One *property* of coal is its black, rocklike appearance; another property is that it will burn when kindled. If a scientist is asked to identify a black, rocklike material thought to be coal, one of the first tests he will probably make will be to see if the material will burn. If he finds that the material will burn and if it has other properties of coal, he will conclude that it *is* coal; that is, he will *identify* the material as coal.

Why Study Physics?

There are many practical reasons for studying physics. Some of these are described in the following paragraphs. You will find many more as you take part in explorations into the field of physics.

1. To get a better understanding of our universe. Science is founded on the belief that everything in the universe, from the giant stars in the heavens to the tiny particles that make up an atom, operates in an orderly fashion in accordance with natural laws. When we come to understand these laws we realize that we can count on certain effects to follow their causes as surely as day follows night. Your study of physics should help you understand why the earth stays in its orbit as it revolves around the sun year after year, for example, and why the compass needle points north at some places on the earth and not at others.

2. To learn how science and invention are helping to change the world in which we live. Electric refrigeration, radio, television, jet propulsion, and atomic power are among the scientific developments and inventions that have become important during the last quarter-century. All of these affect the things we can do and the way we live. Your study of physics should help you gain a better understanding of these and other scien-

2

tific developments and their influence on our civilization.

3. To learn how to use and control machines and mechanical appliances more intelligently. Engines and motors are used with other machines to do a large share of the routine work of the world. Your study of physics should make clear to you how engines and motors work, the sources of power for these machines, and how their power output can be controlled. Many of the mechanical and electrical appliances used in everyday life are based on simple physical principles. Even many toys depend on some physical principle for their operation. When you understand these principles, you will be better able to understand and use the mechanical devices you find in everyday life.

4. To get experience in determining the causes of different physical effects that you may observe. A study of physics will introduce you to some of the methods scientists have used to discover the facts we now know about the science of physics. It will help you to understand how the general laws and principles of physics have come into existence. Furthermore, it will provide many opportunities for you to discover and solve problems in science for yourself. Some problems for you to solve are suggested in the chapters of this book. Your teacher will probably suggest others. The best problems for you, however, will be ones you find and work out for yourself. *How, why, how many*, and *how long* are among the many questions you should learn to ask yourself and try to answer as you study different topics in physics.

How Scientists Solve Problems

The laws and principles of physics, in general, have not been discovered and developed by following any fixed set of steps like those in the proof of a proposition in geometry. Scientists work on problems in many different ways. There are, however, a few steps or procedures that investigators in science usually follow more or less closely in attempting to solve a scientific problem. Among these steps are the following:

To recognize that there is a problem to be solved.

To determine just what the problem is.

To gather as much information about the problem as possible from observation, from books, from magazines, and from other scientists.

To sort out this information, organize it, and determine what parts of it are important in solving the problem.

To find ways of fitting the facts, observations, and important items together into a pattern that will lead to a possible or tentative conclusion.

To test this conclusion by experiment or otherwise to see if it agrees fully with experience and known facts. Conclusions that are contrary to experience and tested facts are usually considered false or unsound and are rejected.

When scientists are working on unsolved problems, they do not always follow these steps in the order given. In fact, they may omit some of the steps entirely. However, some important rules for solving a problem are the following:

Be open-minded; examine all the available evidence.

Consider different ways of solving the problem.

Test tentative conclusions by experiment or by comparing them with known facts, if possible.

Do not draw hasty conclusions.

Do You Have a Hobby?

Have you ever had a camera of your own or have you ever been interested in making good photographs? Have you ever built a miniature railroad or torn down and rebuilt an automobile engine? Have you ever tried to fix a radio or had an interest in building one of your own? These and many similar interests often develop into fascinating hobbies that may last through a lifetime. If you have already found an interest of this kind, your study of physics can help you to gain a better understanding of the underlying principles involved and enable you to explore the field of your hobby a bit further. If you have never had any particular interest in any aspect of physical science, your study of physics may open up some field or activity that you would like to investigate further as a hobby.

Physics and Your Future

You may find exploration in the field of physics so interesting that you will want to choose this field for your life work. Do you know what kinds of work you might do as a *physicist?*

Many physicists are employed in research laboratories. Some of them work with chemists, engineers, and mathematicians on problems of the physical universe—problems that are more difficult and advanced than those you will encounter in this book. Many private industries employ trained physicists to study ways of making better products and making them more efficiently. Other physicists devote their efforts to teaching students the facts, principles, and laws of the universe of physics. Engineers employ their knowledge of physics in designing and building bridges, railroads, airplanes, electric power plants, and machines for many purposes. These are some of the possible outlets open to you if you decide to make physics your life work.

Still other occupations and professions offer opportunities to apply the principles of physics. Doctors, dentists, meteorologists, geologists—to name only a few—make a great many practical applications of physics in their professions. A modern farmer must know how to put into practice many physical laws and principles. A housewife will find many uses for the principles of physics.

Divisions of Physics

Everyday occurrences that seem quite simple may involve several different physical processes operating together at the same time. In most cases it is easier to observe and study one process, one operation, or one set of related ideas at a time. This is one reason why the subject matter of physics is usually organized into several large parts or divisions such as mechanics, heat, sound, electricity, light, and atomic physics. In this book each of these large divisions is called a *unit.*

These units or divisions are for convenience only and are not separate compartments of the subject of physics. Physical events and processes often involve several of these divisions at once. Facts, principles and theories that are found in one division will occur in other divisions. The general facts and principles of mechanics are most closely interlinked with those in all the other divisions. This is why the first explorations in this book are into the area of mechanics.

Unit **1.**

Mechanics in Our World

PREVIEW

We live in a mechanical age, an age in which machines play an ever-increasing role. Business, industry, and science rely more and more on machines to do their routine work. The tasks of everyday life are lightened and shortened by the use of mechanical labor-saving appliances. Many machines, such as the lever and the wheel, are of such ancient origin that there is no clear record of when or by whom they were first used. These devices and others like them are so simple and elementary that it is often hard to realize that they are actually machines. Typewriters, printing presses, automobiles, and other more complicated mechanical devices are built from many simple machines fitted together.

The world of mechanics deals with different types of elementary machines but is more directly concerned with general effects, principles, and laws common to all of them. Forces—pushes and pulls—and the motion of objects on which forces act are among the general effects associated with machines. Work, energy, and power are other such effects. Methods and systems for measuring these and other physical quantities are of prime importance in physics, engineering, and other branches of physical science.

In this unit on mechanics you will begin the story of matter and energy, how they are related, and how one affects the other. Each of the six units of this book is concerned with some part of this story.

1.

Matter and Measurement:
The Tools of Our Science

MATTER AND ENERGY

Do you realize that sound, heat, light, electricity, and radio waves are fundamentally different from water, air, wood, glass, metals, and stone? Sound, heat, light, and similar things are forms of *energy*. Water, air, wood, and kindred things are *materials;* that is, they are composed of *matter*. Our whole physical universe, when reduced to its simplest terms, is made up of just two things, *energy* and *matter*. How these two behave, how they interact one with the other, and how we control them make up the substance of two basic physical sciences, physics and chemistry.

6

HOW MATTER DIFFERS FROM ENERGY

Matter has certain features or properties that enable us to recognize it easily. Energy, in general, does not have these properties.

1. Matter occupies space. We can measure the amount of space a body of matter occupies; we call this its *volume*. It is easy to understand the meaning of such expressions as a "gallon of water" and a "cubic foot of stone," for water and stone are both matter. A "gallon of heat" and a "cubic foot of light" are meaningless, however, because heat and light are both forms of energy and we usually regard energy as not occupying space.

2. *Matter has mass.* We all know from experience that the earth exerts a pull or force of attraction on an apple held in the hand. This pull is called the *weight* of the apple. Your weight, which may be expressed in pounds, indicates how much the earth pulls on your body. Every bit of matter on the earth has weight. Weight is directly related to the *mass* of a body, that is, to the amount of matter in it.

We also know from experience and observation that it takes a stronger push (by hand) to start an automobile to move than is required to start a baby carriage or a scooter. We know, too, that once the heavier body is moving at a given speed, it is harder to stop than the lighter one moving at the same speed. This tendency of matter to *resist change* in its condition of motion is called *inertia.* Every bit of matter in the universe has inertia. Inertia, like weight, is directly related to the mass of a body; the greater its mass, the greater is its inertia. We may say, then, that every particle of matter has mass, as indicated by its weight (if on earth) and by its inertia.

The heat that warms an electric laundry iron does not change appreciably either the weight of the iron or its inertia. Heat, light, sound, and other forms of energy do not possess mass, at least in any amount that we can easily observe. Because heat is weightless, the early scientists called it one of the "imponderables," meaning "without weight." In special cases it has been observed that energy may act as if it, too, has inertia. Figure 1–1 illustrates some easily recognizable differences between matter and energy.

3. *Matter appears to be granular in structure.* When we look at a piece of iron, a drop of mercury, or a handful of graphite, we may find it difficult to believe that each of these is made up of units or particles so small that they cannot be seen even with the aid of the most powerful microscope. Nevertheless, scientists have evidence which indicates that every chemical *element* is composed of submicroscopic units called *atoms.* As a further challenge to our imaginations, the evidence indicates that each atom is built up of still smaller particles.

Fig. 1–1. A rock is a body of matter; it has mass and weight and requires force to move it. Radio waves are energy; they do not have mass and weight.

Scientists have found about 90 different chemical elements that occur in nature. Besides these, several new elements not found in nature have been produced from natural elements by artificial means. Each chemical element has as its basic unit an atom which is different from the atoms of every other element. When two or more atoms of different kinds unite chemically they form a *compound*. Examples of common compounds are water, table salt, sucrose (table sugar), aspirin, baking soda, and carbon dioxide. Units of compounds formed by combined atoms may be called *molecules*. The term *molecule* is also used to refer to a group of atoms of the *same kind* which act together as a unit. Suppose that a piece of copper (one of the chemical elements) were to be divided again and again until there remained a particle so small that it could not be divided further and still be copper. This smallest possible particle is sometimes called a *molecule* of copper. It would consist of a single atom of copper. For other elements, such as oxygen, the molecule consists of two or more atoms. The number of known kinds of molecules is very large and hundreds of new kinds of molecules are discovered every year.

Energy, unlike matter, is not made up of molecules and atoms. However, in special cases, energy seems to act as if it consisted of small units or packets called *quanta*. A quantum of energy differs in a number of ways from a molecule or atom of matter.

Scientists who deal with the physical universe must deal with both matter and energy. The chemist is interested chiefly in changes in matter, but energy is always involved in these changes. The physicist is interested primarily in energy, but energy is nearly always associated with matter.

8

▶Do You Know?

1. What are the names of two elements that have been produced artificially?
2. How does a chemical element differ from a compound?
3. How many atoms may a molecule have?
4. What are some ways in which physics differs from chemistry?
5. Discuss three ways in which matter differs from energy.

MEASUREMENT

Students of the sciences in which a great deal of progress has been made find themselves confronted, time after time, with such questions as How much?, How many?, How large?, and How long a time? To answer these questions, the *size* or *magnitude* of things must be known with some degree of precision and exactness. In everyday usage, we may speak of a *large* crowd of people, a *high* mountain, and a *long* period of silence. These adjectives do not give us any precise or accurate knowledge of the size of the crowd, the height of the mountain, or the duration of the silence. What one person considers a *large* crowd may appear to be a *small* one to another person. This type of general information in which size or magnitude is a matter of purely *personal opinion* is totally inadequate for engineering and scientific work and even for everyday transactions in our highly mechanized world. Much more precise information about the size of things is required to build and operate power plants, telephone systems, and radio stations; to split atoms; and even to drive an automobile on the highway. Physics is a *quantitative* science; that is, it is largely concerned with size and number. Its great progress in recent

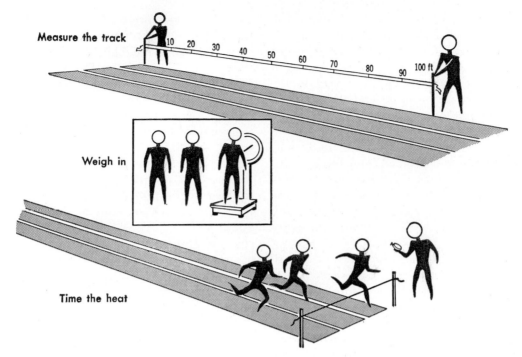

Fig. 1–2. Mass or weight, length, and time are fundamental quantities in the gymnasium as well as in science.

years has come about largely because methods for precise and accurate measurement of the size of things have been perfected. Lord Kelvin, one of the greatest English physicists of the nineteenth century, once said:

I often say that when you can measure what you are speaking about and express it in numbers, you know something about it; but when you cannot measure it, when you cannot express it in numbers, your knowledge is of a meagre and unsatisfactory kind. It may be the beginning of knowledge, but you have scarcely in your thoughts advanced to the stage of science, whatever that may be.

Things We Measure

We *measure* almost everything we buy or sell. If you live on a farm you may have to *measure* (weigh) such things as grain or vegetables or milk and cream. *Weighing* is merely measuring weight. If you want to use a board, you may have to measure its *length*. You may sell apples and potatoes by the *bushel*, but the bushel, too, is a unit of measure. If you want to know how long it is until dinner time, you will probably consult a watch or clock, which measures *time*.

The grocer sells sugar, flour, and other food products by the pound; so he, too, has to measure things. A skillful cook usually measures (weighs) the butter and flour she uses to make a cake. She uses a thermometer to measure the *temperature* of the oven. She may use a clock to measure the *time* the cake is in the oven.

These everyday measurements are similar to those which the scientist makes. He may work more slowly and be more careful and accurate than we need to be with the common measure-

9

ments we make every day, but he still has to measure the same kinds of things. Things which can be measured are called *quantities*. Basic or fundamental quantities are those which we regard as the simplest and most general. We use fundamental quantities for building more complex quantities, as when we form square centimeters (surface) and cubic centimeters (volume) from linear centimeters (length). We find in science as well as in our everyday life that the things we have to measure can generally be reduced to three fundamental quantities:

Length, as when we measure a board.

Mass, as when we weigh sugar.

Time, as when we measure the duration of a class period.

Some of the complicated quantities that we measure in the physical world may involve more than one of these three fundamental quantities. For example, when an object is moved, distance in feet, mass in pounds, and time in seconds may all three be involved.

English Units of Length

For everyday purposes, we measure lengths in miles, rods, yards, feet, and inches. These are called *English* units of length because they were brought from England by the early settlers. To refresh your memory, examine Table 1–1.

►You Will Be Interested to Know

Many of the units of length that have been used in the past and some of those used today were originally derived from the length of some part of the human body. The hand, the digit, the palm, and the foot are illustrations of units named for parts of the body. King Henry I of England, who reigned in the twelfth century, decreed that the distance from the point of his nose to the end of his thumb should be the lawful yard of that time. In the sixteenth century the lawful rod was the sum of the lengths of the left feet of the first 16 men lined up as they left church on Sunday morning. Such units have undergone many changes through the years. The *foot* has ranged in length from 9.75 to 19 of our present inches during the course of centuries.

Metric Units of Length

The metric system of weights and measures is used in everyday transactions in more than 25 countries of the world. The United States and the members of the British Commonwealth of Nations are the only great manufacturing and trading nations in which this system has not come into general use. Even in these countries some of the more recent branches of industry and engineering use this system, wholly or in part. The metric system is used almost universally in all scientific work.

The *meter* is the standard or basic metric unit of length; all other metric units of length are multiples or submultiples of the meter. Examine Table 1–2 carefully.

Table 1–1.   English Units of Length

1 mile	= 320 rods (rd)	= 1,760 yards (yd)	= 5,280 feet (ft)	= 63,360 inches (in.)
	1 rd	= 5½ yd	= 16½ ft	= 198 in.
		1 yd	= 3 ft	= 36 in.
			1 ft	= 12 in.

The metric units of length in common use are the kilometer, the meter, the centimeter, and the millimeter. Notice that all numbers used in Table 1–2 are multiples or submultiples of *ten*. This is the general plan on which the metric system was constructed and for this reason it is described as a *decimal* (ten) system. You are already familiar with our decimal system of dollars and cents, so you will recognize the convenience of the metric over the English system in making measurements and computations.

Metric Prefixes

The metric system is used in measuring many quantities besides length. In each case, the unit begins with a *prefix* that gives the scale of the unit. You should have no difficulty with this system, wherever you may encounter it, if you will learn these prefixes now. To illustrate:

A *millimeter* (mm) is one-thousandth of a meter (m).

A *milligram* (mg) is one-thousandth of a gram (g).

A *milliampere* (ma) is one-thousandth of an ampere (amp).

A *kilometer* (km) is 1,000 meters.

A *kilogram* (kg) is 1,000 grams.

A *kilowatt* (kw) is 1,000 watts.
The other prefixes are used in the same way. The prefixes are shown in Fig. 1–3. Two additional prefixes should be mentioned here, even though you will not encounter them very often. One is *micro*, which means one-millionth. The *micron* (used instead of *micrometer*, which has another meaning) is one-millionth of a meter. It is used in measuring the wavelength of light and radiant heat. The *microampere* (μa) is one-millionth of an ampere, a unit used in electricity. The *microvolt* (μv) and the *microfarad* (μf) are likewise units used in electricity. The other prefix is *mega*, which means one million. A *megohm* is one million ohms, a unit used in electricity. A *megacycle* (Mc) is one million cycles. You have no doubt noticed this unit on an FM radio dial.

Changing Metric Units

The metric stairway shown in Fig. 1–3 provides an easy scheme for changing a quantity from one metric unit to another. Suppose you know that the length of a cross-country course is 3.00 kilometers (km) and you want to find this length in centimeters (cm). For each step down on the stairway of Fig. 1–3, you must multiply the original number by 10; for each step up you must divide the original number by 10. It is five steps down from *kilo* to *centi*. So

$$3.00 \text{ km} = 3.00 \times 10 \times 10 \times 10$$
$$\times 10 \times 10 \text{ cm}$$
$$= 300,000 \text{ cm}$$

We could have obtained this result at

Table 1–2. Metric Units of Length

1 kilometer (km) = 10 hectometers	= 100 decameters	= 1000 meters (m)	
1 hectometer	= 10 decameters	= 100 m	
1 decameter	= 10 m		
1 meter (m) = 10 decimeters	= 100 centimeters (cm)	= 1000 millimeters (mm)	
1 decimeter	= 10 cm	= 100 mm	
1 cm	= 10 mm		

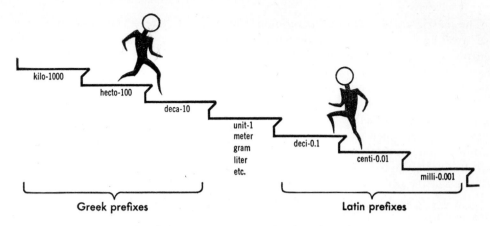

kilo-1000

hecto-100

deca-10

unit-1
meter
gram
liter
etc.

deci-0.1

centi-0.01

milli-0.001

Greek prefixes

Latin prefixes

Fig. 1–3. A metric stairway for changing units.

once by moving the decimal point in the original number *five places to the right,* one place for each step down. In a similar way, if we know that a given electric current is 5,000 *milliamperes* (ma), we can express this current in *amperes* (amp) by moving the decimal point in the original number three places (three steps up) to the *left.* Thus

$$5{,}000 \text{ ma} = 5.0 \text{ amp}$$

Why We Need Standards

In the days when commodities were exchanged by barter and when all the parts of any manufactured article were made and fitted together by hand in one small shop, it was of little consequence if the foot and the pound used in one part of the country were not exactly equal to the foot and pound used in another section. With the rise

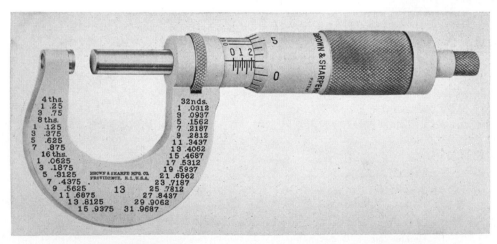

A micrometer caliper used for precise measurements of small lengths. The object to be measured is placed between the jaws, and the thimble at the right is turned until the spindle makes contact with the object. Measurements to one ten-thousandths of an inch can be made with this instrument.

12

Aerial view of the National Bureau of Standards. This Bureau is custodian of the national standards of mass and length. Laboratory and industrial weights and length-measuring devices are checked against "working standards," which in turn are compared at intervals with the standard kilogram and the standard meter. This Bureau is the principal agency of the Federal government for fundamental research in physics, mathematics, chemistry, and engineering. (*National Bureau of Standards*)

of modern commerce and trade and with the development of large-scale factory methods of production, definite standards of length and mass for the whole country became an absolute necessity. A standard of length is a definite fixed length in terms of which the lengths of units such as the foot and the centimeter are defined. Today it is of prime importance that the inch and the pound used in one shop manufacturing parts for a machine be *exactly* the same as the inch and pound used in another shop, if the products of these shops are to fit together when assembled into one machine.

In science, too, it is essential that a single standard be used in measuring a given quantity so that a scientist in one part of the world can use with confidence the results of measurements made by other scientists elsewhere. For these reasons, the governments of the world, at a cost of considerable sums of money and much careful labor, have developed and set up definite objective standards of length, mass, and time.

International Standard Meter

One of these standards is the International Standard Meter, which is the

13

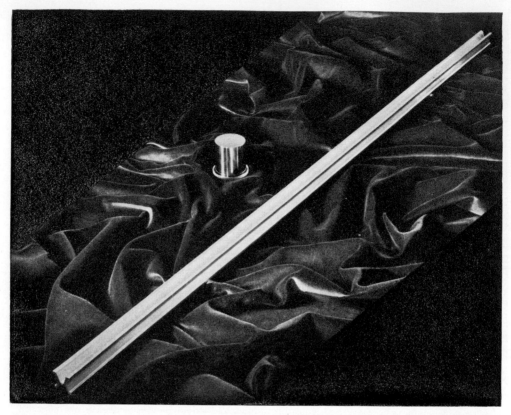

The standard meter bar and the standard kilogram of the United States are kept in the vaults of the National Bureau of Standards, Washington, D.C. (*National Bureau of Standards*)

distance between two fine cross lines, one near each end of a special bar made of 90 percent platinum and 10 percent iridium. The distance is taken at the temperature of melting ice, 0° centigrade (C). This valuable meter bar is carefully preserved in the vaults of the International Bureau of Weights and Measures at Sèvres, a suburb of Paris, France. Since the International Standard Meter is the length in terms of which the metric units of length are defined, it is called a *primary* standard of length. It is the primary standard for scientific work in all countries and for industrial and commercial purposes in many of the principal countries of the world.

14

Accuracy of Our Measuring Tools

At the time the International Standard Meter bar was made, 31 bars, all as nearly alike as possible, were constructed. From these 31 bars one was selected for the International Standard. The other 30, called *prototype bars*, were assigned by lot, two to each subscribing country. The two prototype bars in the United States are kept in the vaults of our National Bureau of Standards at Washington, D.C. While neither of our prototype bars is of *exactly* the same length as the International Standard, still the amount by which each one varies from the International Standard Meter

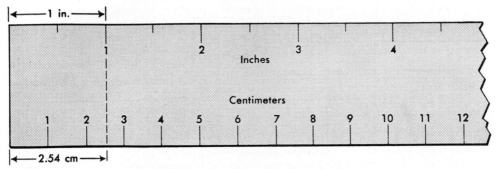

Fig. 1–4. There are 2.54 cm in 1 in.

is known. So if we should ever have an occasion to check the accuracy of one of our better measuring tools, we might have this check made against one of the prototype bars at the National Bureau of Standards. The prototype meters are very rarely used for such a purpose. *Secondary standards*, made as nearly like the prototype meter bars as possible, are used for all routine check measurements.

Converting Measurements

When we study physics or read news dispatches from foreign countries, we often have to translate centimeters into inches or kilometers into miles. Changing the units in which a length or other quantity is expressed from metric to English units or English to metric units is called *converting*. To convert 10 in. to centimeters we have to multiply the 10 by 2.54, obtaining 25.4 cm. The number 2.54 is called a *conversion factor*. You should become thoroughly familiar with the conversion factors given in Table 1–3.

▶You Will Be Interested to Know

The metric system was invented in France during the period of the French Revolution, when the French people were designing a complete new order for practically everything. The metric system became the official system for that country by a decree of the National Assembly in 1790. The present International Meter bar was made nearly a century later. It was officially accepted in 1889. This bar is kept in an underground vault which may not be opened oftener than once a year, and then only in the presence of three officials each of whom has a key to a different one of the three locks on the door.

UNITS FOR AREA AND VOLUME

Square centimeters (cm²), square meters (m²), and square kilometers (km²) are used in the metric system to measure areas, just as square inches (in.²), square feet (ft²), and square miles are used in

Table 1–3. Conversion Factors for Length

1 m	=	39.37 in.
1 cm	=	0.3937 in. (about 0.4 or ⅖ in.)
1 km	= 39,370	in. = 0.621 mile (about ⅝ mile)
1 in.	=	2.54 cm
1 mile	=	1.61 km

15

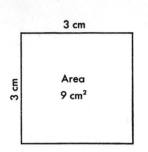
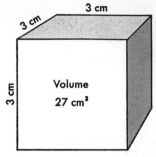

Fig. 1–5. Area involves two measured lengths. Volume involves three measured lengths.

the English system. Cubic centimeters (cm³) and cubic meters (m³) are used to measure volume.

Suppose we wish to find the area of the square face shown in Fig. 1–5, each side of which is 3 cm in length. We proceed as follows:

$$\text{Area} = 3 \text{ cm} \times 3 \text{ cm} = 9 \text{ cm}^2$$

Notice that the unit (cm) is treated in exactly the same way that you learned to treat the letters (a, b, x, y, etc.) in algebra. We can find the volume of the cube in Fig. 1–5 in the same way.

$$\text{Volume} = 3 \text{ cm} \times 3 \text{ cm} \times 3 \text{ cm}$$
$$= 27 \text{ cm}^3$$

With a system like this, it is a simple matter to represent the fourth, fifth, or any other number of dimensions of space, even though we can visualize and draw a diagram of only three dimensions. In chemistry and sometimes in

physics the abbreviation cc is used for cubic centimeters.

Measurement by the Liter

For many purposes we use pints (pt), quarts (qt), and gallons (gal) to express volumes in the English system. The *liter* (pronounced lee-ter) is used for corresponding purposes in the metric system. In countries that use the metric system, gasoline, milk, and other liquids are bought and sold in liters, deciliters, and centiliters. Except for very exact measurements, we use 1 liter and 1,000 cm³ to represent the same amount of volume. Thus a hollow cube 10 cm on an edge has a volume of 1,000 cm³ and would hold approximately 1 liter. This approximation is good to 27 parts in 1,000,000. The liter is sometimes used as the unit for measuring the volume of a given mass of gas. Glassware used in chemistry laboratories is often marked in

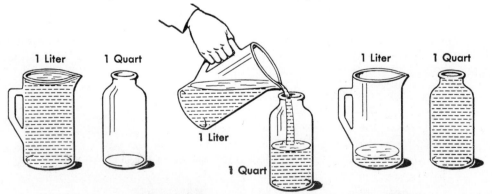

Fig. 1–6. One liter is slightly more than 1 qt; it is equivalent to 1.057 qt.

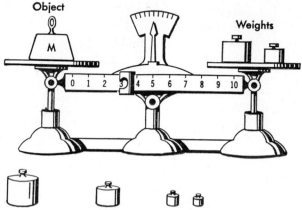

Fig. 1–7. Weighing an object with a beam balance.

milliliters (ml). For all practical purposes 1 ml is the same as 1 cm³.

Units Used in Measuring Mass

Every bit of matter has some mass, as we have already seen. In everyday usage we do not distinguish clearly between the *mass* of a body and its *weight*. *Mass* refers to the *amount of matter* a body contains, while weight refers to the pull the earth exerts on it. A *pound of mass* is a definite amount of matter that still remains a pound wherever in the universe it may be taken. A *pound of weight* is the amount of force or pull with which the earth attracts a pound of mass at a definite location on the earth's surface. If we could place a body whose mass is 1 lb in a rocket and send it 100 miles above the earth's surface, its inertia and its mass would still be exactly 1 lb. The attraction of the earth for this body at this altitude would be lessened so that its weight would be only about 0.95 lb.

When we weigh a body on a beam balance, as in Fig. 1–7, the effect of the pull of the earth on the object M is just balanced by the effect of its pull on the weights in the pan. If the balance, weights, and the object M could be

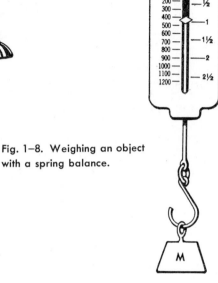

Fig. 1–8. Weighing an object with a spring balance.

enclosed in a rocket and sent without disturbing their arrangement to a point 100 miles above the earth, the weights and the object M would still be balanced. The attraction of the earth for M would be reduced by this change in position, but its attraction for the weights in the pan would at the same time be reduced by a corresponding amount. For this reason, measurements with a beam balance are not affected by position.

When we weigh a body with a spring balance, as in Fig. 1–8, the attraction of the earth for the object M stretches the coiled spring of the balance. This stretching continues until the opposing force set up by the stretched spring just equals the pull of the earth on M. At 100 miles above the earth, this pull would be less than at the surface and so the spring would not be stretched so far. The weight indicated by the spring

17

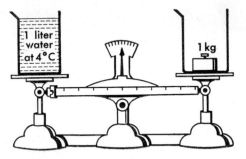

Fig. 1–9. One liter of water at 4° C weighs 1 kg and has a mass of 1 kg.

balance at this point would, therefore, be less than on the ground. Measurements with a spring balance are affected by changes in the earth's attraction.

The units of weight such as the pound, the kilogram, and the gram have the same names as the corresponding units of mass.

International Standard of Mass

The International Standard Kilogram is the mass of a platinum-iridium cylinder, also carefully preserved at the International Bureau of Weights and Measures. Our National Bureau of Standards at Washington, D.C., has two copies in the form of prototypes of this International Standard Kilogram. One of these prototypes is shown in the photograph on page 14.

The gram, a thousandth part of the kilogram, is a very small unit of mass. Our coin, the nickel, has a mass of approximately 5 g. The mass of a liter of pure water at 4°C is exactly 1 kg. So the mass of a milliliter of water under these conditions is 1 g. For all practical purposes we take the mass of 1 cm³ of water, under the same conditions, as 1 g. We can say also that the *weight* of 1 liter of pure water at 4°C is 1 kg and that the *weight* of 1 cm³ of water is 1 g.

In countries that use the metric system, sugar, flour, and other commodities are bought and sold in *kilos* (kilograms), just as we are accustomed to deal in pounds. If you were to travel by air in the countries using this system, both you and your baggage would be weighed in kilos.

What Is a Kilogram of Matter?

If you were sent to the store for a kilo of butter do you think you would be able to carry it home? By definition, a *pound* of mass in the United States is 1/2.2046 kg. This definition is the basis for the following conversion factors:

$$1 \text{ kg} = 2.20 \text{ lb}$$
$$1 \text{ lb} = 453.6 \text{ g}$$
$$1 \text{ oz} = 28.35 \text{ g}$$

You will readily see that the pound and the half-kilogram represent about equal masses (and equal weights). You could probably carry home the kilogram of butter without much help.

Table 1–4.   Units of Mass

English
1 ton = 2,000 pounds (lb) = 32,000 ounces (oz)
        1 lb   =   16 oz

Metric
1 metric ton = 1,000 kilograms (kg) = 1,000,000 grams (g) = 1,000,000,000 milligrams (mg)
               1 kg   =   1,000 g   =   1,000,000 mg
                                    1 g   =   1,000 mg

Standard time signals originate at the United States Naval Observatory in Washington, D.C. (*U.S. Naval Observatory*)

How Long Is a Second?

The standard unit of time for all purposes is the *second* (sec). A second is defined as 1/86,400 of the mean (average) solar day. The solar day is the interval of time between the instant the sun passes through its highest point in the heavens today and the instant it passes through its highest point tomorrow. This interval varies somewhat throughout the year; so a mean or average value is taken in defining the *second*. The number of seconds in a mean solar day is thus 86,400. Our standard of time depends in this way on the motion of the earth. Fortunately, we do not have separate units of time in the English and metric systems. The second is the standard in both systems. We sometimes use the time units *milliseconds* and *microseconds*.

Astronomers and physicists work together in keeping a constant check on standard clocks to see that they do not get out of step with the motion of the earth. Some of the most accurate clocks are controlled by a plate of quartz crystal in the same way that the *frequency* of the signal from a radio station is controlled. The National Bureau of Standards has announced the development of a new and extremely accurate kind of clock, controlled by the vibrations (to-and-fro motion) of molecules of ammonia gas. It is predicted that a clock of this kind may be able to indicate seconds with greater accuracy than any other known type of time indicator.

1. In the cgs (centimeter-gram-second) system of units, length is expressed in centimeters, mass in grams and time in seconds. What units are used in the fps (foot-pound-second) system?
2. For what purposes is the *hand* (a unit of length) used? How many inches equal a *hand?*
3. For what purposes is the fathom used? How many feet are in a fathom?
4. For what purposes is the furlong used? How many feet or rods are in a furlong?
5. How many feet are in a nautical mile? Is this longer or shorter than a "statute" mile? How much?
6. Why were the International Standard Meter bar and the International Standard Kilogram cylinder made of platinum-iridium alloy?
7. Why was the International Standard Meter bar made with its peculiar cross-sectional shape?
8. How can you get Naval Observatory time, or other standard time in your locality?
9. What is the basis for the saying, "A pint's a pound, the world around"?
10. Why do some states prohibit by law the use of spring balances in grocery stores, meat shops, and other places where weighed commodities are sold?
11. In football we sometimes have "five yards for off side." How does the referee measure off the 5-yd penalty?

DENSITY AND SPECIFIC GRAVITY

A quart bottle can hold about 2 lb of milk, but it can hold about 28 lb of mercury. It may at first seem strange to you that such widely different masses of milk and mercury can be placed in a quart bottle, but this is one of the differences that enable us to distinguish between milk and mercury.

What Is Density?

It is often important to know how much mass of a given material can be packed into one unit of volume; how many grams of milk or mercury are in 1 cm³. This number, which is different for different materials, is called *density*. **Mass per unit volume is called the mass density of a material.** In algebraic notation, $D_m = m/V$, where D_m is the *density*, m the *mass*, and V the *volume* occupied by that mass of material. The densities of solids and liquids are usually expressed in pounds per cubic foot (lb/ft^3) or in grams per cubic centimeter (g/cm^3). The densities of gases are often expressed in ounces per cubic foot (oz/ft^3) or in grams per liter ($g/liter$).

EXAMPLE: A cube of iron measures 10 cm on an edge and has a mass of 7,860 g. What is the density of this iron?

SOLUTION: The volume of the iron

$$V = 10 \text{ cm} \times 10 \text{ cm} \times 10 \text{ cm}$$
$$= 1,000 \text{ cm}^3$$

the mass

$$m = 7,860 \text{ g (given in the example)}$$

the density

$$D_m = ? \text{ (to be found)}$$

By definition, density is mass per unit volume, so

$$D_m = \frac{m}{V}$$

Substituting the values for the letters,

$$D_m = \frac{7,860 \text{ g}}{1,000 \text{ cm}^3} = 7.86 \text{ g/cm}^3$$

Grams divided by cubic centimeters gives grams per cubic centimeter.

In practical work we often wish to know the weight of a unit volume of a material.

The weight per unit volume is called the weight density of a material.

The density $D_W = W/V$, where W is the weight of the material that occupies a volume V. Both kinds of density are generally expressed in units that have the same name, such as pounds per cubic foot (lb/ft^3) or grams per cubic centimeter (g/cm^3). For example, the mass density of iron may be 7.86 g (of mass) /cm^3; its weight density is then also 7.86 g (of weight) /cm^3. Notice that the numerical values of these two densities are the same. For these reasons we often use the term density without specifying whether it is mass density or weight density and consider

$$\text{Density} = \frac{\text{mass}}{\text{volume}} \text{ or } \frac{\text{weight}}{\text{volume}}$$

Densities of Materials

You have perhaps heard the question, "Which is heavier, lead or feathers?" This is a tricky question because it gives no indication of the volume of lead and the volume of feathers involved. If the question were, "Which is *denser*, lead or feathers?" the answer could easily be found. All we would need to do to find this answer experimentally is to weigh *equal volumes* of lead and feathers and compare these weights. The material with the greater weight (lead) must then have the greater density. Weight and density are sometimes confused in everyday usage.

We shall have frequent use for the values of the density of water and the density of mercury. You should fix these values well in mind.

Density of pure water = 1 g/cm³
or 62.4 lb/ft³
Density of mercury = 13.6 g/cm³

Uses of Density Measurements

If we know the density of water and the capacity of a water tank we can

Table 1-5. Densities of Some Common Materials
[The densities are in grams per cubic centimeter; the temperatures of the liquids are in degrees centigrade. The densities of the solids were measured at 0°C.]

Solids		Liquids	
Wood, oak	0.6–0.9	Gasoline	0.68–0.74
Ice	0.917	Ethyl alcohol at 20°C	0.789
Glass	2.4–2.8	Pure water at 4°C	1.00
Stone	2.5–3.0	Sea water at 0°C	1.028
Aluminum	2.7	Glycerin at 20°C	1.26
Iron	7.86	Carbon tetrachloride at 20°C	1.595
Copper	8.92	Mercury at 4°C	13.6
Silver	10.5		
Lead	11.34		
Gold	19.3		
Platinum	21.37		

readily compute what the contents of a tank full of water will weigh without actually weighing the water.

EXAMPLE: What is the weight of water in a full tank whose capacity is 1,000 ft³?

SOLUTION: In this example

$$V = 1{,}000 \text{ ft}^3$$
$$D = 62.4 \text{ lb/ft}^3$$
$$W = ? \text{ (to be found)}$$

From the definition of density

$$W = V \times D$$

Substituting the numerical values for the letters,

$$W = 1{,}000 \text{ ft}^3 \times 62.4 \text{ lb/ft}^3$$
$$= 62{,}400 \text{ lb}$$

In this same way an engineer can compute the weight of a piece of machinery or part of a bridge or building before it is actually constructed. He needs to know only its volume and the density of the material of which it is to be made. He can thus compute beforehand the load (weight) every part of a structure

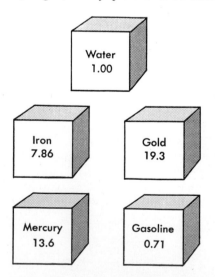

Fig. 1–10. Water is the standard or base for specific gravity. Its specific gravity is 1.00.

has to support and determine whether the design is of sufficient strength.

Sometimes the density of a substance helps us identify it. If you are given a small piece of silvery metal and asked to find out what it is, you may start by weighing it and then finding its volume. You can then compute its density. From its appearance, the metal may be any one of a number of pure metals or alloys, but if you find its density to be 21.4 g/cm³ you will be pretty sure the sample is platinum. Other tests, probably chemical tests, are necessary to establish its identity with still greater certainty.

What Is Specific Gravity?

We often need to know how the density of one material compares with that of another material. We may want to know that the density of gold (19.3 g/cm³) is 1.84 times the density of silver (10.5 g/cm³) or that the density of silver is 3.9 times that of aluminum (2.7 g/cm³). It would require a very large table to show all such possible comparisons of one material with another. You can easily see that it would be much simpler to select some one material as a standard of density and compare the densities of all other materials with this standard. This is, in effect, what scientists have done. Water has been chosen as the standard of density for solids and liquids. Air is usually chosen as the standard for gases, although other standards are sometimes used.

The ratio of the density of any substance to the density of the material chosen as a standard (water or air) is the specific gravity of the substance.

Figure 1–10 shows blocks or containers all of the same volume. The first is water, whose weight is its volume times the density of water. The second is a block of iron whose weight is the same volume times the density of iron. The ratio of the weight of the iron to that of the water is

$$\frac{\text{Wt of volume } V \text{ of iron}}{\text{Wt of volume } V \text{ of water}}$$

$$= \frac{V \times \text{density of iron}}{V \times \text{density of water}}$$

$$= \frac{\text{density of iron}}{\text{density of water}}$$

$$= \begin{array}{l} \text{specific gravity of the iron} \\ \text{(by the definition above)} \end{array}$$

The specific gravity of a material is the ratio of the weight of a given volume of this material to the weight of an equal volume of the standard (water or air).

Sometimes this ratio is called the *specific weight* or the *specific density* of the material, instead of its *specific gravity*. You will notice that specific gravity is always the ratio of two weights, and so it is a *pure number*, such as 3 or 5.25, without any unit associated with it.

Computing Specific Gravity

EXAMPLE 1: A cubic foot of iron weighs 490.5 lb, while a cubic foot of water weighs 62.4 lb. What is the specific gravity (sp gr) of the iron?

SOLUTION:

$$\text{Sp gr} = \frac{\text{wt of a given volume of material}}{\text{wt of equal volume of standard}}$$

$$= \frac{\text{wt of 1 ft}^3 \text{ of iron}}{\text{wt of 1 ft}^3 \text{ of water}}$$

$$= \frac{490.5 \text{ lb}}{62.4 \text{ lb}} = 7.86$$

EXAMPLE 2: A volume of 5 cm³ of mercury weighs 68 g, while the same volume of water weighs 5 g. What is the specific gravity of mercury?

SOLUTION:
Sp gr of mercury

$$= \frac{\text{wt of 5 cm}^3 \text{ of mercury}}{\text{wt of 5 cm}^3 \text{ of water}}$$

$$= \frac{68 \text{ g}}{5 \text{ g}} = 13.6$$

You have noticed that the number (13.6) that expresses the specific gravity of mercury, is the same as the number that expresses its density in grams per cubic centimeter. This did not happen by accident. The men who set up the metric system were careful to define the cubic centimeter and the gram in such a way that for all practical purposes 1 cm³ of water weighs 1 g at 4°C and so water has a density of 1 g/cm³ and a specific gravity of 1.

From a table of densities in grams per cubic centimeter such as Table 1–5, you can read at once the specific gravities of the substances listed, since these densities have the same numerical values as the corresponding specific gravities. You cannot do this when the densities are expressed in English units, pounds per cubic foot, for example. In the English system the density of mercury is 13.6 times the density of water, that is

$$\begin{aligned} \text{Density of mercury} &= 13.6 \times 62.4 \text{ lb/ft}^3 \\ &= 848.6 \text{ lb/ft}^3 \end{aligned}$$

The value of the specific gravity of a given material does not depend on the *kind* of units (English or metric) used to express volume and weight, so long as the same units are used both for the material and for the standard (water).

Using Specific Gravity

Specific gravity is used in much the same way as density. We can compute the weight of a known volume of a given material or the volume of a known

23

weight if we know the specific gravity of the material. These problems are simple when metric units are used, but are more complicated in English units.

EXAMPLE: What is the weight of 150 ft³ of iron whose specific gravity is 7.86?

SOLUTION: To solve this problem we need first to know the weight of 150 ft³ of water. This is

$$\text{Wt of water} = V \times D \text{ (of water)}$$
$$= 150 \text{ ft}^3 \times 62.4 \text{ lb/ft}^3$$
$$= 9,360 \text{ lb}$$

Then

Wt of iron =
sp gr of iron × wt of equal volume
of water
$$= 7.86 \times 9,360 \text{ lb}$$
$$= 73,570 \text{ lb}$$

From this example, you will see that

$$\text{Weight} = \text{specific gravity} \times \text{volume} \times \text{density}$$

of a body   of material of   of the   of the
the body   body   standard
(water)

►**Do You Know?**

1. What are some materials which have specific gravity higher than that of platinum?
2. Could any material have a specific gravity of zero? Give the reason for your answer.
3. What is the specific gravity of the solution in a fully charged automobile battery?
4. Discuss the meaning of specific gravity and density.
5. Explain why length, mass, and time are called fundamental quantities in physics.
6. What complications would you expect if the metric system were put into use for everyday measurements in our country?

HIGHLIGHTS

Physics, one of the basic physical sciences, deals with *matter* and *energy*. Matter occupies space and has mass. Energy does not possess these properties.

Length, mass, and *time* are fundamental quantities in physics.

The *meter* is the standard metric unit of length.

$$1 \text{ m} = 39.37 \text{ in.} \qquad 1 \text{ in.} = 2.54 \text{ cm} \qquad 1 \text{ km} = 0.621 \text{ mile or } \tfrac{5}{8} \text{ mile}$$

The International Standard Meter bar and the International Standard Kilogram cylinder are both made of platinum-iridium and are kept at the International Bureau of Weights and Measures at Sèvres, near Paris, France. Two prototypes of each are deposited in the vaults of the National Bureau of Standards in Washington, D.C.

The *liter* is used in liquid measure.   1 liter = 1.057 qt

1 kg = 2.20 lb   1 lb = 453.6 g

The *second* is the standard unit of time. The length of the second is determined from the period of rotation of the earth.

$$1 \text{ sec} = \frac{1}{86,400} \text{ of a mean solar day}$$

Density is mass per unit volume, $D_m = m/V$, or weight per unit volume, $D_W = W/V$.

The density of water is 1 g/cm³ or 62.4 lb/ft³.

Specific gravity is the ratio of the weight of a body of a given material to the weight of an equal volume of water (for solids and liquids). The standard used for gases is usually air.

PROBLEMS: GROUP A

1. If you walk ½ mile to school, how many inches do you travel? If you were in a "metric" country and walked ½ km to school, how many centimeters would you travel? Which is easier to compute? Why?

2. If you had to lift 25 lb of sugar, how many ounces would you lift? If you bought 2 kg of sugar in a "metric" country, how many grams would you get? Which is easier to compute? Why?

3. If 6.00-in. automobile tires are manufactured for export to a "metric" country, what would be their size, expressed in centimeters?

4. Suppose you read in a news article that a certain town is 100 km from Paris. If you want to tell a friend who is not acquainted with the metric system about this town, how many miles should you say it is from Paris?

5. Suppose you have a friend in a "metric" country with whom you correspond. He writes that (*a*) his height is 160 cm, (*b*) his weight is 70 kg, (*c*) his family uses 2 liters of milk a day, (*d*) he ran in the 100-m dash at a track meet at school, (*e*) his family automobile averages 8 km per liter of gasoline, and (*f*) he rode on a train 125 km to a neighboring city in an hour. Change the units in these statements to our everyday units so that you can explain this letter to your friends who may not know the metric system of units.

6. Suppose you measured a small swimming tank with a meter stick and found it to be 2 m deep, 4 m wide, and 6 m long. How many kilograms of water would be required to fill this tank to ½ m from the top?

7. A silver half-dollar weighs about 12.5 g. What is the total value in milligrams of the weights you would have to put on the pan of a balance like that in Fig. 1–7 to weigh a half-dollar coin?

8. Suppose you found in the laboratory that the density of a sample of metal is 556.6 lb/ft³. What is the specific gravity of this sample? If this sample is a pure metal, what does its specific gravity indicate it might be?

9. A nickel weighs approximately 5 g. How many nickels would be needed to weigh a kilogram?

10. A carat, used in weighing diamonds and other precious stones, is equivalent to 200 mg. How many grams does a 3-carat diamond weigh?

11. What is the weight in kilograms of 2 liters of glycerin?

12. What is the weight in kilograms of 5 liters of carbon tetrachloride?

13. How many seconds are in a 30-day month?

14. What is the weight in pounds of 1 ft³ of ice?

15. What is the weight in pounds of 0.5 ft³ of copper?

16. A large glass flask has a capacity of 25 liters. How many quarts will this flask hold? If the flask is filled with distilled water, how many kilograms will the water weigh?

1. The manufacturer of a certain automobile recommends an air pressure of 26 lb/in.^{2} for the tires. If this model of automobile were exported to a "metric" country, what air pressure (in kilograms per square centimeter) would probably be recommended?

2. Airliners commonly reach speeds of 400 miles per hour (mph). How would this speed be described in a "metric" country?

3. The Empire State Building in New York City is 1,250 ft high. A television transmitting antenna mast is mounted on top of this building. How many meters is the base of this mast above the street?

4. If the gasoline tank of an automobile holds 15 gal and is entirely empty, how many liters of gasoline would a driver in a "metric" country have to buy to fill the tank?

5. If the driver in the previous problem has to pay the equivalent of 12 cents for a liter of gasoline, how much more or less expensive is this than the regular gasoline in your community today?

6. If your school laboratory has in stock 250 cm^3 of mercury in a bottle, how many pounds would this mercury weigh? How many kilograms would the mercury weigh?

7. If a ton of water is stored in a tank, how many cubic feet of space does this water occupy?

8. Suppose you find that a 0.5 ft^3 sample of sandstone weighs 68.7 lb. What is the specific gravity of this sandstone?

9. The speed of sound is approximately 750 mph. What would this speed be if expressed in kilometers per hour?

10. A million metric tons of water is stored in a reservoir. How many cubic meters of space does this water occupy?

11. If 0.5 ft^3 of solid glass weighs 81.25 lb, what is the specific gravity of the glass?

12. An automobile weighs 3,400 lb. What is its weight in kilograms?

13. When the current price of coal is $18 per ton, how much per ton would you save or lose by buying the same grade of coal at $20 per metric ton?

14. When the current price of milk is $1 per gallon, how much would you lose or save on a gallon by buying at a price of 20 cents per liter?

15. If an automobile were equipped with a metric speedometer, how many kilometers per hour would this instrument read at 40 mph?

THINGS TO DO

1. How many cups in a quart? Count the number of kitchen measuring cups of water required to fill a quart milk bottle or container. Why might it be useful to know the number of cups in a quart?

2. Obtain a ruler marked in centimeters and measure your height. Multiply the number of centimeters you get by 0.4 and see if you get approximately your height in inches. Compare results of three trials.

3. "A pint's a pound the world around." Check the truth of this old saying by weighing an empty pint container, filling it with water, and weighing it again. How much does the water weigh? Is the old saying true? Discuss.

4. How long is your step, or pace? Pace off 10 or any other convenient number of steps. Measure the distance you moved with a tapeline or yardstick. What is the average length of your pace? Why might it be useful to know this?

Forces in Liquids:
Buoyancy and Gravity

FORCE AND PRESSURE

The earth exerts a pull on every body near it. This pull is the *weight* of the body and is one kind of *force*. We call this force the *force of gravity*, the *force due to gravity*, or often merely *gravity*. The pull of a stretched rubber band is also a force. The push of the wind against your body is likewise a force. The lift of an inflated balloon is a force. The thrust of expanding ice as water freezes, the attraction of a magnet for an iron nail, and the push of compressed air against the walls of an automobile tire are still other forces.

A force is a push or a pull which tends to start, stop, or otherwise change the motion of a body on which it acts.

Forces do not always actually result in a change in motion because they are often balanced by other opposing forces.

Units Used in Measuring Forces

You have already learned that the pull of the earth on a *pound of mass* (at the surface of the earth) is a *pound of force*. The earth's pull on a *kilogram of mass* is a *kilogram of force*. For every unit of mass we have a corresponding unit of force that bears the same name.

It is common practice to use pounds, kilograms, grams, and similar units to express not only a force due to gravity, but other kinds of forces as well. Thus the *pull* in the rope of a sled may be 50 lb, the *stretching force* in a wire may be 25 kg, and the *attracting force* of a

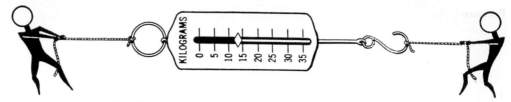

Fig. 2–1. A spring balance can be used to measure forces.

magnet for a piece of iron may be 100 g.

There is a miniature unit of force with which you will need to become acquainted. This is the *dyne* (from the Greek word for power). A dyne is so small that 980 dynes are equivalent to only 1 g of force. If you hold a nickel (mass, 5 g) on your extended finger you will have to exert a force of about 4,900 dynes to keep the coin from falling. We will find many uses for this very small unit of force.

How We Measure Forces

One device for measuring forces directly is the *spring balance*. This type of

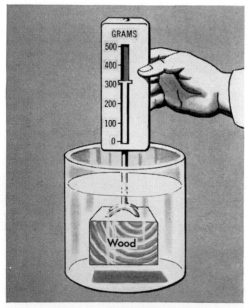

Fig. 2–2. A compression balance can be used to measure the force required to push a wood block under water.

28

balance can be used to measure not only weights—forces due to gravity—but also other forces such as the pull exerted by the boys on the two segments of rope shown in Fig. 2–1. Compressing (squeezing) forces can be measured with a *compression balance*, as shown in Fig. 2–2. The coiled spring in this type of balance is pushed together rather than stretched by the force that it measures. Other more complicated machines called *dynamometers* are used to measure very large forces, such as the pull of a tractor or a locomotive.

A scale marked off in suitable divisions is usually mounted under the pointer of one of these force-measuring balances so that the pointer by its position indicates the amount of force in pounds, kilograms, or other force units. In many situations it is very difficult, if not impossible, to measure the total force involved. If we wish to know the total compressing force of water on a submerged submarine, or the total push of water against a large dam, it may be much more convenient to compute the force than to measure it directly. We will examine methods by which such computations are made after we have learned about pressure.

What Is Pressure?

When a force is distributed over a considerable area, we often need to know the amount of force that acts on 1 ft^2 or on 1 cm^2 of the area. This amount of force is called *pressure*.

Pressure is the amount of force per unit area.

$$P = \frac{F}{A}$$

Pressure and *force* are often confused. To illustrate how these terms should be used, suppose some water in a bucket exerts a *force* of 15 lb on the bottom. If the bottom has an area of 30 in.², the amount of force per square inch, or the *pressure* this water exerts on the bottom, is $\frac{15\ lb}{30\ in.^2} = 0.5\ lb/in.^2$ Some other units commonly used to express pressure are the following:

lb/ft², pounds per square foot
kg/m², kilograms per square meter
g/cm², grams per square centimeter
dynes/cm², dynes per square centimeter

We often speak of the pressure exerted by such familiar things as gas, air, water, and steam as so many *pounds* or so many *grams*. What we really mean is *pounds per square inch* or *grams per square centimeter*. But since everyone concerned usually understands what we mean in these cases, we sometimes shorten the expressions by omitting the *per square*. . . . To avoid misunderstanding we shall use the full expressions throughout this book.

How to Compute Total Force

Since pressure is the amount of force per unit area, the total force acting on any given surface is the average pressure on that surface multiplied by its area.

Force = average pressure × area
$$F = P \times A$$

EXAMPLE: The average air pressure in a tank is 50 lb/in.² The total area of the inside walls of this tank is 1,200 in.² What is the total outward force exerted on the tank by the compressed air?

SOLUTION:

$$F = P \times A = 50\ lb/in.^2 \times 1{,}200\ in.^2$$
$$= 60{,}000\ lb$$

Notice that the units for pressure and area used in computing total force must be *consistent*, that is, if pressure is expressed in pounds per *square inch*, area must be expressed in *square inches*. If pressure is expressed in grams per *square centimeter*, area must be expressed in *square centimeters*.

►Do You Know?

1. What is the average pressure of the gas used for fuel in homes?
2. What is the average pressure in the water pipes in homes?
3. What is the air pressure usually carried in the tires of automobiles?
4. Give the definitions for force and pressure.
5. Name several forces which you see in action on your way to and from school.

PRESSURE CAUSED BY GRAVITY

Nearly everyone who swims has noticed the compressing force exerted on his body by the water in a pool, a lake, or the sea. If you have dived into a body of water you know, too, that this force becomes noticeably greater as you go down deeper into the water. This force is caused by the weight of the water, that is, by the force of gravity. You are undoubtedly aware that this force is not all *downward* or *upward*, but presses in on your body from all directions. These facts are easily verified by simple tests.

Force Due to Pressure

If you press your finger against the rubber diaphragm of the exploring tube shown in Fig. 2–3a you will notice that

29

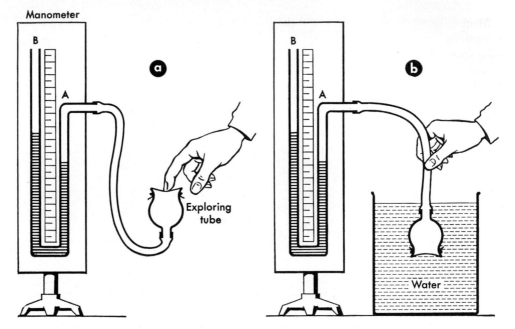

Fig. 2–3. A manometer and exploring tube for testing force and pressure under water.

the liquid in the arm *A* goes down while that in arm *B* goes up. The harder you press the greater the difference in levels in the two arms becomes. This *difference in levels* is thus an indicator of the total force pushing against the rubber diaphragm. It is likewise an indicator of the *average pressure* on the diaphragm because the area of the diaphragm does not change much unless you push it in quite far. This pressure-measuring instrument, or gage, is called a *manometer*.

Imagine that the exploring tube of the manometer is pushed down to a convenient depth in a large jar of water, as shown in Fig. 2–3b. Notice that the manometer indicates that there is a definite force on the diaphragm. If the exploring tube is now turned about in different directions, with the center of the diaphragm always at the same depth, the levels of the liquid in arms *A* and *B* will remain *unchanged, regardless of the direction the exploring tube is turned.*

At a given depth in water, the force due to pressure is the same in every direction (downward, upward, and sidewise).

This force is always perpendicular to any surface that the water touches. A hollow body submerged in a liquid is subjected to this force just as are the walls of the container.

Pressure Depends on Depth

If you will watch the manometer of Fig. 2–3 as the exploring tube is pushed deeper and deeper into the water you will notice a steady *increase* in the *difference in levels* of the liquid in the two arms. This indicates a steady increase in the *average pressure* on the diaphragm. You have noticed that the force due to pressure at a given depth is the same in all directions, so it will make no difference in this test whether the exploring tube is held with the diaphragm up, down, or sidewise.

More careful measurements made with a sensitive manometer or other pressure gage show that when the depth is *twice* as great, the pressure is *twice* as much. At *three* times the original depth the pressure is *three* times the original pressure, and so on. This fact is shown in Fig. 2–4. In Fig. 2–5, the pressure indicated by each gage in Fig. 2–4 is plotted against its corresponding depth. The individual points are then connected to give a straight line. If any other liquid is used in place of water in the test suggested in Fig. 2–4, another straight-line graph similar to that in Fig. 2–5 is obtained. The actual pressure at any depth, however, depends on the kind of liquid used. When two quantities are related as pressure and depth are here so that their graph is a straight line, the first (the effect) is said to be *directly proportional* to the second (the cause).

The pressure at any point below the surface of a liquid is directly proportional to the depth.

Quantities that influence or help produce any effect are often called *factors* of that effect. Thus we may say that depth below the surface is one *factor* upon which the pressure at a point within the liquid depends.

How should the depth be measured? In the case of a large body of water, there is no question that the depth is the *vertical* distance from the surface down to the point where we want to know the pressure. But consider the cases shown in Figs. 2–6 and 2–7. The water pressure must be the same at the bases of all the tubes in Fig. 2–6 at the points where they join the connecting tank, provided the tank is level. If this were not true, water would flow in the tank from tubes of higher pressure to tubes of lower pressure, until the pressures were equalized. Since water stands at the same level in

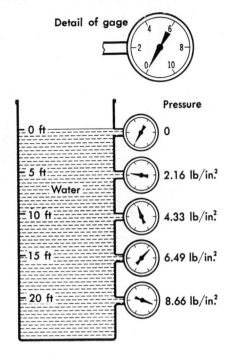

Fig. 2–4. The gages in the side of the tank indicate that pressure in water increases with depth.

all five tubes, the *vertical distance* from the surface to the base is the same for the bent tubes as for the straight ones. The

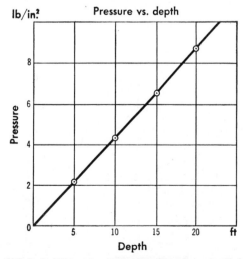

Fig. 2–5. When the pressure at a given depth is plotted against the corresponding depth and the points connected, a straight-line graph is obtained.

31

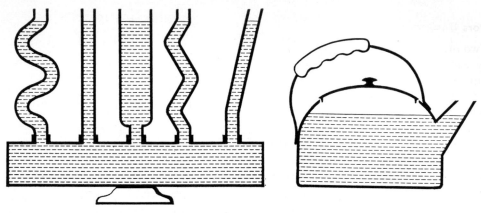

Fig. 2–6. Water stands at the same level in all tubes connected at the base.

Fig. 2–7. Water stands at the same level in the teakettle and in the spout.

actual lengths of these water columns, however, are quite different for different tubes. In tubes connected at their bases, as in Fig. 2–6, the *same vertical distance from surface to base produces the same pressure at the base*. This principle applies also to the water in the teakettle and its spout in Fig. 2–7. The depth is the *vertical* distance from the surface level to the level of the pressure point.

Pressure Depends on Density

If we were to push the exploring tube of Fig. 2–3 into carbon tetrachloride (a nonflammable cleaning fluid) we would find the pressure at a given depth about 1.6 times as great as in water at the same depth. In gasoline, the pressure would be only about 0.7 times as great as at an equal depth in water. If we had enough mercury for a trial, we would find a pressure more than 13 times that in water at corresponding depths. All these liquids have different densities.

The pressure at any given depth below the surface of a liquid is directly proportional to the density of the liquid.

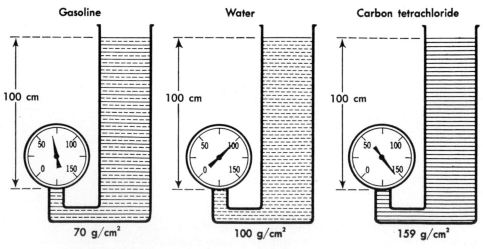

Fig. 2–8. Pressure at a given depth is greater in a more dense liquid.

Factors Unrelated to Pressure

Two other factors that you might possibly expect to affect the pressure in a liquid are (1) the volume of the liquid and (2) the shape of the body of liquid. A simple test for the effect of these factors, devised three centuries ago by the famous French scientist Blaise Pascal, is shown in Fig. 2–9. Three vessels (Pascal's vases) of different shapes but with bases having equal areas are used. The three vessels are filled with water to the same level and the pressure at the base of each is measured by means of the gage. It is easy to observe that the gages all indicate the same pressure for the same water level. This simple test shows that (1) pressure at the base does not depend on the *shape* of the vessel or container and (2) pressure at the base does not depend on the *volume* of liquid in the container. This means that the pressure at the base of a $\frac{1}{2}$-in. pipe filled with water to a height of 10 ft is no different from the pressure 10 ft below the surface of a large lake, if the water in both has the same density.

How Pressure Is Calculated

We have found that the pressure at a given depth in a liquid depends on only two quantities, the *depth* and the *density* of the liquid, and is directly proportional to each of them. These relationships can be expressed in one equation.

$$\text{Pressure} = \text{depth} \times \text{density}$$
$$P = H \times D$$

where H is the depth and D is the weight per unit volume of the liquid (weight density).

EXAMPLE: What is the pressure at a point 1 m below the surface of a fresh-water lake?

SOLUTION: Here

$$H = 1 \text{ m} = 100 \text{ cm} \quad \text{and} \quad D = 1 \text{ g/cm}^3$$

so

$$P = H \times D = 100 \text{ cm} \times 1 \text{ g/cm}^3$$
$$= 100 \text{ g/cm}^2$$

Notice that *consistent* units must be used for H and D. When the indicated operation is performed on the units shown, a correct unit of pressure, grams per square centimeter, is obtained.

Let us now consider an example using English units.

EXAMPLE: Compute the pressure at a point 10 ft below the surface of water in a pool.

SOLUTION: Here

$$H = 10 \text{ ft} \quad \text{and} \quad D = 62.4 \text{ lb/ft}^3$$

so

$$P = H \times D = 10 \text{ ft} \times 62.4 \text{ lb/ft}^3$$
$$= 624 \text{ lb/ft}^2$$

If we wish to know this pressure in *pounds per square inch*, which is the more customary way of expressing pressure, we shall have to divide the result just obtained by 144, the number of square inches in 1 ft².

$$P = \frac{624 \text{ lb/ft}^2}{144 \text{ in.}^2/\text{ft}^2} = 4.33 \text{ lb/in.}^2$$

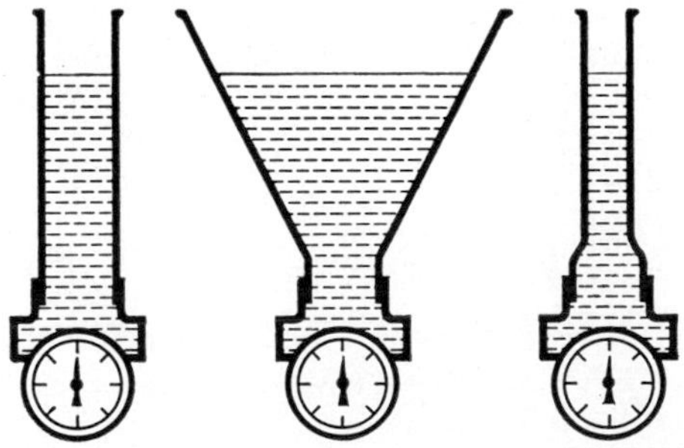

Fig. 2–9. Pascal's vases. Pressure at the bottom does not depend on the size or shape of the vessel.

33

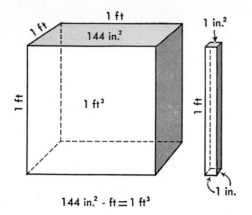

144 in.² - ft = 1 ft³

Fig. 2–10. A square inch-foot, as shown at the right, is the volume of a column 1 in.² at the base and 1 ft high.

The units have been carried through in this solution so that you may see just how *pounds per square foot* become *pounds per square inch*.

In every problem of this type in which the depth is given in *feet* and the density of the liquid in pounds *per cubic foot*, we have to perform this division by 144 to find the pressure in pounds *per square inch*. It is convenient to make this division only once and use the value obtained for solving future problems in pressure. This division results in a new unit of volume, the square inch-foot, as shown in Fig. 2–10. It results also in a

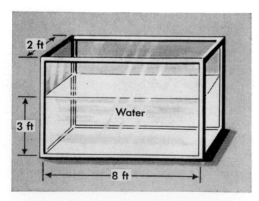

Fig. 2–11. The total force of water against the bottom, sides, and ends of this tank is 8,611 lb.

new unit of density, pounds per square inch-foot, lb./in.²-ft. The density of pure water expressed in this new unit is then

$$\frac{62.4 \text{ lb/ft}^3}{144 \text{ in.}^2/\text{ft}^2} = 0.433 \text{ lb/in.}^2\text{-ft}$$

Let us now see how the use of this new unit of density simplifies the computations when we wish to find the pressure at a point 10 ft below the surface of a pool of water.

SOLUTION:

$H = 10$ ft and $D = 0.433$ lb/in.²-ft

so

$$P = H \times D = 10 \text{ ft} \times 0.433 \text{ lb/in.}^2\text{-ft}$$
$$= 4.33 \text{ lb/in.}^2$$

Notice that the computation is shortened and the units come out correctly.

Pressure and Outward Force

Figure 2–11 shows a rectangular tank partially filled with water. We know from experience that the water pushes outward on the ends and sides of this tank, as well as downward on the bottom. What is the total force pushing outward on the front side of this tank? We need to know two things to compute this force: (1) the *area* of the sidewall in contact with the water and (2) the *average pressure* of the water on this area. The area in contact with the water is

$$A = 3 \text{ ft} \times 8 \text{ ft} = 24 \text{ ft}^2$$

The *average pressure* of the water can easily be found when the sidewall is a rectangle. The pressure at a point at the very top of the water is zero. The pressure at a point at the bottom edge of the sidewall is exactly the same as the pressure at a point on the bottom of the tank, because these two points are at the same depth. This pressure is expressed by

$$P = H \times D = 3 \text{ ft} \times 62.4 \text{ lb/ft}^3$$
$$= 187.2 \text{ lb/ft}^2$$

In the special case of a rectangular sidewall, the *average* pressure on the wall is the average of the pressure at the top surface of the water and that at the bottom of the wall, so for this sidewall

$$P_{av} = \frac{0 + 187.2 \text{ lb/ft}^2}{2}$$
$$= 93.6 \text{ lb/ft}^2$$

This *average* pressure is the same as the actual pressure at a point *halfway* between the top surface of the water and the bottom. Can you show why this is true? For a rectangular sidewall we may write

$$P_{av} = \frac{H}{2} \times D$$

The total outward force on the side of the tank is

$$F = P_{av} \times A$$
$$= 93.6 \text{ lb/ft}^2 \times 24 \text{ ft}^2$$
$$= 2,246 \text{ lb (more than a ton)}$$

See if you can compute the total outward force on all sides and bottom of the tank shown in Fig. 2 11. Does your result check with the value shown under the illustration?

Figure 2–12 shows a case where the average pressure is *not* the same as that at a point halfway down the sidewall. Can you think of other cases where this is true?

How Cities Get Water

The systems that supply water for large cities are generally quite complicated. Many of them represent outstanding engineering achievements. New York City brings its water from large reservoirs high in the Catskill Mountains.

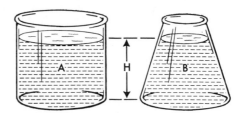

Fig. 2–12. The average pressure on the side of vessel A is the same as the actual pressure at a point halfway down in the liquid. This is not true in vessel B.

Los Angeles obtains its water from the Sierra Nevadas. Cleveland draws its water from Lake Erie at a point several miles from shore. Chicago takes its water supply from Lake Michigan. Some cities obtain water from drilled wells, while still others draw from lakes, rivers, and streams. The size, location, and industries of a city depend in a large

This storage tank is 75 ft high and holds 750,000 gal of water. (*Photo by Robert H. Sage*)

35

measure on the quality and quantity of water available.

All water systems have one problem in common. They must supply enough pressure to push the water from the faucet to operate the shower, lawn sprinkler, garden hose, and other devices the consumer may attach. Stationary water pressures of the order of 25 to 50 lb/in.² are common. Generally this pressure is obtained by gravity. It is for this reason that water is stored in large reservoirs or elevated standpipes and storage tanks on hills and mountain tops, above the level of the city. The water system then takes full advantage of the law we have just discussed, $P = H \times D$. You should remember that this equation can be used to compute the pressure at a point along such a system only when the water in the pipes is not flowing. When water is moving through the pipes, the pressure at any point is lower than the value computed from this equation. Why should this be true?

▶Do You Know?

1. Is the pressure 5 ft below the surface of a large fresh water lake the same as that at an equal depth in a swimming pool, if the water has the same density in both cases? Explain.
2. Why is the pressure 10 ft below the surface of the ocean greater than that 10 ft below the surface of a fresh water lake?
3. What is meant by the expression, "Water seeks its own level"?
4. Describe different methods by which cities are supplied with water. How is pressure for city water supply maintained?
5. What chemicals may be used in treating city water supply? How may softened water be provided in city water supply?

36

6. How is water commonly supplied in farm homes?
7. There is a Dutch legend about a small boy named Hans, who discovered a hole in the sea dyke and stopped the flow of water with his hand until assistance arrived. How could a small lad hold back the whole North Sea?

PASCAL'S LAW

When you try to push with your finger on the surface of water in a drinking glass you soon discover that the water moves out from under your finger so that you cannot exert much force on the water. If you place a stopper in a bottle that has been completely filled with water and push on the stopper, you can exert considerable force on the water. How do these two situations differ?

How Liquids Transmit Pressure

When a liquid is entirely enclosed in a tank or other container, pressure can be set up in the liquid by a mechanical force exerted on its surface from the outside. Figure 2–13 shows how pressure produced by an external force acting on the surface of a liquid is transmitted throughout the liquid. At every point in the liquid the pressure is increased by 10 lb/in.² (in this example) over and above the original pressure. An additional *force* pushes outward against all the walls of the container. These facts are expressed in Pascal's law.

Pressure caused by an external force applied to an enclosed liquid is transmitted undiminished throughout the body of the liquid.

Because the surface of the enclosed liquid presses against the large area of its container, a large bursting force may be produced by a relatively small external force exerted on the liquid. The following example will help you see why.

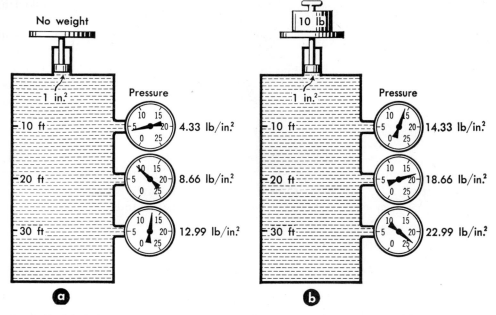

No weight

1 in.²

Pressure

10 ft .... 4.33 lb/in.²

20 ft .... 8.66 lb/in.²

30 ft .... 12.99 lb/in.²

a

10 lb

1 in.²

Pressure

10 ft .... 14.33 lb/in.²

20 ft .... 18.66 lb/in.²

30 ft .... 22.99 lb/in.²

b

Fig. 2–13. (a) With no pressure applied to the surface of the liquid, $P = H \times D$. (b) When a weight causing a pressure of 10 lb/in.² on the surface is added, $P = (H \times D) + 10$ lb/in.²

EXAMPLE: Find the additional outward force exerted against the walls of a bottle filled with water, when a tight stopper is pushed in so that it exerts a force of 5 lb on the water. The area of the end of the stopper is 0.5 in.² and that of the inside walls of the bottle is 250 in.²

SOLUTION: The amount of external *force per unit area* on the water surface is

$$P = \frac{\text{force exerted by stopper}}{\text{area of end of stopper}} = \frac{5 \text{ lb}}{0.5 \text{ in.}^2}$$
$$= 10 \text{ lb/in.}^2$$

An equal amount of force acts against *every* square inch of the inside surface of the bottle. Hence the total bursting force is

$$F = P \times A = 10 \text{ lb/in.}^2 \times 250 \text{ in.}^2$$
$$= 2,500 \text{ lb}$$

Notice that the initial force of 5 lb has resulted in a total force of 2,500 lb, a force *multiplication* of 500 times.

▶**Do You Know?**

1. Why is water safer than air or steam for testing the strength of a hot-water tank?

2. What is the "hydrostatic paradox"? How does Pascal's law serve to explain this paradox?

3. Make a list of the names, purposes, and locations of machines with which you are acquainted that operate on

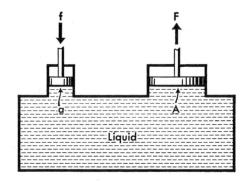

Fig. 2–14. The principle of the hydraulic press.

37

the principle expressed in Pascal's law.

4. Explain how a force of a few pounds on the brake pedal of the hydraulic brake system of an automobile is changed into a force large enough to stop the vehicle.

5. What fluid is used in the hydraulic hoists in your neighborhood filling stations?

Pascal's Law Applied

Consider the apparatus shown in Fig. 2–14. When a small force is applied to the smaller piston the larger piston moves and exerts a large force against its load. How are these forces related?

Let f = amount of force applied to the smaller piston in Fig. 2–14

a = area of the face of this piston in contact with the liquid

F = amount of force exerted by the larger piston against its load

A = area of the face of the larger piston in contact with the liquid

Pressure due to the weight of the liquid is usually so small in comparison to the pressure set up by the force f on the smaller piston that it may be neglected. Then, the pressure in the liquid resulting from the force applied to the smaller piston is $P = f/a$. By Pascal's law this is also the pressure on the face of the larger piston. The total force exerted by the liquid against the larger piston is the same as that exerted by the piston against its load, if the piston is free-moving. This force may be expressed by $F = P \times A$.

Substituting f/a for P gives

$$F = \frac{f}{a} \times A$$

$$= f \times \frac{A}{a}$$

Dividing both sides of this equation by f gives the relation

$$\frac{F}{f} = \frac{A}{a}$$

In a hydraulic system the force exerted by the larger piston is to the force exerted on the smaller piston as the area of the larger piston is to the area of the smaller piston.

The face of a piston is usually circular. It is proved in geometry that the areas of two circles are to each other as the squares of their diameters. So for circular piston faces we may write

$$\frac{F}{f} = \frac{A}{a} = \frac{D^2}{d^2}$$

where D represents the diameter of the larger piston and d the diameter of the smaller one. If the diameter of the larger piston is 10 times that of the smaller one, the force exerted by the larger piston will be 100 (or 10^2) times the force applied to the smaller one. This assumes that the pistons are free-moving, that is, are free from friction.

A number of common mechanical devices operate on the principle expressed in Pascal's law. The list includes the hydraulic brake system for an automobile shown in Fig. 2–15, hydraulic freight elevators used in factories and other buildings, hydraulic jacks used in service garages, hydraulic presses used in factories and testing laboratories, and many others. Hydraulic presses may be built to exert forces as large as 1,000 tons or more.

Some hydraulic machines use water for the liquid. Others use oil or a similar fluid. In the hydraulic brake system of an automobile a special liquid or brake fluid is used. This fluid must not freeze or become thick in cold weather. Liquids are better than air or steam for machines of

38

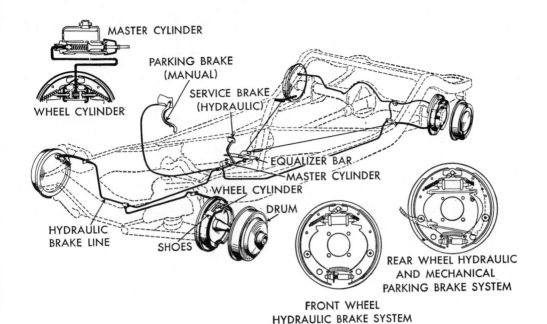

MASTER CYLINDER

WHEEL CYLINDER

PARKING BRAKE (MANUAL)

SERVICE BRAKE (HYDRAULIC)

EQUALIZER BAR

MASTER CYLINDER

WHEEL CYLINDER

DRUM

HYDRAULIC BRAKE LINE

SHOES

REAR WHEEL HYDRAULIC AND MECHANICAL PARKING BRAKE SYSTEM

FRONT WHEEL HYDRAULIC BRAKE SYSTEM

Fig. 2–15. A hydraulic brake system uses the principle of Pascal's law to stop an automobile.

this type, because if the cylinder should burst under the high pressure to which it is subjected, the pressure in a liquid is relieved at once without any great external damage. Steam or air under the same conditions would be likely to cause the cylinder to explode.

ARCHIMEDES' PRINCIPLE

If you stand deep in water you are aware of a force pushing upward on your body, in addition to the compressing force which we have already discussed. When you are in water you seem to "lose weight." If you try to lift a stone or other object, you will notice that it, too, seems to weigh less under water than in air. The upward or supporting force exerted by the water on objects immersed in it is called a *buoyant force* and the general effect is called *buoyancy*. Every liquid exerts a buoyant force on any object immersed in it.

Buoyant Force

Study carefully the series of operations shown in Fig. 2–16.

The test illustrated in Fig. 2–16, when done carefully, shows that the buoyant force of the water on the stone is just equal to the weight of the water displaced by the stone.

When liquids other than water are tried in this test, it is found that they, too, buoy up the stone with a force that is just equal to the weight of the displaced liquid. When any solid object that is not porous is completely submerged in a liquid, *it displaces a volume of the liquid just equal to its own volume.* So the weight of the displaced liquid is the weight of a body of the liquid whose volume is the same as that of the submerged object.

Because of the buoyant force, the submerged body *appears* to weigh less; the net downward pull that it exerts on the balance is reduced, even though the

39

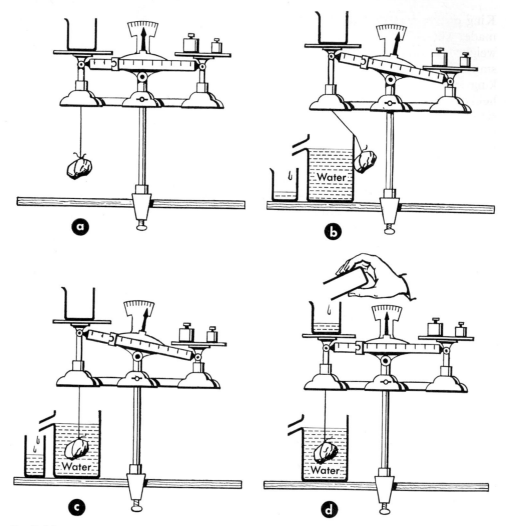

Fig. 2–16. Archimedes' principle. (a) The weights on the right pan just balance the stone and beaker on the left. (b) The overflow can is filled with water to the level of the spout. Excess water caught in a beaker is discarded. (c) The *dry* catch can placed under the spout catches all the water that overflows when the stone is placed in the water in the overflow can. Notice that the stone now seems to weigh less than at first. (d) Balance is restored when the water that overflowed is poured into the beaker. What conclusion can you draw from this experiment?

earth pulls on the body as hard as ever. The apparent loss in weight of any object submerged in a liquid is equal to the weight of an equal volume (the displaced volume) of the liquid.

The principle expressed in this statement is known as *Archimedes' principle.*

40

▶**You Will Be Interested to Know**

Archimedes, a noted mathematician and scientist, lived during the third century B.C. in the ancient Grecian city of Syracuse on the island of Sicily. According to an interesting story, Hiero,

King of Syracuse, ordered a new crown made. The gold for the new crown was weighed out and delivered to the goldsmith. When the crown was finished, the king suspected that the goldsmith had held out some of the gold and substituted silver or some other less precious metal for it. Hiero commanded Archimedes to find out whether the crown was pure gold.

One day while Archimedes was in a public bath, it suddenly dawned on him that the buoyant effect of water provided the long-sought key to the solution of his problem. In his excitement, he is said to have leaped from the bath and run naked down the street shouting "Eureka! Eureka!" which means, "I have found it!" The story further relates that Archimedes' tests proved that the goldsmith had stolen some of the gold. This is probably one of the first incidents on record of the use of experimental science in crime detection.

Buoyant Force and Density

Study carefully the operations shown in Fig. 2–17.

You will notice in Fig. 2–17*b* that the block in water appears to be the heavier. This can mean only that the buoyant force of carbon tetrachloride on one block is greater than the buoyant force of water on the other one.

The buoyant force acting on an object submerged in a liquid and the apparent loss in weight of the object increases as the density of the liquid increases.

Why An Object Sinks

When the buoyant force acting on an object submerged in a liquid is less than its actual weight (the actual pull of the earth on the object), the object will sink. We could, then, say that the submerged object apparently loses only part of its actual weight. The volume of the displaced liquid is the same as that of the submerged object, but its weight is less than that of the object. So the density (weight per unit volume) of the liquid is less than that of the object. *The density of any object that sinks in a liquid must be greater than that of the liquid itself.*

When the buoyant force acting on a submerged body is just equal to the weight of the body, the body appears to lose all its weight. It will then neither

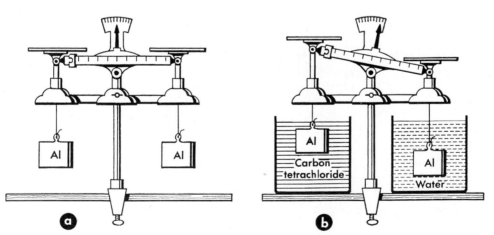

Fig. 2–17. (a) Two blocks of aluminum of equal size and weight are balanced. (b) The blocks now are not balanced. Why?

41

Fig. 2–18. When the fish neither rises nor sinks, its average density is exactly the same as that of the water.

sink or rise of its own accord in the liquid. *Its density must be exactly the same as that of the liquid.* If you float in water with just your nose out, the *average* density of your body must be the same as that of the water. This exact balance in density is generally hard to maintain. A fish is equipped with an air bladder which compresses and expands to change its average density. This device enables the fish to maintain this delicate balance with seeming ease, as shown in Fig. 2–18.

Why an Object Floats

It may surprise you to learn that Archimedes' principle applies also to bodies that float. When the actual weight of an object is less than that of the liquid it displaces, the object will be forced upward out of the liquid. It will rise above the surface of the liquid and float with only part of its volume submerged in the liquid. The weight of the volume of liquid displaced by the floating object must just equal the actual weight of the object itself. A floating object must apparently *lose all of its weight*, but to do so it needs to be only partly submerged. The *average* density of a floating body must be *less than* that of the liquid in which it floats. The less the density of the floating object, the smaller fractional part of its whole volume is under the liquid, as illustrated in Fig. 2–19.

Empty steel gasoline drums, steel pontoons, and steel ships float even though the density of steel is more than seven times that of water. Because of its shape each of these devices displaces a much greater volume of water than the actual volume of steel it contains. The *average* density of each of these is less than that of water. The weight of the water each displaces, however, is just equal to its own weight. It is only because of their large *displacement* that bodies such as these keep afloat.

The Hydrometer

A *hydrometer* is an instrument for indicating the specific gravity of a test

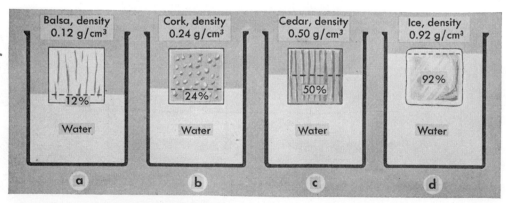

Fig. 2–19. A floating body sinks in a liquid until it displaces a volume of liquid whose weight is exactly the same as that of the floating body.

S.S. *United States.* One of the fastest and most modern passenger ships. (*United States Lines*)

liquid in which it floats. A common type consists of a glass bulb, loaded at one end so that it floats upright. The other end is a narrow neck or stem in which the printed specific gravity scale is mounted. When placed in a test liquid, this bulb settles down until the weight of the liquid it displaces is just equal to its own weight. Thus a given hydrometer will ride higher in a denser liquid and sink deeper in one less dense. The scale reading at the surface level of the liquid in which the hydrometer is floating indicates the specific gravity of the liquid, as shown in Fig. 2–20.

Hydrometers are used in many manufacturing and industrial processes. Special types are used to measure the specific gravity of milk, sirups, and other

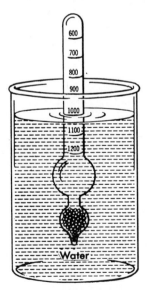

Fig. 2–20. Hydrometers are used for measuring the specific gravity of liquids.

43

liquids. Hydrometers with special scales are used to determine the freezing points of antifreeze radiator solutions. Hydrometers in syringes are used to measure the specific gravity of the sulfuric acid solution in the cells of storage batteries and thus determine how fully the batteries are charged. You may find that a hydrometer indicates a specific gravity of 1250 for the solution in your automobile battery. This really means a specific gravity of 1.250, but the decimal point is generally omitted. This practice of omitting the decimal point is familiar to baseball fans, who understand that a bat-

ting average of 300 really means 0.300. It is not customary to write 1,250 for specific gravity.

►**Do You Know?**

1. Is it easier to float in fresh water or in sea water? Why?
2. Why is it difficult for a swimmer to sink in the water of Great Salt Lake in Utah?
3. Are there kinds of wood that will not float in water? If so, what are their names?
4. What is a Cartesian diver, or bottle imp? How does one work?
5. Is it easier to keep afloat in water 6 ft deep than in water 2 ft deep? Why?
6. The density of ordinary stone is about 2.50 g/cm³, while that of sea water is about 1.03 g/cm³. Water is only slightly compressible even under very great pressures. Explain why a stone dropped overboard at a very deep place in the ocean will or will not sink to the bottom.
7. Of what materials are life belts made?
8. For what purposes are buoys used?
9. What is the specific gravity of fresh water?
10. When the amount of antifreeze in the solution in an automobile radiator is increased does the test hydrometer ride higher or sink deeper into the solution?
11. When an automobile battery is fully charged, does the test hydrometer ride higher or sink deeper into the solution than when the battery is half-charged?
12. Are there industries in your vicinity that use hydrometers for testing purposes? If so, what liquid materials do they test?

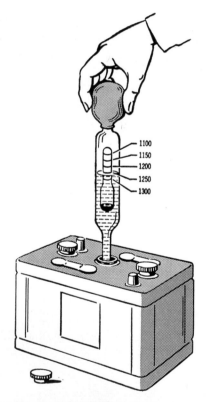

Fig. 2–21. A syringe hydrometer is used to determine how fully a storage battery is charged. A reading of 1250 to 1300 (1.250 to 1.300) indicates full charge for most types of automobile batteries. A reading of 1175 or lower indicates a discharged battery.

WORKING UNDER WATER

How far down can you dive in water? The depth is probably not more than a few feet, because, without auxiliary apparatus, you cannot carry enough air with you to breathe. Expert divers sometimes go down 30 or 40 ft without special equipment and remain under for several minutes. In some parts of the world sponges, oysters (sometimes with pearls), and other marine products are collected by divers without mechanical equipment.

Underwater Devices

In repair and rescue work, in exploring and raising sunken vessels, and in recovering cargo and treasure from wrecked ships, it is often necessary for divers to descend to considerable depths and remain there at work for an hour or more at a time. The diver must be free to move about and use his hands while on the bottom. For this type of work *diving suits* and *diving helmets* of different kinds are used. When several men are required to work together within a limited area on the sea bottom and when greater freedom of the hands and body of the worker are required, a *diving bell* is sometimes used. Air pressure inside a diving bell prevents water from entering and allows the worker to move about in air rather than in water.

Caissons are used for underwater construction work, in laying the bases for piers, bridges, and viaducts that extend over water. They are used also in digging tunnels under rivers. A caisson is similar in principle to a diving bell. It is usually designed to be used in a fixed position for a longer period of time. Air pressure must hold the water out of the caisson so that men may be able to work in the chamber.

The standard Navy deep-sea diver's dress and equipment weigh approximately 190 lb. (*Official Department of Defense photo*)

You will find additional interesting information on how these devices work in any good encyclopedia.

Dr. Charles W. Beebe, a noted biologist and undersea explorer, made a number of successful expeditions down more than $\frac{1}{2}$ mile to the ocean floor in a large hollow steel sphere called a *bathysphere*. The greatest depth reached by Dr. Beebe was 3,028 ft. He was accompanied on this trip by an assistant, Otis Barton. Some 15 years later in the summer of 1949, Barton himself broke this depth record in a new and improved diving device called a *benthoscope*. The benthoscope was a $57\frac{1}{2}$-in. steel sphere, $1\frac{3}{4}$ in. thick, fitted with clear quartz windows 3 in. thick. It carried enough oxygen gas in cylinders to last the occupant 6 hr. After several unsuccessful trials Barton descended in the benthoscope to a new record depth of 4,500 ft.

U.S. Navy submarine rescue bell (surfacing). (*Official Department of Defense photo*)

The benthoscope used by Otis Barton for his depth dive. (*Hancock Foundation, University of Southern California*)

Over two hours were required for the trip down and back. During this entire time Barton was able to talk by telephone with members of his crew on the ship above and tell them of the strange creatures he was seeing.

In 1953, Professor Auguste Piccard, a Swiss scientist, accompanied by his son Jacques, dived to a depth of 10,330 ft in the waters off the Italian coast. The oddly shaped diving device that Piccard used was called a *bathyscaphe*.

Keeping Alive Under Water

Two major problems that must be solved by anyone who would work or explore under water are (1) how to get air to breathe and (2) how to withstand the water pressure.

To solve the first problem a diver must either take a reserve supply of air down with him or must get it from the surface through a tube. In ordinary diving without apparatus, the diver takes down only the air he can store in his lungs. When this is exhausted he must rise to the surface for more or perish. In some modern types of diving equipment, the diver carries his reserve supply of air compressed in a steel cylinder fastened to his back. A helmet fits over his head and he releases the air from the cylinder into this helmet as needed. The used air escapes into the water through a valve. The air pressure inside the helmet must be at least as great as that of the water outside.

Another type of underwater equipment used primarily by swimmers requires a mask that covers the face and two or three steel cylinders of compressed air that are strapped to the back. Outlets from the cylinders to the mask enable the swimmer to breath through the nose and mouth. About five pounds of lead fastened to a belt around the swimmer's waist help him to sink in the water. Flippers worn on the feet assist in swimming.

A submarine also carries its own air supply. The pressure of the atmosphere within one of these underwater ships is nearly the same as that of the air above the water. Air-conditioning equipment is installed to restore the depleted oxygen and remove the excess carbon dioxide that accumulates in this atmosphere as it is breathed.

In some types of deep-sea diving equipment, fresh air is pumped from the surface to the submerged diver through a tube. The used air passes through a valve in the diver's helmet into the water outside. Fresh air is pumped under pressure into diving bells and caissons. In all these cases the air pressure under which the workman or diver works is practically equal to that of the water outside. The pressure on the diver increases as he goes deeper.

Withstanding Water Pressure

For every 100 ft of depth, pressure in fresh water increases about 43.3 lb/in.² and in sea water about 44.6 lb/in.² If the surface of a diver's body is 16 ft², then at 100 ft down in sea water he is squeezed by the water with a crushing force of over 50 tons. This force will vary with the size of the diver but in any event it is stupendous. When using diving suits and helmets, a diver has to withstand this full crushing force. How much he can endure determines how deep he can go with equipment of this kind. The limit is usually 400 ft or less, although a record test dive of 500 ft has been reported.

In submarines and devices like Beebe's bathysphere, Barton's benthoscope, and Piccard's bathyscaphe, the crushing force of the water is sustained by the steel shell. This permits the occupants to live in an atmosphere that has nearly the same pressure as that of the air at the surface of the water. The crushing force of the water outside limits the maximum depth of submarine operation to about 400 ft. At too great a depth the hull of a submarine would be crushed in like an eggshell.

►Do You Know?

1. Why can submarines not operate at depths of ½ mile?
2. How does a submarine dive and surface?
3. Describe how a caisson is used.
4. What sources of power are used to operate the engines of a submarine? Are the same sources used when the submarine is on the surface as when it is submerged?
5. What is a *snorkel?*
6. How were Beebe and Barton able to see fish and other marine animals when they were more than one-half mile below the surface of the sea?

HIGHLIGHTS

Force is a push or pull that tends to change the motion of a body on which it acts.

Pressure is the amount of force per unit area. $P = F/A$

The *total force* on a surface is the average pressure at that surface multiplied by its area. $F = P_{av} \times A$

Liquids exert pressure at all points below their surface because they have weight. The force due to this pressure at any point is the same in all directions.

The pressure at any point in a liquid due to its weight is equal to the depth of the point times the density of the liquid. $P = H \times D$

The pressure at any point in a liquid due to its weight does not depend on the size or shape of the container.

Pressure limits the depth to which men can descend in water to about 400 ft unless the diving device supports the force due to the weight of the water.

Pascal's law: Pressure produced by an external force applied to an enclosed liquid is transmitted undiminished throughout the body of the liquid.

In a hydraulic press

$$F/f = A/a = D^2/d^2$$

Archimedes' principle: A body immersed in a liquid is buoyed up by a force equal to the weight of the displaced liquid, or the apparent loss in weight of a body immersed in a liquid is equal to the weight of the displaced liquid.

The *buoyant force* on a given submerged body is greater in a denser liquid.

A *hydrometer* is used for testing the specific gravity of storage battery solutions, antifreeze solutions, sirups, milk, and other liquids.

Diving suits, diving helmets, diving bells, caissons, the bathysphere, the benthoscope, the bathyscaphe, and similar devices are used for underwater work.

Two major problems encountered in working under water are (1) how to get air to breathe and (2) how to withstand the water pressure.

PROBLEMS: GROUP A

1. What is the water pressure on a diver when he is 10 m below the surface of a fresh-water lake?

2. What is the water pressure on a diver when he is 50 ft below the surface of a fresh-water lake?

3. How much is the total force of water on the bottom of an aquarium which is 100 cm long and 50 cm wide and is filled with water to a depth of 40 cm?

4. How much is the total force of water on one of the 100- by 40-cm sides of the aquarium in the previous problem?

5. A force of 10 lb is applied to the smaller piston of a hydraulic press. The area of this piston is 0.5 in.² while the area of

the larger piston is 500 in.² How much force does the larger piston exert against its load under these conditions?

6. Explain how Archimedes could have gone about detecting the crime of the goldsmith. Use numbers if possible.

7. A stone weighs 250 g in air and 150 g when submerged in water. What is the volume of the stone? What is its specific gravity?

8. A rectangular block of wood 12 cm long, 8 cm wide, and 4 cm high weighs 225 g. What is the specific gravity of this wood?

9. A piece of iron weighs 500 g in air and 433 g when submerged in water. What is the specific gravity of this iron? What would be the weight of 1 ft³ of this iron?

10. What was the approximate water pressure on the outside of the bathysphere when Dr. Beebe was 3,028 ft down (in sea water)? What was the approximate pressure on the benthoscope at a depth of 4,500 ft? In sea water the density and hence the pressure at a given depth is about 1.03 times that in fresh water.

11. A rectangular block of glass 4 by 6 by 20 cm weighs 1,248 g. What is the specific gravity of this glass?

12. A lead plummet weighs 1,000 g in air and 912 g when immersed in water. What is the specific gravity of the lead?

13. What is the volume of a boat anchor which weighs 6 kg in air and 5.2 kg when under water?

14. What is the total force acting against the face of a rectangular dam 50 ft long and 20 ft high when the water stands 5 ft below the top of the dam?

15. What is the total force of water on the body of a diver 150 ft below the surface of fresh water, if the area of the surface of his body is 16 ft²?

16. The bottom of a barrel has an area of 350 in.² It is filled with fresh water to a depth of 2 ft. What is the total force of water on the bottom of the barrel?

17. A boy who weighs 160 lb in air can float in water with his body just submerged. Under these conditions, what is the total volume displaced by his body? What is the *average* density of his body? Could this boy float in the same way if he gained 5 lb? Explain.

18. If the area of the surface of a boy's body is 12 ft², how much total force is exerted on his body by the water when he dives to an average depth of 8 ft in fresh water?

19. A fresh egg which weighs 40 g just floats in salt water. The specific gravity of the salt water is 1.2. What is the volume of the egg?

20. A steel gasoline drum setting on end is 2.5 ft high. This drum is fitted with a 1-in. pipe which extends upward 17.5 ft. The drum and pipe are then completely filled with water. What is the water pressure on the bottom of the steel drum?

GROUP B

1. What is the average pressure on a submarine 200 ft below the ocean surface?

2. What is the total force of water on the bottom of a rectangular tank 10 ft long and 8 ft wide when it is filled with fresh water to a depth of 5 ft?

3. What is the total force of the water against one of the 10- by 5-ft sides of the rectangular tank in the preceding problem?

4. What is the total force of water against the face of a dam 100 ft long, when the water at the face of the dam is 10 ft deep and the stream backs up for a distance of 1 mile?

5. Suppose the diameter of the master

cylinder of a hydraulic brake system is 0.5 in. and that of a brake cylinder is 1 in. If the force exerted on the master piston is 50 lb, what is the force exerted by the piston of the brake cylinder on the lever attached to the brake shoe?

6. What is the net lifting force exerted by a watertight gasoline drum filled with air when it is completely submerged in fresh water? The drum is 18 in. in diameter and 3 ft high and weighs 50 lb. (Such drums are sometimes used to support floating diving platforms at bathing beaches.)

7. A glass stopper weighs 50 g in air, 30 g when immersed in water, and 35 g when immersed in a sample liquid. What is the specific gravity of the sample liquid?

8. A cork stopper weighing 12 g in air is attached to a lead sinker, which alone weighs 50 g under water. When both cork and sinker are under water their combined weight is only 12 g. What is the specific gravity of the cork?

9. The density of sea water is approximately 1.03 g/cm³. What is the total force of water on a submarine submerged to an average depth of 200 ft? Assume that the outside surface of the submarine is 7,500 ft².

10. If the diameter of the smaller cylinder of a hydraulic press is 2 in. and the diameter of the larger cylinder is 30 in., how much force is exerted against the load by the piston of the larger cylinder when a force of 100 lb is applied to the piston of the smaller cylinder?

11. The specific gravity of wood in a sample block is 0.65. The sample block is 4 by 5 by 2 in. This block floats in water on a 4 × 5 face. How many inches is the surface of the water from the top of the floating block?

12. A barge when loaded with coal sinks an additional 24 in. into fresh water in which it floats. The barge is 30 ft wide and 80 ft long and rectangular. What is the weight of the coal?

THINGS TO DO

1. Does a floating body have weight? Weigh some water in a pan. Float an apple in the water and weigh again. The floating apple "loses all of its weight." But do your scales show that this is true? Explain.

2. Can you find the volume of an apple? Obtain a bowl large enough to hold the apple easily. Set the bowl in a larger pan and fill the bowl level full of water without spilling any over into the pan. Push the apple into the bowl so that it is completely submerged in the water. Pour the overflow water into a measuring cup and measure its volume. This should be the same as the volume of the apple. Explain why. NOTE: One cup is equal to ½ pt, or 14.44 in.³

3. Make a Cartesian diver that will rise or sink at your command. Obtain a narrow cylindrical medicine bottle, fill it partly full of water, and invert it in water in a milk bottle. The milk bottle should be filled to within about ¼ in. of the top. Adjust the amount of water that enters the medicine bottle so that it just floats. Then stretch and tie a sheet of rubber from an old inner tube or a toy balloon over the mouth of the milk bottle so that air cannot get in or out of the bottle. If the medicine bottle is properly adjusted, it should sink when you push in on the stretched rubber top and rise again to the surface when you release this pressure. Explain why the "diver" works this way.

3.

Forces in Gases:
Fluids in Action

AIR PRESSURE

We live in an ocean of air just as under-water animals live in an ocean of water. This ocean of air envelops the entire earth and extends upward several hundred miles. We spend most of our lives on the floor or bottom of this vast ocean of air, which we call the *atmosphere*.

Air Has Weight

Can anything as "light as air" possibly have any weight? A good way to find an answer to this question is to try to weigh some air. Let us look at the experiment represented in Fig. 3–1. When we pump the air out of the hollow metal sphere with a vacuum pump, the sphere weighs less than when it is filled with air. This simple test shows clearly that air has weight.

Because air has weight and volume, it also has density. Careful measurements show that the density of very dry air at 0°C and normal atmospheric pressure is 0.001293 g/cm³, which is equal to 1.293 g/liter. In English units, this amounts to 1.29 oz/ft³. As the temperature rises, the density of air decreases so that at 20°C it is only 1.20 g/liter. Water vapor in the air also lowers its density. In an empty classroom 20 ft wide, 30 ft long, and 10 ft high the air alone (at ordinary temperatures) weighs a little less than 480 lb, as you can easily compute for yourself.

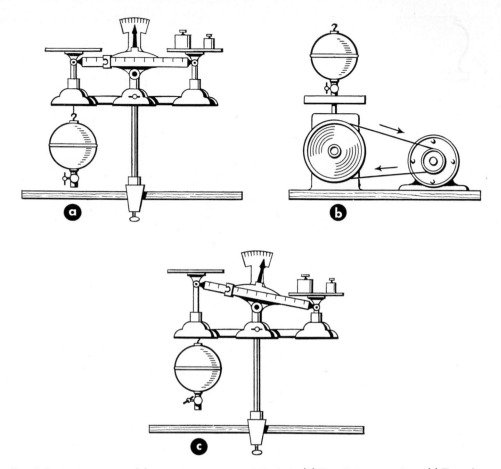

Fig. 3–1. Air has weight. (a) The hollow sphere is full of air. (b) The air is pumped out. (c) The sphere now weighs less.

Forces in Air Due to Its Weight

We found that water exerts a force at every point below its surface because it has weight. Since air likewise has weight, should we not expect it also to exert a force on the things about us at the bottom of this great ocean of air? For an answer, look at Fig. 3–2.

When we pump some of the air out of the bell jar in this experiment, air on the outside *pushes* in upon the rubber diaphragm. If we pump out enough air the diaphragm may burst. This simple test is good evidence that air *does* exert a

52

force on the rubber diaphragm. The amount of force per unit area exerted by the air is *air pressure*.

►You Will Be Interested to Know

The experiment shown in Fig. 3–3 was first performed about 1650 by Otto von Guericke, the versatile mayor of the Prussian city of Magdeburg. His experiments attracted attention and he was invited to stage a demonstration before the Emperor and his court. For this large-scale demonstration, von Guericke used two hemispheres about 22 in. in diameter. He hitched eight horses to each

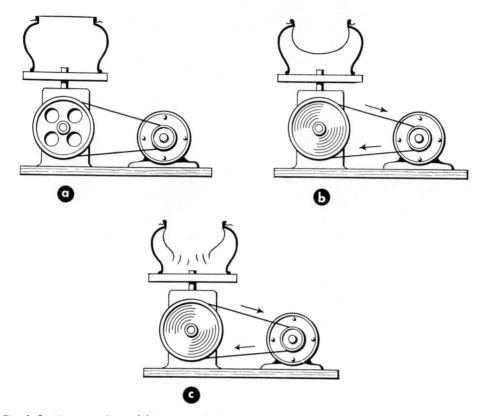

Fig. 3–2. Air exerts force. (a) A sheet of rubber is tied over the mouth of the bell jar. (b) Air is pumped out of the bell jar. (c) The force of air above breaks the rubber sheet.

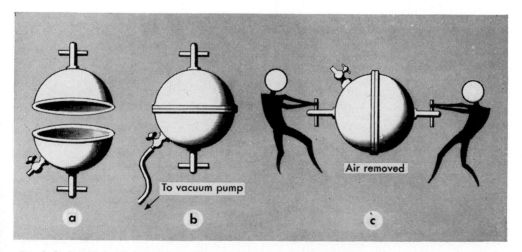

Fig. 3–3. Magdeburg hemispheres. A large force is required to pull them apart when air has been pumped out. Why?

hemisphere. After the air had been pumped out with the new vacuum pump, which von Guericke had previously invented, the horses were barely able to pull the hemispheres apart. Eight horses and a strong tree could have done just as well, but this would have been much less spectacular.

Measuring Air Pressure

One of our best ways of measuring air pressure was devised by Torricelli, an Italian scientist, about three centuries ago. Figure 3–4 shows how apparatus can be set up for this method.

After you have first filled the thick-walled glass tube with mercury in this experiment, you can hold a finger over the open end and invert the tube—placing this end under the mercury in the dish, as shown in Fig. 3–4b. When you remove your finger some of the mercury will run out of the tube, but a column 27 to 30 in. high will remain. Why does not all of the mercury flow out when the tube is inverted?

This effect is easy to understand when you recall that outside air presses downward on the open surface of the mercury in the dish and the column of mercury in the tube presses downward on the layer at its base. These two pressures taken at the same level must be equal when the mercury is at rest, according to Pascal's principle. The pressure on the base layer of the mercury column is $P = H \times D$, where H is the height of the column and D is the density of the mercury. This must also represent the pressure of the air on the surface of the mercury in the dish.

Air pressure is directly proportional to the height of the mercury column supported by it.

The pressure exerted by air can be expressed in different ways. We may speak of air pressures of 30 in., 75 cm, and 740 mm. In each case, the expressed

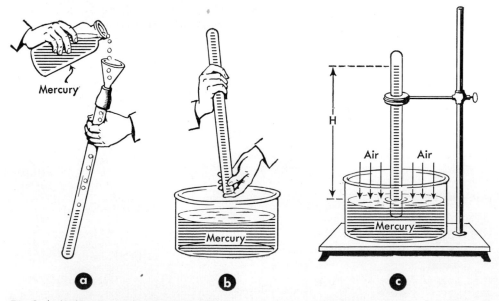

Fig. 3–4. Making a simple barometer to measure air pressure. (a) The glass tube is first filled with mercury. (b) It is then inverted in a dish of mercury. (c) Force due to air pressure then supports the mercury column H units high.

length refers to the *height* of the corresponding mercury column that the air can support at the moment. Of course, air pressure, like any other pressure, may be expressed in pounds per square inch or in grams per square centimeter.

EXAMPLE: Air pressure at a certain time was 740 mm of mercury. What is the value of this pressure in grams per square centimeter?

SOLUTION: $P = H \times D$

Here

$$H = 740 \text{ mm} = 74 \text{ cm}$$
$$D = 13.6 \text{ g/cm}^3 \text{ (mercury)}$$

so

$$P = 74 \text{ cm} \times 13.6 \text{ g/cm}^3$$
$$= 1,006 \text{ g/cm}^2$$

The Mercurial Barometer

The *mercurial barometer* is basically a Toricellian tube arranged for measuring air pressure. A glass tube for the mercury is usually enclosed in a metal housing with only the upper end of the tube and the mercury column exposed to view. A means is provided for setting the level of the mercury in the cup to the lower pointer or end of the scale before taking a reading. On a barometer fitted with a suitable *vernier scale* the height of the mercury column can be read directly to 0.1 mm or 0.01 in.

What Is a Millibar?

The *millibar* is a unit used by the weather services of the United States and other countries to express barometric pressure. It is equal to 1,000 dynes/cm².
(A *bar* is 1,000,000 dynes/cm².)
1 mm of mercury = 1.333 millibars
1 in. of mercury = 33.78 millibars

What Is One Atmosphere?

The height of the mercury column in a barometer at any location varies from day to day and often from hour to hour, because the pressure of the air is not constant. Furthermore, as Pascal discovered several hundred years ago, the height of the mercury column varies with altitude. It is greater at sea level than on a mountain top.

An *atmosphere* (atm) is a unit of pressure sometimes used in expressing the pressure exerted by gases and liquids. It is approximately equal to the *average* air pressure at *sea level* over an extended period of time, and is defined more precisely as follows:

$$1 \text{ atm} = 14.7 \text{ lb/in.}^2$$
$$= 1,033.6 \text{ g/cm}^2$$
$$= 29.9 \text{ in. of mercury}$$
$$= 760 \text{ mm of mercury}$$
$$= 1,013.25 \text{ millibars}$$

These definitions are not all exact equivalents but represent values commonly used.

The Aneroid Barometer

A mercury barometer is an excellent instrument for use in permanent locations where it can be mounted rigidly and does not need to be moved about frequently. It is not very convenient on shipboard, on planes, or for other portable use. The *aneroid* barometer is much more satisfactory for such purposes because it contains no liquid, is reasonably small and light, and can be moved easily from place to place. It is rugged, so that it is not unduly affected by rocking and vibration.

An aneroid barometer as shown in Fig. 3–5 contains a hollow airtight metal drum whose top springs in and out very slightly as air pressure on it changes.

The motion of the top is transmitted through, and magnified by, gears and levers to move a pointer across a dial. The scale on this dial may be marked in equivalent inches, or millimeters of mercury, or in millibars.

Usually an aneroid has to be checked against a mercury barometer from time to time to ensure that its readings are correct. Aneroid readings, also, have to be corrected for temperature when precise values are required. A barometer of this type can be made so sensitive that you can easily see a small change in its reading when you lift the barometer from the floor to the top of a table.

The Altimeter

Measurements made in different ways indicate that air pressure decreases with altitude as we go higher into the atmosphere. The average rate of fall for the first few thousand feet is approximately

1 in. of mercury for each 900 ft rise
1 mm of mercury for each 10 m rise

When the barometer reads 760 mm at sea level, it will read only about 660 mm at the top of a 1,000-m mountain and 460 mm in a plane 3,000 m above sea level. Again, when the barometer reads 30 in. at sea level, it will read only about 29 in. at a point 900 ft above sea level, and 20 in. on a mountain top 9,000 ft high. The rate of change of air pressure with altitude is not uniform, however, and these approximate values can be used only for elevations less than about 10,000 ft.

Because air pressure varies in a definite way with elevation, the dial of an aneroid barometer can be marked in feet or meters of elevation. An aneroid barometer marked in elevation units is one type of *altimeter* very commonly used by aviators. An altimeter must be set so that it reads *zero feet* at ground level, if its dial readings are to indicate directly the distance above ground. This instrument must be reset each time just before it is taken aloft to measure elevation.

Because of differences in air pressure at a given time from one ground station to another, an aneroid type of altimeter

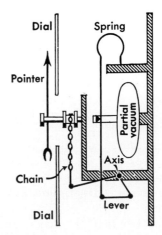

Fig. 3–5. An aneroid barometer indicates air pressure. The diagram shows the arrangement of the main parts of an aneroid. (*Photo from the Taylor Instrument Company*)

is not a very reliable indicator of the actual distance of a plane above ground, especially on long flights. Other types of altimeters using principles of radio and radar are often used to provide a pilot or navigator with a better check on his distance above ground.

Altimeters of the aneroid type are available for use on automobiles. Have you ever seen one of these installed on a car?

How a Lift Pump Works

Lift pumps, such as the one diagramed in Fig. 3–6, are often used to pump water from boats, shallow wells, or cisterns. On the upstroke of the piston, air pressure on the water in the tube is reduced and the greater pressure on the water in the well causes water to flow up the tube past the open lower valve and into the cylinder to follow the piston. On the downstroke of the piston, the lower valve closes. The trapped water in the cylinder moves past the valve (now open) in the piston to the space above. On the next upstroke, the piston valve closes and the water trapped above it flows out the spout while air pressure causes more water to flow into the cylinder. Air pressure cannot cause water to rise farther than about 32 to 34 ft, as we have seen, so the greatest practical distance this pump can be placed above the water level is from 26 to 30 ft. A pump of this type may dry out when not in use so that the piston on its upstroke can no longer reduce air pressure inside the cylinder. Air pressure outside, then, is not sufficient to raise water in the pipe and the pump delivers no water. In this event, water is sometimes poured into the top of the cylinder to "prime" the pump, that is, to help seal the valves when they close. Priming often enables the pump to operate again.

The Simple Force Pump

A simple force pump is shown in Fig. 3–7. Notice that there is no valve in the piston and that a valve is inserted in the outlet line. An *air dome* is often connected to the outlet line to obtain a steadier flow of water.

This type of pump can force water over considerable elevations, but the cylinder of the pump must be close enough to the surface of the water supply so that the existing air pressure can raise water into the cylinder. For all practical purposes this limiting height is 30 ft or less.

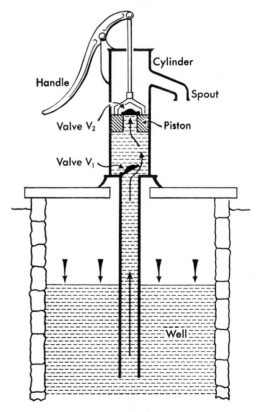

Fig. 3–6. A simple lift or pitcher pump. This pump delivers water through the spout only on the upstroke of the piston.

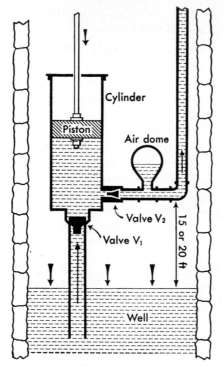

Fig. 3–7. A simple force pump. This pump delivers water to the outlet pipe only on the downstroke of the piston.

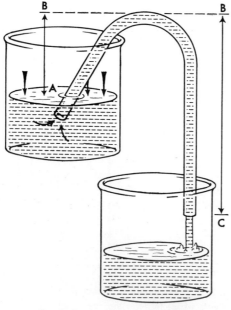

Fig. 3–8. A siphon in operation.

How the Siphon Works

A bent tube with its shorter arm placed in a tank of liquid and its longer arm free, as shown in Fig. 3–8, will serve to remove liquid from a tank. Such a device is called a *siphon*. Once the siphon is started, the liquid will flow from the upper tank due to the air pressure on the surface of the liquid. If there are two liquids in the tank, such as milk and cream, the siphon can be arranged to remove the lower liquid without disturbing the one above.

There are several ways of starting a siphon. Air can be removed from the longer arm by any means at hand until the flow of liquid starts. The tube can be filled with the liquid and its ends held shut until the tube is in position. When the ends are then opened, the flow of liquid from the tank will usually start.

For a siphon to continue operating, two conditions must be satisfied: (1) The vertical distance AB in Fig. 3–8 must not exceed the distance to which air pressure can raise water. This means 30 ft or less in practice. (2) The vertical distance BC in Fig. 3–8 must be greater than the distance AB.

Water will "flow uphill" in part of the siphon but no siphon can deliver water to a higher level than that from which it started.

►You Will Be Interested to Know

Scientists have not always explained these effects we have just examined in the way we now do. The ancient Greeks believed and taught that the rise of liquids in straws and tubes occurs because "nature abhors a vacuum." This explanation satisfied most people until the time of Galileo, about 1600. Galileo became skeptical of this explanation when he observed that water would rise only about 26 ft in the pump in a certain well. He died before he could test the ancient explanation experimentally, but his pupil Torricelli carried on with his ideas and established the fact that air pressure causes liquids to rise in tubes, as we have already seen. Pascal in Paris became much interested in air pressure. His brother-in-law, L. Perrier, lived near a convenient mountain at Clermont in south-central France. Pascal induced him to carry a barometer several times up and down this mountain side and observe the results. On each trial he found a difference of more than 3 in. in the barometer reading from the foot to the top of the mountain. These experiments showed clearly that the height of the mercury column decreases with elevation and thus overthrew the ancient theory that "nature abhors a vacuum."

How High Is Our Atmosphere?

We know both the density of air in the lower layer of our atmosphere and the pressure it exerts. With the same information about water, we could solve the equation $P = H \times D$ for H and calculate how deep the water must be. But when we try to apply this equation to our atmosphere, we find that we really do not know what value to use for the density of air. Air, and in fact any gas, is very easily compressed, whereas water is almost incompressible. As a result, the density of air falls off along with pressure at higher levels of the atmosphere. Should we use for the density of air its value at sea level, or its value at some other level? Without knowing the value of D, we *cannot calculate the height of our atmosphere from the pressure equation.*

We do, however, have direct ways of exploring the upper atmosphere. We can send up instruments to measure such effects as air pressure, temperature, humidity, and winds. These airborne instruments may either make records of the effects they measure, or may send the information back to the ground by short-wave radio. In some cases flasks are sent up in balloons or rockets to trap air at different levels and bring the samples down for laboratory analysis.

The chief means of carrying instruments into the upper atmosphere are:

1. Airplanes. With pressurized cabins and oxygen for the personnel, planes can operate up to elevations of 50,000 ft or more.

2. Manned balloons. Balloons with men aboard have reached heights of well over 13 miles. A pressurized gondola and oxygen for the occupants are required for such trips.

3. Sounding balloons. Hydrogen-filled balloons have carried instruments aloft some 24 miles. The instruments parachute to earth when the balloon bursts.

4. Rockets. Huge rockets have carried instruments more than 100 miles into the upper regions of the atmosphere. Air at very low pressure and density is found even at this height.

We have some more indirect ways of exploring the upper atmosphere from the ground. Among these are:

1. The aurora. Auroral displays are visible almost every night near the north and the south magnetic poles. Sometimes they can be seen in the middle latitudes. They are believed to be due to electric discharges in the upper atmosphere. Measurements indicate that most of the streamers and curtains are from 60 to 100 miles above the earth, but occasional faint glows have been observed at 600 miles.

2. Radio sounding. A short pulse of radio signal sent directly upward may return like an echo. By knowing the speed of a radio wave and measuring the

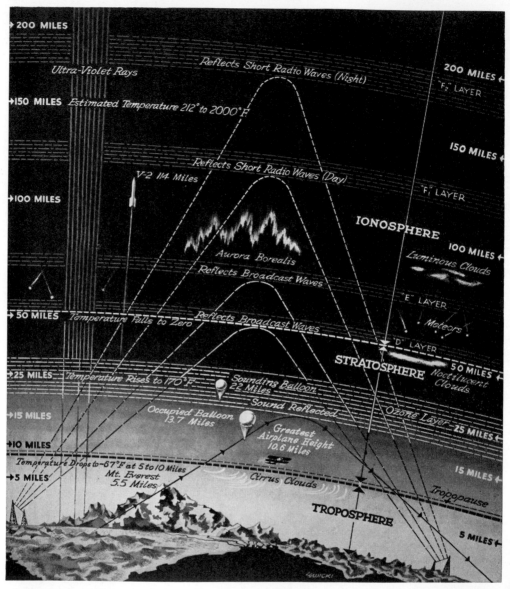

The structure of our atmosphere. (The New York Times Magazine; drawn by James Lewieki)

time for the echo to return, we can compute the apparent distance out to the reflector. There is evidence that many of the atoms in air at great heights are *ionized*, or electrically charged. Air in an ionized condition acts as a reflector for radio waves. So the distance up to reflecting layers of air can be calculated.

In this way, it is found that there is one layer 60 to 90 miles above the earth and another at 100 to 250 miles.

The information we have obtained concerning the height of our atmosphere can be used to reconstruct a picture of what it is probably like. The illustration above shows such a reconstruction.

The lower region in which we live is called the *troposphere*. In this region are clouds and winds. Temperature drops off more or less regularly with altitude, about 3.5 Fahrenheit degrees for every 1,000 ft. The troposphere extends up about 30,000 ft. Above this is a region called the *tropopause*, in which the temperature is practically constant at about 67°F below zero. The tropopause is the base of an extensive region immediately above it, called the *stratosphere*. What air is present in the stratosphere is mostly in layers. Some of these layers have been explored and named. In the *ozone layer* the temperature is almost high enough to boil water. The region above the stratosphere is called the *ionosphere*. Several different layers which play important roles in radio transmission have been discovered in the ionosphere, as we have already mentioned.

Our ocean of air has no definite top surface in the same sense that an ocean of water has a surface. Our atmosphere gets less and less dense at greater heights and eventually becomes so thin that only a few molecules per cubic meter remain at the outer fringe.

▶**Do You Know?**

1. Explain why "suction cups" stick to window glass.
2. If water were used in place of mercury in a Torricellian tube, how many times as high as the mercury would the water rise? Explain.
3. Why is it necessary to punch *two* holes in a condensed-milk can to get the milk to flow out readily?
4. Why do we have to remove the cap from a gasoline can to get the liquid to flow steadily from the spout?
5. Why is it easier to remove the lid from a fruit jar after we "let in air"?
6. What is the particular name of the

aurora visible in the *northern* hemisphere? What is the name of the one visible in the *southern* hemisphere?
7. Do you know any other effects that accompany unusual auroral displays?
8. How could von Guericke have used a tree or post to replace eight of the horses used in his famous experiment with the hemispheres?
9. How does an airdome help to produce a steady flow of water from a single action force pump?

THE AIR WE BREATHE

Our atmosphere is a mixture of several gases. Chief among these are nitrogen and oxygen, but argon, water vapor, carbon dioxide, and lesser amounts of neon, krypton, and several other gases are also present. A sample of air near the earth contains these gases in approximately the following percentages by volume:

Nitrogen	77.3 (about $\frac{4}{5}$)
Oxygen	20.8 (about $\frac{1}{5}$)
Water vapor	0.92
Argon	0.92
Carbon dioxide	0.03
All other gases	0.03

This means that of every 1,000 cm³ of air, about 773 are nitrogen gas, 208 are oxygen, 9.2 are argon, and so on. The proportions vary somewhat from time to time and from place to place. In breathing we take oxygen from the air we inhale and give carbon dioxide and water vapor to the air we exhale.

How We Breathe

You may be surprised to learn that even our breathing is a mechanical process that depends on air pressure. Figure 3–9 shows what we do to breathe.

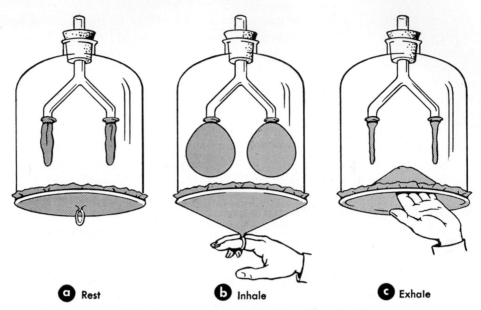

ⓐ Rest   **ⓑ** Inhale   **ⓒ** Exhale

Fig. 3–9. This apparatus shows how breathing takes place.

When we inhale we automatically raise our ribs and depress our diaphragm so that our chest cavity is enlarged. This reduces the air pressure within this cavity below that of the atmosphere outside. Air then *pushes* into the lungs, just as it pushes into the rubber balloons in Fig. 3–9*b*. Notice that we have no way

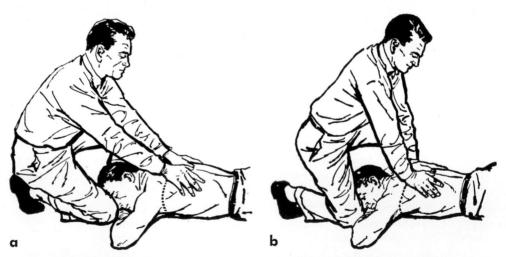

a   b

Back-pressure arm-lift method of artificial respiration, adopted by the American Red Cross. The victim is placed prone with the elbows bent and with one hand upon the other. The cheek is placed on the hand with the face turned slightly to one side. The operator kneels on one knee at the head of the victim. (*a*) The operator places his hands on the victim's back so that the thumbs just touch and the hands are just below a line running between the armpits. (*b*) He then rocks forward slowly, keeping the elbows straight, until his arms are approximately vertical, exerting steady pressure

62

to *draw* air into the lungs; it can only be *pushed* in from outside. When we exhale, we reduce the chest cavity and increase the pressure within it. This pushes the air out of the lungs in the same way that air is pushed out of the balloons in Fig. 3–9c.

Anything that interferes with our ability to raise and lower the air pressure within our chest cavity interferes with breathing. When this ability is impaired by accident or disease, it is sometimes necessary to employ *artificial* means of assisting or maintaining the process of respiration (breathing).

How Air Pressure Affects Us

If you weigh 120 lb, the surface of your body is approximately 12 ft² in area. With an air pressure of 14.7 lb/in.², there is a total air force of more than 12.5 tons pressing inward on your body. Why does this not crush you? The explanation of this condition is that the blood and other fluids in the tissues of the body are adjusted to exert an equal counterbalancing pressure. If the air pressure outside were changed very much, you would at once become aware of the effect of pressure.

Reduced air pressure encountered at high altitudes affects us in several ways. With lower outside pressure, our lungs are not filled so completely when we inhale. With lower density, we actually get fewer molecules of air in each "breath." So we must breathe more times per minute to get the amount of oxygen our bodies require, that is, we become "short of breath." If the outside pressure is reduced very much, the pressure of the blood and other liquids in the body is no longer balanced. Our bodies then tend to burst. In some cases, blood vessels near the surface of delicate tissues may be ruptured, causing hemorrhages in the eyes, ears, and breathing passages.

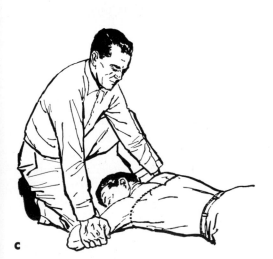
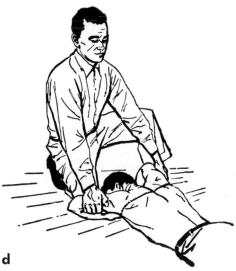

c d

upon the chest. (c) Then he rocks backward, slowly sliding his hands to the victim's arms just above the elbows. (d) Continuing to rock backward, he raises the arms until resistance and tension are felt at the victim's shoulder. Then he drops the arms and thus completes a full cycle. The cycles are repeated 12 times per minute, the expansion and compression phases being of equal length, and the release periods of minimum duration. (*The American National Red Cross*)

Stratoliners that fly at high altitude are equipped with superchargers to supply enough air for the engines. Their cabins are sealed and "pressurized" so that even at great heights the occupants experience an air pressure only slightly less than that on the ground. With similar arrangements for the safety and comfort of passengers, planes with rocket engines may be able to travel far into the stratosphere.

Men who work under water are subjected to *increased* air pressure, as we have already seen. Workers in tunneling operations under rivers and other bodies of water work in chambers (caissons) in which the air pressure is sometimes raised to 3 or 4 atmospheres to keep out the water. It is necessary that the pressure on a workman on those jobs be increased *gradually* as he enters the tunnel through one or more compression chambers. When he leaves work he must go through a gradual decompressing process before he is ready to live comfortably again under normal air pressure.

Nitrogen from the air dissolves in the blood of deep-sea divers and others who work under increased air pressure. If the pressure on the diver's body is not reduced very slowly when he comes up from a dive, this dissolved nitrogen is likely to form bubbles in the blood stream and cause a very painful and dangerous disease known as *bends*. It has been found that helium does not dissolve in blood as readily as nitrogen, so many divers now use a mixture of helium and oxygen gases for under water breathing. In this "synthetic air," helium takes the place of the nitrogen of natural air. Divers using this helium gas mixture are able to come up from depths of several hundred feet in a few minutes without experiencing painful results, whereas with natural air an hour or more may be required.

64

▶Do You Know?

1. How does the change in pressure affect a deep-sea fish when it is caught and hauled to the surface?
2. Why does a parachute jumper have to take precautions to prevent his ear drums from bursting when he falls rapidly?
3. Why are partly filled fountain pens likely to leak ink when taken aloft in a plane?
4. Would it be possible to breathe in a vacuum? Why?
5. Explain how the human body withstands the enormous force exerted on it by the air. Why do we not feel the force of the air on our body?

AIR PRESSURE AND WEATHER

Weather forecasts are important to many people. Day-to-day changes in air pressure at a network of weather stations form one of the bases on which weather predictions are made.

How Air Pressure Is Recorded

The barometer is a very good instrument for measuring air pressure at any one time and place, but when a continuous record over a period of hours or days is required, an instrument that automatically records this pressure is much more convenient. Such an instrument is called a *barograph*. A barograph is essentially an aneroid barometer with a type of fountain pen attached to the pointer. The pen moves across a sheet of ruled paper attached to a cylinder that is driven slowly by clockwork. The pen traces a graph of the barometric pressure on the ruled paper during the interval of time that the cylinder has been rotating. We can read directly from such a graph the barometric pressure that

This barograph is tracing a permanent record of air pressure on the chart of the rotating drum. (U.S. Weather Bureau)

existed at any time during the interval covered. These records are permanent and may be filed for future reference and study.

The United States Weather Bureau and weather services maintained by the different airlines use barographs to record air pressure. Sometimes barographs are used in airplanes to obtain a continuous record of the altitude during a flight.

What Are Isobars?

The United States Weather Bureau maintains hundreds of weather stations in different locations throughout the country. Each of these stations collects data on such weather elements as visibility, wind velocity and direction, temperature, humidity, barometric pressure, and precipitation. Each station transmits its weather information to a central office at regular times. Barometric pressures (reduced to sea level) are plotted on a map of the United States at the central office and lines are drawn on this map through stations that report the same air pressure. Such lines are called *isobars*, that is, lines of equal pressure. The photograph on page 66 shows the isobars for a particular day. Many of the isobars are closed curves. Notice that pressure in millibars is marked on each isobar.

Regions of high barometric pressure called *highs* and regions of low pressure called *lows* are marked on the map. Highs and lows move across our continent, in general, from west to east, although many pressure areas do not follow a regular course. In high-pressure areas the weather is usually fair, clear, and cooler. In low-pressure areas the weather is likely to be warmer and cloudy, often accompanied by rain or snow. Warm and cold *fronts* where warmer and colder air masses meet are often more reliable indicators of weather changes than are the highs and lows.

Since weather conditions play such an important role in agriculture, shipping, transportation, travel and many of our personal outdoor activities, advance weather information is of great value to us. Weather maps are so important to navigation that they are transmitted regularly by radio facsimile to ships at sea. The safety of air travel depends to

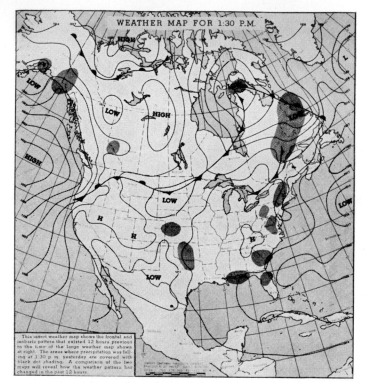

WEATHER MAP FOR 1:30 P.M.

Weather map for Monday, July 20, 1953, 1:30 P.M. (*U.S. Weather Bureau*)

such a degree on reliable weather information that air lines require new weather maps issued several times each day. Farmers and others whose work is dependent on weather have learned to appreciate the value of advance weather information.

Radiosonde

Information concerning weather conditions in the upper atmosphere is obtained from several sources. Planes in flight report weather by radio. A special weather plane may be sent up to explore conditions above a landing field. A great deal of information is obtained by a system called *radiosonde*. A radiosonde unit consists of a balloon that carries aloft weather instruments and a short-wave radio transmitter. The transmitter automatically sends back to a ground station information concerning weather

conditions at different levels. When the balloon bursts, the instruments are parachuted to earth and thus are often recovered undamaged.

►Do You Know?

1. From what central office are weather maps for your area issued?
2. How could you use daily weather maps posted on a bulletin board in your school?
3. What is the significance of a *rapidly* falling barometer reading?
4. Do you know any station at which radiosonde equipment is used? Where?
5. Do you know anyone who has found radiosonde equipment that has parachuted to earth after the balloon burst? What should be done with such equipment when it is found?
6. Find out if your local telephone com-

pany or some other agency in your community furnishes weather reports by phone. If so, how could you use this service?

7. To what department of our Federal government does the United States Weather Bureau belong?

ARCHIMEDES' PRINCIPLE IN GASES

Do you recall that an object immersed in a liquid is buoyed up by a force equal to the weight of the liquid it displaces? We shall now investigate whether this principle of Archimedes operates in air and other gases, as well as in liquids. Liquids and gases can be made to *flow* through a tube or pipe, so they are both called *fluids*. Figure 3–10 shows what happens when we weigh a hollow metal sphere first in air and then in a vacuum. The sphere must be sealed airtight.

The hollow sphere seems heavier when the air is removed! We can interpret this to mean that the sphere is buoyed up by a force and seems to lose weight when it is in air, just as a body does when it is immersed in water. But the cylinder must at the same time be buoyed up and appear to lose weight, for it also is in air. The sphere, however, has a greater volume, and so displaces a greater weight of air. If the amount of buoyant force depends on the weight of the displaced air, then the sphere in air should appear to lose *more* weight than the cylinder. Figure 3–10 shows that this happens. Careful measurements show that the buoyant force and hence the apparent loss in weight of an object in air is just equal to the weight of the displaced air. The same effect can be observed in any gas.

A body immersed in a fluid is buoyed up by a force equal to the weight of the displaced fluid.

To find the real weight of any object that we weigh in air, we would need to correct for the buoyant force of the air both on the object and on the weights we use to counterbalance it. This correction is so small, however, that we never consider it except in the most precise weighings. If your weight were corrected for the buoyant effect of air, your real weight would be only 2 or 3 oz more than that now indicated by the scales.

Balloons that float or rise in air do so because the weight of the air they displace is equal to or greater than the

A radiosonde balloon with parachute, instrument case, and miniature radio transmitter attached. (*U.S. Weather Bureau–L. E. Johnson*)

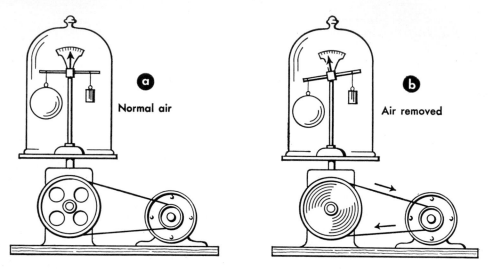

Fig. 3–10. Archimedes' principle holds for air.

combined weight of the balloon, the gas it contains and the load attached to it. The weight of the gas used to fill the balloon must be "lighter than air." Two gases, hydrogen and helium, are commonly used to fill balloons although some of the early ones were filled with hot air or household fuel gas. Hydrogen, mixed with air, is explosive when ignited by a spark. Helium is not flammable. The net lifting force of a given volume of any gas is the weight of the displaced air *minus* the weight of the gas. The net lifting force of helium is about 90 percent that of a corresponding volume of hydrogen. Table 3–1 shows how these two gases compare in density and lifting force.

▶You Will Be Interested to Know

Helium was first discovered on the sun. Nearly all the world's supply of helium is obtained from the natural gas from wells in the Panhandle of Texas. Its extraction and distribution are under direct control of the United States government. The cost of helium dropped from about $2,500 per cubic foot prior to 1917 to the present cost of about 1 cent per cubic foot because of the discovery of richer sources and the development of improved methods of extraction.

▶Do You Know?

1. Why does a toy balloon or a soap bubble filled with household fuel gas

Table 3–1. Comparison of Hydrogen, Helium, and Air

Gas (at 0°C and 760 mm of mercury)	Weight of 1 ft³, oz	Net lifting force of 1 ft³, oz
Hydrogen	0.090	1.201
Helium	0.177	1.114
Air	1.291	0

rise to the ceiling when released in a room?

2. What factors determine the height to which a hydrogen-filled balloon released outdoors can rise?
3. About what percentage of a sample of the natural gas extracted from the Texas fields is helium?
4. Why were the production and distribution of helium in the United States placed under direct governmental control?
5. Birds have hollow bones. How does this fact aid or hinder the flight of birds in air?

PRESSURE AND ITS EFFECTS

A gas always exerts a pressure on every surface that it touches. Under some conditions this pressure may be very low, but under others it may become quite high.

Pascal's Law for Gases

When we apply pressure on the surface of any enclosed gas, the gas compresses, but at the same time it exerts an equal pressure on any surface it touches, just as liquids do. Thus Pascal's law applies to gases as well as to liquids.

Pressure in an enclosed fluid produced by an external force applied to the fluid is transmitted undiminished throughout the body of the fluid.

Boyle's Law

If you squeeze an inflated rubber balloon, its volume becomes smaller but the pressure inside may become great enough to break the rubber. Is there any definite relation between the volume and the pressure of the air in the balloon? To find an answer to this question, let us examine the effects shown in Fig. 3–11.

In Fig. 3–12, the volumes indicated in Fig. 3–11 are plotted against their corresponding pressures. Notice that the graph obtained is not a straight line, but a portion of a curve. This particular curve is called a *hyperbola*. When we have plotted this curve for a given body of gas we can predict what the volume of this body of gas will be at any pressure if the temperature remains constant. *When two quantities are so related that one is doubled when the other is halved, one is tripled when the other is divided by three and so on, one quantity is* inversely proportional *to the other.*

The volume occupied by a body of gas is inversely proportional to its pressure, if its temperature remains constant.

This general law for gases was first formulated and expressed by Robert Boyle, an English scientist of the seventeenth century. It is now universally known as *Boyle's law.*

All gases follow this law quite closely except when they are near the temperature and pressure at which they change into a liquid (*liquefaction point*). The law assumes that the temperature of the gas is the same every time its pressure and volume are measured and also that the number of molecules in the body of gas remains constant.

You will notice from the data in Fig. 3–11 that in

    a. $PV = 20 \times 120 = 2,400$
    b. $PV = 40 \times 60 = 2,400$
    c. $PV = 60 \times 40 = 2,400$
    d. $PV = 80 \times 30 = 2,400$

So, one way of stating Boyle's law in mathematical terms is

$$P_1 V_1 = P_2 V_2$$

where P_1 and V_1 refer to the pressure and volume of the gas under one set of con-

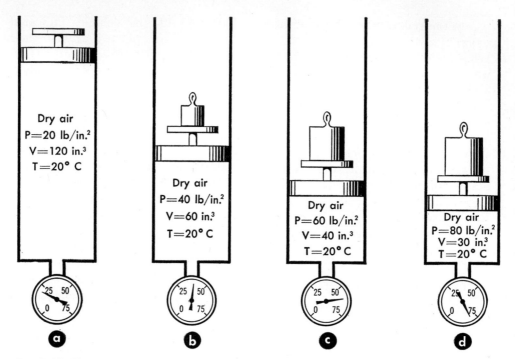

Fig. 3–11. The volume and pressure of a body of gas. The piston is assumed to be leakproof and to move freely in the cylinder. Pressure indicated by the gage *includes* that of the atmosphere which pushes down on the piston. (a) Notice the original values of P, V, and T. (b) When the original pressure is doubled, the volume is reduced to half the original volume. (c) When the original pressure is multiplied by three, the volume becomes one third the original volume. (d) When the original pressure is multiplied by four, the volume becomes one-fourth of the original volume.

ditions, and P_2 and V_2 refer to the pressure and volume under a second set of conditions. Another way of writing this law is

$$PV = k$$

where k stands for a constant. In Fig. 3–11, $k = 2,400$, but k will have a different value for a different mass of gas or a different temperature. Still another way of writing this same equation is

$$P_1/P_2 = V_2/V_1$$

You can easily test the validity of this form of the equation by substituting the corresponding numbers for the P's and V's from Fig. 3–11.

Density and Pressure

The same molecules are packed into smaller space when the pressure on a body of gas is increased. So the number of molecules per unit volume is increased by an increase in pressure. For this reason, the mass per unit volume and the weight per unit volume (density) of the gas are increased by increasing pressure. Careful measurements show that the density of any gas at constant temperature is *directly* proportional to its pressure.

$$D_1/D_2 = P_1/P_2$$

where D_1 is the density of the gas when its pressure is P_1 and D_2 is its density when the pressure is P_2.

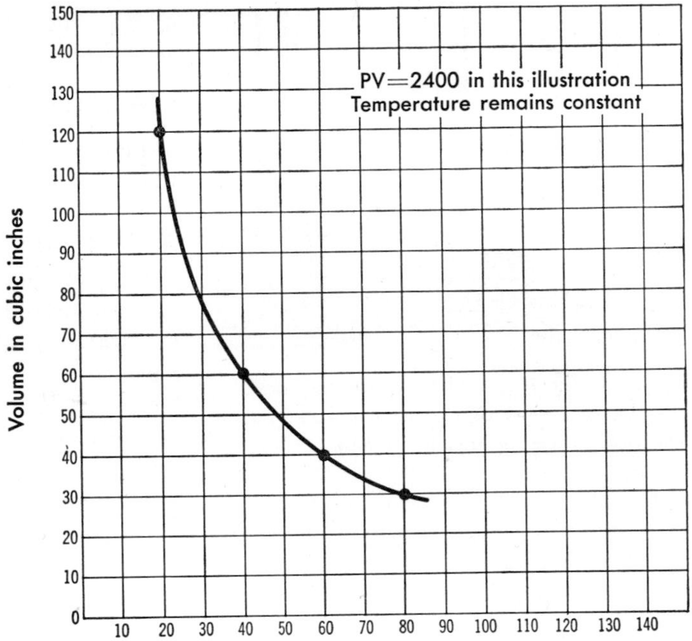

Fig. 3–12. How the volume of a gas varies with pressure.

PV=2400 in this illustration
Temperature remains constant

Volume in cubic inches

150
140
130
120
110
100
90
80
70
60
50
40
30
20
10
0

10 20 30 40 50 60 70 80 90 100 110 120 130 140

Pressure in pounds per square inch

▶Do You Know?

1. Why would a change in temperature of a gas during expansion or compression prevent the gas from following Boyle's law?
2. What is meant by "gage pressure," and how does this pressure differ from the P used in Boyle's law?
3. Is water pressure, computed from the equation $P = H \times D$, "gage pressure" or total pressure? Explain.
4. Explain the relationship of two quantities which are inversely proportional.
5. Explain how Pascal's law applies to gases as well as to liquids.

FLUIDS IN MOTION

Have you ever noticed that the flow of water from a tap *decreases* when another nearby tap is opened? When the demand is heavy, water pressure at service outlets of a water system often falls, even though the water level in the standpipes or the reservoir is maintained. These effects are due to the fall in pressure that occurs when any liquid *flows* through a pipe. You can see from the diagram in Fig. 3–13 how this principle works.

The fall in pressure is due to friction between the moving fluid and the walls

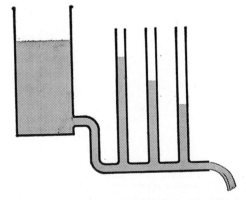

Fig. 3–13. Pressure is indicated by the height water rises in the side tubes. This pressure falls off as the water flows along the outlet pipe.

71

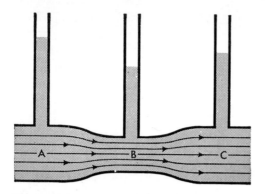

Fig. 3–14. The speed of flow increases and the pressure decreases as the flowing water passes into a constriction or neck in the tube.

of the pipe and between different layers of the fluid that move at different speeds. This internal friction between layers of a fluid is called *viscosity*. The higher the viscosity, the greater the internal friction, the slower the fluid will flow and the more the pressure will fall off in a given distance. Frictional force between the fluid and the pipe is relatively greater in a small pipe than in a larger one, so a fluid moves more freely through the

larger pipe. *The equation $P = H \times D$ does not apply to a moving liquid.*

Rate of Flow and Pressure

Figure 3–14 shows what happens to the pressure when a stream of water flows through a constriction in the pipe. As the water moves from A to B it must speed up; as it moves from B to C it must slow down. In the region where the water is speeded up, *its pressure is reduced.*

When a fluid passes through a constriction or around an obstacle in such a way that the stream is speeded up, the pressure within the fluid decreases.

This is known as *Bernoulli's effect.* Figures 3–15 and 3–16 show applications of this effect.

What Are Streamlines?

Lines indicating the paths of particles in a stream of fluid are called *streamlines*. The lines indicating the paths of particles of water in Fig. 3–14 are streamlines. Notice that these streamlines

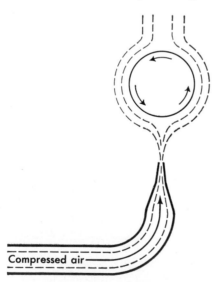

Fig. 3–15. Why does the Ping-pong ball stay in the stream of air?

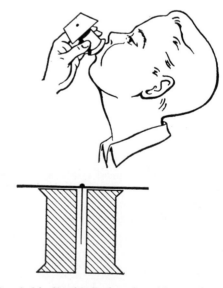

Fig. 3–16. Should the boy be able to blow the cardboard disk off the spool?

never cross one another. In the region where the flow is faster the lines are crowded together; where the flow is slower they are farther apart. The relative spacing of the streamlines indicates the relative speed of flow at different points along the path. Where the lines are crowded the water pressure is less.

Crowded streamlines mean reduced pressure.

Fluids do not always move in layers or streamlines. When a stream meets an obstacle, the regular motion may be broken up into whirls and eddies. A churning motion of this type is called *turbulence,* and the forward flow of the fluid is described as *turbulent.* Much more energy and power are used up in pushing along a turbulent stream than in pushing along one that moves in streamlines.

Why a Baseball Curves

When a pitcher throws a curve, he gives the ball a twisting motion that causes it to spin as it moves toward home plate. The direction and amount of curve depend on the direction and rate of spin together with the speed at which the ball travels. Notice in Fig. 3–18 that the ball drags some air with it as it spins. In this way it deflects the streamlines so that they are *crowded* below the ball. This indicates that the net air pressure here is less than normal and less than that on the top side of the ball. The pitched ball "drops" because a force due to this difference in air pressure *pushes* it down faster than it would normally fall. A spinning ball always "follows its nose," that is, it always tends to curve in the direction that its forward edge is spinning. If you keep this rule in mind, you can predict which way a ball will curve when given a particular spin.

In tennis, golf, handball, and other

Fig. 3–17. Streamlining reduces the driving power required for higher speeds.

games using balls, curves can be produced by giving the ball a spin.

Streamlines Aid Airplane Flight

A large part of the force required to keep an airplane in the air comes from

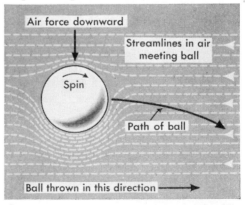

Fig. 3–18. How streamlines cause a "drop."

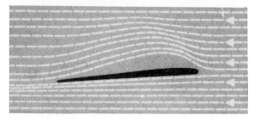

Fig. 3–19. Streamlines of air across an airplane wing.

the streamline effect on its wings. Aviators sometimes speak of this as the "vacuum effect on the upper surface of the wings."

Figure 3–19 shows how streamlines of air move across an airplane wing. Notice that these lines are crowded along the upper surface. Air pressure on this surface is accordingly less than it would be in still air. Pressure on the under surface of the wing is greater

than that on the upper surface. This results in a net lifting force on the plane.

The flow of air across a wing and other parts of a plane can be photographed and studied by placing a model of the wing or plane in a wind tunnel. The model remains fixed, while the air flows through the tunnel at speeds that can be regulated. Air speeds greater than a mile per second can be obtained in some wind tunnels. These speeds are used for study of models of planes designed to fly at speeds faster than sound (supersonic speeds).

▶Do You Know?

1. Why is the boy unable to blow the cardboard off the spool in Fig. 3–16?
2. How does one "cut" a tennis ball to make it drop rapidly?
3. Why does "slicing" make a golf ball curve in its flight?
4. What are the advantages of "streamlining" trains?
5. Why do door handles, license plates, and other projections from the body of an automobile cause an increase in gas consumption when a car is driven at high speed?

HIGHLIGHTS

Air *weighs* 1.293 g/liter or 1.29 oz/ft³ at 0°C and a pressure of 760 mm of mercury.

Air exerts *pressure* on everything it touches. The normal value of this pressure at sea level is 14.7 lb/in.² or 1033.6 g/cm².

Air pressure is measured with a *barometer*. In the mercury barometer, the amount of pressure is indicated by the height of the mercury column supported by the air. This height is about 30 in. or 760 mm at sea level.

The height of the mercury column is less at *greater altitudes*. At any one place it fluctuates also with air conditions.

An *aneroid* barometer is a barometer without liquid. An *altimeter*, used for measuring the altitude of airplanes, is a special type of aneroid barometer.

74

The *millibar* is the international unit for measuring air pressure. One atmosphere equals 1013.25 millibars.

In the process of *breathing*, air is forced into the lungs by air pressure outside the body.

Isobars are lines of equal barometric pressure plotted on a map.

Balloons rise because they follow *Archimedes' principle*. The total weight of a rising balloon including the bag, the gas, and the load, must be less than the weight of the displaced air.

Hydrogen and *helium* may be used to fill balloons. Hydrogen is flammable. Helium is not flammable.

Boyle's law: The volume of a given body of gas at constant temperature is inversely proportional to its pressure.

$$P_1/P_2 = V_2/V_1 \quad \text{or} \quad PV = k$$

Where streamlines are crowded together, pressure within the fluid is reduced. This is *Bernoulli's effect*.

Streamlining trains, automobiles, airplanes, and boats *reduces the amount of power* required to drive them at high speeds.

Bernoulli's effect provides the *lift* on the wings of airplanes.

PROBLEMS: GROUP A

1. Compute the weight of air in a room 12 by 14 by 8 ft. Take the density of air as 0.08 lb/ft³.

2. A barometer reads 29.04 in. of mercury in a valley and 25.64 in. on a nearby mountain top. Approximately how many feet is the mountain top above the valley?

3. What is the greatest height over which a fresh-water siphon can work when the barometric pressure is 29.40 in. of mercury?

4. What volume of gas at atmospheric pressure must be compressed in a tank whose volume is 200 liters in order that the total pressure may be increased to 5 atmospheres?

5. What will be the volume of a body of gas at standard pressure (760 mm of mercury) if the gas occupies 150 cm³ at 740 mm pressure?

6. Read the barometer in your classroom or laboratory and from this reading compute the greatest height to which a lift pump can raise fresh water in your vicinity.

7. The pressure in a tank of oxygen is 2,000 lb/in.² What part of the original oxygen has been used when the pressure in the tank has dropped to 500 lb/in.²?

8. Compute the weight of air in an auditorium which is 70 ft long, 40 ft wide, and 20 ft high. Take the density of air as 0.08 lb/ft³.

9. When the barometer reads 745 mm of mercury, what will be its reading in inches of mercury?

10. When a barometer reads 730 mm of mercury, what would be its reading in millibars?

11. When a barometer reads 1,000 millibars, what would be its reading in millimeters of mercury?

12. What is the greatest distance (theoretical) the cylinder and piston of a lift pump may be placed above the surface

of water in a well and still work when the barometer reads 29.6 in. of mercury?

13. What would be the volume of a body of gas at standard pressure (760 mm) if the gas occupies 500 cm³ at a pressure of 1,000 mm of mercury? Assume that the temperature of the gas does not change.

14. A barometer taken aloft in an airplane reads 24.00 in. of mercury when a similar barometer on the ground reads 29.40 in. What is the approximate height of the plane above the ground?

GROUP B

1. Refer to the definition of the millibar on p. 55 and convert the following barometer readings to millibars: 27.5 in., 28.8 in., 735 mm, 746 mm.

2. When the barometer reads 28.77 in., what is the maximum height atmospheric pressure can raise fresh water in a good lift pump?

3. What is the total force of air holding together two Magdeburg hemispheres 4 in. in diameter? Take air pressure at 15 lb/in.² The force is that on an *area equivalent to one great circle of the sphere*, $A = \pi r^2$.

4. If 100 ft³ of helium at 0°C and 760 mm pressure is used to inflate the bag of a balloon weighing 1 lb, what is the net lifting force this balloon can exert?

5. To what volume will the air in a tire expand when released into the atmosphere? The tube has a volume of 1,500 in.³ and the pressure is 35 lb (gage). Take atmospheric pressure as 15 lb/in.²

6. The density of oxygen is 1.11 times that of air. What is the weight of oxygen in a 2-ft³ cylinder in which the gage pressure is 1,200 lb/in.² and the temperature 0°C? Take normal atmospheric pressure as 15 lb/in.²

7. How much time will be required to use the compressed household fuel gas in a 1-ft³ cylinder under a pressure of 500 lb/in.² if gas is used at the rate of 10 ft³/hr at a pressure of 15 lb/in.²? (Total, not gage, pressure.)

8. What is the density of air in a flask that has been evacuated to a pressure of 0.001 mm of mercury? (Total, not gage, pressure.)

9. When air pressure is 740 mm of mercury, what is the maximum height over which gasoline (specific gravity 0.72) can be siphoned?

10. When a barometer reads 29.00 in. of mercury, what would be its reading in millibars?

11. Otto von Guericke is said to have made a glass barometer and filled it with red wine. If the specific gravity of the red wine was 0.90, what could have been the height of the wine column when the barometric pressure was equivalent to 740 mm of mercury? Why was the height of the column probably less than this value?

12. A cylinder contains 2 ft³ of carbon dioxide at a pressure of 50 lb/in.² What volume will this gas occupy if allowed to escape into the atmosphere without any change in temperature? Assume atmospheric pressure is 15 lb/in.²

13. When air pressure is 725 mm of mercury, what is this pressure in grams per square centimeter?

14. For a certain body of gas $P \times V = 15,000$ when P is expressed in pounds per square inch and V in cubic feet. What will be the volume occupied by this gas when its pressure is 50 lb/in.²?

15. What is the greatest height (theoretical) that the top of a siphon tube may be above the surface of milk in a bottle and still work as a siphon? The specific

gravity of milk is 1.03. Assume the barometric pressure is 745 mm.

16. Otto von Guericke used hemispheres 22 in. in diameter in one of his demonstrations. What was the total force holding these hemispheres together, if all the air was removed from inside the hemispheres? Take air pressure as 15 lb/in.^{2} The force is that on an area equivalent to one great circle of the hemispheres, $A = \pi r^2$.

17. A spherical weather balloon 1 m in diameter is filled with hydrogen gas at atmospheric pressure. If the balloon and trappings weigh 1 lb, what net lifting force can this balloon exert? The volume of a sphere is $\frac{4}{3} \pi r^3$.

18. Assume that the volume of your body is 2 ft^3 and that the density of air is 1.29 oz/ft^3. With what force does the air buoy up your body?

19. A barometer taken down into a mine reads 31.00 in. of mercury when a similar barometer at the surface reads 29.5 in. What is the approximate depth of the mine?

THINGS TO DO

1. Fill a water glass level full of water. Slide a file card over the top of the glass and hold this card against the glass as you turn the glass upside down. Explain what happens. NOTE: Do this experiment over a sink or basin.

2. Obtain an empty rectangular can such as is sometimes used for turpentine, varnish, and other liquids. Be sure the can is empty and well rinsed out, for turpentine and varnish are highly flammable. Put about ½ in. of water in the can and heat to boiling. Then stopper the can tightly and quickly put it under a stream of cold water from a faucet. Describe and explain what happens.

3. Streamlines cause unexpected effects. Hold two sheets of paper so that they hang vertically about ½ in. apart. Then blow downward between the two sheets. Try to account for what happens. Hold the narrow edge of a strip of thin paper (8 or 10 in. long) against your lower lip and blow along the upper surface of the paper strip. Notice what happens and explain why.

4. Hold a water glass under water so that it becomes entirely filled. Then turn the glass bottom up and lift it from the water. Where does the glass seem to weigh least and where does it seem heaviest? Explain.

Forces and Motion:
Laws of Motion

BALANCED CONCURRENT FORCES

In the preceding chapters you have studied a number of different forces and have learned what these forces do. Do you now have such a clear mental image of a force that you can draw a picture of a particular one? Such a picture will need to show the features which enable us to identify that force and distinguish it from all others. The distinguishing features of a force are the following:

1. Its *magnitude*, that is, the number of pounds, grams, kilograms, dynes, or other units in the force.
2. Its *direction*, that is, whether it acts upward, downward, or at some stated angle.

3. Its *point of application*, that is, the point on a body at which it acts.

Drawing a Diagram of a Force

You may be able to think of several ways of incorporating these characteristics into a picture or diagram. The usual way of doing this is to represent the force by means of a simple straight line, with these conventions:

1. The *length* of the line represents the *magnitude* of the force. A suitable linear scale is selected, and from this the length of the line required to represent a given magnitude is determined. Suppose we wish to represent a force of 50 kg. If we choose the scale 1 cm = 10 kg, then a line 5 cm long is required to represent the

50-kg force. We might have selected any other convenient scale, but then the line representing the 50-kg force would have a different length.

2. The *direction* of the line in the diagram represents the *direction* of the force. An arrow head is generally placed at the end of the line to show exactly which way the force is directed. It is customary to use conventional map directions in the diagram (top of diagram, north; bottom, south; right, east; left, west) when the force direction is given in these terms. Suppose a force of 50 kg acts toward the southeast. We should represent this force as shown in Fig. 4–1.

3. The point of application is indicated on the diagram by putting numerical dimensions on parts of the figure. Suppose a force of 50 kg acts obliquely downward at a point 2 ft from the center of a 10-ft horizontal beam and makes an angle of 45 deg with the shorter end of the beam. This force should be diagramcd as shown in Fig. 4–2. If the reproduction of this figure were to scale, the length of the line *OA* would be 5 cm. Note that the scale is 1 cm = 10 kg.

You will notice that forces are a different kind of quantity than specific gravity, temperature, and age. Forces not only have magnitude, as other quantities do, but have *direction* as well. Such quan-

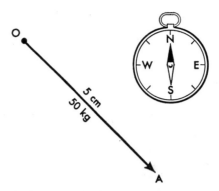

Scale: 1 cm=10 kg

Fig. 4–1. A force of 50 kg acting southeast at the point O.

tities are called *vector quantities*. Quantities, such as temperature and age, which have magnitude but not direction are called *scalar quantities*. You know from elementary arithmetic how to add, subtract, and otherwise use scalar quantities. You will need to learn new methods to perform corresponding operations with vector quantities. Sometimes the results are surprising!

Balanced Forces

Forces always *tend* to start, stop, or change the motion of the body on which they act. However, when one force is just *balanced* by one or more other forces acting at the same point, the tendency of the first force to move the point is just counteracted by that of

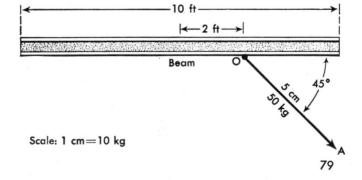

Fig. 4–2. A force of 50 kg acting obliquely downward at a 45 deg angle. This force is applied at the point O, 2 ft from the center of a 10-ft beam.

Scale: 1 cm=10 kg

79

Scale: 1 inch = 50 pounds

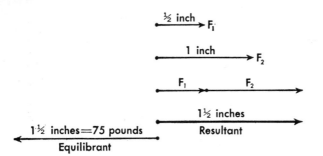

Fig. 4–3. Graphic method of finding the resultant and equilibrant of parallel concurrent forces that act in the same direction.

the other force or forces. Sets of forces that nullify one another in this way are called *balanced forces;* the bodies on which the forces act are *in equilibrium.*

Concurrent Forces

When two or more forces *act at the same point* at the same time, they are described as *concurrent.* Concurrent forces may act parallel to one another or they may act in different directions. *Two* concurrent forces can be balanced only if they are equal in magnitude and act in exactly opposite directions.

Suppose one boy pulls with a force of 25 lb on a rope tied to a tree at the same time that a second boy pulls with a force of 50 lb in the same direction on the rope. What is the total force exerted

on the tree by the two boys together? In this problem we are asked to find the *resultant* of the two forces exerted by the boys.

The resultant of two or more concurrent forces is the single force that would produce the same effect as all the individual forces acting together.

In Fig. 4–3, the 25-lb force exerted by the first boy is represented by F_1, a line $\frac{1}{2}$ in. long. The 50-lb force exerted by the second boy is represented by F_2, a line 1 in. long. F_1 and F_2 have the same direction. To find the resultant of these two forces, we place F_2 so that its origin (beginning end) is on the terminus (tip end) of F_1, that is, we lay the vectors end to end, without changing their magnitudes or directions. Then the

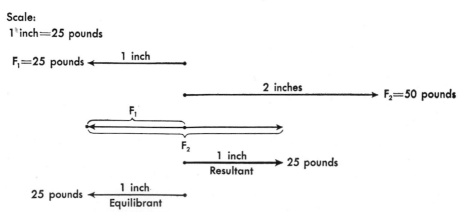

Fig. 4–4. Graphic method for finding the resultant and equilibrant of parallel concurrent forces that act in opposite directions.

80

straight line from the origin of F_1 to the terminus of F_2 is the *resultant* of these two forces. From the diagram you can see that the length of the resultant is $1\frac{1}{2}$ in., which represents $1\frac{1}{2} \times 50$ lb = 75 lb according to the scale used. The direction of this resultant is the same as that of the two forces.

Unless something breaks, this resultant 75-lb force will produce no motion. It must therefore be balanced by another equal and opposite force set up by the tree to which the rope is attached. This equal and opposite force is called the *equilibrant* of the two forces F_1 and F_2.

For concurrent forces, the resultant and the equilibrant are equal in magnitude and opposite in direction.

If the first boy pulls on the rope so that he opposes the second one, we can find the resultant and the equilibrant by the same method, as shown in Fig. 4–4. You will notice that the scale used in this figure is different from that in Fig. 4–3.

Right-angle Concurrent Forces

Let us now consider an example in which two forces are perpendicular to each other.

EXAMPLE: Two boys, one on each bank of a stream, are holding a boat with ropes, as shown in Fig. 4–5. One boy pulls with a force of 40 lb and the other with a force of 30 lb. The ropes make a right angle where they are tied to the boat. What single force would produce the same effect as these two forces acting together and what is the *drag* of the boat?

SOLUTION: *Method* 1. On a sheet of paper draw two lines OM and ON at right angles to each other as shown in Fig. 4–6.

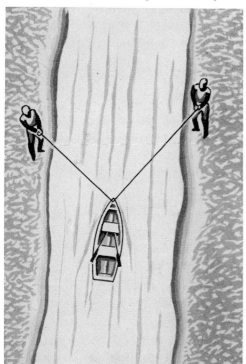

Fig. 4–5. Two boys hold a boat in a stream.

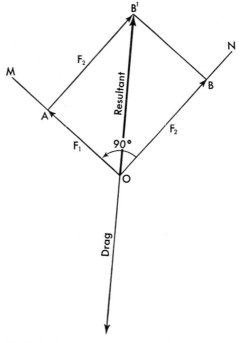

Fig. 4–6. Graphic method for finding the resultant force and drag of the boat in Fig. 4–5.

OM and *ON* represent the directions of the two forces. Using the scale of 1 in. equal to 20 lb, measure off *OA* on line *OM* equal to $1\frac{1}{2}$ in. The vector *OA* represents the 30-lb force F_1. Along *ON* measure off the vector *OB* equal to 2 in. to represent the 40-lb force F_2. From point *A* draw line *AB'* parallel and equal in length to the vector *OB*. Then *AB'* also corresponds to the 40-lb force F_2. Thus we have in effect placed the origin of F_2 on the terminus of F_1. The straight line *OB'* from the origin of F_1 to the terminus of F_2 then represents the resultant of these two forces. If we construct this diagram carefully, we should find that *OB'* is $2\frac{1}{2}$ in. long. By the scale used, this represents 50 lb. So the resultant force effective in holding the boat in the stream is 50 lb; it is directed upstream. The drag of the boat, directed downstream, is the equilibrant of the forces exerted by the boys. This, of course, is also 50 lb.

Method 2. To find the resultant of the two forces F_1 and F_2, we could have constructed the parallelogram *OAB'B* with sides F_1 and F_2. The diagonal *OB'* of this parallelogram represents the resultant of the two forces. By measuring the length of this diagonal and applying the scale, we can find how many pounds it represents.

Method 3. Since the figure *OAB'* in your drawing is a *right* triangle, apply a theorem learned in geometry and compute the hypotenuse from the two sides. Thus $\overline{OB'}^2 = \overline{OA}^2 + \overline{AB'}^2$. We may substitute for each of these lengths the force for which it stands. $\overline{OB'}^2$ is the resultant, or R^2. So we may write

$$R^2 = 30^2 + 40^2 = 2{,}500$$

Hence

$$R = \sqrt{2{,}500} = 50 \text{ lb}$$

82

►You Will Be Interested to Know

The theorem in geometry which states that the sum of the squares on the two sides of a right triangle is equal to the square on the hypotenuse is generally attributed to Pythagoras, an ancient Greek philosopher of the sixth century B.C. One of the best known sets of *whole* numbers that satisfy the conditions for the sides of a right triangle is 3:4:5. Of course, any multiple of this set, such as 30:40:50 in the example above, also satisfies the right triangle conditions. This is in reality the same set, however. There are innumerable other sets of *whole* numbers which satisfy these conditions. Among them are 5:12:13 and 8:15:17.

Concurrent Forces at Any Angle

Methods 1 and 2 of the preceding section enable us to find the resultant of two or more concurrent forces, regardless of the angle between them.

EXAMPLE: A piece of rope, which will safely stand a tension (stretching force) of 500 lb, is stretched between two posts, as shown in Fig. 4–7. What is the greatest weight that this rope can support at its center when the two parts of the rope form an angle of 150 deg?

SOLUTION: Draw the lines *OM* and *ON*, as in Fig. 4–8, with the included angle 150 deg. Then on *OM* lay off *OA* 2.5 cm long to represent F_1, the 500-lb force permissible in one side of the rope. Likewise on *ON* lay off *OB* 2.5 cm long to represent F_2, the 500-lb force permissible in that side of the rope. At *A*, the terminus of F_1, construct *AB'* parallel and equal to *OB*. This places the origin of F_2 on the terminus of F_1. The straight line *OB'* from the origin of F_1 to the terminus of F_2 represents the resultant of these two forces. Notice that the resultant is directed vertically upward from O toward B'. When we lay off the angle and distances carefully, we find that the length of OB' is 1.3 cm. This corresponds to 260 lb by the scale used. The person standing on the rope in Fig. 4–7 could weigh up to 260 lb before the rope is overloaded! Notice that the weight that can be supported is less than the tension in the rope when the forces act at this angle.

This same method can be used to find the resultant when the two forces act at an angle less than a right angle. In fact, by laying the vectors end to end in this manner, we can find the resultant of any number of concurrent forces. If there are more than two forces, this method will result in a polygon of more than three sides, but in every case the following is true:

The straight line from the origin of the first vector to the terminus of the last one represents the resultant of the forces.

The vectors may be taken in any order and the same resultant obtained. The process of finding the resultant of several forces is sometimes called the *composition of forces.*

Components of a Force

In many problems we know the magnitude and direction of the resultant (or equilibrant) of two concurrent forces. When we also know the directions of the forces themselves, we can find the magnitude of each of them by reversing the steps used in finding resultants. The process of dividing a force into two *components* is called the *resolution of the force.*

EXAMPLE: A boy pulls on the rope of a sled with a force of 75 lb. The rope

Fig. 4–7. The tightrope problem.

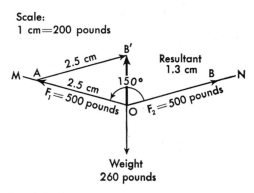

Scale:
1 cm=200 pounds

Fig. 4–8. Graphic method for solving the tightrope problem. The resultant is less than the tension in either rope.

makes an angle of 30 deg with the surface of the snow. What is the component of this force effective in pulling the sled ahead?

SOLUTION: *Method* 1. In Fig. 4–10, OR is taken 3.75 cm long, at an angle of 30 deg with the horizontal line OH, to represent the 75-lb force exerted by the boy on the sled rope. AR is perpendicular to OH. Then OA represents the *component* of OR in the horizontal direction. OA measures 6.5 cm, corresponding to 65 lb, so the force effective in pulling the sled ahead is 3.25 lb. AR represents the vertical component of the 75-lb force. The length of AR is 1.875 cm. This

83

Fig. 4–9. The sled problem.

Scale:
1 cm=20 pounds

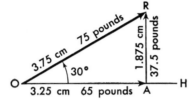

Fig. 4–10. Graphic method for solving the sled problem. Only the horizontal component of the force is effective in pulling the sled ahead.

represents a vertical force of 37.5 lb effective in lifting the front end of the sled upward.

Method 2. You will notice in Fig. 4–10 that the triangle OAR is a 30–60-deg right triangle. In such a triangle, the length of the shorter side is always one-half that of the hypotenuse. So $AR = \dfrac{OR}{2}$ and $OA = \dfrac{OR}{2}\sqrt{3}$. When we know that OR represents 75 lb, we can easily compute each of the two components.

►Do You Know?

1. Do you know any other vector quantities besides forces? Name them.

2. Do you know any other scalar quantities besides those mentioned? What are they?

84

3. Can you think of any other examples of balanced forces? Name them.
4. When 3 in. in a diagram represents 75 lb, what is the *scale* used?
5. Two forces, one of 25 lb and the other of 30 lb, act simultaneously at the same point. What is the largest and the smallest resultant that these two forces can have as the angle between them changes from 0 to 180 deg?
6. Under what conditions is the tension in a rope greater than the weight of the load the rope supports?

FORCES AT DIFFERENT POINTS

Forces not only can cause an object to move along a straight or curved path but also can cause it to turn or spin as a wheel on its axle.

The Moment of a Force

In Fig. 4–11 the weight of each child acts downward at a different point on the teeter board, while the support exerts a force upward at the center point. These forces are shown diagrammatically in Fig. 4–12. The board tends to turn about point O, so we regard this point as the *axis* of the system. The total weight of the two children must be borne by the support, so the force F_3 must be equal to the sum of F_1 and F_2.

Whether the girl at the left goes up or down or is just balanced by the boy at the right depends both on her weight and on how far she is out on the board from the support. In more technical language, the turning effect of the force F_1 about axis O depends not only on the magnitude of that force, but also how far from the axis the force is applied. The turning effect of a force about a given axis is called the moment of that force.

The moment of a force is measured

by the product of the magnitude of the force and the perpendicular distance from the axis to the line of action of the force.

Moment = force × perpendicular
distance to axis

In Fig. 4–12, the moment of the force F_1 about the axis O is $F_1 \times AO$, while that of F_2 about the same axis is $F_2 \times OB$.

When Moments Are Balanced

In Fig. 4–11 the weight of the boy tends to turn the teeter board in one direction around its support while the weight of the girl tends to turn it in the opposite direction. *Moments* which tend to turn a system in the direction the hands of a clock move are called *clockwise* and those which tend to turn a system in the opposite direction are called *counterclockwise*. In Fig. 4–12, the moment of the force F_2 about the axis O is clockwise; that of F_1 is counterclockwise.

Careful measurements with apparatus similar to that of Fig. 4–13 prove that the bar is balanced only when *the sum of all the clockwise moments is equal to the sum of all the counterclockwise moments.*

When two or more forces act at *different points* on a body, two conditions must be fulfilled to have equilibrium: (1) The sum of all the forces (or components) in any one direction must be equal to the sum of all the forces (or components) in the opposite direction and (2) the sum of all the clockwise moments about any axis must just equal the sum of all the counterclockwise moments.

What Is Torque?

Engineers and mechanics often speak of the starting *torque* of a motor, the

Fig. 4–11. A teeter board illustrates moments.

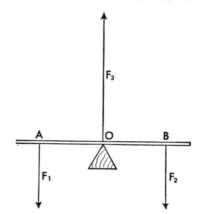

Fig. 4–12. Forces and moments on a teeter board.

torque in the drive shaft of an automobile, and the *torque* produced by a force acting on a bar or lever. By *torque,* they mean the moment of the force involved. The *starting torque* of a motor is the product of the force that the motor can, in starting, develop at the rim of a pulley attached to its shaft, multiplied by the radius of the pulley. *Torque* is thus only another term for the moment of a force.

In computing a torque or moment of a

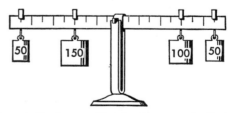

Fig. 4–13. For equilibrium, the sum of all the clockwise moments must just equal the sum of all the counterclockwise moments.

85

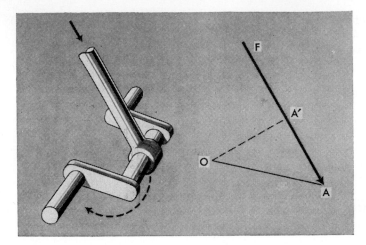

Fig. 4–14. Torque in a crank-shaft.

force, does it make any difference which distance from the axis to the force we take? Consider the crankshaft represented in Fig. 4–14. In the position shown, the force applied to the crank is in the direction of the connecting rod. This is not perpendicular to the radius of the crank. In such a case the torque

F

W   W   W   W   W   W   W   W   W   W   W

W

Fig. 4–15. The ruler balances at its center of gravity.

86

produced by the force F is $F \times OA'$ rather than $F \times OA$. OA' is the *perpendicular* distance from the axis to the *line of action* (the direction line) of the force. The "distance from the axis" involved in torques and moments of force is always the *perpendicular distance* from the axis to the *line of action* of the force.

Center of Gravity

You know from experience that there is some point at which the ruler in Fig. 4–15 will just balance on the sharp edge of the block. This point is called its *center of gravity*, although, strictly speaking, the center of gravity lies inside the ruler and a little above this balance point. If the ruler is straight and has the same density throughout, its center of gravity lies at its geometric center. If the ruler is heavier at one end than at the other, then its center of gravity lies nearer the heavier end.

Suppose we think of the ruler as made up of many exceedingly small units of volume. Each of these tiny units of volume has a small weight, and each small weight is a force acting downward. These small forces are at different distances from the sharp edge of the block, which is the axis of the balanced ruler. So there are many different moments acting on the ruler, some of them clockwise and some counterclockwise. When we move the ruler across the sharp edge to find its balance point, we are actually locating by trial and error the point on the ruler about which the clockwise and counterclockwise moments are just equal. This point is the *center of gravity* of the ruler.

The *weight* of the ruler is the sum of all these small downward forces. It is this resultant force that presses down on the sharp edge of the block. The force that the block must exert upward to support the ruler is the equilibrant of this weight. Thus one single upward force applied at the center of gravity just balances all of the many individual downward forces distributed along the ruler.

The combined weight of all the parts of a body acts like a single downward force concentrated at the center of gravity of that body.

For many purposes we may treat a body as if it were a weightless system, with a concentrated force equal to its actual weight acting downward at its center of gravity.

EXAMPLE: Suppose a meter bar balances on a sharp edge placed at its 50-cm mark as shown in Fig. 4–16. A 100-g weight is then attached to the bar at the 10-cm mark and the bar with this load balances at the 35-cm mark. What is the weight of the meter bar alone?

SOLUTION: From the first balance, we see that the center of gravity of the bar alone is at the 50-cm mark. We may now replace the actual bar with an imaginary weightless one and place a downward force W, equal to the un-

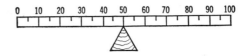
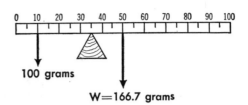

Fig. 4–16. A method for finding the weight of a meter bar.

known weight of the bar, at the 50-cm mark of this imaginary bar. The conditions for the second balance of the bar are shown in Fig. 4–16. Setting the clockwise and the counterclockwise moments equal,

$$W \times 15 \text{ cm} = 100 \text{ g} \times 25 \text{ cm}$$

from which

$$W = 166.7 \text{ g, the weight of the bar}$$

What Is a Plumb Line?

Builders often use plumb lines to determine whether a wall or chimney is

Fig. 4–17. A plumb line on a transit.

exactly vertical. Surveyors use the same simple device to obtain a vertical line.

A plumb line consists of a piece of cord attached to a heavy metal bob. The bob is often made of lead, hence the name *plumb* (*plumbum*, Latin, lead). The free end of the cord is attached to a nail or other support. In this way the metal bob is suspended so that it is free to swing about the nail as an axis. Any body suspended in this way *eventually comes to rest with its center of gravity as low as possible*. Any line parallel to the cord is then "plumb," or vertical.

Stability

If a solid body resting on a base returns to its original position after it has been tipped a little, it is said to be in *stable equilibrium*. The brick resting on the table in Fig. 4–18a is in stable equilibrium. Notice that it cannot be tipped or overturned *unless its center of gravity is first raised*.

A body balanced so that it cannot return to its original position but topples over following a slight tipping is said to be in *unstable equilibrium*. The brick balanced on one edge in Fig. 4–18b is in unstable equilibrium. Notice that any slight turning *causes the center of gravity of this brick to fall, without first rising*.

The baseball in Fig. 4–18c is in neutral equilibrium. If it is moved slightly in any direction on the level table, it neither topples over nor returns to its original position. As it is rolled along, its center of gravity neither rises nor falls.

There is a simple way of knowing in advance whether a body, resting on a given base, will be stable or will topple over when released. If the plumb line through its center of gravity falls within the boundary of the base on which it

rests, the body will not topple over, but if this plumb line falls outside the boundary of the base, the body will overturn automatically when released.

A body is more stable if it requires a greater force to overturn it. A given weight of material is more stable when it has a shape such that its center of gravity must be raised farther to overturn it. For a given weight, that design will be more stable in which (1) the center of gravity is lower and (2) the area of the base is larger.

These principles of stability are utilized in the designing of automobiles with lower and lower centers of gravity.

►You Will Be Interested to Know

The famous leaning tower of Pisa, Italy, presents an interesting study in stability. This tower is 179 ft high, with walls 13 ft thick at the base. It is built entirely of marble. Its construction was begun in 1174 and 200 years were required to complete it. It seems to have been designed as a vertical tower, but apparently began to lean while still under construction. The original footing was inadequate and partially successful attempts have been made to reinforce this with concrete. The tower was $15\frac{1}{2}$ ft out of plumb in 1829 and $16\frac{1}{2}$ ft out in 1910. It was from the top of this tower that Galileo dropped two weights in the famous experiment to find out about falling bodies.

►Do You Know?

1. What is the purpose of ballast in a ship?
2. Do you know any uses for plumb lines, other than those mentioned in the text? Name them.
3. Where is the center of gravity of a finger ring located?
4. How does the rider that you slip

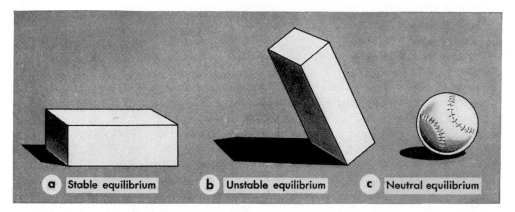

| a Stable equilibrium | b Unstable equilibrium | c Neutral equilibrium |

Fig. 4–18. Stable, unstable, and neutral equilibrium.

along the beam of a trip scale produce a balance?

5. Do you know any common situations where you make use of a torque? Name them.

6. Why do the linesmen on a football team usually crouch down and place their hands on the ground just before a play starts?

7. Do you know of any devices, other than those mentioned in the text, in which stability is increased by intentionally lowering the center of gravity? What are they?

8. Do you know of any devices in which greater stability is secured by enlarging the base? Name them.

9. Why is the base of a floor or desk lamp usually made heavy?

10. A class of small toys, with hemispherical bases, always turn upright, no matter how they are dropped on the floor. How is the toy constructed to accomplish this effect?

MOTION FROM UNBALANCED FORCES

Motion results when a force is not balanced by an equal and opposite force. Many forces succeed in moving the objects on which they act, while others only hinder or retard motion.

Speed

When we observe an automobile moving along a highway, one of the first questions we are likely to ask ourselves is, "How fast is that car traveling?" This is a question of such prime importance to the safety of riders and pedestrians alike that the speedometer is standard equipment on all cars and laws are enacted prescribing the speeds at which cars may be driven under various conditions. The *speed* of a moving object is an essential characteristic of its motion.

Speed is the distance traveled in one unit of time. It may be expressed in miles per hour (mph), feet per second (ft/sec), centimeters per second (cm/sec), or in any one of a variety of other units of this kind. The abbreviation mi/hr is sometimes used for miles per hour and fps for feet per second.

It is convenient to remember that 60 mph is equivalent to 88 ft/sec. As a working approximation, $1\frac{1}{2}$ times the number of miles per hour indicated on the speedometer is the number of feet you are traveling each second.

89

Velocity

The speedometer indicates speed of travel but tells nothing about direction. Speed is a scalar quantity; it has only magnitude. When we say that a car is driven north at 50 mph, we state not only how fast but also in what direction the car is traveling. 50 mph northward is a *velocity. Velocity is a speed with a direction.* It is a vector quantity, like force. We are not always careful to distinguish between speed and velocity.

A body in motion may have two or more velocities at the same time. In such a case, the resultant velocity may be found by the same methods as those used for forces earlier in this unit.

EXAMPLE: A boy heads a rowboat directly across a stream which is flowing at the rate of 3 mph. With the same effort, the boy could row the boat 4 mph in still water. What is the path and actual speed of the boat, that is, what is its velocity?

SOLUTION: The velocities are represented in Fig. 4–19. The actual velocity

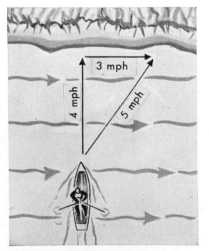

Fig. 4–19. The resultant velocity of the boat is 5 mph with respect to the ground.

of the boat is the resultant of the 4 mph velocity across the stream and the 3 mph velocity of the stream. The velocity of the boat is 5 mph in the direction indicated in the illustration.

Speed, Time and Distance

When a body moves at a speed that does not change, both the speed and the motion are described as *uniform.* You know that an automobile driven at a *uniform speed* of 44 ft/sec for 100 sec will travel 4,400 ft. This distance is obtained by multiplying the speed by the length of time this speed was maintained. In mathematical symbols

$$S = v \times t$$

where S stands for the distance traveled, v, the uniform speed of motion, and t, the length of time this speed was maintained. If you know any two of these quantities, you can find the third one by use of this relationship.

Speeds That Are Not Uniform

In ordinary traffic driving, uniform speeds cannot be maintained for extended periods of time. Suppose that a 120-mile trip is made in 4 hr. In all probability the driving will not be uniform, either in speed or in direction. However, we can easily see that the *average* speed for this trip is 120 miles/ 4 hr = 30 mph. In mathematical symbols

$$\bar{v} = \frac{S}{t}, \quad S = \bar{v} \times t, \quad \text{and} \quad t = \frac{S}{\bar{v}}$$

where $\bar{v}$ stands for the *average speed* and S and t are the distance and time, respectively. Most actual motions are not uniform for more than very short periods, and in many cases we can know only average speeds. These relationships hold for any type of motion for which average speeds can be found.

What Is Momentum?

An automobile coasting down a grade gains *momentum;* as it slows down to a stop it loses momentum. The momentum of a moving body depends on its speed. A heavy truck at a given speed has more momentum than a bicycle moving at the same speed. Thus the momentum of a moving body depends also on the mass of that body. We all know from experience that the greater the momentum of a moving body the harder it is to stop.

The term *momentum*, as used in physics and engineering, has a special and definite meaning. *The momentum of a moving body is a quantity measured by the product of the mass of the body and its velocity.*

$$\text{Momentum} = \text{mass} \times \text{velocity}$$

An automobile whose mass is 3,000 lb, moving 45 mph (66 ft/sec) has a momentum of 3,000 lb $\times$ 66 ft/sec = 198,000 lb-ft/sec (read pound-feet per second). Other units of momentum are formed in the same way.

Newton's Laws of Motion

Philosophers and scientists through the ages have tried to find simple laws or principles that are equally true for all kinds of motion. It was difficult or impossible to discover such laws before the concepts of force, mass, velocity, momentum, and other properties of motion were developed and clearly defined. Many of the early students of the physical universe found it difficult to distinguish between mass and weight, just as do high school students today! The early Greek philosopher Aristotle expressed what he thought were principles or laws of motion; some of his statements were later found to disagree with experimental evidence and, so, had to be abandoned.

Galileo, of whom we shall hear more, studied the motion of bodies experimentally and discovered some general laws of motion that we still use. Sir Isaac Newton, an English mathematician and physicist of the late seventeenth century, in his book *Principia*, published in 1686, set forth the fundamental relationship between force and motion in three simple, concise statements. We now call these statements *Newton's laws of motion*. We shall first state these laws and then explore their meaning.

First Law of Motion (The Law of Inertia): Every body tends to remain in a state of rest, or in uniform motion in a straight line, unless acted upon by an external force.

Second Law of Motion (The Law of Momentum): The rate of change in momentum of a body is directly proportional to the force applied. This change occurs in the direction of the force.

Third Law of Motion (The Law of Reaction): For every action force, there is an equal and opposite reaction force.

The First Law of Motion

In simpler language, the first law states that any body now at rest cannot be set in motion unless an outside force acts on it. This is understandable in the case of inanimate objects, such as a book or a piece of stone. If you leave your textbook in your desk you expect to find it there later. If you do not find it, you infer that some "external force" has acted on the book in your absence.

An animate object, such as your dog, presents a different situation. If you leave him at some particular spot and fail to find him there on your return, does this indicate that some "external force" has been acting on your dog, too? If it were not for the force of friction between the ground or floor and your dog's feet, he, too, would be powerless to move from the spot where he was left. Here the floor or the earth supplies the external force.

The second part of the law states that a body now in motion continues to move indefinitely with uniform motion in a straight line. This at first seems contrary to experience, for all moving bodies with which we are acquainted slow down and eventually come to rest, unless force is applied to maintain their motion. But this slowing down is attributed to the action of an external force, friction. If friction could be entirely eliminated, a body now in motion would not slow down unless some other form of external force was applied to it.

The uniform motion that a body tends to maintain is along a straight-line path. An external force is required to change even the *direction* of motion. A body moving with uniform speed around a circle must have an outside force acting on it, for it is constantly changing direction. This force is called a *centripetal force*.

A force can affect the motion of a body in three ways: (1) set the body in motion or speed it up, (2) slow down or entirely stop the body, or (3) change the direction in which the body is moving.

The tendency of a body to resist any change in its speed or direction of motion is *inertia*. All matter possesses inertia, and that is exactly what this first law of motion asserts.

Examples of Inertia

When a car is stopped suddenly, passengers and loose objects continue to fly forward, for bodies in motion tend to remain in motion. If the car is started suddenly, passengers are pressed back against the seats, for bodies at rest tend to remain at rest. When the car turns an abrupt corner, passengers slide toward the outside of the curve, because bodies in motion tend to remain in motion in a *straight line*. When you stamp your feet to remove snow or mud from your shoes, you are relying on inertia to do the job. When you drive the head on the handle of a hammer by striking the opposite end of the handle, you are again relying on inertia to perform this task.

What Is Acceleration?

We often discuss the "pick-up" of this or that automobile. By "pick-up" we generally mean how quickly the car can increase speed. Suppose an automobile starts from a dead stop and, at the end of 5 sec, is going 30 mph. It has picked up speed at the average rate of 6 mph for every second it was in motion. Its *acceleration* is accordingly 6 mph/sec. This may be written as 6 mi/hr-sec or 6 mi/hr/sec. But 6 mph/sec is equivalent to 8.8 ft/sec^2. This may be written as 8.8 ft per sec per sec or 8.8 ft/sec/sec. **Acceleration is the rate at which the velocity or speed of a body changes per unit of time.**

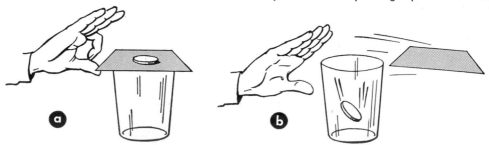

Fig. 4–20. Inertia of the coin prevents it from moving with the snapped card.

For a body starting from rest (a dead stop)

$$a = \frac{v}{t}$$

where a is the average acceleration of the body, and v is its velocity at the end of time t.

When a body is slowing down, it has *negative acceleration*. This is often called *deceleration* or *retardation*. The efficiency of brakes on an automobile is frequently expressed in terms of the deceleration they can produce in the motion of the machine.

A body moving with uniform motion in a straight line does not change its velocity at all as time proceeds. Its acceleration is, therefore, *zero*. It is only while its velocity is increasing, decreasing, or changing direction that a body experiences any acceleration. The motion of a body which has acceleration is called *accelerated motion*.

The Second Law of Motion

The second law of motion asserts that the rate at which the momentum of a body changes is directly proportional to the force producing the change. Thus a larger force will change the momentum of a given body faster than a smaller force. A force *twice* as large will change the momentum *twice* as fast.

For all ordinary velocities, the mass of a body is the same regardless of what its velocity may be. So the only way the momentum of a given body can change is through a change in its velocity, and the time rate of change of velocity is acceleration.
The second law of motion may be stated as follows:
The acceleration produced in the motion of a body is directly proportional to the force acting on that body.

Fig. 4–21. Acceleration is important at the start of a dash.

The acceleration given the body is always in the direction of the applied force.

Let us now incorporate these facts into an equation.

$$\text{Force} = \frac{\text{change in momentum}}{\text{time}}$$

$$= \frac{\text{mass} \times \text{change in velocity}}{\text{time}}$$

$$= \text{mass} \times \text{acceleration}$$

$$F = ma$$

For greater acceleration of a given body, a larger force must be used. Even a small force is able to set a large mass into rapid motion if it is allowed sufficient time and is unopposed by friction and other resisting forces. The size of the force required to set a given mass in motion depends not on the mass alone, but also on how fast the body is to pick up speed, that is, on its acceleration. The engine of an automobile must furnish a large force when a quick "pick-up" is demanded by the driver. It is more economical of gasoline to accelerate less rapidly when starting and when passing other cars on the highway. It is also more economical of brake linings to decelerate more slowly when coming to a stop.

93

Fig. 4–22. Action and reaction in two episodes.

What Is a Dyne?

It should now be clear that the size of a force depends both on the mass it moves and on the acceleration it gives to that mass. That force which can accelerate one gram of mass at the rate of one centimeter per second per second is called a *dyne*. One gram of force is the pull of the earth on one gram of mass. There are 980 dynes in one gram of force.

$$1 \text{ dyne} = \frac{1 \text{ g-cm}}{\text{sec}^2} \text{ (read gram-centi-meter per second per second)}$$

$$= \frac{1}{980} \text{ g of force}$$

What Is a Poundal?

That force which can accelerate one pound of mass at the rate of one foot per second per second is called a *poundal*. This is the unit in the English system that corresponds to the dyne in the metric. There are 32 poundals in one pound of force or weight. The poundal is seldom used in practical work.

The pound, gram, and other units of force whose values depend on the pull of gravity on given masses are called *gravitational* units. The dyne and the poundal do not depend on any other force and so are called *absolute* units.

Not All Motion Is Accelerated

We know from observation that an automobile, starting from a dead stop on a straight level highway, will not continue to pick up speed indefinitely, even with the accelerator pedal pushed down to the floor board. Eventually the machine will reach a limiting speed, if all goes well, and thereafter will travel at an approximately uniform rate. In practically every case with which we are acquainted, a force acting on a body does not continue to accelerate that body indefinitely, as the second law of motion indicates it should. How can we account for this fact?

As a body picks up speed, frictional forces between the body and the surrounding air, or between moving parts, increase rapidly. Ultimately these resisting forces become as great as the force applied to produce the motion. When this condition is reached, the net unbalanced force applied to the body is zero. From there on, the body continues to move at a uniform speed in accordance with the first law of motion.

94

The Third Law of Motion

A book lying on a table exerts a downward force (action) on the table. The table, in turn, exerts an equal force (reaction) upward on the book. In diving off the end of a rowboat, you exert as much force on the boat as the boat exerts on you. Since these forces persist for the same length of time, namely while you are in actual contact, you and the boat each *acquire the same amount of momentum*. The same situation occurs when a gun is fired. The momentum of the gun is equal in amount and opposite in direction to that acquired by the bullet or projectile.

Two Kinds of Force

If you whirl a metal ball tied to one end of a cord while the other end is held in your hand, you at once become aware of the outward pull of the cord on your hand. To cause the moving ball to deviate from a straight line, you have to exert a force on it through the cord. This pull which you have to exert is called a *centripetal force*. The outward pull of the ball through the cord on your hand is called a *centrifugal* force. These two forces constitute action and reaction and are equal in magnitude and opposite in direction. A centripetal force changes the *direction* of a velocity rather than its magnitude or speed. From one point of view a centrifugal force is a real force only to a person who is part of the rotating system. We shall treat it here as a real force, but we should always remember that it comes into existence only because the body at the end of the cord tends to remain in motion in a *straight line*.

If you whirl the ball on the end of the cord faster, you will easily notice that you will have to pull harder on the cord.

If you make the cord longer and keep the ball whirling at the same speed (along the arc) you will find that the pull you must exert on the cord is lessened. Finally, if you substitute a heavier ball for the original one and whirl it at the same speed and distance as before you will find that you need to pull harder on the cord. When all these effects are taken into account, we find that they are related in the manner expressed in the following equation:

$$F_c = \frac{mv^2}{r}$$

where F_c = centrifugal (or centripetal) force, expressed in *dynes* or *poundals*

m = mass of the rotating object, expressed in grams or pounds

r = radius of the circular path of the object, expressed in centimeters or feet

v = velocity, expressed in centimeters per second or in feet per second

To obtain the centrifugal force expressed in grams of force, we have to divide the number of dynes by 980 (the number of dynes in one gram). To obtain the centrifugal force expressed in pounds of force, we have to divide the number of poundals by 32 (the number of poundals in one pound). We may then write the equation

$$F_c = \frac{mv^2}{980r} \text{ g } \quad \text{and} \quad F_c = \frac{mv^2}{32r} \text{ lb}$$

We must always be careful to use centimeters, grams, and seconds when we wish to obtain grams of force; and feet, pounds, and seconds when we wish to obtain pounds of force.

EXAMPLE: A 5-lb weight is attached to a string 2 ft long and whirled so that it makes 2 revolutions per second. What is the tension (stretching force) in the string?

SOLUTION: The circumference of the circular path of the weight is

$$C = 2\pi r = 2 \times 3.14 \times 2 \text{ ft} = 12.56 \text{ ft}$$

Since the weight makes 2 revolutions per second, its speed along its path is

$$v = 12.56 \times 2 = 25.12 \text{ ft/sec}$$

From the problem

$$m = 5 \text{ lb} \quad \text{and} \quad r = 2 \text{ ft}$$

so

$$F_c = \frac{mv^2}{r} =$$

$$\frac{5 \times 25.12 \times 25.12}{2} \text{ poundals}$$

$$= 1{,}577 \text{ poundals}$$

To express this force in *pounds* we have to divide by 32; thus

$$F_c = \frac{1{,}577}{32} = 49.3 \text{ lb}$$

Effects of Centrifugal Force

Mud flies from a moving wheel because of centrifugal force. Wheels on machines sometimes fly apart when the centrifugal force becomes too great. Tracks have to be banked to counteract centrifugal force when the turns are taken at high speed. Skaters, bicyclists, and bobsled riders lean toward the inside when making a turn in order to use the force of gravity to counterbalance some of the centrifugal force. Centrifugal force is often responsible for skids on slippery highways.

96

Uses for Centrifugal Force

Many devices are designed to take advantage of centrifugal force. Centrifugal pumps for water, vacuum sweepers, and the whirling-drum type of wringers used in laundries are devices of this type. You can probably think of many others.

A machine called a centrifuge is used extensively to separate liquids that have different densities. A cream separator is one type of centrifuge. This machine separates the cream from the whole milk by whirling the whole milk at very high speeds. The more dense skim milk goes to the outside of the rotator and the less dense cream is crowded to the inside. The two are drawn off from the machine through separate spouts.

Other centrifuges are used for testing milk for butterfat content, for removing coarse carbon particles, grit, and sludge from used lubricating oils and for separating corpuscles from the plasma of blood in the preparation of serums. Centrifuges have countless other industrial and laboratory uses. Supercentrifuges and ultracentrifuges, operating at speeds as high as 50,000 revolutions per minute (rpm) or more, are in use. A special machine of this type can be used to separate light molecules from heavier ones.

►Do You Know?

1. By how much does the momentum of an automobile change when its speed is changed from 30 to 60 mph?
2. What is the physical purpose of the running start of a broad jump?
3. Under what condition will a 140-lb football player have more momentum than a 180-lb player?
4. Do you know any other uses for centrifugal force than those mentioned in the text?

5. The polar diameter of the earth is almost 27 miles shorter than its diameter at the equator. How may centrifugal force be used to account for this difference?

6. If you were standing on a bathroom scale in an elevator that is just starting upward, would the weight registered on the scales be greater or less than your actual weight?

7. After the elevator has reached its steady speed, how would the registered weight compare with your actual weight?

8. When the elevator is slowing down for a stop, how would the registered weight compare with your actual weight?

9. Answer questions 6, 7, and 8 for an elevator starting downward.

10. If you are inside a coach of a train moving 75 mph and you toss a ball upward, will you be in position to catch the ball when it falls? Explain.

11. Some lawn sprinklers rotate when water flows through them. What force causes this rotation?

UNIVERSAL FORCE OF GRAVITATION

When Newton was seeking an explanation of why the moon stays in its orbit around the earth and why the earth and other planets move in orbits, as they do, around the sun, he found that he could explain these motions satisfactorily if he assumed the following:

Every particle in the universe attracts every other particle with a force that is directly proportional to the product of their masses and inversely proportional to the square of the distance between their centers of gravity. These assumptions have since been carefully tested by experiment and found to be true. We now call this statement Newton's law of universal gravitation.

This law may be expressed in the form of an equation.

$$F = G \frac{m_1 m_2}{r^2}$$

where F is the force of mutual attraction between two bodies whose masses are m_1 and m_2, respectively, and whose centers of gravity are r units apart.

The force F comes out in dynes when the masses m_1 and m_2 are expressed in grams and the distance between centers, r, is in centimeters. In this case, G, the constant of universal gravitation, has been found by careful measurement to be 6.664×10^{-8}. To reduce the attraction to grams of force we have to divide the number of dynes by 980.

The force of attraction is in *poundals* when the masses are expressed in pounds and the distance in feet, provided G is taken as 1.068×10^{-9}. To reduce the attraction to pounds, we have to divide the number of poundals by 32.

Notice that if the two bodies under consideration are moved twice as far apart, their mutual attraction is only one-fourth as great; if they are three times as far apart, their mutual attraction is but one-ninth as great, and so on. This is why the law of universal gravitation is called an *inverse-square law*.

For any masses that are of convenient size to handle, the gravitational force between them is so small that it can be detected only with very sensitive instruments. The mutual attraction between two golf balls when their centers are 10 cm (4 in.) apart is only about 0.0000013 dyne. For this reason it is difficult to make a classroom test of the law of universal gravitation.

When one of two attracting bodies is the earth and the other an object on or near the surface of the earth, their mutual attraction is called *gravity*.

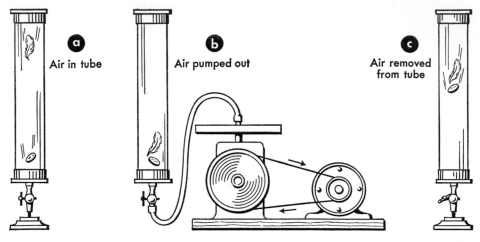

a Air in tube

b Air pumped out

c Air removed from tube

Fig. 4–23. The feather and disk experiment.

Mass and Weight

We are now able to distinguish more clearly between *mass* and *weight.*

Mass is a property that all matter possesses. It shows itself in two ways: (1) by mutual attraction and (2) by inertia. The mass of a body does not depend on its position on the earth or in the universe, nor upon the presence of other masses in its vicinity. For all ordinary speeds, the mass of a body does not depend on the speed it may have.

A body has weight because it possesses mass and because this mass is attracted to the earth by the force of gravity. If a body is removed to a point farther from the center of the earth, the attraction of the earth for that body decreases, in accordance with the law of universal gravitation. The earth is slightly flattened so that the direct distance from pole to pole is about 27 miles less than the diameter at the equator. For this reason, the force of gravity on a body at either pole is greater than at the equator.

Centrifugal force due to rotation of the earth tends to counteract the pull of gravity on a body. Centrifugal force is greatest at the equator and diminishes as we go north or south of this line toward a pole of the earth. The weight of a body depends on the combined effect of gravity and this centrifugal force. Since the pull of gravity becomes greater and centrifugal force less as either pole is approached, it follows that the *weight* of a body increases as it is moved toward a pole of the earth. This increase is small, however, and amounts to but 5 parts in 1,000 between the equator and a pole. A bag of sugar that weighs 1,000 g at the equator would weigh 1,005 g at either pole. The weight difference would have to be detected by a spring balance and not by a beam balance. See page 17 for the explanation.

Freely Falling Bodies

A stone released in the air falls rapidly, but a leaf flutters slowly to the ground. Clearly, these objects do not fall with the same acceleration. But let us try a feather and a piece of metal in a glass tube from which the air has been withdrawn, as shown in Fig. 4–23.

When there is air in the tube the metal disk falls much faster than the feather. After the air has been pumped out, both fall at practically the same speed.

Except for the retarding effect of air, a light body falls with the same acceleration as a heavy one.

When we wish to show that air resistance is to be disregarded in the fall of a body, we describe the body as "freely falling." All freely falling bodies have the same acceleration. They fall with *uniformly* accelerated motion.

►You Will Be Interested to Know

Aristotle, in ancient Greece, taught that the heavier a body, the faster it falls. If one body is twice as heavy as another, then, according to Aristotle, the heavier body should fall twice as fast as the lighter one. He undoubtedly never tested this idea to see if nature really acts in this manner. No one seems to have raised openly any question of this teaching of Aristotle until Galileo dared to challenge its validity. One day, probably in the year 1590, this young instructor of mathematics in the University of Pisa, Italy, is reported to have climbed to the top of the famous leaning tower in that city and, in the presence of a group of students and a few skeptical faculty members, dropped simultaneously two metal balls of different weights. It is probable that these balls were made of iron, one of 100 lb and the other of 1 lb. To the amazement of the students and the consternation of the professors, these two balls struck the earth below at practically the same time. Although we today would consider this quite conclusive evidence that bodies do not fall with speeds proportional to their weights, Galileo's

fellow instructors who witnessed this demonstration refused to be convinced, for they had unshakable faith in everything that Aristotle had taught many centuries before.

How Fast Do Bodies Fall?

The acceleration of freely falling bodies is constant, as we have just seen, as long as the force of gravity is constant. The letter g is customarily used to represent this acceleration. The value of g does not depend on the size, shape, or mass of the falling body. But we have seen, also, that the net force of gravity does change slightly with latitude—distance from the equator—and with altitude. So we should expect the value of g to change slightly from place to place. Careful measurements show that this is true.

For most engineering and scientific work, the standard value used for g is 980 cm/sec². This is equivalent to about 32 ft/sec², which is generally used as the standard value when English units are involved. A slightly higher value is used for very precise work with English units.

Laws of Freely Falling Bodies

The so-called laws of freely falling bodies are a series of statements or mathematical equations which express the relationship existing among the four quantities, time, acceleration, velocity, and distance traveled. By means of these laws, a great deal of information concerning falling bodies can be learned. In the next few sections, we shall develop these laws and show how they can be used. We shall consider here only the laws for (1) freely falling bodies, the effect of air resistance neglected, and (2) bodies starting from rest or slowing down to a dead stop. We shall use letters with the following significance:

$t =$ number of seconds elapsed since the action started

$g =$ acceleration due to gravity

$a =$ any acceleration at all

$v =$ velocity at *the end* of any specified number of seconds, the end-of-the-second velocity

$\bar{v} =$ *average* velocity during a specified period of time

$S =$ total distance traveled by the body since it started to move, or slow down

Acceleration, Velocity, Time

If a body starts from rest and falls freely, it will have a velocity of 32 ft/sec

Start	0 feet	0 ft/sec
1 sec	16 feet	32 ft/sec

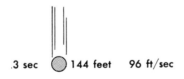

2 sec	64 feet	64 ft/sec

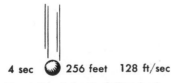

.3 sec	144 feet	96 ft/sec

4 sec	256 feet	128 ft/sec

Fig. 4–24. A freely falling body.

at the *end* of the first second. At the *end* of the second second its speed will have increased 32 ft/sec more so its velocity will be 64 ft/sec. Each second its velocity increases 32 ft/sec over what it was one second before. This is what we mean by a constant acceleration of 32 ft/sec². The velocity at the end of any number of seconds is $v = gt$ for freely falling bodies. For final velocity, in general, $v = at$ for any body with uniformly accelerated motion.

EXAMPLE: What is the velocity of a freely falling body at the end of 6 sec of fall?

SOLUTION:

$$v = gt$$
$$= 32 \text{ ft/sec}^2 \times 6 \text{ sec}$$
$$= 192 \text{ ft/sec}$$

Average Velocities

Since the velocity increases in regular uniform steps from second to second, the *average* velocity during any time is

$$\text{Average velocity} = \frac{\text{initial velocity} + \text{final velocity}}{2}$$

Since we expect to deal only with cases where the body starts from rest, we may set the initial velocity equal to zero. The final velocity at the end of t seconds is gt (or at), so we may write

$$\bar{v} = \frac{0 + v}{2} = \frac{0 + gt}{2} = \frac{1}{2} gt$$

This means that the *average velocity during a fall of t seconds is one-half the velocity at the end of t seconds.*

For average velocity, in general,

$$\bar{v} = \frac{1}{2} at$$

for any body with uniformly accelerated motion.

Distance, Acceleration, Time

When we know the average velocity for any type of motion over an interval of time, we can always find the distance that the body travels in that time, for

Distance = average velocity × time

For a freely falling body

$$S = \bar{v} \times t = \tfrac{1}{2}\, gt \times t = \tfrac{1}{2}\, gt^2$$

since $\bar{v} = \tfrac{1}{2}\, gt$ as we have just shown. In general, for any body with uniformly accelerated motion

$$S = \tfrac{1}{2}\, at^2$$

Notice that the distance a body falls is directly proportional to the *square* of the number of seconds it has been falling. It will fall 4 times as far in 2 sec as it falls in 1 sec, 9 times as far in 3 sec, 16 times as far in 4 sec, and so on. This is shown in Fig. 4–24.

EXAMPLE: How far will a freely falling body fall in 5 sec?

SOLUTION:

$$\begin{aligned} S &= \tfrac{1}{2}\, gt^2 \\ &= \tfrac{1}{2} \times 32 \text{ ft/sec}^2 \times 5^2 \text{ sec}^2 \\ &= 400 \text{ ft} \end{aligned}$$

Velocity, Acceleration, Distance

Since $v = gt$, $t = v/g$. Substituting this value for t in the equation $S = \tfrac{1}{2}\, gt^2$ gives

$$S = \frac{1}{2} g \left(\frac{v}{g}\right)^2 = \frac{v^2}{2g}$$

Hence

$$v^2 = 2gS \quad \text{and} \quad v = \sqrt{2gS}$$

In general, $v^2 = 2aS$ and $v = \sqrt{2aS}$ for any body with uniformly accelerated motion. Notice that the end-of-the-second velocity is directly proportional

to the square root of the distance traversed by the falling body.

EXAMPLE: What is the velocity of a freely falling body when it has fallen 900 ft?

SOLUTION:

$$\begin{aligned} v &= \sqrt{2gS} \\ &= \sqrt{2 \times 32 \text{ ft/sec}^2 \times 900 \text{ ft}} \\ &= \sqrt{64 \times 900 \text{ ft}^2/\text{sec}^2} \\ &= 8 \times 30 \text{ ft/sec} = 240 \text{ ft/sec} \end{aligned}$$

Acceleration in g Units

Airplane pilots often speak of the acceleration their ships acquire in power dives and in pulling out of such dives in terms of g, the acceleration due to gravity. An acceleration of 3 g means three times the acceleration due to gravity, 3×32 or 96 ft/sec². The *velocity* at which we travel has no apparent effect on our bodies. It is only when we are required to *change velocity* that we may experience unpleasant and even dangerous results. The amount of acceleration our bodies can withstand without serious results is limited. About 5 g seems to be the upper safe limit for most persons but this undoubtedly differs with individuals. For very short periods of time higher values of acceleration can be endured. There is evidence that persons subjected repeatedly to multiples of g become accustomed somewhat to its effects. Pilots in planes traveling at very high speeds may be unable to see and even lose consciousness momentarily if the ship is turned too suddenly from its course, thus producing multiples of g. Modern airplanes are tested at as much as 12 g.

Vertical Upward Motion

A baseball thrown straight up rises with diminishing velocity until it momentarily comes to rest at the top of its flight. It then reverses its motion and begins at once to fall back to the earth. If air resistance is negligible, it will take the ball as long to fall to the earth as it took to rise to the top of its flight. The negative acceleration or deceleration due to gravity on the upward flight is just equal to the positive acceleration on the way down. So the ball will have the same speed when it passes a given point going up and going down.

EXAMPLE: A baseball is thrown upward with a speed of 64 ft/sec. How far will it rise and how long will it remain in the air?

SOLUTION: If we find how far the ball will have to fall to acquire a speed of 64 ft/sec we will at the same time find how far it will rise, for these two distances are equal.

$$v^2 = 2gS$$

so

$$S = \frac{v^2}{2g}$$

$$v = 64 \text{ ft/sec}$$

$$g = 32 \text{ ft/sec}^2$$

Hence

$$S = \frac{64 \text{ ft/sec} \times 64 \text{ ft/sec}}{2 \times 32 \text{ ft/sec}^2}$$

$$= 64 \text{ ft}$$

Fig. 4–25. The two balls released from the gun on the
stand fall to the floor in the
same time.

102

Let t represent the number of seconds required for the ball to fall from the top of its flight to the earth; then v is the velocity at the end of t seconds, just before the ball strikes the ground.

$$v = gt,$$

so

$$t = \frac{v}{g} = \frac{64 \text{ ft/sec}}{32 \text{ ft/sec}^2} = 2 \text{ sec}$$

The time of falling is 2 sec, so the time of rising is also 2 sec. The total time the ball is in the air is, therefore, 4 sec.

Horizontal Motion

When the trigger of the spring gun in Fig. 4–25 is pulled, a piston is driven forward. This releases the ball at A so that it falls vertically downward. At the same time the piston strikes the ball B, giving it a horizontal velocity. Careful observations show that, if the two balls are ejected from the gun simultaneously, they both strike the floor at the same time, even though the ball B has to travel over a longer path.

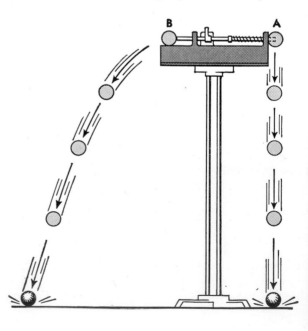

A stone thrown horizontally from the top of an overhanging cliff will strike the earth below in practically the same time that it would require to drop straight down. The path of any body projected with a *horizontal* velocity is a parabola. As the body falls, the *horizontal* component of its velocity remains nearly constant. The vertical component increases just as the velocity of any freely falling body increases. That is, it moves at a constant speed horizontally, but falls faster and faster until it strikes the ground.

The path of a projectile is called its *trajectory*. The horizontal distance a projectile travels before striking the ground is called its *range*. The angle which the path of a projectile makes with the horizontal at its beginning is called its *elevation*.

If air resistance can be neglected, the greatest range for a projectile fired at a given velocity occurs when the elevation is 45 deg, as shown in Fig. 4–26.

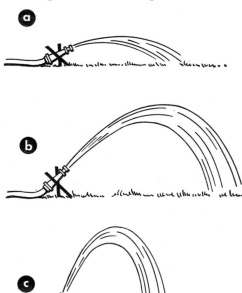

What Is Terminal Velocity?

Air resistance retards the fall of bodies so that they are not freely falling for long. This is a fortunate effect for us, because if raindrops were freely falling they would strike the earth with terrific speeds and do great damage. Air resistance increases very rapidly with speed. Any body falling through the air will continue to pick up speed but at a diminishing rate until the retarding force of friction on it equals the pull of gravity. When this condition is reached, the net force on the body is zero and the body will then continue to move with nearly a *uniform velocity* called its *terminal velocity*.

The terminal velocities of raindrops range from a few feet per second up to about 25 ft/sec. The larger ones have the greater terminal velocities. The terminal velocities of snowflakes are but a few feet per second. A parachutist reaches a terminal velocity of from 16 to 24 ft/sec, while a human body falling without a parachute may reach a velocity as high as 175 mph, or about 2,60 ft/sec.

If a projectile is shot vertically upward, is there any possibility that it may never fall back to the earth again? The acceleration due to gravity decreases as a body gets farther from the earth, and if the body were to start with sufficient velocity it might still have some forward speed left after it has traveled so far out into space that the retarding acceleration due to gravity has become negligible. The initial velocity that a body must have to escape from the earth in this way is called the *escape velocity*. It is possible to calculate the escape velocity.

Fig. 4–26. The maximum range of a garden hose occurs when the angle of elevation is about 45 deg.

If air resistance is neglected, the escape velocity from the earth is just a little less than 7 miles per second, about 25,000 mph. Do you think there is any present prospect of a projectile attaining such a speed?

►**Do You Know?**

1. If Newton's law of universal gravitation holds for the earth and the sun, why are they not pulled together?
2. What causes tides in the ocean?
3. Is a stone dropped into the sea a freely falling body? Explain.
4. Do you know any other bodies besides freely falling ones that move with uniformly accelerated motion? What are they?

MOTION OF THE PENDULUM

The back-and-forth motion of a playground swing, the to-and-fro motion of a rocking chair, the vibration of a piano string all represent a type of motion that differs from any we have discussed heretofore. When a body moves with a rhythmic to-and-fro motion along a straight line, we often say it has *periodic motion*. This is an exceedingly common type of motion in nature.

The motion of the bob of a large pendulum such as that used in a grandfather's clock is periodic, so we shall use the pendulum for our study of this type of motion.

What Is a Pendulum?

A simple *pendulum* consists essentially of a large mass, called the bob, suspended by a cord, wire, or light rod from an axis about which it is free to turn. When the pendulum bob in Fig. 4–27 is pushed to one side from O, its position of rest, the force of gravity tends to pull it back toward O again. Its momentum carries it through O to the other side, and gravity again pulls it back toward O. Thus the force of gravity and the effect of inertia keep the pendulum swinging until air resistance and other frictional forces finally stop it entirely.

The distance L from the point of suspension S to the center of gravity C of the bob is called the *length* of the simple pendulum. The distance OA that the bob swings from O is called the *amplitude* of the swing. AB is the *arc* through which the pendulum swings. The time, generally in seconds, required for the pendulum to make a complete swing or vibration from O to A to O to B back to

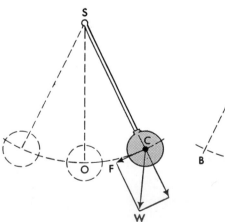 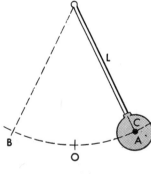

Fig. 4–27. The swing of a pendulum.

O again is called the complete *period* of the pendulum. Astronomers and clock-makers are accustomed to call the time for a swing from *O* to *A* to *O* a period. This is just half a complete period. The *frequency* of the pendulum is the number of complete vibrations it makes in one second.

$$\text{Frequency} = \frac{1}{\text{period}}$$

One complete vibration is called a *cycle*, so frequency is often expressed in *cycles per second* (cps).

The Period of a Pendulum

The period of a simple pendulum, whose arc is small, depends on only two factors, its length and the acceleration caused by gravity. From mathematical considerations and careful experimental tests it has been shown that

$$T = 2\pi\sqrt{\frac{L}{g}}$$

where *T* is the number of seconds required for a *complete* swing, *L* is the length in centimeters, and *g*, the acceleration caused by gravity, is expressed in centimeters per second per second. *T* comes out in seconds, also, when *L* is in feet and *g* in feet per second per second.

Tests show clearly that the period of a pendulum *does not* depend on (1) the mass of the bob, its volume, or the material of which it is made; or (2) the arc of swing, if the arc is small. (For an arc as large as 60 deg, the period of a pendulum is increased about 1.5 percent above that given by the equation above.)

►**Do You Know?**

1. For what is a Foucault pendulum used?
2. Does a pendulum clock that has been adjusted to keep correct time at sea level on the equator gain or lose time when carried northward?
3. Would a pendulum with a lead bob have a different period than one of the same length with an iron bob? Explain.
4. What kinds of timepieces were used before the invention of the pendulum clock?
5. What might be the longest possible pendulum which could be operated? Explain your answer.

HIGHLIGHTS

Forces are *vector* quantities—they have both *magnitude* and *direction*. Scalar quantities have magnitude without direction. Forces, velocities, and accelerations are vectors.

Forces must be combined with due regard to direction as well as magnitude. The process of combining forces is called *composition of forces*.

The *resultant* of two or more forces acting at the same point is the one single force which would have the same effect as the several forces together.

The *equilibrant* of two or more forces is the single force which counterbalances these forces. The equilibrant is equal in magnitude and opposite in direction to the resultant.

105

The *resolution* of a force is the process of finding the *components* of this force in specified directions.

The *torque*, or *moment*, of a force is the tendency of that force to produce rotation about a given axis. It is equal to the product of the force and the perpendicular distance from the axis to the line of action of the force.

For *equilibrium* in a system (1) the sum of the clockwise moments must equal the sum of the counterclockwise moments about any axis and (2) the sum of the components of the forces in any direction must equal the sum of the components of the forces in the opposite direction.

The *center of gravity* of a body is a point about which the body just balances. The entire weight of the body may be considered to act at its center of gravity.

Newton's laws of motion are (1) law of inertia: tells what a force *does*; (2) law of momentum: tells how to measure a force; and (3) law of reaction: asserts that forces occur in pairs.

Centrifugal force acts outward away from an axis of rotation.

Centripetal force tends to pull a rotating body toward the center of rotation.

$$F_c = \frac{mv^2}{r}$$

Acceleration is the time rate of change of velocity. $a = v/t$

A steady force produces uniformly accelerated motion.

The law of universal gravitation:

$$F = G\frac{m_1 m_2}{r^2}$$

The *weight* of a body is the force of gravity on that body.

When air resistance may be neglected, bodies fall with *uniformly accelerated motion*.

The *acceleration due to gravity*, g = 980 cm/sec² or 32 ft/sec², varies slightly with altitude and latitude.

The laws of falling bodies:

$$v = gt \qquad \bar{v} = \frac{v}{2} = \tfrac{1}{2}gt \qquad S = \tfrac{1}{2}gt^2 \qquad v^2 = 2gS$$

The *escape velocity* from the earth is about 25,000 mph.

The period of a pendulum is given by $T = 2\pi\sqrt{L/g}$.

1. An automobile is driven 360 miles in 12 hr. What is the average speed on this trip?

2. How far will an airplane fly in 8 hr at an average speed of 250 mph?

3. What is the average acceleration of a bullet that leaves the muzzle of a rifle with a speed of 1,000 ft/sec, if it requires 0.005 sec to move through the barrel?

4. How many dynes of force are required to give a 500-g iron ball a velocity of 25 cm/sec in 5 sec?

5. Express in *grams* the force required in Problem 4.

6. A wind is blowing from the south with a velocity of 30 mph. What will be the apparent speed and direction of the wind to the occupants of an automobile driven westward at 40 mph? HINT: The motion of the automobile is equivalent to a wind of 40 mph *from the west*, from the point of view of its occupants.

7. A boy pushes with a force of 40 lb on the handle of a lawn mower. The handle makes an angle of 45 deg with the horizontal. What is the component of this force effective in pushing the mower ahead? Solve by the force-triangle method and then check your result by direct computation.

8. A uniform bar 5 ft long balances on a knife-edge at its mid-point. When a 50-lb weight is attached to the bar 1 ft from one end, the bar then balances at a point 1 ft from its mid-point. What is the weight of the bar?

9. A meter stick weighing 150 g balances on a knife-edge at its mid-point. A 100-g weight is then hung at the 65-cm mark. Where must a 50-g weight be hung to again balance the stick at its mid-point?

10. How far does a stone, dropped from a tower, fall in the first half second?

11. What would be the average acceleration of an automobile which started from rest and reached a speed of 30 mph in 10 sec?

12. At an average speed of 600 mph, how long will it take a jet-engine plane to travel 2,500 miles?

13. A boy rows a boat across a stream, always heading directly for the opposite shore. The stream has a flow of 6 ft/sec and the boy can row the boat in still water at a speed of 8 ft/sec. Under these conditions, how fast will the boat move with respect to the bottom of the stream?

14. How far will a baseball, dropped from the top of a stadium wall, fall in 1.5 sec? Neglect air resistance.

15. An automobile is started from a dead stop with an acceleration of 16 ft/sec^2. Express this acceleration in *g* units.

16. A wooden bar 10 ft long weighs 40 lb. It balances on a sharp-edge fulcrum placed at its mid-point. Where will it balance if a 5-lb weight is hung 6 in. from one end?

17. If a force of 10 lb gives a certain body an acceleration of 5 ft/sec^2, what acceleration will a force of 25 lb give to this body?

18. A silver half-dollar weighs 12.5 g. How many dynes of force are required to hold a half-dollar and keep it from falling?

19. A girl lifts a 10-lb bag of sugar from the floor to the top of a table. Express in *poundals* the average force she must use to do this.

20. A boy pulls on a doorknob with a force of 10 lb. The knob is 26 in. from the door hinges. What is the largest value of torque the boy can exert on the door under these conditions? Explain your answer.

107

1. Show by a force diagram how the forward force on a sailboat originates when the boat is tacking across the wind.
2. Show by means of a force diagram why a kite remains aloft in a wind. There is very little Bernoulli effect on a kite.
3. When one drives a car into gently falling snow, the flakes appear to approach the windshield with considerable speed and almost horizontally. Explain this effect by means of a velocity diagram.
4. A plank 10 ft long has one end resting on the ground and the other on a platform 5 ft high. A 200-lb barrel is being rolled up the plank. What force parallel to the plank is required to just hold the barrel from rolling back down the plank and with what force does the barrel press perpendicularly against the plank?
5. How much average force is required to accelerate a 3,000-lb car at the average rate of 7 ft/sec²? HINT: Your answer will probably come out in poundals; divide by 32 to reduce it to pounds.
6. A ball thrown vertically upward rises 150 ft and then begins to fall back to the earth. With what velocity did it start? (Neglect air resistance.)
7. How long does the ball in Problem 6 remain in the air?
8. What is the length of the simple pendulum that ticks off a second every time it passes through its position of rest? Such a pendulum is called a "seconds pendulum." Assume that g is 980 cm/sec² at the point where this pendulum is located.
9. An automobile changes speed from 30 to 60 mph in 22 sec. What is its average acceleration in feet per second per second?
10. A locomotive moving 60 mph directly eastward emits a smoke plume from its smoke stack. A wind whose velocity is 25 mph is blowing from the north at the same time. Set up a diagram to represent these velocities and show the direction of the smoke plume.
11. Compute the force of attraction between two 10-kg iron spheres whose centers are 20 cm apart. Express your answer in dynes.
12. How many seconds will be required for a stone dropped from the edge of a cliff to fall to the base 32 ft below? Neglect air resistance.
13. How many seconds are required for a freely falling body starting from rest to acquire a velocity of 80 ft/sec?
14. An automobile is traveling at a steady rate of 44 ft/sec when the driver pushes the gas pedal and causes the automobile to accelerate uniformly to 66 ft/sec in 1 min. What is the *average* speed of the automobile during this minute?
15. A tightrope walker stands at the midpoint of a 20-ft rope the ends of which are attached at equal heights to two posts. The walker weighs 160 lb and the two sections of the taut rope form an angle of 120 deg. Draw a force diagram to scale to represent the weight of the walker and the forces in the two sections of the rope. Determine graphically how much tension is in the rope.
16. Neglecting air resistance, how fast would the weight dropped by Galileo from the top gallery of the leaning tower of Pisa have been falling when it struck the ground approximately 165 ft below?
17. How many seconds would have been required for the weight dropped by Galileo from the leaning tower to reach the ground 165 ft below? Neglect air resistance.

THINGS TO DO

1. Obtain a pail with a handle or bail similar to a child's sand pail. Fill this pail about half full of water. Then swing the pail and water in a vertical circle without having the water fall out when the pail is upside down at the top of the circle. Explain why the water stays in the pail. NOTE: Do this outdoors.

2. How does a jet engine develop propelling force? To demonstrate the principle, inflate a toy balloon with air and then suddenly release the air and the balloon. Explain why the balloon moves as it does.

3. Can you pull a string straight? Tie a book to the *middle* of a heavy string several feet long. Hold the string in your hands, with each hand about 18 in. from the book. Can you pull the string so tight that it does not sag at the book? Explain.

4. Obtain a glass or plastic tube about ½ in. in diameter and 18 or more inches long. Fit a stopper into one end of this tube and fill the tube with water or a mixture of glycerin and water if possible. Hold the tube to the light and drop *small* lead shot or other small pieces of metal into the top of the liquid. Watch these objects as they fall through the liquid. Do they seem to fall with uniformly accelerated motion? Why? Do larger or smaller objects seem to reach the greater speed? Why?

5.

Energy and Power:
Machines at Work

FORCES IN ACTION

How many horses can you drive? A few generations ago an average driver could handle one or two horses, but an expert was required to manage the four- and six-horse teams used on stagecoaches. Now a driver of an automobile has at his command 100 or more horsepower, while the pilot of an airplane and the engineer of a modern locomotive have thousands of horsepower under finger-tip control. The average factory worker in our country has at his service mechanical power equivalent to that of more than 10 horses or 100 men. Handpower has given way to mechanical power in almost all industries and services. High wages and

a high standard of living, unequaled in any other major country of the world, are largely due to the fact that a worker in the United States with modern machinery can produce more and better goods in less time than he could produce by handpower alone.

What Is Work?

You may be surprised to discover that you become tired out from *physical labor* in which *you do no mechanical work*. In fact, it is quite possible that you may find a task in which you do *no* work even more tiring than one in which you actually do work. The reason for this situation is that the term *work* used in mechanics has a much more definite and

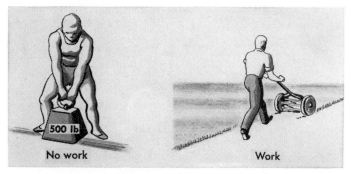

Fig. 5–1. Exerted effort does not always do work.

No work

Work

restricted meaning than it has in everyday use.

Suppose you push on a stalled automobile and succeed in moving it. You then do mechanical work on the car. Even if you provide only a part of the force that is applied to move the car, still you do work on it. But if you push and *fail to move the car*, you do no mechanical work on it, no matter how hard or how long you continue to push. *A force does work when it exceeds all resisting forces and moves the body on which it acts.* A force does no work when it does not exceed the resisting forces and fails to move the body to which it is applied. *Both a force and a motion are necessary when work is done.*

How Work Is Measured

People often ask how much work is involved in any enterprise that is undertaken. If we limit the question to mechanical work, the answer is often easy to obtain. Suppose you lift a 25-lb sack of flour from the floor to the top of a table 3 ft high, as shown in Fig. 5–2. The average force you have to exert is 25 lb. A little more than this is required to start the sack upward and a little less when the sack is slowing down just before it comes to rest on the table top. The 3-ft distance you move the sack vertically is called its *displacement*. The amount of work you do on the sack of flour is then 25 lb × 3 ft = 75 ft-lb (read foot-pounds).

$$\text{Work} = \text{force} \times \text{displacement}$$
$$W = F \times S$$

Consider another case shown in Fig. 5–3. If you pull on a 200-lb block of ice with a horizontal force of 50 lb and fail to move the block, you do no work. But

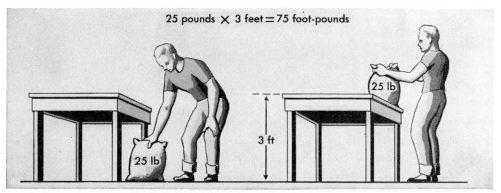

25 pounds × 3 feet = 75 foot-pounds

25 lb

25 lb

3 ft

Fig 5–2. Work done in lifting a weight.

111

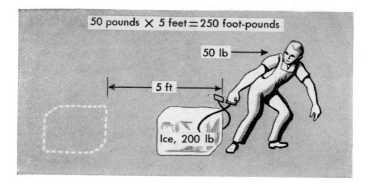

50 pounds × 5 feet = 250 foot-pounds

50 lb →

5 ft

Ice, 200 lb

Fig. 5–3. Work equals the force times the displacement. Both must be in the same direction.

if you succeed in pulling the block 5 ft along the floor on which it is lying, then you do work on the ice. The amount of this work is, 50 lb × 5 ft = 250 ft-lb.

Notice that the weight of the block of ice has nothing to do *directly* with the amount of work done in moving it. The *force you apply* and the distance you move the block in *the direction of this force* are the only two factors involved in the amount of work you do on the block.

In some cases the displacement is not in the same direction as the applied force. Consider the boy pulling on the sled in Fig. 5–4. The applied force is in the direction of the rope, while the sled moves ahead in a horizontal direction. The force that the boy must exert on the rope at the angle shown is greater than he would have to exert horizontally to pull the sled along. So if we multiply the

actual force F that the boy exerts on the rope by the displacement S that the sled moves ahead, we obtain too large a value for the work done. To compute the work in a situation like this, we should first find the *horizontal component* of the force in the rope and multiply this component by the horizontal displacement of the sled, that is, the distance it moves ahead. Part of the force exerted by the boy in Fig. 5–4 does no useful work at all because it is perpendicular to the displacement. In measuring work, the *force involved and the displacement must be in the same direction.*

Work = component of force in direction of motion × displacement

Units of Work

When a force of one pound succeeds in moving a body one foot, the amount of work done is *one foot-pound*. The foot-

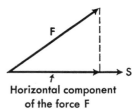

F

Horizontal component of the force F

Fig. 5–4. When the force and displacement are in different directions, the component of the force in the direction of the displacement must be used to compute work.

pound is the most commonly used unit of work for all practical purposes. Other units are formed by compounding a force unit with a distance unit in the same way. Thus such units as the gram-centimeter (g-cm), the kilogram-meter (kg-m), and the foot-ton (ft-ton) are sometimes used. All of these are *gravitational* units because they involve gravitational units of force.

You will recall that the dyne is a very small unit of force. When a *dyne* succeeds in moving an object one centimeter, one dyne-centimeter of work is done. This is such an important unit for scientific purposes that it has been given a distinctive name of its own, the *erg*. The erg is a miniature work unit, just as the dyne is a miniature force unit. In fact the erg is so small that it takes 4,900 ergs to lift a United States nickel vertically one centimeter and about 13.6 million to make one foot-pound.

When a larger unit of the same nature as the erg is needed, we use the *joule*, which is equivalent to 10 million ergs.

$$1 \text{ joule} = 10^7 \text{ ergs} \quad 1 \text{ joule} = 0.736 \text{ ft-lb}$$

The joule is equivalent to about $\frac{3}{4}$ ft-lb.

The erg and the joule are *absolute* units of work in the metric system. The force units they involve do not depend on the pull of gravity. The corresponding unit in the English system is the *foot-poundal*. Foot-poundals are convenient units for use in physics and other science books, but are seldom used elsewhere. Engineers use formulas that convert these units to foot-pounds at once and thus avoid using foot-poundals.

What Is Energy?

In Fig. 5–5a, an 11-lb weight W_1 rests on a hinged shelf while a 10-lb weight W_2 is on the floor. A rope passing over a pulley connects these two weights. When the shelf is dropped out of the way (Fig. 5–5b), we know from experience that W_1 will begin to fall and W_2 to rise, provided friction in the pulley and rope is not too great.

Work must be done on W_2 to raise it. This work is done by W_1 in falling to the floor. When W_1 is resting on the shelf, it has *capacity for doing work*. The work for which it has a potential capacity can be realized by allowing it to fall to the floor.

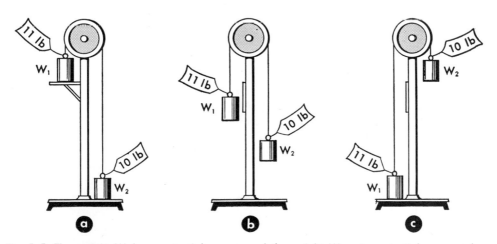

Fig. 5–5. The weight W_1 loses potential energy and the weight W_2 gains potential energy when the shelf is dropped and W_1 is allowed to fall.

Fig. 5–6. The moving hammer has kinetic energy.

The capacity of a body or system of bodies for doing work is called energy.

While on the shelf, W_1 has energy because of its position with respect to the earth. It is said to possess *potential energy*.

A hammer, used to drive a nail in a board, is moving at a considerable speed just as it is about to strike the nail. On striking, the hammer is stopped, and it does work on the nail in driving it into the board. So the hammer has a *capacity for* doing work at the instant of contact. This capacity is *due to its motion* rather than to its position with respect to the earth. Energy due to motion is called *kinetic energy*. The hammer has kinetic energy at the instant of contact with the nail.

A way of finding out how much energy a body or system of bodies possesses is by determining how many ergs, joules, or foot-pounds of work it can do. The capacity for doing work can be measured in terms of work. Consequently, the units used in measuring most forms of

114

energy are the now-familiar units of work, the erg, the joule, the foot-pound, and like units.

Potential Energy

In Fig. 5–5, the weight W_1 at first has potential energy because of its position with respect to the earth and the floor. If it were higher, it could do more work in falling to the floor and so would have more potential energy. If its weight were greater, it likewise would have more potential energy for it could do more work in falling. Its potential energy is measured by *how much work is required to lift it vertically from the floor to the shelf* on which it rests. We already know how to compute this work, since the force we have to apply to lift an object is its weight and the displacement we need to produce is the vertical distance from the floor to the shelf. So we may write

$$\text{Potential energy} = \text{weight} \times \text{height}$$
$$= W \times H$$

If the 11-lb weight W_1 in Fig. 5–5 is 8 ft above the floor, its potential energy with respect to the floor is 11 lb × 8 ft = 88 ft-lb.

Consider a rubber ball at the end of a stretched rubber cord, as shown in Fig. 5–7. Work had to be done on the ball and rubber cord to get the system in its strained condition. When the ball is released, it can do work just as truly as can the weight in Fig. 5–5. So a ball at the end of a stretched rubber cord possesses potential energy. Stretched and compressed springs, wound watch springs, bent steel rods, compressed air— in fact, all elastic systems under strain —*possess potential energy because of their condition*.

A piece of soft iron and a nearby magnet together possess potential energy, for, if free to move, they will pull to-

Fig. 5–7. Potential energy is stored in the stretched rubber string.

gether and thereby do work. Likewise, a rubber rod charged with static electricity and a light piece of cork in the same vicinity exert attractive forces one on the other. If they are free to move, they too can do work. These systems possess potential energy because of their condition.

Gunpowder, dynamite, TNT, and other explosives have large stores of potential energy. Gasoline possesses about 100 million ft-lb of potential energy per gallon. This type of potential energy may be called *chemical potential energy.*

So while some bodies possess potential energy because of their position with respect to the earth, others have potential energy because of their condition of strain or their chemical composition.

Kinetic Energy

Any body in motion possesses *kinetic energy* (KE), for it is capable of doing work on some other body or system when it is stopped. We know from experience that an automobile moving at a given speed can do more work, in coming to a dead stop, than can a bicycle moving at

One gallon of gasoline could lift the Statue of Liberty 220 ft. (*Sinclair Refining Company*)

115

the same speed. The larger the mass of the moving body the more kinetic energy it possesses at a given speed. We also know from observation that an automobile moving 40 mph does more work in stopping than it would do if it had been moving only 20 mph. So the kinetic energy of a moving body depends also on its speed.

From a mathematical analysis that can be verified by experiment, we find that

$$KE = \frac{mass \times (velocity)^2}{2}$$
$$= \frac{mv^2}{2}$$

This equation is sometimes confusing to students because, with it, kinetic energy comes out in absolute units—ergs or foot-poundals. For example, the kinetic energy of a golf ball whose mass is 45 g, moving with a speed of 20 m/sec (2,000 cm/sec) is

KE = ½ mv^2
= ½ × 45g × (2,000 cm/sec)²
= 90,000,000 dyne-cm
= 90,000,000 *ergs*
= 9 *joules*

The kinetic energy of a 3,000-lb automobile moving 30 mph (44 ft/sec) is

KE = ½ mv^2
= ½ × 3,000 lb × (44 ft/sec)²
= 2,904,000 *foot-poundals*

If we wish to know this kinetic energy in *foot-pounds*, we shall have to divide our result by 32, the number of foot-poundals in one foot-pound. This gives 90,750 ft-lb for the kinetic energy of the automobile. If we write the equation for kinetic energy as KE = $\frac{mv^2}{2 \times 32}$ we can find the number of foot-pounds directly from the equation.

Are Your Brakes Working Well?

The motor of an automobile, in doing mechanical work on the car, gives it speed and, hence, kinetic energy, $mv^2/2$. As drivers, we should be impressed with the fact that this kinetic energy increases as the *square* of our speed, as shown in Table 5–1.

To stop a moving body, its kinetic energy must be converted into heat, mechanical work, or some other form of energy. Under ordinary circumstances,

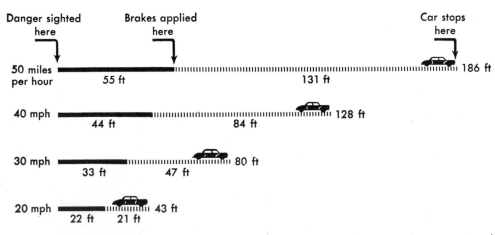

Fig. 5–8. The stopping distance of an automobile traveling at different speeds. (*From a National Safety Council chart*)

116

the kinetic energy of a moving car is changed into heat by the action of the brakes, the engine, and road and wind friction. In a collision, it is this kinetic energy that causes the destruction. Many serious accidents could probably be avoided if every driver were more "kinetic-energy conscious" when he presses down the accelerator!

Conservation of Energy

In addition to the potential and kinetic forms of mechanical energy, we recognize sound, heat, light, radio waves, and other radiations also as forms of energy. Mechanical energy is changed into heat energy when work is done against friction. Heat is converted into mechanical energy in the gasoline engine. Any form of energy can be converted more or less completely into other forms of energy. For this reason, we believe that these various forms are only different aspects of energy.

Workers in physical science make extensive use of a fundamental assumption which may be stated in the following two ways: (1) The total amount of energy in the universe is unchanging or

(2) energy can be transformed from one form into another but can neither be created nor destroyed. Thus when we do mechanical work in sliding a brick along the floor, we expect the total amount of frictional heat and other forms of energy produced to equal the mechanical work we do on the brick. When gasoline is burned in an engine to produce mechanical work, we expect the total amount of mechanical energy and wasted heat energy to equal the potential energy of the gasoline. In every case where energy is changed from one form to another, we expect the total amount of energy after the change to equal the energy before the change took place.

This principle that energy can be transformed but can neither be created nor destroyed is called the *law of conservation of energy.*

Energy and Mass

Our chief source of energy is the sun. An immense stream of energy is being radiated from the sun continuously day and night and this process has been going on probably for billions of years. Measurements indicate that about 4,300,000 ft-lb are radiated every second from each square foot of the sun's surface. The amount radiated from the whole surface is so great that it is almost beyond our comprehension.

Scientists have long been perplexed by the question of where all of this energy comes from. If it came from the sun's own heat, then the sun should long ago have become quite a cold body. A number of other sources have been suggested and found inadequate. A theory that has gained quite wide acceptance is based on the assumption that in the interior of the sun, where temperatures estimated as high as 20,000,000°C and pressures as

Table 5–1. Kinetic Energy of a 3,000-lb Automobile at Different Speeds

Speed of car, mph	Kinetic energy of car, ft-lb (approx)	Relative kinetic energy
5	2,521	1
10	10,083	4
20	40,333	16
30	90,750	36
40	161,333	64
50	252,080	100
60	363,000	144
70	494,077	196
80	645,333	256

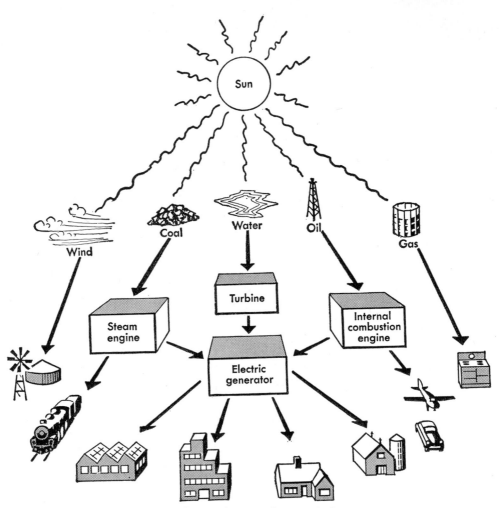

Fig. 5–9. Our chief source of energy is the sun.

great as 1,330,000,000 atmospheres exist, *atoms are being transformed into other atoms, losing mass and yielding energy in the process.* Thus, under extremely high temperatures and pressures mass would be changing into energy. It is also believed that energy may, in special cases, change into mass. So today we find that the law of conservation of energy has to be extended to embrace another law much used by chemists, the law of conservation of mass.

The total amount of mass and energy in the universe is constant.

118

If this change of mass into energy is taking place, we can assume that the sun must be losing mass. The amount of mass required to account for the energy the sun is radiating has been calculated at about 4 million tons per second. You may wonder why the mass of the sun has not all radiated away and vanished long ago at this rate. The total mass of the sun is about 2.2×10^{27} tons, so even at the tremendous rate at which its atoms may be changing, 150 billion years would be required for its mass to decrease only 1 percent.

What Is Power?

We speak in familiar terms of 60-watt electric lamps, 50-kilowatt (kw) radio stations and 100-horsepower (hp) gasoline motors. We are accustomed to gage the size of a device or machine by the amount of *power* it develops or consumes. What do we mean by power?

Earlier in this chapter we discussed how much work is done when the sack of flour is lifted from the floor to the table and the block of ice is pulled along the floor, but did not inquire *how much time* is required to do this work. When we want to know *how fast* as well as *how much* work is being done, we are concerned with *power:*

Power is the time rate of doing work.

$$\text{Power} = \frac{\text{work}}{\text{time}}$$

Power is work per unit time.

If one joule of work is done in one second, the power developed is one *watt*. A *kilowatt* is 1,000 watts. There is no particular power unit that corresponds to one foot-pound per second, but 33,000 foot-pounds per *minute* or 550 foot-pounds per *second* is one *horsepower*.

1 hp = 746 watts = about $\frac{3}{4}$ kw

Suppose the motor raises the car of an elevator with its occupants, weighing 2,000 lb in all, a distance of 200 ft in 2 min. The total amount of work done by the motor is

2,000 lb × 200 ft = 400,000 ft-lb

The average rate at which this work is done is 400,000 ft-lb/2 min, which is 200,000 ft-lb/min. This is equivalent to 200,000/33,000 or 6.06 hp.

An engine rated at 100 hp does not always do work at this rate. It may work at a much slower rate at times, and again at a much slower rate at times, and again it may work at a somewhat faster rate for short periods. The power rating merely indicates how fast the engine *can* do work under specified operating conditions. The rate at which it actually *does* work at any instant depends on the load that is placed on it, as well as on its own capacity.

Some Natural Sources of Power

An enormous amount of power comes to us directly from the sun. Much of this is absorbed or reflected by our atmosphere, but, on the average, about 646,000 hp per square mile reaches the earth's surface, where it is converted largely into heat. We have as yet no effective means of utilizing this solar power *directly* for mechanical work.

Fuels—coal, gas, oil, and wood—constitute our most important source of power. Water in waterfalls, rapid streams, and storage reservoirs is another important source of power. Winds and ocean tides, too, are capable of furnishing power but they are not very effectively harnessed as yet.

Another possible source of natural power lies within the very atoms of which matter is built. Scientists long have dreamed of ways to tap this almost limitless reservoir of power. The amount of power realized from the few atoms used in early laboratory experiments was very small. From these small beginnings and an enormous amount of research and development came the atomic bomb of World War II. Methods are being worked out to control the release of energy from atoms. The atoms of matter itself may eventually become our chief source of power.

►You Will Be Interested to Know

The distinctive names of the units of work and power are of interesting origin.

119

The name *erg* comes from the Greek word *ergon*, which means *work*. The joule was named for James Prescott Joule, a nineteenth-century English scientist who experimented with heat and mechanical energy. The watt was named for James Watt, a Scottish engineer and inventor, who is credited with developing the steam engine (about 1770).

At the time the first steam engines were built, horses were used to operate the machinery in the coal mines, mills, and breweries of Scotland and England. The first engines were used to replace these horses and it became the custom of the manufacturers to rate their engines in terms of the number of horses they could replace. It is not clear whether the value of 33,000 ft-lb/min was arrived at by actually measuring the average power draft horses then in service could develop or whether this number represents a good estimate, rounded off for convenience in use. The term *horsepower* long ago ceased to have any reference to the power of a horse.

►Do You Know?

1. In Fig. 5–2 will you do more work in lifting the sack of flour if you swing it in an arc from the floor to the table top than if you lift it vertically upward? Explain.
2. If you push on the side of a building, how much work do you do?
3. When you lift an object you do work against gravity; that is, the force of gravity is the opposing force that your force must exceed. Against what do you do work when you push a book across the top of a desk? When you stretch a rubber band? When you throw a baseball? When you set a marble in motion?
4. What becomes of the work you do in pushing a book across a table top?

In stretching a rubber band? In setting a marble in motion?
5. In which of the situations listed in question 3 is the work you do recoverable, wholly or in part?
6. What becomes of the potential energy of a raindrop when it falls to the earth?
7. When is the energy of a pendulum all potential and when is it all kinetic?
8. Once an automobile has reached a steady speed, the engine must continue to do work on it to maintain this speed. What becomes of this work?
9. What kind of energy is possessed by water in a storage reservoir? By water at the foot of a waterfall?
10. What kind of energy is stored in spinning flywheels?
11. What is meant by "white coal"?
12. Have any engines been developed that operate directly from the sun's energy? How do they operate?
13. What is the horsepower rating of the engine in your family automobile?
14. What is the horsepower rating of the motor on your vacuum sweeper, washing machine, refrigerator, or electric fan?
15. Make a list of some new jobs or new kinds of work open to you which have been created by the introduction of machines to replace handpower. Make also a list of the jobs or kinds of work that these machines replaced.

MACHINES AID IN DOING WORK

Every worker in the home, on the farm, and in the factory is to some degree an engineer who controls and directs power through machines that do the actual work.

What a Machine Does

Consider the lever represented by the pump handle in Fig. 5–10. To operate this pump we have to exert a force on the handle. The handle in turn exerts a force on the rod to lift the piston and water. We shall call the force exerted on a machine the *input* or *effort force* and designate it by F_i; we shall call the force exerted by the machine on a load connected to it the *output force* and designate it by F_o. Thus the push we exert on the pump handle is the input force F_i and the force the handle exerts on the rod is the output force F_o. We know from experience that the output force in this illustration is greater than the input force, so we may think of this machine as *multiplying force*. Some machines are designed specifically to multiply force.

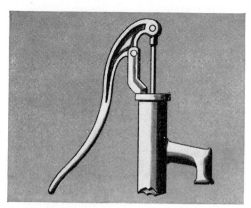

Fig. 5–10. The pump handle is a lever used to multiply force.

The fish-line reel represented in Fig. 5–11 is a combination of several simple machines. The input force F_i is applied to the handle of the crank and the output force F_o is exerted on the line. The line reels in faster than the crank is turned so F_o moves faster and farther than F_i. We may therefore think of this reel as a machine for *multiplying speed and distance*. Some machines are designed specifically to multiply speed and distance.

Fig. 5–11. The fish-line reel multiplies speed and distance.

In the pulley represented in Fig. 5–12 the input force is in one direction and the output force is in another direction. This machine serves chiefly to *change the direction* of force, for the force is not larger nor does it move faster than the load. Some machines are designed specifically to change the direction of force.

We do work on the handle of the pump in Fig. 5–10 when we push it down a certain distance. The handle, in turn, does work on the piston and water when it lifts them. We may, then, consider

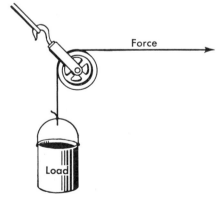

Fig. 5–12. This pulley changes the direction of force.

121

that the pump handle transfers work or energy from our hand to the piston and water. In the same way, we may say that the broom in Fig. 5–13 transfers energy from the hands of the operator to the floor. Some machines are designed specifically to transfer energy from one place to another.

Some machines are used chiefly to *transform* energy from one form to another. These are generally more complicated machines like the steam engine, the gasoline engine, and the electric generator and motor.

A machine may serve several of these purposes at the same time, but no machine yet devised can multiply both force and speed simultaneously.

Mechanical Advantage

When we speak of the *mechanical advantage* (MA) of a machine as 2 or 5 we refer to a particular characteristic of that machine. By mechanical advantage we mean the ratio of the output force exerted by the machine to the input force we apply to the machine. Thus we may write

$$MA = \frac{\text{output force}}{\text{input force}} = \frac{F_o}{F_i}$$

Fig. 5–13. A broom is used to transfer energy.

If the output force of a certain lever is 100 lb when a force of 25 lb is applied to it, the mechanical advantage of the lever is $100/25 = 4$. If the output force of any machine is greater than the input force, the mechanical advantage of that machine is *greater than 1*. Conversely, a machine whose mechanical advantage is greater than 1 *multiplies force.*

We can also see from the preceding equation that if the mechanical advantage of a machine is less than 1, the output force it can exert is less than the input force applied to it. Such a machine *reduces force.* When the mechanical advantage of a machine equals 1, the machine neither multiplies nor reduces force. If we know the mechanical advantage of any machine we can compute how much input force must be applied to it to produce a given output force.

EXAMPLE: The mechanical advantage of a certain lever is 5. How much force must be applied to the lever to lift a weight of 250 lb?

SOLUTION: Since

$$MA = \frac{\text{output force}}{\text{input force}} = \frac{F_o}{F_i}$$

$$F_i = \frac{F_o}{MA} = \frac{250}{5} \text{ lb} = 50 \text{ lb}$$

The Law of Machines

In every machine that does mechanical work, the applied input force F_i must move the part of the machine on which it acts through some distance S_i, so the effort force *does work on the machine.* The amount of this work, called the *work input,* may be expressed by

Work input = input force × distance moved

$$= F_i \times S_i$$

The machine, in turn, exerts an output force F_o on the load, and this force moves the load through a distance S_o. The work that the *machine does on the load* is called the *work output* and may be expressed as

Work output = output force × distance force moves load

$$= F_o \times S_o$$

By the law of conservation of energy, a machine can neither create nor destroy energy. So if there were no friction or other energy losses in the machine, the work output and the work input would be exactly equal.

Work output = work input
$$F_o \times S_o = F_i \times S_i$$

This is sometimes called the *law of machines*.

No machine is entirely free from friction. The *useful* work output is always less than the actual work input. In some machines, however, friction is so small that it can be neglected for practical purposes. If we include the energy spent in working against friction as part of the output, we can always apply the law of machines to any of the simple machines we shall consider.

Mechanical Efficiency

The ratio of the useful work output to the work input of a machine is called its *efficiency*. This ratio is usually expressed as a percentage. An efficiency of 75 percent means that the useful output is 75 percent of the input.

$$\text{Eff.} = \frac{\text{useful work output}}{\text{work input}} \times 100\%$$

or

$$= \frac{\text{useful power output}}{\text{power input}} \times 100\%$$

The useful work output of a machine is always less than its input, because some energy is wasted in doing work against friction and in other ways. No machine can have an efficiency greater than 100 percent and none in practice can quite equal this figure because of friction.

Perpetual Motion

If the useful power output of a machine were greater than its power input, the machine could be made to run itself indefinitely, with perhaps a little power left over for other purposes. Any machine which purports to operate in this way is called a *perpetual-motion machine*. The scheme behind such a machine violates the law of conservation of energy, and is an attempt to get something for nothing. Hundreds of such machines have been designed, and many inventors who have had but little regard for this law have spent years on will-o'-the-wisp schemes for circumventing the law of conservation of energy. All models of such machines have failed to operate.

▶Do You Know?

1. Name one machine that is used chiefly to multiply force; to multiply speed; to change the direction of a force; to transfer energy; to transform energy.
2. Can the mechanical advantage of a machine be 250? 0.25? Explain.

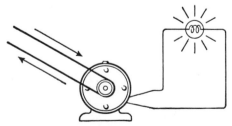

Fig. 5–14. An electric generator *transforms* mechanical energy to electrical energy.

123

3. Can the efficiency of a machine be 250? Explain.
4. Give a definition of mechanical advantage. How large or how small can the mechanical advantage of machines be?
5. Define efficiency. Explain how the meaning of efficiency in physics may be different from its meaning in everyday life.

THE SIMPLE MACHINES

We usually think of a machine as an assembly of intricate parts, properly designed and fitted together to do some special type of work. When we examine the individual parts of such a machine, we may be surprised to find that it is built up of variations of a relatively few very simple devices, used over and over again. The six simple machines are:

Lever	Inclined plane
Wheel and axle	Wedge
Pulley	Screw

You have probably not thought of these simple devices as machines at all, yet out of these are built most of the machines in use today. We shall confine our discussion to the simple machines and a few of their combinations.

The Lever

The *lever* was one of the first machines ever used by man. Its origin is pre-

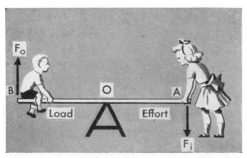

Fig. 5–15. A teeter board acts as a lever.

124

historic. Archimedes is reported to have been so impressed with the force-multiplying property of the lever that he said, "Give me a place to stand and rest my lever and I can move the earth." In everyday language, a lever is often called a *pry*. In *prying* the lid off a can of paint, a knife or a screwdriver may be used as a lever.

Many of our common tools and utensils such as shovels, brooms, nutcrackers, pincers and pliers, ice tongs, table knives, forks, and spoons are used as levers. Some types of door latches are levers. Scales used for weighing wagons and trucks are usually made up of a series of levers. The bones of our arms and legs are essentially levers. If you will examine any complicated machine, you are likely to find a number of levers.

A lever consists of a rigid bar, or its equivalent, pivoting about an axis or support called a *fulcrum*. The effort or input force is applied at some point along the bar, and the output force is exerted against the load placed at another point. In operation, the input force is generally sufficient to move the lever and the load so work is *done on the lever* by the effort and the lever, in turn, *does work on the load*.

In Fig. 5–15, the girl is applying the effort or input force F_i as she pushes down on the board. The weight of the child is the load. The board exerts the output force F_o upward tending to lift the child. The fulcrum of the lever is where the board rests on its support. Suppose this point is marked O. We shall call the distance OA the *effort arm* and the distance OB the *load arm*.

Classes of Levers

Levers are classified according to the relative positions of effort, load, and fulcrum.

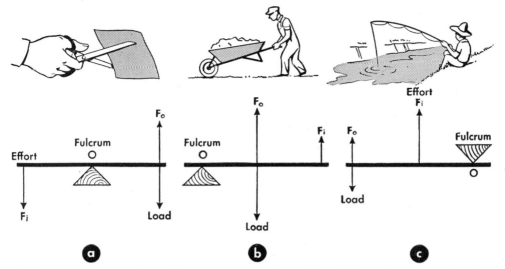

Fig. 5–16. (a) First-class lever; fulcrum between load and effort. (b) Second-class lever; load between effort and fulcrum. (c) Third-class lever; effort between fulcrum and load.

In *first-class levers* the fulcrum is between the load and the effort.

In *second-class levers* the load is between the effort and the fulcrum.

In *third-class levers* the effort is applied between the fulcrum and the load.

What Is Leverage?

When we know how much output force a given effort or input force can set up, we can compute the mechanical advantage, F_o/F_i, for the lever. We call this the *real* or *actual mechanical advantage* to distinguish it from the *ideal* or *theoretical mechanical advantage* which the machine would have if it were entirely free from friction.

In order that a lever of any class shall just be balanced (equilibrium), it is necessary that the sum of the moments of forces acting on the lever to produce clockwise rotation shall be equal to the sum of the moments of the forces acting on the lever to produce counterclockwise rotation. We explored this problem of equilibrium in Chapter 4. It is usually customary and convenient to take the fulcrum as the axis about which the moments of the acting forces are computed. So, if we may neglect the weight of the board in Fig. 5–15, the condition for balance is

Load force $\times$ load arm $=$
$$\text{effort force} \times \text{effort arm}$$

From this relation we can obtain the proportion

$$\frac{\text{Load force}}{\text{Effort force}} = \frac{\text{effort arm}}{\text{load arm}}$$

When the lever is just balanced, the output force F_o exerted by the lever on the load must be equal to the force the load exerts on the lever (equilibrium). So we may write for this lever

$$\text{MA} = \frac{F_o}{F_i} = \frac{\text{load force}}{\text{effort force}}$$
$$= \frac{\text{effort arm}}{\text{load arm}} = \frac{OA}{OB}$$

If we can measure the effort arm OA and the load arm OB and take their ratio, we can obtain the mechanical advantage of

125

this lever without setting it up and without applying any input force or load to it at all. The mechanical advantage we obtain in this way is that of an *ideal* lever in which there is assumed to be no friction when the lever moves. This value, $\frac{\text{effort arm}}{\text{load arm}}$, is the *ideal*, or theoretical, mechanical advantage of the lever. Its *real* mechanical advantage is expressed by $\frac{\text{actual output force}}{\text{actual input force}}$. In finding the real mechanical advantage of a machine, we must make full allowance for friction. The real mechanical advantage of most machines is smaller than the ideal mechanical advantage.

EXAMPLE: In a certain lever the length of the effort arm is 5 ft and that of the load arm is 1 ft. A force of 22 lb must be

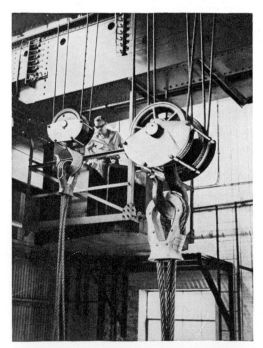

Pulleys play important parts in the operation of shops and factories. (*John A. Roebling's Sons Company*)

applied to lift a weight of 100 lb. What are the real and the ideal mechanical advantages of the lever?

SOLUTION: The ideal mechanical advantage is

$$\frac{\text{Effort arm}}{\text{Load arm}} = \frac{5 \text{ ft}}{1 \text{ ft}} = 5$$

The real mechanical advantage is

$$\frac{\text{Output force}}{\text{Input force}} = \frac{100 \text{ lb}}{22 \text{ lb}} = 4.54$$

Workmen and engineers often speak of mechanical advantage as *leverage*. When a mechanic wants to get more leverage, he shortens the load arm or lengthens the effort arm of his lever.

Mechanical Efficiency of Levers

The efficiency of a machine is its useful work output divided by its work input. Because frictional forces are relatively small in a well-designed lever, the work output of the lever is very nearly equal to its work input and so its efficiency is high. The efficiency of some levers is more than 99 percent. It can be shown by mathematical analysis that the efficiency of any machine is also given by

$$\text{Efficiency} = \frac{\text{real MA}}{\text{ideal MA}} \times 100\%$$

In the example given under What Is Leverage? the efficiency of the lever is

$$\text{Efficiency} = \frac{4.54}{5} \times 100\% = 90.8\%$$

The Weight of the Lever Bar

The weight of the lever itself is usually quite small in comparison to the other forces acting on it. However, *except when the fulcrum is at the center of gravity of the bar*, its weight produces a moment that adds either to that of the effort or to that of load. If the weight of the bar tends to rotate the lever in the same direction as the effort, the *total work input* is that due to the effort *plus* that due to the weight of the bar acting at its center of gravity. If, on the other hand, the weight of the bar tends to rotate the lever in the same direction as the load, then the *total work done by the lever* is the work done on the load *plus* that done on the weight of the bar. These facts must be taken into consideration when we wish to make a precise calculation of the work input, the work output, and the efficiency of a lever.

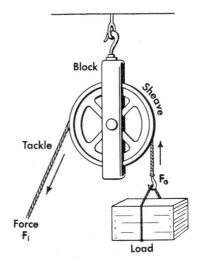

Fig. 5–17. The parts of a pulley.

Pulleys

Pulleys are used to raise and lower awnings and venetian window shades. The sash cords for the counterweights of windows pass over pulleys. Elevators and dumbwaiters operate on pulleys. Power shovels, cranes, trucks equipped with hoists, and automobile service cars generally make use of pulleys. On the farm, pulleys are used in hay-stacking equipment, in pulling stumps, and in many other operations. Pulleys have a wide variety of uses in shops and factories.

A simple pulley consists of a grooved wheel, called the *sheave*, and a frame, called the *block*, which supports the axle on which the sheave turns. A rope, called the *tackle*, passes through the groove in the sheave and connects the effort to the load. A "block and tackle" is then merely two blocks each consisting of one or more sheaves, together with the rope used for connecting them.

Fixed Pulleys

Figure 5–18 shows a single *fixed pulley* in use. The block is fastened to a fixed point at the top of the flagpole. The sheave turns but the block does not

move along with the load. The effort force and the output force are exerted at opposite ends of the same rope. They are equal if the cords are parallel and if there is no friction in the rope or pulley. In practice, the effort force must be a little larger than the output force since it must counterbalance an additional force due to friction.

The *ideal* mechanical advantage of a pulley of this type is 1. As a machine, this pulley multiplies neither force nor

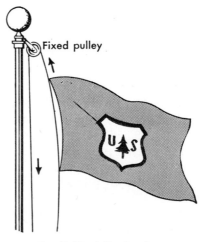

Fig. 5–18. A fixed pulley.

127

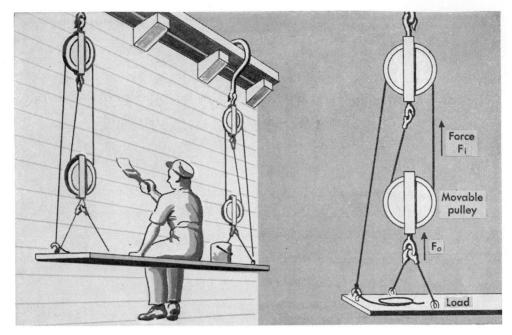

Fig. 5–19. Movable pulleys in use.

speed. It serves only to change the direction of the effort force and to transfer energy.

The distances the effort force and the output force move are the same. So, with the actual effort just slightly greater than the output force, the work input is only slightly greater than the useful work output. For this reason, the efficiency of a pulley of this type is usually greater than 90 percent, unless there is undue friction at the axle of the sheave.

Movable Pulleys

Figure 5–19 shows a *movable pulley* in operation. Notice that the movable pulley is attached to the ladder, which with the painter constitutes the load. This pulley moves along with the load. One end of the rope is fastened to the block of the fixed pulley and the effort force is applied at the other end of the rope after it has passed around the two pulleys.

If the input force pulls the end of the rope down 10 ft then the output force will lift the ladder only one-half this distance, because each of the two sections of rope supporting the ladder will be shortened only 5 ft. When the input force moves a distance S_i, the output force moves the load a distance $S_o = S_i/2$. If we neglect friction,

Work output = work input (law of machines)

so
$$F_o \times S_o = F_i \times S_i$$

We can obtain from the preceding equation an expression for the *ideal* (no friction) mechanical advantage of this pulley system in the same way we did for the lever.

$$\mathrm{MA} = \frac{F_o}{F_i} = \frac{S_i}{S_o} = \frac{S_i}{S_i/2} = 2$$

A single movable pulley multiplies force by 2 and divides speed and distance by 2.

If the positions of the load and the effort were interchanged, the pulley would multiply speed and distance by 2 and divide force by 2.

Multiple Pulleys

A great many combinations of pulleys can be made. Each combination has its own characteristics and purposes. One of the most common combinations is shown in Fig. 5–20. To find the mechanical advantage of a set of pulleys connected in this way, we have to note that one piece of rope is used to thread them. If that rope is free to move over the sheaves of the pulleys, *every section must have the same force in it as every other section.*

In Fig. 5–20 the total force pulling upward on the lifeboat is then $4\,F_i$, the force in the single rope, for there are four sections of rope attached to the boat. If there are n sections of rope pulling on the load, there will be a total force of $n \times F_i$ acting on it. This total force is the output force F_o. Hence, $F_o = n \times F_i$ and $F_o/F_i = n$, where F_o/F_i is the ideal mechanical advantage of the combination of pulleys.

The ideal mechanical advantage of a combination of pulleys is equal to the number of sections of rope attached to the load.
Because of friction, the real mechanical advantage will be somewhat smaller than this value.

The Wheel and Axle

A wheel, fastened rigidly to an axle or to another wheel so that both must turn together, constitutes a *wheel and axle.* The axle is generally mounted in a frame with bearings to facilitate its use. There are so many variations of this machine that we sometimes have difficulty in recognizing it. A crank sometimes takes the place of a wheel. A rope, chain, or belt may be attached to the wheel to connect it to the effort. Sometimes the wheel has cogs cut in its rim and these mesh with another cogwheel to form part of a train of gears.

Figure 5–21 shows a few of the uses of this machine. Doorknobs, door keys, food grinders, water faucets, screwdrivers, grindstones, radio dials and knobs, gear wheels in watches and clocks, transmission and differential gears in automobiles are all different forms of the wheel and axle.

The wheel and axle is represented schematically by the diagram in Fig. 5–22, where r_w represents the radius of the wheel and r_a the radius of the axle. Suppose the effort force moves far enough to turn the wheel once around. It must then move a distance $2\pi r_w$, the circumference of the wheel. At the same time the axle must turn once around and the

Fig. 5–20. A pulley system with a mechanical advantage of 4.

129

Fig. 5–21. Examples of the wheel and axle.

load must move a distance $2\pi r_a$, the circumference of the axle. During this operation, work input $= F_i \times 2\pi r_w$ and work output $= F_o \times 2\pi r_a$. If we neglect friction, these two amounts of work are equal (law of machines), so

$$F_i \times 2\pi r_w = F_o \times 2\pi r_a$$

from which we can find the ideal mechanical advantage

$$\frac{F_o}{F_i} = \frac{r_w}{r_a} = \frac{\text{radius of wheel}}{\text{radius of axle}}$$

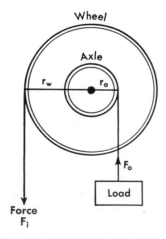

Fig. 5–22. The parts of an ideal wheel and axle.

130

Since the radius of the wheel is greater than that of the axle in the usual case, the mechanical advantage is generally greater than 1. Thus this machine multiplies force at the expense of speed and distance. If the positions of the effort and the load were interchanged, the machine would multiply speed and distance at the expense of force, for the mechanical advantage would then be less than 1.

The Inclined Plane

An *inclined plane* consists of a smooth sloping surface up which a load is pushed or pulled.

An inclined plane can be represented schematically as shown in Figs. 5–23 and 5–24.

The effort force is usually applied parallel to the plane, as shown in Fig. 5–23. Suppose the effort force moves the load up the plane a distance L, the length of the plane. The work input is then $W = F_i \times L$ units. The weight of the load acts vertically *downward*, so we should consider the output force of the machine to act vertically upward. When the load moves a distance L up the plane it moves through a vertical

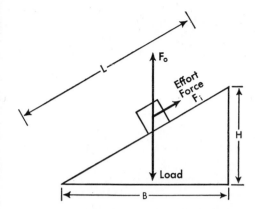

Fig. 5–23. An inclined plane with the effort parallel to the plane.

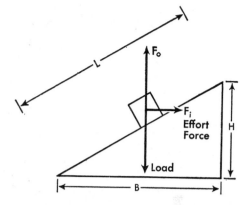

Fig. 5–24. An inclined plane with the effort parallel to the base.

distance equal to the height H of the plane. So the work done by the machine on the load is $W = F_o \times H$. If we neglect friction, the work output should just equal the work input (law of machines), so

$$F_i \times L = F_o \times H$$

We can find the expression for the mechanical advantage from this equation in the same manner as in previous cases.

$$MA = \frac{F_o}{F_i} = \frac{L}{H}$$

Thus L/H is the ideal mechanical advantage of the inclined plane. Notice that this mechanical advantage is determined entirely from the physical dimensions of the machine.

Since L is always greater than H, the mechanical advantage of this machine when used as shown in Fig. 5–23 is always greater than 1. It multiplies force at the expense of speed and distance. Some inclined planes have the effort force parallel to the base, rather than parallel to the plane, as shown in Fig. 5–24. The mechanical advantage in this case is B/H. The mechanical advantage with this arrangement is less than when the effort force is parallel to the plane.

EXAMPLE: A force of 50 lb is required to pull a sled and its load weighing 200 lb (total) up a hill which rises 20 ft in every 100 ft (measured along the surface of the hill). What are the real and the ideal mechanical advantages and the efficiency of this hill considered as an inclined plane?

SOLUTION:

$$\text{Real MA} = \frac{\text{output force (or load)}}{\text{effort force}}$$

$$= \frac{200 \text{ lb}}{50 \text{ lb}} = 4$$

$$\text{Ideal MA} = \frac{\text{length}}{\text{height}} = \frac{100 \text{ ft}}{20 \text{ ft}} = 5$$

$$\text{Efficiency} = \frac{\text{real MA}}{\text{ideal MA}} \times 100\%$$

$$= \frac{4}{5} \times 100\% = 80\%$$

The Wedge

A *wedge* is a piece of wood, metal, or other suitable material, two opposite faces of which are divergent planes, as shown in Fig. 5–25. The effort force pushes the wedge under the load and thus exerts an output force. A wedge is in reality a double inclined plane, with

131

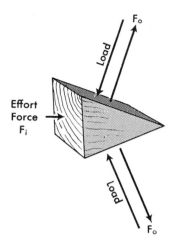

Fig. 5–25. A wedge and its forces.

the effort force applied parallel to the base.

Nails and tacks of all kinds, hatchets and axes, chisels and carpenters' planes, knives, swords, and bayonets are all wedges. Needles and pins, awls, punches, and even the thorns of rose bushes are wedges. You will doubtless be able to identify many other wedges among the tools and utensils with which you come in contact every day.

What Is a Self-locking Machine?

The ideal mechanical advantage of a wedge can be expressed in a form similar to that for the inclined plane. But a wedge must have friction—a great deal of friction—to be of much use. Without friction, a wedge driven into a log would come out after the sledge blow is delivered. This sometimes happens when the wood in the log is wet and frozen so that friction is greatly reduced. Since a wedge usually stays where we leave it when the effort force is removed, we call it a *self-locking machine*. By mathematical analysis and from experimental data we find the following rule:

In a self-locking machine, the real mechanical advantage is less than half the ideal mechanical advantage and the efficiency of the machine is less than 50 percent.

The Screw

Screws are used in worm gears, food choppers, drills for wood and metal, and jacks for raising cars. Windmills, electric fans, and airplane propellers are types of screws. Corkscrews and fruit-jar lids are also types of screws.

The threads of a screw constitute a spiral inclined plane, while the lever arm and the shaft together form a wheel and axle. The threads are usually cut so that the screw advances, or moves away from you, as it is turned clockwise. Such a screw has *right-hand threads*. Some screws, designed for special purposes, have *left-hand threads*. Such screws must be turned counterclockwise, that is, to the left, to advance the screw. A wood screw must be turned to the right to drive it and to the left to loosen it. The nut of an ordinary bolt tightens when

Fig. 5–26. The threads of a screw form a spiral inclined plane.

turned to the right and loosens when turned to the left.

To be of any use, the screw must generally be self-locking. Friction must be great enough so that the nut of a bolt will not immediately unscrew when the wrench is removed from it, and the wood screw will not unscrew when the screw driver is lifted. This means that the efficiency of such a screw must be less than 50 percent and its real mechanical advantage less than half its ideal, as was indicated earlier in this chapter.

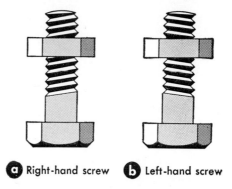

ⓐ Right-hand screw   ⓑ Left-hand screw

Fig. 5–27. Right- and left-hand screws.

►Do You Know?

1. How may a shovel be either a first-class or a third-class lever?
2. What class lever is a pair of ice tongs? The oars of a rowboat? A pump handle? The accelerator pedal on an automobile? The brake pedal?
3. When the mechanical advantage of a lever is $\frac{1}{3}$, how many times does it multiply speed?
4. When the mechanical advantage of a lever is 4, how many pounds of effort are required to lift a 100-lb weight?
5. If you wish to use a lever to increase speed but not change the direction of the applied force, what class lever would you use?
6. Why can the efficiency of a lever not equal 100 percent?
7. If the effort and the load in Fig. 5–20 were interchanged, what would be the mechanical advantage of the pulley system then?
8. Do you know any uses for pulleys around your home, other than those mentioned in the text? If so, are the pulleys of the fixed or of the movable type?
9. "A pulley is a lever in disguise." Can you justify this statement?

10. How would you identify the parts of a wheel and axle in a skate key? a window-shade roller?
11. "The wheel and axle is really a continuously operating lever of the first class." How would you justify this statement?
12. Is the inclined plane a special type of lever, as the pulley and the wheel and axle seem to be? Explain.
13. When you climb up the slope of a toboggan slide you do work against gravity and increase your potential energy. What becomes of this potential energy when you slide down?
14. Do you know any uses for left-hand screws? Name them.
15. The propeller of an airplane automatically changes *pitch* when the plane reaches high altitudes. What does this mean?

FRICTION

A ball rolling along a smooth surface is slowed down and eventually stopped by the force of friction. An automobile speeding along a level highway is opposed by friction between the tires and the road, as well as by air resistance, another form of friction. In addition to these, there is friction between the moving parts of the motor and in the trans-

Fig. 5–28. If friction should vanish.

mission system of the car. When two *parts of a machine slide or roll one across the other, frictional forces appear, opposing the motion.*

In any machine with moving parts, force must be exerted against friction as well as on the load. Thus *work must be done against friction when the machine operates.* This work is converted into heat and does not increase the potential or kinetic energy of the load. It cannot be regained when the load is allowed to do work on something else. The heat developed is generally not in a useful form, so this part of the input energy is wasted. It represents the toll that friction exacts in every mechanical operation. Because of this toll, perpetual motion is impossible.

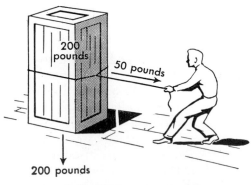

200 pounds

50 pounds

200 pounds

Fig. 5–29. Friction opposes motion.

Friction Is an Aid

We have seen that wedges, nails, screws, bolts, and other self-locking machines would be useless without friction. If railroad tracks and highways offered no friction to moving wheels, they could handle no traffic. Everyone who has tried to walk over smooth ice knows that motion is slow and uncertain when friction is reduced. If friction should vanish entirely, walking would be impossible. Without friction, automobile brakes of the present type would be useless. Lead pencils and chalk, without friction, could not leave even a faint mark. So you see that while we would like to banish friction in some situations, we find it a necessary aid in others.

When one surface *slides* across another, the friction between them is described as *sliding friction.* When one surface rolls along another, the friction between them is described as *rolling friction.*

Coefficient of Sliding Friction

Suppose a force of 50 lb is required to pull a 200-lb box along a floor as shown in Fig. 5–29. Then the ratio $50/200 = 0.25$ is called the *coefficient of friction* between the box and the floor. For any two given surfaces, the coefficient of sliding friction equals the force of friction divided by the perpendicular force with which the two surfaces are pressed together.

The coefficient of friction is always a

Table 5–2. Some Coefficients of Friction

Wood on wood, dry	0.25–0.50
Metals on metals, dry	0.15–0.20
Smooth surfaces, continually greased	0.05
Steel on agate, dry	0.20
Earth on earth	0.25–1.00

number. The preceding relationship indicates that if we multiply the force with which one surface presses on the other by the coefficient of friction, we obtain the *force of friction*. This force of friction is equal to the force we have to exert to slide one of the surfaces over the other. If the coefficient of friction between two surfaces is 0.2 and one surface presses on the other with a force of 500 lb, the force we would have to exert to slide one across the other is 0.2 × 500 lb = 100 lb. The coefficient of friction depends not only on the material of the two surfaces, but also very much on their smoothness and general condition.

Ball bearings have less friction than sliding bearings. (SKF Industries, Inc., Philadelphia, Pa.)

How to Reduce Friction

There are several ways in which friction in machinery can be reduced:

1. Use smooth, well-polished surfaces. In the wearing-in process in new machinery, the moving surfaces become polished and otherwise modified so that friction is reduced.
2. Use metals with low coefficients of friction for the moving parts. Bronze, brass, and babbitt metal are used for bearings for steel shafts because these metals have low coefficients of friction against steel.
3. Substitute ball or roller bearings for sliding bearings and thus change from sliding to rolling friction.
4. Use a lubricant, such as soap, oil, grease, or graphite, on the surfaces that rub together. The lubricant fills in the surface irregularities and a thin layer of it clings to each surface so that sliding now takes place between layers of the lubricant rather than between metals.

►Do You Know?

1. How does sand or cinders thrown on icy pavement affect the coefficient of friction between the surface of the pavement and the tires of passing cars?
2. Why do locomotives sometimes need sand on the track to start a heavy load?
3. Why do gym and tennis shoes have rubber soles rather than leather?
4. Why is it easier to walk on an icy surface when you wear rubbers over your shoes?
5. How may water on the surface of a paved highway act as a lubricant?

Roller bearings, too, have less friction. (SKF Industries, Inc., Philadelphia, Pa.)

135

HIGHLIGHTS

Work involves both a force and a displacement in the direction of the force. $W = F \times S$

The foot-pound, gram-centimeter, and the kilogram-meter are gravitational units of work.

The erg, joule, and foot-poundal are absolute units of work.

$$1 \text{ ft-lb} = 32 \text{ foot-poundals} \quad \text{and} \quad 1 \text{ joule} = 10,000,000 \text{ ergs}$$

Energy is the capacity for doing work. The units are the same as those of work.

Potential energy is energy due to position, condition, or chemical composition. The potential energy of a body due to its elevation is

$$\text{Potential energy} = \text{weight} \times \text{height}$$

Kinetic energy is energy due to motion.

$$KE = \tfrac{1}{2}\, mv^2 \text{ (foot-poundals or ergs)}$$

The law of conservation of energy asserts that energy can be neither created nor destroyed in any transformation that takes place.

Power is the time rate of doing work. $P = W/t$.

The *watt*, the *kilowatt*, and the *horsepower* are units of power. $1 \text{ hp} = 746 \text{ watts}$

The simple machines are the lever, the wheel and axle, the pulley, the inclined plane, the wedge, and the screw.

The law of machines asserts that the total work output equals the total work input.

The real mechanical advantage of a machine is $\dfrac{\text{output force}}{\text{effort force}}$.

The efficiency of a machine is

$$\text{Efficiency} = \frac{\text{useful work output}}{\text{work input}} \times 100\%$$

$$= \frac{\text{useful power output}}{\text{power input}} \times 100\%$$

In a *lever*, load $\times$ load arm $=$ effort $\times$ effort arm, if friction is neglected.

A *fixed pulley* changes the direction of a force only.

For a *movable pulley*, the ideal mechanical advantage is equivalent to the number of sections of rope supporting the load.

In a *wheel and axle*, the ideal mechanical advantage is $\dfrac{\text{radius of wheel}}{\text{radius of axle}}$.

In an *inclined plane*, the ideal mechanical advantage is $\dfrac{\text{length of plane}}{\text{height of plane}}$ when the effort is parallel to the plane.

The *wedge* and the *screw* are self-locking machines in which the efficiency is less than 50 percent and the real mechanical advantage less than half the ideal.

The *coefficient of sliding friction* is the force of friction divided by the perpendicular force with which the surfaces are pressed together.

PROBLEMS: GROUP A

1. How much work is done in lifting 1 ft³ of fresh water 10 ft vertically? By how much is the potential energy of this water increased?
2. How much work does a boy weighing 130 lb do against gravity when he walks up a flight of stairs 20 ft high?
3. If ½ min is required for the boy to mount the stairs in Problem 2, at what average horsepower does he work?
4. How much work is done against gravity when a loaded airplane, whose total weight is 10 tons, ascends to an elevation of 10,000 ft?
5. The water storage tank shown on p. 35 holds 750,000 gal when filled. The average height of this water is 65 ft above the ground. What is the potential energy of the water in a full tank? Assume 1 gal of water weighs 8 lb.
6. What is the potential energy of 1 ft³ of water on the brink of Niagara Falls 165 ft above the river below?
7. What is the kinetic energy of a 140-lb boy running 10 ft/sec?
8. A force of 20 kg is required to pull a 100-kg box of sand along a wooden floor. What is the coefficient of friction between the box and the floor?
9. What is the efficiency of an electric motor which requires an input of 10 kw when it is delivering 10 hp?
10. A lever has a real mechanical advantage of 10. How much force is required to lift a 500-lb weight with this lever?
11. What must be the real mechanical advantage of a lever that lifts a load of 20 lb when an effort of 50 lb is applied to it?
12. The effort arm of a lever is 6 ft and the load arm 1 ft. What is the ideal mechanical advantage of this lever? By how much does it reduce speed?
13. A block and tackle has six sections of rope pulling parallel on the movable block. How much does this machine reduce speed? How much does it multiply force, if friction is neglected?
14. The radius of the crank of a windlass is 12 in. and that of the axle is 2 in. How much does this machine reduce speed? How much does it multiply force, if friction is neglected?
15. The radius of the crank of a brace used to drill holes in wood is 6 in. When a 1-in. (diameter) bit is used in this brace, what is the ideal mechanical advantage of the wheel and axle thus formed?
16. How much work is done against gravity when a 3,400-lb automobile is driven up a mountain road between two towns whose elevations are 1,000 and 7,500 ft above sea level? Express your answer in foot-pounds.
17. When a horizontal force of 50 lb is required to pull a 250-lb sled along the surface of ice on a lake, what is the coefficient of friction between the runners of the sled and the ice?
18. What horizontal force will be required to pull a 125-lb block of ice at a uniform speed along a level slide if the coefficient of friction between ice and the slide is 0.15?
19. Draw a schematic diagram of a system of pulleys with which a force of 50 lb could lift a weight of 250 lb if there were no friction.

20. Draw a schematic diagram of a block-and-tackle system with which a force of 150 lb could lift a weight of 600 lb, if there were no friction.

21. Draw a schematic diagram of a block-and-tackle system in which the load will move four times as fast as the effort force.

22. Show by means of a diagram with dimensions marked what kind of lever should be used to lift a weight of 20 kg by applying an *upward* effort force of 100 kg.

23. Show by a diagram with dimensions marked what kind of lever should be used to lift a weight of 100 kg by applying a *downward* effort force of 20 kg.

24. The length of an inclined plane is 25 ft. What must be its height in order that a force of 25 kg could pull a weight of 250 kg up the plane at a uniform rate, if there were no friction?

GROUP B

1. What average power does a 130-lb boy develop when he climbs a 100-ft hill in 3 min?

2. A horse hitched to a plow pulls with an average force of 150 lb and walks 2½ mph. How much average power does he develop?

3. How many tons of coal can an engine working at an average rate of 25 hp hoist from a mine 200 ft deep in 10 hr, if friction can be neglected and an empty car going down the shaft just balances the weight of the car alone that is coming up.

4. A tractor pulls with a force of 1,000 lb in dragging a log that weighs 3,000 lb along level ground. What is the coefficient of friction between the log and the ground?

5. A tractor pulls with an average force of 1,000 lb in hauling a load up a hill 2,000 ft long. How much work does the tractor do?

6. If the tractor in Problem 5 pulls the load up the hill in 5 min, what average horsepower does it develop?

7. Two boys carry a 100-lb load on a 5-ft pole, one boy at each end and the load between them. The load is 2 ft from one boy. How much must each boy lift to support the load?

8. A pump is required to raise water 50 ft at the rate of 600 gal/min. At what average horsepower must the pump work? Assume 1 gal of water weighs 8 lb.

9. If the efficiency of the pump in Problem 8 is 75 percent, how much power must be supplied to operate it?

10. Show by means of a diagram how a lever may be used to enable a man to lift a 200-lb weight by applying an *upward* effort force of only 50 lb. Mark suitable dimensions on your diagram.

11. Show by means of a diagram how the speed at the point of a lever system where the effort force is applied may be "multiplied" by 4, so that the load moves four times as fast as the effort force.

12. A bridge is 50 ft long. A 3,400-lb automobile is parked on this bridge so that its center of gravity is 15 ft from one end of the bridge. How much weight due to the automobile rests on each abutment (end support) of the bridge?

13. A rifle bullet weighs 30 g and has a speed of 400 m/sec. Compute the kinetic energy of this bullet. What is the momentum of the bullet?

14. A tractor drawing a farm machine exerts a force of 1,000 lb on the draw

bar and travels at a rate of 15 mph. How many horsepower must it develop to do this?

15. What is the kinetic energy of a 3,600-lb automobile traveling at 40 mph? Your answer will probably come out in foot-poundals and should then be converted into foot-pounds.

16. What is the kinetic energy of a 120-lb skater moving at a speed of 22 ft/sec? If your answer comes out in foot-poundals, convert it to foot-pounds.

17. A playground teeter board 12 ft long balances at its mid-point. A 100-lb girl is sitting on the board 5 ft from the mid-point. Where must a second girl who weighs 120 lb sit to balance the first girl?

18. Show why it would be impossible for an electric motor to do mechanical work at the rate of 16,500 ft-lb/min, when its electric input is 250 watts.

THINGS TO DO

1. Obtain a raw egg and a hard-boiled egg marked for identification. Place each egg in a pie pan and whirl each so that it spins around its shorter axis. How does the behavior of the hard boiled egg differ from that of the raw one? Explain.

2. Obtain a rubber hot-water bottle fitted with a stopper and a rubber tube. Lay this rubber bottle on a flat surface, place a stack of books on it and blow as much air as you can into the bottle. Do the books rise? What principles are illustrated?

3. Obtain two pulleys, such as those used for raising awnings. With these pulleys and a piece of heavy cord, make a pulley system that has an ideal mechanical advantage of 3. In what direction do you have to pull to lift a laundry iron off the floor with this block and tackle?

4. Obtain a rubber overshoe and place a few stones or other weights in it. Pull the overshoe, sole down, over the smooth dry surface of a worktable. Sprinkle a small area of the surface of the worktable with water and try pulling the overshoe over it again. In which case is friction greater? Explain.

6.

Forces between Molecules:
Adhesion and Cohesion

MOLECULES AND ATOMS

Probably no one has an imagination adequate to comprehend the vastness of of the universe in the heavens revealed to the astronomer by his telescope. The earth is just a tiny speck in this vast universe. Some of the stars seen with the more powerful telescopes are so far away that it takes a billion years for the light they send out to reach us, traveling at the rate of more than 186,000 miles every second of that time. At the other extreme in size are molecules and atoms and their components. These are so small that the imagination again is inadequate to comprehend their minute size.

What Is an Atom?

All matter, whether it exists as a gas, a liquid, or a solid, is composed of exceedingly small building blocks, called *atoms*, as was noted in Chapter 1. Atoms are so small that no person has ever seen one, even when armed with the most powerful microscope. All our knowledge of atoms comes from indirect evidence, yet we are sure they exist.

Atoms do not all act alike. A given atom, when brought near other atoms under suitable conditions, may show a strong attraction for atoms of a particular kind, and little or no attraction at all for atoms of other kinds. Because of

140

these attractions, atoms arrange themselves into closely bound groups that act as units. These compact groups of atoms may be called *molecules*. Under some circumstances, an atom may leave one group and attach itself to another group to form a new molecule. This process is called a *chemical reaction*. Molecules are broken up and new ones formed in chemical reactions. It is with this type of change that chemistry is chiefly concerned.

Scientists have classified all of the known kinds of atoms into about 100 different types on the basis of their chemical behavior. This number includes the atoms that occur in nature as well as those that have been produced by artificial means. Each of the different types is called a chemical element. Out of these chemical elements are built all the various kinds of material substances known in our universe.

The atoms of one element have different average mass and weight from those of another element. The mass of any atom is extremely small. A hydrogen atom is the lightest of all atoms. The mass of a typical hydrogen atom is only 1.66×10^{-24} g. If you wish to see what this number looks like, write a decimal point followed by 23 zeros and these

followed by 166. One cubic centimeter of water has a mass as great as 6.0×10^{23} atoms of hydrogen. Fortunately we do not have to weigh hydrogen atoms singly or count them one by one! All the people in the United States could not count the atoms in a single gram of hydrogen in 350 million years, if each person counted one atom every second, 8 hours a day, and 365 days a year, without interruption. A typical oxygen atom has a mass about 16 times that of a hydrogen atom, while a typical atom of uranium, the heaviest natural element, has a mass about 238 times that of a hydrogen atom.

It has been discovered that some of the chemical elements have several kinds of atoms that *behave the same way in chemical reactions but have different masses*. For example, three different kinds of natural hydrogen atoms have been found, two of chlorine, three of neon, and four or more of lead. Atoms of the same element that differ only in mass are called *isotopes*. Hundreds of isotopes have been discovered. A large majority of the chemical elements have two or more of them. So, while there are about 100 different chemical elements, there are nearly a thousand different kinds of atoms, counting isotopes.

Fig. 6–1. Atoms are clannish but often change partners.

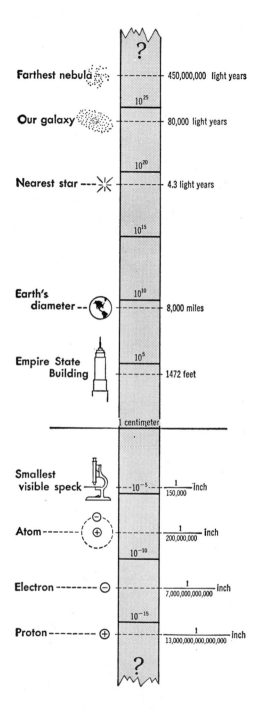

Farthest nebula	10^{25}	450,000,000 light years
Our galaxy		80,000 light years
	10^{20}	
Nearest star		4.3 light years
	10^{15}	
Earth's diameter	10^{10}	8,000 miles
Empire State Building	10^{5}	1472 feet
	1 centimeter	
Smallest visible speck	10^{-5}	$\frac{1}{150,000}$ inch
Atom	10^{-10}	$\frac{1}{200,000,000}$ inch
Electron		$\frac{1}{7,000,000,000}$ inch
	10^{-15}	
Proton		$\frac{1}{13,000,000,000,000}$ inch

Fig. 6–2. Size scale of the universe. (*Adapted from This Physical Universe*, Clark, Johnson, and Cocka-day, *McGraw-Hill Book Company, Inc.*)

What Is a Molecule?

Atoms combine to form molecules. Some molecules, such as those of mercury vapor, consist of a single atom. A molecule of water in the form of steam has two hydrogen atoms and one of oxygen. Its chemical formula is H_2O. A molecule of carbon dioxide has one atom of carbon (C) and two of oxygen (O_2). Its chemical formula is CO_2. A molecule of sugar (sucrose) has 45 atoms—22 of hydrogen, 12 of carbon, and 11 of oxygen. Its chemical formula is $C_{12}H_{22}O_{11}$, but it may be written in the form of a diagram, called a *structural formula*. A structural formula shows how the atoms in the molecule are arranged and bound together.

Some materials such as gasoline are mixtures of different chemical substances and so contain a number of different kinds of molecules. The molecule is often considered the smallest division of matter which has the same properties as the substance of which it is a part. Molecules are quite clearly identified in gases. In some solids and liquids, molecules are difficult or impossible to identify.

Each molecule has its own mass and weight. Its mass is the sum of the masses of all the atoms that the molecule contains. Likewise its weight is the sum of the weights of all of its atoms. The mass of an object such as a rubber ball is the sum of the masses of all its molecules. The weight of the ball is the sum of the weights of all the molecules it contains.

It is probable that heavier molecules are also larger, whether the greater weight is due to heavier atoms or a larger number of lighter ones. But even the larger molecules with several hundred atoms are too small to be seen with the best optical microscope. It has been estimated that it would take about 1,000 average-sized molecules laid end to end (if molecules have ends) to appear as the faintest dot in the field of a high-power optical microscope. An instrument called an *electron microscope* produces shadow pictures of very small objects. Some of the smallest objects visible with the electron microscope are believed to be large molecules.

The Kinetic Theory of Matter

The *kinetic-molecular theory of matter* assumes that: (1) Gases and liquids and some solids are composed of molecules. (2) These molecules are in ceaseless random motion. (3) Any one molecule has frequent collisions with its neighbors, bouncing off with a new speed and a new direction. (4) Molecules show strong attractions for one another when they are very close together. When they are a little distance apart, they are quite indifferent to their neighbors.

A great many phenomena can be quite satisfactorily explained on the basis of this kinetic-molecular theory.

States of Matter

Matter may exist as a gas, a liquid, or a solid. Let us see how each of these states is explained by the kinetic theory.

1. In a *gas* the molecules are relatively far apart and exert practically no attraction on one another. They have freedom to move in all directions and consequently fill up the vessel in which the gas is confined. Gas molecules migrate freely from any part of the vessel to any other part, so a *gas maintains neither a definite volume nor a definite shape.*

2. The molecules or other basic particles in a *liquid* are closer together than in a gas. More attracted to each other, they do not have as much freedom

RCA permanent-magnet electron microscope with operator. *(Radio Corporation of America)*

An electron-microscope picture of single crystals of the necrosis virus, showing their molecular arrangement. The small spheres are believed to be single molecules. This micrograph was made with an electron microscope with a magnification of 10,400 times. *(Dr. R. Wyckoff, National Institute of Health)*

143

of motion as gas molecules have. This stronger attraction holds the molecules within the body of the liquid and forms a boundary or free surface in case the liquid does not completely fill its container. A liquid takes the shape of the vessel in which it is placed but does not always fill it as a gas would do. In other words, *a liquid maintains a definite volume but not a definite shape.*

3. In a *solid*, molecules or other basic particles are still farther restricted. Closer than in a liquid, they are quite strongly bound to their neighbors on all sides. They cannot readily move from one part of a solid object to another. Their motion, like that of a bird in a cage, is limited to a very small region in the immediate vicinity of their base positions. For these reasons, *a solid maintains both its volume and its shape.*

►You Will Be Interested to Know

The idea that matter is made up of small individual particles, just as a pile of sand is made up of grains, is not entirely a modern one. The philosophers of the ancient world pondered deeply over the question of how matter is constructed. Democritus, a Greek philosopher who lived in the fifth century B.C., was a strong advocate of the hypothesis that all matter is built up of tiny

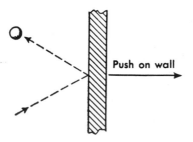

Fig. 6–3. A molecule strikes the wall of its container and bounces off.

particles. Four centuries later, the Roman poet and scholar Lucretius enlarged on this hypothesis of Democritus. With these early philosophers, the problem of how the material world is constructed could be solved only by speculation. They had little or no experimental evidence to support their views. It was not until the nineteenth century that this ancient idea was revived and a mass of evidence collected from experiments to support it. Our present kinetic-molecular theory is a most useful tool in explaining a wide variety of phenomena.

►Do You Know?

1. Do you know the names of 10 common chemical elements? List them.
2. Is the number of hydrogen atoms which weigh as much as 1 cm^3 of water, as given previously, exact or just a "round number"? Explain.
3. Give the chemical formula for a molecule of water.
4. Why do we speak of the *kinetic-molecular* theory of matter?
5. Define the terms atom and molecule.
6. Name and describe one example of each of three different states of matter.

PRESSURE AND DIFFUSION

A number of physical processes or phenomena can be explained by the assumption that molecules are in ceaseless random motion.

What Causes Gas Pressure?

In Chapter 2 we touched very lightly on the reason why a gas exerts pressure. Let us now examine the matter further in the light of the kinetic-molecular theory. Assume that a rapidly moving molecule of gas, in the course of its wandering, bumps into the wall of its container. This molecule acts like a perfectly elastic ball and in the average case bounces off again with the same speed it had when it was approaching the wall. Its direction, however, is changed by the collision. This can be done only by the action of an "outside force," as we found in Chapter 4. The outside force is furnished by the wall of the container, which pushes on the molecule while the two are in contact. The molecule, in turn, must push on the wall. The effect is similar to that which occurs when a basketball bounces off the backboard. If only one or two molecules collided with a square inch of wall in a second, this wall would receive separate impacts for each collision, but each one would be so small that we could never detect it. When a billion or so such collisions occur in a second, the individual blows tend to blend into one steady force, which is the pressure we measure. Pressure exerted by a gas is thus due to the hammering of the confined molecules against the wall of the container.

The more molecular collisions on a square inch of surface in a second, the larger the pressure of the gas becomes. A vacuum pump removes molecules from a bell jar so that there are fewer left to collide with the container wall every second. *In this way, it reduces pressure.* Forcing the same number of molecules into smaller space without slowing them down increases the number of collisions per second with the container wall. So reducing the volume of a gas, while keeping its temperature constant, increases its pressure, as Boyle's law indicates it should.

Brownian Movement

If you illuminate the minute particles of carbon in smoke or in a thin layer of

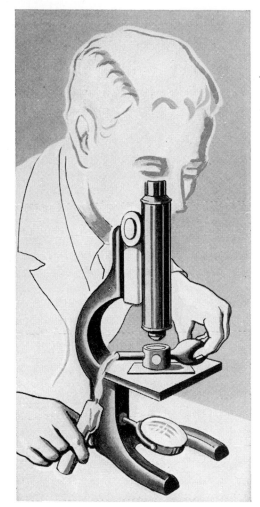

Fig. 6–4. Apparatus for observing the Brownian movement of particles of smoke from a candle or match.

india ink with a strong light and at the same time focus a microscope on them, you will see a rapid movement of these little particles. Imagine you are witnessing a fast volley-ball game in which you can see only the ball as it is struck by invisible players. The motion of this ball is very much like that of an individual carbon particle as seen in the microscope. Whirling and dancing, it appears to move in short zigzag jumps

145

Fig. 6–5. The Brownian movement of a particle of smoke as seen through a microscope.

as if buffeted about by blows first from one direction and then from another. This phenomenon was first discovered by a Scottish scientist, Robert Brown, in 1827 and in his honor is now called *Brownian movement*.

Although the objects we see zigzagging about under the microscope *are not molecules*, they are extremely small. If we assume that the molecules of air in which a carbon particle is suspended are in rapid motion among themselves then it is certain that some of them must bump into this particle from time to time. When more molecules happen to strike the particle from one direction at a given instant than from the opposite direction, the particle will be given a push. This push may set the particle in motion if the particle has exceedingly small mass. Such a motion will continue until the same event happens again. Then the particle may be stopped or turned sharply in a new direction. In this way, the kinetic theory accounts for the erratic motion of the particle observed in the microscope.

Evaporation

Water sprinkled on the sidewalk on a dry day soon disappears. Wet clothes hung outdoors soon become dry. We say that, in cases such as these, the water *evaporates*. This means that it changes from a liquid to a gas and is borne away by the surrounding air.

What explanation does the kinetic theory offer for evaporation? Molecules

146

of a liquid are in rapid motion. They are perfectly free to move, except when they try to pass through the surface of the liquid. The attraction of other molecules in the liquid then pulls them back and prevents their escape. However, if a molecule that comes darting up to the surface of the liquid should have enough speed and hence enough kinetic energy ($\frac{1}{2} mv^2$), it may be able to break the bonds that hold it back and pass right through into the air above. There it is free to move about as a gas molecule. There are always some molecules that have the speed necessary to break through, so evaporation occurs. They acquire this higher speed from their collisions with other molecules.

Raising the temperature of a liquid increases the speed of its molecules and thus increases the probability that a molecule will have enough kinetic energy to break through when it strikes the surface. This is why liquids evaporate faster when their temperature is raised.

Often molecules of a liquid have considerable speed and kinetic energy left *after* they break through the surface. In Fig. 6–6, a method is shown to utilize this residual kinetic energy to produce a kind of large-scale Brownian movement. When the mercury in the evacuated tube is heated, many of its molecules break through its surface and bombard the small colored glass particles from beneath. The dance of the glass particles due to these impacts resembles somewhat the motion of carbon particles in smoke.

Sublimation

"Dry Ice"—solid carbon dioxide—changes directly from a solid to a gas without forming any liquid, under ordinary conditions. Moth balls placed in clothing vanish after a period of time.

Even water ice, on a day when the temperature is below freezing, changes in the same way. We often say that these solids "evaporate," but it is more correct to say that they *sublime*.

The molecules or particles of a solid are ordinarily bound to definite positions and are free to move only short distances from these positions. When a molecule acquires enough kinetic energy, it may be able to break loose from its confines and pass into the surrounding air as a gas molecule. It may acquire this amount of kinetic energy from collisions with its neighbors or from outside sources. In this way, the kinetic theory accounts for sublimation.

Diffusion

We know from experience that odors, both the pleasing and the disagreeable varieties, spread rapidly through still air. If lilacs are brought into a room, their characteristic odor can soon be noticed in every part of the room. The odor of fuel gas from a leaking jet soon permeates every part of the laboratory. Glue factories have long been noted for the odor that fills the air in their immediate vicinity.

The odor of any substance is caused by molecules given off by that substance. When these molecules enter the nose, they stimulate the olfactory nerves and give rise to their characteristic odor. Our noses are excellent detectors for certain kinds of molecules.

The rapid spread of odors can mean only that molecules, escaping from the source of odor, are in motion and that this motion carries them considerable distances through the surrounding air. They must pass among the molecules of air and in so doing cannot avoid collisions. These collisions will slow them down or speed them up and, in practi-cally every case, will change their directions. So their motions will usually not be along a straight line for more than a small fraction of a millimeter.

The spread and intermingling of the molecules of one substance among those of another substance is called *diffusion*. Diffusion occurs most readily in gases, less readily in liquids, and very slowly or not at all in solids.

Rate of Diffusion

If we pump the air from a glass vessel and then introduce a little colored gas, such as bromine, we notice that the colored gas fills the evacuated vessel in a flash. If the colored gas is introduced without first pumping the air out of the vessel, diffusion takes place more slowly.

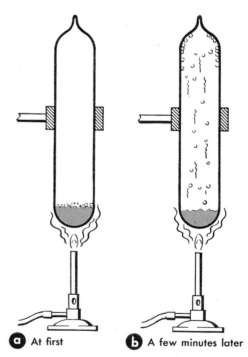

a At first   **b** A few minutes later

Fig. 6–6. (a) Fine pieces of colored glass on mercury in a glass tube with air removed. (b) When the mercury boils, the separate pieces of glass fly around in the tube as if buffeted by a force from below.

147

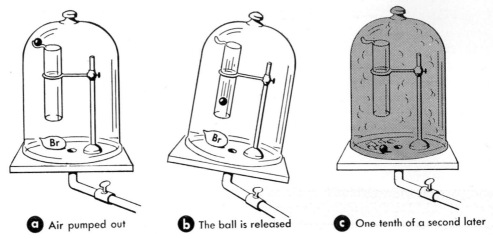

(a) Air pumped out   (b) The ball is released   (c) One tenth of a second later

Fig. 6–7. Bromine gas (Br₂) diffuses to fill the evacuated bell jar in a flash when the glass capsule is broken by the falling ball.

The presence of air molecules slows down the rate of diffusion but does not prevent it.

If a flask containing ammonia gas is connected to another flask containing hydrogen chloride gas, as shown in Fig. 6–8, the heavier hydrogen chloride will diffuse upward into the ammonia and the lighter ammonia will diffuse downward into the hydrogen chloride. You can watch the progress of this diffusion by observing the white cloud formed where the two gases meet. If you have studied chemistry you may be acquainted with this reaction. The two gases will eventually become thoroughly mixed in both of the flasks, even though the hydrogen chloride is more than twice as heavy as the ammonia and has to move upward against the force of gravity to diffuse into the upper flask.

When water and alcohol are stirred or shaken together, they mix thoroughly and give a clear solution. They will not again separate of their own accord. Two such liquids are said to be *miscible*. Some

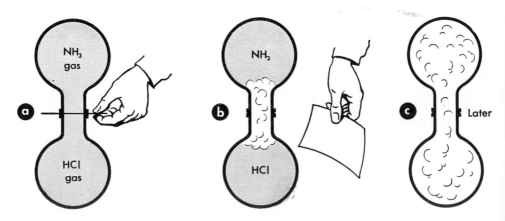

Fig. 6–8. Two gases become thoroughly mixed by diffusion.

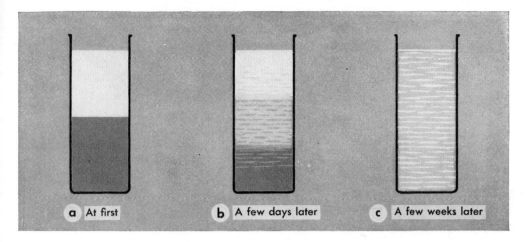

| a | At first | b | A few days later | c | A few weeks later |

Fig. 6–9. Diffusion of liquids. (a) Copper sulfate solution (blue) below with clear water above. (b) Some diffusion of the copper sulfate into the water. (c) Complete mixing by diffusion.

liquids, like water and oil, will not mix. If shaken together in a flask, the oil will form in little droplets and give a cloudy liquid. When allowed to stand for a little while, the oil will separate out in a layer on top of the water. Oil and water are said to be *immiscible*. Name two other immiscible liquids.

When two *miscible* liquids are brought into contact without mixing, they will diffuse slowly, one through the other. Figure 6–9 shows what happens in the course of several weeks with copper sulfate solution placed in a container of water.

Evidence shows that atoms or molecules of one solid may sometimes diffuse through those of another solid with which it comes in contact, although the process is exceedingly slow at ordinary temperatures. Experiments have been reported in which lead atoms were detected throughout a piece of gold after the gold had been in contact with lead for a period of months.

The rate of diffusion in all states of matter is speeded up by a rise in temperature.

Sorting Molecules with a Sieve

In Fig. 6–10a, a porous cup made of unglazed earthenware has been fitted with a stopper and a glass outlet tube. The outlet tube is connected through a rubber tube to a manometer which indicates the pressure inside the porous cup. At the start, the pressure inside the cup is the same as that outside and the liquid stands at the same height in the two arms of the manometer.

A glass beaker has been inverted over the porous cup. In Fig. 6–10b, household fuel gas is flowing into the beaker. Notice that the pressure inside the porous cup *has already risen*. It will continue to rise for several minutes and then will gradually drop back practically to the original pressure.

In Fig. 6–10c, the beaker has been removed and the porous cup again is exposed to the outside air. The pressure within the cup has fallen below that outside. It will continue to fall for several minutes and then will gradually rise again to approximately that of the air outside.

149

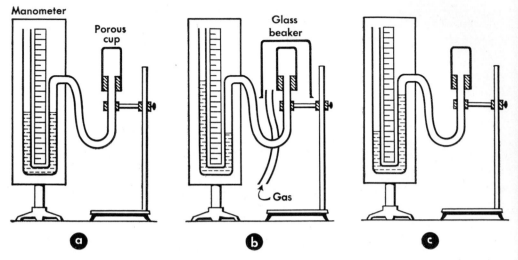

Fig. 6–10. A porous cup acts as a sieve for separating molecules of different size and speed.

Molecules of household fuel gas are lighter and probably smaller than air molecules. At a given temperature, they travel at higher speeds than air molecules. When household fuel gas is first admitted to the inverted beaker, its smaller, speedier molecules pass readily through the porous wall of the cup. The larger molecules of air have greater difficulty in getting through the pores. So the original air molecules and the gas molecules that have diffused through the porous wall unite in producing a higher pressure inside the cup. This is why the pressure rises in Fig. 6–10b. After a while, enough air molecules are able to get out through the porous wall to equalize the pressure inside and out.

When the beaker is then removed, the outside of the cup is soon again surrounded by air. Gas molecules diffuse out through the porous wall and reduce the pressure inside, as shown in Fig. 6–10c. Eventually enough air molecules from the outside get through the porous cup to equalize the pressure on the two sides of the wall again. Different gases may be used for this experiment.

The porous wall acts as a kind of sieve or filter for separating molecules that have different masses. A porous wall is not a perfect filter, however, for some of the heavier, slower-moving molecules (air) get through along with the lighter, faster-moving ones (household fuel gas), as we can see from the above experiment. A lighter gas can be almost completely separated from a heavier gas by this process if the first gas that comes through the wall is collected and filtered over again several times. This process is the basis of one method used to separate the isotopes of an element such as uranium.

Membranes, too, have the property of allowing some molecules to pass through them freely, while preventing other molecules from passing. Such membranes are described as *semipermeable.* Cell walls, animal tissues, parchment paper, and even some forms of cellophane act as semipermeable membranes under suitable conditions. A liquid may pass through a semipermeable membrane, while a solid dissolved in liquid is held back.

150

1. The collisions between molecules that have been discussed are *perfectly elastic*. Is the collision of two billiard balls also perfectly elastic? Explain.
2. Is a tennis ball perfectly elastic? How can you find out?
3. A moth ball placed in clothing may completely disappear after some months. What becomes of its molecules?
4. Do you know any substances that sublime, other than those mentioned in the text? Name them.
5. Explain how gases exert pressure on solid surfaces.
6. What is it that we see when we observe Brownian movement under the lens of a microscope?

COHESIVE AND ADHESIVE FORCES

In accepting the assumption that the molecules of solids, liquids, and gases are in ceaseless motion, we should not overlook the fact that solids do not fly apart into molecular fragments and liquids do not evaporate and vanish in an instant. To account for this, another assumption must be included in the kinetic theory: Molecules attract one another when they are close together.

The force of attraction between adjacent molecules of the *same material*, such as molecules in this sheet of paper, is called *cohesion*. Your pen point is kept from crumbling by cohesion between molecules of the metal of which it is composed.

When the attraction is between molecules of *different materials*, the force is called *adhesion*. Graphite from a lead pencil is held on the paper on which you write by adhesion. Adhesive tape sticks to the skin because of the force of adhesion between molecules of unlike kind. Mucilage, pastes, glues, and cements are materials whose molecules have strong attraction for those of the materials on which they are used.

Part of the force of cohesion is probably gravitational. It is believed that the law of universal gravitation holds for molecules as well as for larger bodies of matter. But molecules seem bound together with a force much stronger than gravitation, one that falls off more rapidly than gravitation as they get farther apart. So it is believed that cohesion includes other forces in addition to gravitation.

There is no evidence that adhesion is any different from cohesion in its fundamental nature. The two names serve only to indicate whether the attraction

Fig. 6–11. Cohesion involves attracting forces between molecules of the same kind; adhesion involves attracting forces between molecules of different kinds.

Fig. 6–12. The sewing needle can be supported by the surface film of water.

is between molecules of the same or different materials.

Surface Tension

Have you ever seen steel float on water? This would seem to contradict Archimedes' principle, for steel is more than seven times as dense as water. Yet you can easily prove for yourself that, under special conditions, steel does float on water.

Bend a hairpin or a piece of fine wire to form a yoke for holding a sewing needle, as shown in Fig. 6–12. Then gently lay the needle on the surface of water in a cup or tray. With a little practice, the yoke can be slipped from under

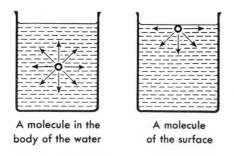

A molecule in the   A molecule
body of the water   of the surface

Fig. 6–13. Cohesive forces acting on a molecule of water.

152

and the needle left riding on the water.

If you look closely, you will see that the needle rides in a cradle or depression in the surface, with the surface itself unbroken. If you push one end of the needle so that it breaks through the surface, it will sink at once to the bottom.

The surface of the water acts as if it were an elastic film, something like a sheet of stretched rubber. The needle, lying on this surface, stretches the film, as the cradle shows. The film is quite strong, since it is able to support the needle. In reality, the needle does not *float* on the water, it merely is supported by this surface film.

Consider a molecule that is within a body of water. It is completely surrounded by other molecules and is attracted by them equally in all directions, as shown in Fig. 6–13. This molecule is in equilibrium since the forces acting on it are all balanced. It can then move about as easily in one direction as in another.

If the molecule happens to be in the surface layer, however, the situation is very different, for there are no water molecules above to attract it. The attracting forces acting downward on it now are not balanced by attracting forces upward, as shown in Fig. 6–13. Should a molecule in the surface layer happen to rise a few molecule-lengths above the surface, it will be pulled back strongly by the molecules below it. If it should be pushed down a little and still remain in the surface layer, it will be pulled back by the other molecules in the layer. This is why the surface layer appears to be elastic.

The elastic force in this surface film is called *surface tension*. The needle in Fig. 6–12 is supported by surface tension. Surface tension will support a razor blade in the same way.

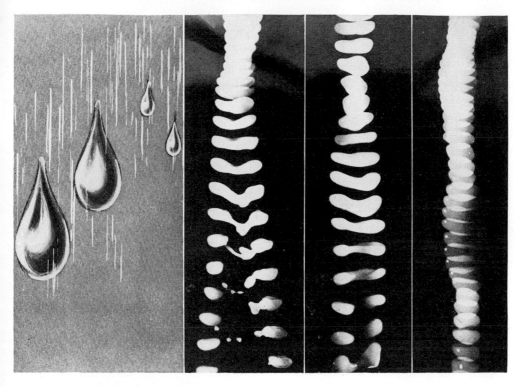

People usually think of raindrops as streamlined and tear-shaped, as shown in the picture at the left. Weather scientists at the General Electric Research Laboratory made the other three pictures of a simulated falling raindrop. These pictures, taken with a high-speed stroboscopic camera, show the drop in successive positions as it falls. (*General Electric Company*)

Why Soap Bubbles Are Round

A thin soap film consists essentially of two surface layers of molecules, back to back. In a bubble, this double film is stretched by the air inside and its surface tension causes a pressure on this confined air. Because of the elastic property of the film, it will tend to shrink to as small an area as possible for the volume of air it has to enclose. It is proved in geometry that a sphere has the least surface for a given volume. The bubble therefore assumes a spherical shape.

If you were to examine with a low-power microscope the cloud of "steam" that issues from the spout of a teakettle, you would find that it is made up of a great many little spheres of water. Raindrops, too, are originally spherical, but friction and other forces acting on them pull them into many shapes as they fall through the air. While some may have tails, as shown in the photograph above, left, others may have many different shapes. Smaller drops have lower terminal velocities and are pulled out less so that they are more nearly spherical when they reach the earth.

If a little mercury happens to spill on the table or floor, it breaks up into droplets that are almost spheres. The force of gravity flattens these droplets somewhat, the larger ones being much more

153

flattened than the smaller ones. These spheres show that mercury has a high surface tension.

In the manufacture of lead shot, melted lead is allowed to drop through holes in a kind of sieve at the top of a tower. These drops of lead, while still liquid, assume a spherical shape because of surface tension. They solidify while falling. The hot solid shot are caught in a tank of water or oil.

When a glass tube or rod is broken, sharp edges are left. To smooth off these edges, the glass worker holds the tubing in a gas flame and heats it until the glass softens. Surface tension then pulls the edge into a rounded shape, as shown in Fig. 6–14. The process is called *fire-finishing*.

Some Surface-tension Effects

When a drop of oil touches the surface of water, the oil at once spreads out in a very thin film over the surface. This effect shows that the surface tension of water is greater than that of oil, for otherwise the drop of oil would retain its spherical shape. Measurements show that the surface tension of oil is only about one-third that of water.

Suppose two matchsticks are laid side by side on the surface of water as shown in Fig. 6–15. If a drop of light oil on the end of a third matchstick is touched to the surface film between the two floating sticks, they will move rapidly apart. The drop of oil spreads and covers the surface between the sticks. Then the surface tension of oil pulls on the inner side of each stick and the surface tension of water pulls on the outer side. Because the sticks move apart, you can see that water has greater surface tension than oil.

The height to which water waves can rise is determined in part by the surface tension of water. When an oil surface is substituted for water, the surface tension is less and waves are reduced. It was once the practice to pour barrels of oil on the surrounding water to calm waves about a ship in distress in a storm. The expression "pour oil on troubled waters" refers to this practice.

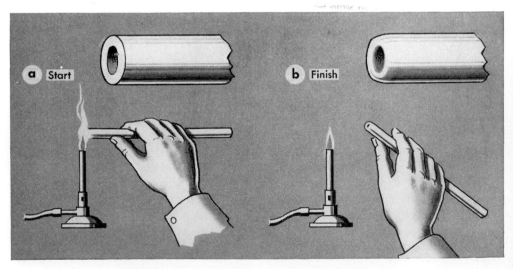

Fig. 6–14. Surface tension rounds the edges of hot glass.

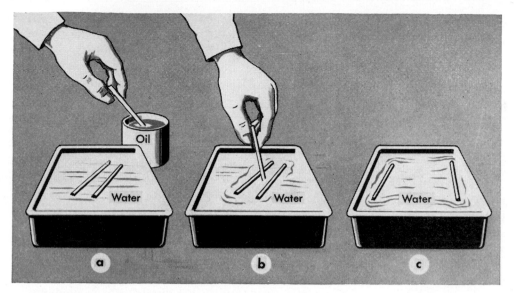

Fig. 6–15. The match sticks move apart when a drop of oil is placed on the surface of the water between them.

Many materials besides oil have less surface tension than water. Among these are alcohol, ether, and dissolved gum camphor. Mercury has a surface tension almost seven times as great as that of water.

Figure 6–16 shows an interesting toy boat that is propelled by surface tension. Camphor dissolving in water reduces the surface tension on the stern and the surface tension on the bow then pulls the boat along. Clean cold water should be used for best results.

Why Liquids Cling to Solids

If we dip a clean glass tumbler in water, we notice that some of the water clings to the glass when the tumbler is removed from the water. We say that water *wets* glass because it spreads out in a thin film over a clean glass surface. This effect indicates that *water molecules are more strongly attracted by adjacent glass molecules than they are by neighboring water molecules.* In other words, ad-

hesion between water and clean glass is greater than cohesion in water.

If a thin film of oil or wax is first applied to the glass, water does not spread over its surface, but tends to collect in globules or drops. The same effect can be noticed on the freshly waxed surface of an automobile when it rains. In these

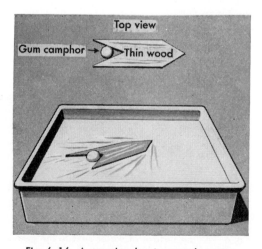

Fig. 6–16. A camphor boat moves in water.

cases, water does *not* wet the surface and cohesion within the water is greater than adhesion between water and the waxed surface. Mercury does not wet wood, glass, or iron, indicating that its cohesive force is greater than its adhesive force with any of these substances.

Because water wets clean glass, the edges of a water surface in a glass beaker are turned up, as shown in Fig. 6–17. This surface is described as *concave upward*, or often just *concave*. Mercury, on the other hand, does not wet glass. Its surface in a glass beaker is turned downward at the edges. Such a surface is called *convex*. Whether a liquid presents a concave or a convex surface, then, depends on whether adhesion with the container wall is greater or less than cohesion among its own molecules.

Capillarity

Ordinarily we are safe in asserting that water seeks its own level and $P = H \times D$, as we did in Chapter 2. But if glass tubes with very small bores are connected as shown in Fig. 6–18, we see at once that water does not always seek its own level. Water rises highest in the tube with the smallest bore and is lowest in the largest tube. With mercury, the situation is even more surprising. Mercury is actually *depressed* in small tubes, and the smaller the tube, the

greater the depression, as shown in Fig. 6–19. From an examination of these and other liquids, we find that the following statement is true:

Liquids rise in small tubes when they wet the tubes, and liquids are depressed in small tubes when they do not wet the tubes.

This effect is called *capillarity*. Tubes with very small bores are called *capillary* tubes, probably because their bores are about the diameter of a hair (*capillaris*, hairlike).

Suppose water rises a given height in a capillary tube of a certain diameter. It has been found that in a similar tube of *half the diameter* of the given tube, water will rise *twice* as far. Thus if water rises 2 cm in a tube 0.2 mm in diameter, it will rise 4 cm in a similar tube 0.1 mm in diameter.

The distance a liquid rises or is depressed by capillarity is inversely proportional to the diameter of the tube.

This relation holds for small tubes, less than a millimeter or two inside diameter, but is not true for larger tubes.

The channel through which water rises does not need to be a straight cylindrical tube. Any fine porous structure will serve the same purpose. The small spaces between crystals in a lump of sugar act as excellent capillary tubes. If one corner of a lump of sugar is dipped in coffee, the rise of the dark liquid through the lump can be easily observed. Towels take up water because of the capillary channels between their fibers. Blotting paper takes up ink for the same reason. Lamps and lanterns use cotton wicks as capillary pipe lines from the oil reservoir to the flame. Wicks are used for a similar purpose in oiling the bearings of small electric motors. The point of your pen is split so that ink can be fed to the paper through the capillary channel between the two parts. Water soaks into

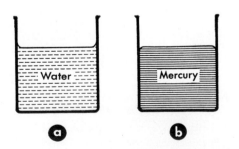

Fig. 6–17. The surface of water next to the glass is concave; that of the mercury is convex.

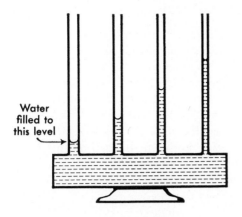

Water filled to this level →

Fig. 6–18. Water rises in glass capillary tubes. Does water always "seek its own level"?

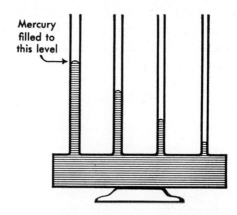

Mercury filled to this level →

Fig. 6–19. Mercury is depressed in glass capillary tubes.

the ground during a rain through capillary channels between the fine particles of soil. When the rain is over, water from the earth returns through similar channels and evaporates. When the soil is cultivated, these minute channels are broken up and larger openings between particles produced. This tends to reduce capillarity and conserve the moisture in the ground for the use of vegetation. Capillarity plays a large part in the rise of sap in trees and plants.

Absorption

We say that towels *absorb* water and blotters *absorb* ink. The ground *absorbs* water during a rain. *Absorbent* cotton is cotton especially treated to improve its absorbing properties. In all these cases, *absorption* is due in part to capillarity.

Liquids *absorb* gases. Molecules of the gas seem to intermingle with molecules of the liquid and we generally say that the gas *dissolves* in the liquid. Air, dissolved in water, provides the oxygen that fish take in through their gills. When water is heated in a pan or a beaker, this dissolved air comes out of solution and collects in small bubbles that can be

seen clinging to the vessel long before the water is ready to boil.

The soda water used in soft drinks is carbon dioxide gas dissolved in water. When the pressure of the gas is raised, more of it dissolves. When the pressure is relieved, most of the gas comes out of solution in the form of bubbles. This causes the fizzing of carbonated drinks.

It has been found that (1) more gas dissolves in a liquid when the temperatures of both are lower, and (2) the amount of gas that can be dissolved in a given liquid is *directly proportional* to its pressure. Thus, twice as much carbon dioxide will dissolve in a cubic foot of water at a pressure of 2 atmospheres as will dissolve at 1 atmosphere if the temperature in both cases is the same.

Adsorption

A film of air clings to the outside surface of glass, metals, and other solids. Special precautions have to be taken to break this film loose from the inside surface of electric light bulbs and radio tubes when they are being pumped free of air in the process of manufacture. A film of moisture forms on the outside

157

surface of electric insulators during humid weather. This film is held very tightly by the solid insulator and does not evaporate as an ordinary layer of water would. For some purposes, this film causes leakage of electricity and interferes with the proper action of the insulator. A film of water surrounds each grain of sand even when the sand appears to be quite dry. Minute dust and smoke particles from the air settle and cling to the walls of our houses and schoolrooms.

This condensing of thin films of liquid, gas, and microscopic solid particles on the outside surface of a solid is called *adsorption*. You will see that adsorption is only a special type of molecular adhesion.

Porous substances have a very large surface area, when we take into account the surfaces within the pores. For this reason, they are sometimes capable of adsorbing large volumes of gas. Fresh charcoal adsorbs some 90 times its own volume of ammonia gas. Specially activated charcoal is used in gas masks to adsorb poisonous gases that may be present in the atmosphere. Butter adsorbs gases readily and for this reason is likely to take up odors from other things, if left uncovered in the refrigerator.

In cases where the gas or liquid is held inside the pores of a solid, it is difficult or impossible to distinguish between *ad*sorption and *ab*sorption. Often no attempt is made to draw any distinction between the two processes.

Viscosity

We have mentioned *viscosity* a number of times and suggested that this property has to do with how readily a gas or a liquid pours or flows through an opening. The more viscous a substance, the more slowly it flows. A more *viscous* substance

158

is not necessarily a *more dense* one.

One layer of a fluid must slide over an adjacent layer when flow occurs. Molecules in one layer attract molecules in an adjacent layer. This cohesive force opposes the motion whenever the liquid flows. So the cohesive force between molecules acts in many respects like friction between solids. For this reason, *viscosity is often called fluid friction.*

The greater the fluid friction, the greater the viscosity and the less readily the fluid flows.

When service station attendants speak of *light* and *heavy* oil, they refer not to its density but to its viscosity. It is customary to indicate the viscosity of engine oil by a number. Number 10 is a light oil. It is less viscous than No. 50, for example.

The viscosity of many fluids increases as the temperature gets lower. Molasses, asphalt, pitch, and a great many other substances show this effect. This is the reason for changing from a heavier to a lighter lubricant in the transmission and differential of an automobile when cold weather approaches. It is also the reason for using a lighter crankcase oil in winter weather. Recently developed silicone lubricants show very little change in viscosity with temperature. Some forms of oil are actually *less* viscous at *lower* temperatures.

Friction Between Two Solids

Friction between two sliding bodies is due in part to the fact that the two surfaces in contact are not perfectly smooth and the hills of one surface tend to settle into the valleys of the other. Then when we try to slide one surface, we have to raise the whole body a slight distance in order to move its hills across the hills of the adjacent surface. But this is only a part of the cause of friction. Some of the molecules of one surface get so close to molecules in the other surface that the force of adhesion becomes appreciable. This adhesive force must be overcome both in sliding and in rolling one surface over another. Lubrication substitutes liquid friction for solid friction.

►**►Do You Know?**

1. What is the name of the force that holds wallpaper on the wall? The force that keeps a brick from crumbling into grains? The force that causes chewing gum to stick to the sole of your shoe?
2. What are the names of insects that skate on the surface film of water?
3. How is surface tension involved in the process of beating the white of an egg?
4. What factors determine how large a soap bubble can get before it bursts?
5. When gas bubbles up through water, why are the bubbles approximately spherical? Why do they become larger as they approach the surface of the water?
6. Do you know any other substance that has a convex surface like mercury? If so, what is it?
7. Why should towels not be starched?
8. Why does a bottle of soda pop not fizz until the cap is removed?
9. Why is a heavier oil used in an automobile engine after the parts become worn and loose?
10. What does "SAE" stand for in the viscosity rating of engine oil?

ELASTIC FORCES

Although individual molecules are exceedingly small and the forces they exert on one another are infinitesimal, when billions and billions of these tiny forces add together, their resultant may be considerable.

When you stretch a rubber band, you notice at once that the band exerts a force that opposes yours. As soon as you release the band, this *restoring* force snaps it back to practically its original length again. When you kick a football, you make a temporary dent in it and increase the pressure inside. This increase sets up a *restoring force* and the dent disappears as soon as the ball leaves your foot. When you bend a meter stick, you must push against its *restoring force*, which causes it to spring back to its original shape when you release the stick. When you twist the spring in a window shade roller, you have to overcome its *restoring force*. As soon as the spring is free, it untwists and rolls up the window shade again.

When we stretch, compress, bend, or twist a body, we change its size and shape and thus produce a *distortion*. All the situations just cited have one thing in common. *A distortion gives rise to a restoring force which brings the body back to its original size and shape when the force that produces the distortion is removed.* **A body or system that assumes its original size and shape after distortion is elastic.**

The restoring forces mentioned above are called elastic forces. Elastic forces have special names. *Tension* exists in the stretched rubber band, *compression* in the dented football, *flexion* or *bending* in the bent meter stick, and *torsion* or *twisting* in the wound spring. *Shear* is the name of an elastic force resisting pincer-like forces, such as those set up by a tin shears in cutting a piece of metal. Elastic forces are due to the action of molecules or groups of molecules.

Tension

The restoring force set up by stretching is called *tension*. Since the behavior of this force is typical of elastic forces in

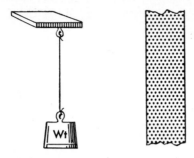

Fig. 6–20. A wire may be imagined to be made up of layer on layer of molecules.

general, we shall now consider it more closely.

Suppose a steel wire is stretched by a weight attached to one end. Imagine that the wire is made up of very many thin layers of molecules, laid one on the other. The molecules in one layer attract those in adjacent layers and thus hold the wire together. When the wire is stretched, each layer is pulled just a little farther from its neighbors. The sum of all these minute displacements is the total stretch of the entire wire. The mutual attraction of molecules in any two adjacent layers is the restoring force. But important shifting of the positions of molecules in the layers must also occur when the wire is stretched, because the restoring force becomes *larger* as the wire is stretched more. If the layers were only *pulled apart*, we should expect the restoring force to become *less* with a greater stretch.

Stretch and Stretching Force

Suppose we set up a coiled-wire spring, as shown in Fig. 6–21, and observe how much this spring stretches when different weights are attached to it. If we plot the stretch produced by a given weight against that weight, we obtain a graph like that shown in Fig. 6–22.

When we remove the weights, the spring should return to its original length

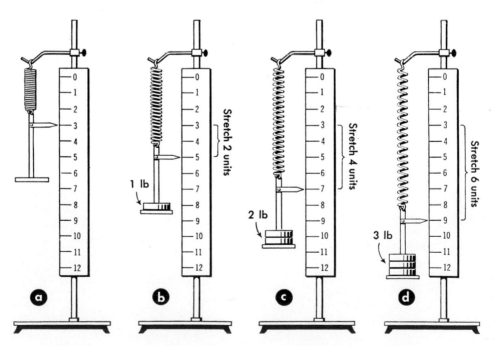

Fig. 6–21. A spring stretches farther when more stretching force is applied to it.

again. If the spring has been stretched too far, however, it will not come back to its original length when we remove the weights. In such a case, the stretching force has exceeded the *elastic* limit of the spring, which has acquired a *permanent set*. The spring then has a new length to which it will return after we remove the weights.

You will notice that the graph in Fig. 6–22 is a straight line. This indicates that when the stretching force is doubled, the stretch is also doubled. **Within the limits of perfect elasticity, the stretch of a spring is directly proportional to the stretching force.**

Stress and Strain

The change in length for each unit length of the straight wire in Fig. 6–20 is called its *strain*. The restoring force per unit area of its cross section is called the *stress* in the wire. Since the elastic force in the wire just balances the force due to the weights hung on it, the stress can be determined from this external force and the cross section of the wire. Stresses and strains exist in all other kinds of elastic distortions, as well as in stretching. **In any elastic system, the stress is directly proportional to the strain, if the elastic limit is not exceeded.** This statement is known as *Hooke's law*. It is named for Robert Hooke, an English physicist of the seventeenth century.

The Elastic Limit

When a force that exceeds the elastic limit is applied to the wire in Fig. 6–20, the wire at first stretches a little and then maintains this new length when the force is removed. But if a force that greatly exceeds the elastic limit is applied, the wire will break.

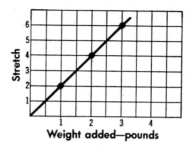

Fig. 6–22. How the stretch of the spring in Fig. 6–21 is related to the stretching force.

The maximum amount of force that a wire can support without breaking depends on the size of the wire and on the *tensile strength* of the material of which it is made. The tensile strength of the substance (steel) is the largest *force per unit-cross-section area* that the wire can support without breaking.

The tensile strengths of materials differ widely, as you will see from Table 6–1.

Many substances do not take a permanent set at all but break as soon as their elastic limit is reached.

Most materials do not assume their full distortion immediately when the distorting force is applied. Some continue to stretch or bend for hours. This effect is called *creeping*. Likewise, most materials do not return to their original

Table 6–1. Tensile Strengths of Various Metals

Metal	Tensile strength, lb/in.²
Gold wire	20,000
Zinc	22,000– 30,000
Aluminum wire	30,000– 40,000
Iron wire, annealed	50,000– 60,000
Bronze	60,000– 70,000
Copper wire—hard-drawn	60,000– 70,000
Steel piano wire	325,000–390,000

size and shape as soon as the distorting force is removed. In fact, some materials, such as a rubber band, never do return to exactly their original size after even a moderate stretch.

Do You Know?

1. Do you know whether Hooke's law applies to the compression of a body of gas when the pressure on it is increased? Explain your answer.
2. Why is steel better than iron for piano and banjo strings?
3. Is there any relation between the *permanent set* acquired by elastic bodies and the *permanent waves* produced by beauty-parlor or home permanent wave operators? Explain your answer.
4. How do shock absorbers on a car work?
5. Explain the meaning of the term *elastic limit*.
6. What is meant by the term *tensile strength*? Compare the tensile strengths of different materials.

HIGHLIGHTS

Matter is built up of *atoms*, which associate themselves into larger units called *molecules*.

There are about 100 different natural and artificial *chemical elements*, each of which has its own kind of atoms.

Each different molecular substance, such as water and carbon dioxide, has its own kind of molecules.

The *kinetic-molecular theory* assumes that (1) gases and some liquids and solids are composed of molecules, (2) the molecules are in ceaseless random motion, (3) molecules frequently collide and rebound, and (4) molecules attract each other at close range.

The *states of matter* are gas, liquid, and solid.

Gas pressure is due to the battering of molecules against the container walls.

Brownian movement is due to molecular bombardment.

Molecules break loose from a liquid to form a gas in the process of *evaporation*.

Molecules break loose from a solid to form a gas in the process of *sublimation*.

Diffusion in gases, liquids, and solids is due to the migration of molecules or other particles.

Cohesion is a force due to the attraction of molecules of the same kind.

Adhesion is a force due to the attraction of molecules of unlike kind.

Surface tension in a liquid is due to cohesive forces on molecules in the surface layer that are not balanced by other cohesive forces.

The *spherical shape* of drops and bubbles is an effect of surface tension.

The force of surface tension is reduced by an increase in temperature.

Liquids in a container have a *convex surface* when they do not wet the container and a *concave surface* when they wet it.

Liquids that wet the inside of a capillary tube *rise in that tube;* those that do not wet the tube are *depressed.*

In *absorption,* a liquid or gas is taken into the body of a solid or a liquid; in *adsorption* a liquid or gas adheres to the surface of a solid.

Liquids absorb gases in varying amounts, depending on temperature, pressure, and other factors.

Viscosity is related to molecular friction.

Elastic forces are set up by bending, stretching, twisting, and shearing.

Hooke's law asserts: Within the limits of perfect elasticity, the stress in an elastic system is directly proportional to the strain.

The *tensile strength* of any material is the maximum stress it can support without breaking.

THINGS TO DO

1. Stretch and tie a handkerchief or a double thickness of cheesecloth over the top of an empty milk bottle. Then pour water through the cloth to fill the bottle level full. Turn the bottle upside down quickly. Repeat the experiment three times. Does the water run out? Explain. NOTE: Perform over sink.

2. Dip the edge of a lump of loaf sugar into coffee. Observe how the coffee rises in the sugar. Explain.

3. Scrape small shavings of gum camphor onto the surface of *clean* water. Observe the motion of the bits of camphor. Then touch the surface of the water with a toothpick that has been dipped in olive oil. What happens? Explain.

4. Float a needle or double edge razor blade on *clean* water. Then try to float the same blade on water with detergent or soap dissolved in it. Explain the different results.

2.

Heat in Our World

PREVIEW

Heat is one of the most common and most useful forms of energy. Without heat there could be no life as we know it and the world would be a cold and dead place indeed! We use heat to cook our food and to warm our houses and school rooms to make them comfortable. Heat makes it possible to solder wires and to weld sheets of metal. Heat produced by radiant energy from the sun melts the snows of winter and warms the land to make the spring and summer seasons. Scientists are searching for some practical means of capturing and storing the enormous amount of heat energy we receive from the sun.

Mechanical work which overcomes friction results in heat. In this process mechanical energy is transformed into heat energy. Other forms of energy, too, are readily transformed into heat energy. The energy of heat can, in turn, be converted into mechanical and other forms of energy. The energy stored in coal and oil, for example, is changed into heat energy when the coal and oil are burned. This heat energy is then used to drive engines and motors.

Heat energy may cause a solid to change to a liquid, as when ice melts, and a liquid to change to a gas, as when water evaporates. Under some circumstances, heat can cause a solid to change to a gas directly, as when "Dry Ice" evaporates. Heat energy may travel through a vacuum, or through liquids, solids, and gases. Heat may cause some objects to expand and others to contract. Temperature is an important effect closely associated with heat. Thermometers are required to measure temperature. These and other effects of heat will be studied in this unit.

Temperature and Expansion:
Measuring Heat Effects

ALL MATTER HAS TEMPERATURE

Temperature is a physical effect that none of us can avoid or disregard for long. One of the first symptoms of illness is a rise in body temperature. The amount and kind of clothing we wear are influenced greatly by the temperature of the atmosphere around us. How we build our houses and make them comfortable to live in is governed to a large extent by the prevailing temperatures in our section of the world. Some parts of the earth are uninhabited because the temperatures there are too high or too low for man to exist and make a living. Life as we know it on the earth cannot exist on most of the other planets partly because of the extreme temperatures existing on other planets.

Why Thermometers Are Needed

"How *hot* is it outdoors?" "How *cold* is the weather?" We have all asked these questions on many occasions. Whether the atmosphere in which we live is hot, warm, mild, or cold is of vital concern to us, because, along with other factors, this affects our health and comfort in a very positive way. You will easily recognize that *hot, warm, mild, cool,* and *cold* are qualitative terms used to describe a condition of matter we call *temperature. All matter, whether solid, liquid, or gas, possesses temperature.*

We can generally tell whether water

is hot, tepid, or cold by dipping our hands in it. We possess a sense of temperature that is adequate for most everyday uses. However, if we are very cold, snow may actually feel warm, whereas, if we are warm, snow may feel decidedly cold. Our sensations are inconsistent and contradictory in these situations. We cannot estimate with much certainty which of two things is warmer or colder when the difference in temperature is small. Our senses are not very accurate or very reliable indicators of temperature.

For modern medical, chemical, and industrial purposes better and more reliable indicators than our gross sense of temperature are necessary. This is one reason why we use *thermometers* to measure temperature.

Galileo's Thermometer

One of the earliest attempts to measure temperature *objectively* was made by Galileo. He is usually credited with the invention of the first thermometer, the principle of which is illustrated in Fig. 7–2. The glass bulb shown in the figure should first be heated gently to drive out some of its air. The end of the glass tube should then be placed under the surface of the oil or water in the cup and the thermometer fixed in an upright position. When the bulb cools, the air in it contracts and outside air pressure forces some liquid up the tube. The level of this liquid in the tube *rises* when we *cool* the bulb and *falls* when we *heat* it. This is just the reverse of the way thermometers to which we are accustomed operate. Perhaps you can think of a reason why the level of the liquid column in Galileo's thermometer may move up or down, even though the temperature does not change. What differences might be observed in Galileo's thermometer when the weather changes from bright and sunny to dark, cloudy, and rainy?

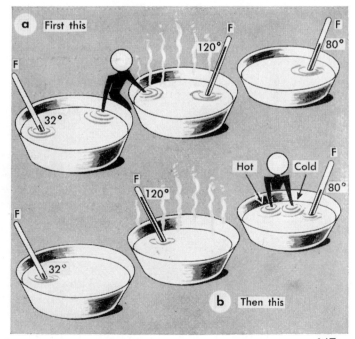

Fig. 7–1. Which hand tells the truth? Is the water in the pan to the right hot or cold?

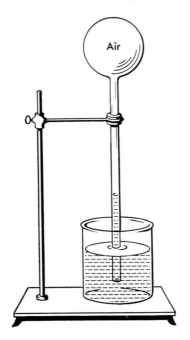

Fig. 7–2. Plan of Galileo's thermometer.

Temperature Scales

Galileo, with his thermometer, could tell that one room was *warmer* or *colder* than another with much greater certainty than a person could tell by "feel." However, even with a thermometer

C

"You'd better believe in signs!"

Fig. 7–3. The sign is important!

whose column changed with temperature, he had no clear way of expressing *how much* warmer or how much colder. He still had to rely on such general terms as hot, warm, tepid, cool, and cold when he referred to temperature. A *temperature scale* had to be invented before temperature could be expressed numerically in degrees.

You will recall that *two* scratches had to be placed on the standard meter bar to fix the length of the meter and its subdivisions. For exactly the same reason, two temperatures are required to fix the value of the degree. These two temperatures are called the *fixed points* of a temperature scale. It has been found by repeated checking with a thermometer that *ice always melts at the same temperature*, under ordinary pressures. So, the melting point of ice is generally taken as one of these fixed points. Steam over boiling water is found always to have the same temperature, provided its pressure is the same. The temperature of steam above boiling water (pure) at a pressure of 760 mm of mercury (1 atmosphere) is taken as the second fixed point of our present temperature scales. This temperature is called the *boiling point of water*. We use *two* different temperature scales, the Fahrenheit and the centigrade. Both scales make use of these same *fixed points*.

Centigrade and Fahrenheit Scales

The *Fahrenheit temperature scale* is the one we use for everyday purposes in the United States and other English-speaking countries. On this scale, the melting point of ice is marked 32° and the boiling point of water 212°. There are 180 Fahrenheit degrees in the temperature interval between these two fixed points.

The *centigrade temperature scale* is used in almost all scientific work. It is also used for everyday purposes by many of the same countries that have adopted the metric system. On this scale, the melting point of ice is marked 0° and the boiling point of water 100°. There are 100 centigrade degrees in the temperature interval between the two fixed points.

Temperatures *above zero* on either scale are written 10°C, 30°F, and so on, with no sign before the number. They are always treated as *positive* numbers in numerical calculations. Temperatures below zero are written −2°C, −10°F, and so on, with a *minus* sign before the number. These are treated as the *negative numbers* of algebra in all numerical calculations.

How to Convert Temperatures

If you look at a thermometer in your classroom and find that it reads 20° you may at first suspect that instrument of indicating a false temperature. But if the thermometer has a centigrade scale, it may easily be telling the truth, for 20° on the centigrade scale corresponds to 68° on the Fahrenheit. Since we often have to convert a temperature reading on one scale to that on the other, we shall need to find a convenient way of doing so.

Consider the thermometer shown in Fig. 7–4. It has two scales, a Fahrenheit scale marked F and a centigrade scale marked C. Notice that the corresponding temperatures on the two scales indicate the boiling point of water and the melting point of ice. Between these two *fixed points* there are 100 centigrade degrees or 180 Fahrenheit degrees. Since 100 centigrade degrees represent the same interval of temperature as 180 Fahrenheit degrees, it follows that 1 centigrade degree must be equivalent to $180/100$ or $9/5$ Fahrenheit degrees.

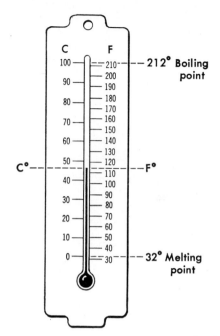

Fig. 7–4. The Fahrenheit and centigrade thermometer scales.

The thermometer column in Fig. 7–4 stands at a point between the melting point and the boiling point. Suppose that the centigrade temperature indicated by this column is represented by C. The column as shown in the figure stands C centigrade degrees above the melting point on the centigrade scale and $9/5 C$ Fahrenheit degrees above the melting point on the Fahrenheit scale. Since the melting point on the Fahrenheit scale is 32° rather than 0°, the mercury column in Fig. 7–4 is $9/5 C + 32°$ above the Fahrenheit zero. This is the Fahrenheit reading, which we may represent by F.

$$F = 9/5 C + 32°$$

If we start with the Fahrenheit temperature reading F and apply similar reasoning, we arrive at the relation

$$C = 5/9 (F - 32°)$$

169

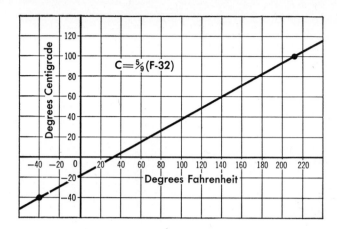

$$C = \tfrac{5}{9}(F-32)$$

Degrees Centigrade

Degrees Fahrenheit

Fig. 7–5. Graphic method for changing temperatures from one scale to the other.

You can check this for yourself by solving the first equation for C. These two equations are the bridges for crossing from one temperature scale to the other.

EXAMPLE: What is the centigrade temperature when a Fahrenheit thermometer reads 100°?

SOLUTION: $F = 100$, $C = $?
By the equation above

$$C = \tfrac{5}{9}(F - 32°) = \tfrac{5}{9}(100° - 32°)$$
$$= \tfrac{5}{9}(68°) = 37.8°$$

EXAMPLE: What is the Fahrenheit temperature when a centigrade thermometer reads $-10°$?

SOLUTION: $C = -10°$, $F = $?
By the equation above

$$F = \tfrac{9}{5}C + 32° = \tfrac{9}{5}(-10°) + 32°$$
$$= -18° + 32° = 14°$$

If you have many temperature readings to change quickly from one scale to the other, you can construct a graph similar to that in Fig. 7–5 and use it to make the conversions. In this graph, Fahrenheit temperatures are plotted along the horizontal or X axis and centigrade temperatures along the vertical or

Y axis. If you are given a Fahrenheit temperature, you can follow out along the X axis until you reach a point that corresponds to this temperature. The *vertical* distance from this point up to the temperature line represents the corresponding centigrade temperature, which you can read directly from the graph. If you are given a centigrade temperature, you can follow up the Y axis until you reach a point that corresponds to this temperature. Then the *horizontal* distance from this point to the temperature line represents the corresponding Fahrenheit temperature, which you can again read directly from the graph.

If you will examine Fig. 7–5 carefully, you will see that only one temperature, namely 40° below zero, is the same on both scales. For all other temperatures it is necessary to write C or F after the degrees to indicate which scale is used, if there can possibly be any doubt.

Special tables which give corresponding values on the two temperature scales have been prepared and may be found in handbooks. Temperatures can be changed quickly from one scale to the other by means of these tables.

170

Temperatures in degrees were not in general use before the eighteenth century. Scales based on such fixed points as "the temperature of ice or snow," "in the severest frost," the temperatures of the bodies of cows and deer, the temperatures of deep cellars and caves, and the temperature of melting butter were used prior to this time, but failed to gain wide acceptance. The older of our present scales was suggested by Gabriel Fahrenheit of Danzig (then in Germany) about 1720. He set the zero at the lowest temperature he could get by mixing snow and salt (actually sal ammoniac). Apparently he thought he could avoid negative temperatures by taking this zero. The temperature of the human body, which he called 96°, was the original upper fixed point of this scale. Later, 32° for the melting point of ice and 212° for the boiling point of water were adopted as the fixed points. With these fixed points, the average normal temperature of the human body turned out to be higher than 96°. The centigrade scale was introduced by Celsius of Uppsala, Sweden, in 1742. This scale is sometimes called the *Celsius scale* in his honor. He first labeled the melting point of water 100° and the boiling point 0°. This was changed within a year or so to the arrangement with which we are now familiar.

►Do You Know?

1. On Galileo's thermometer, would 100°F be higher or lower on the glass stem than 50°F?
2. What is the normal temperature of the human body?
3. What is the difference between cold-blooded and warm-blooded animals?
4. The word *centigrade* comes from two Latin words, *centum* and *gradus*. What is the literal meaning of these words?
5. How is milk pasteurized? What temperatures are used in the process? What are the advantages of pasteurized milk?
6. Does the ordinary process of dishwashing sterilize the dishes? If not, how could dishes be sterilized?

EXPANSION OF SOLIDS

The physical dimensions of a solid body change to a greater or lesser degree when the temperature of that body is changed.

You may have observed that telephone and electric power wires sag in hot weather but become stretched much tighter in cold weather. This indicates that the wires are actually longer when their temperature is higher and shorter when it is lower.

The expansion and contraction of a metal rod with temperature can be demonstrated in the classroom with the simple piece of apparatus shown in Fig. 7–6. The sharp-edged support fits into a groove cut around the rod near one end. At the other end, the rod lies loosely across a small shaft supported on roller bearings. A pointer is attached to one end of this shaft. The pointer moves over a dial when the small shaft turns on the roller bearings. A very small rotation of the shaft produces a noticeable movement of the tip of the pointer.

When the metal rod is heated with a bunsen burner, the pointer moves over the dial to the right, indicating that the rod is getting longer. When ice is placed on the rod, the pointer moves to the left, indicating that the rod is getting shorter.

The amount of expansion and contraction is so small, however, that it would probably escape our notice entirely, if it were not for the multiplying effect of the shaft and pointer.

Coefficient of Linear Expansion

If the metal rod of Fig. 7–6 could be heated uniformly throughout its entire length, every centimeter of it would expand the same amount. The *total* expansion of the rod would be the sum of the expansions of all of its parts. This total expansion of the rod, which we shall designate by X, can be measured with the shaft and pointer in Fig. 7–6, even though it is very small.

If we let L stand for the total length of the rod between the two points of support, then X/L represents the average expansion of a unit length. Both X and L are customarily expressed in the same units—feet, inches, or centimeters.

At the start, the rod will have some temperature t_1, which will likely be the same as that of the surrounding air. When we heat the rod, it will come to some new temperature, t_2. The number of degrees the rod is heated is then $(t_2 - t_1)$.

The average expansion per unit length of the rod for each degree change in temperature is

$$c = \frac{X/L}{t_2 - t_1} = \frac{X}{L\,(t_2 - t_1)}$$

in which c is called the *coefficient of linear expansion* for the material of which the rod is composed.

To illustrate how this coefficient of linear expansion is used, let us consider the following situation. An engineer plans to design a bridge 6,000 ft long. The bridge is to be built of structural steel. In the winter, the temperature of this bridge may fall as low as $-20°F$, while in summer it may reach a tem-

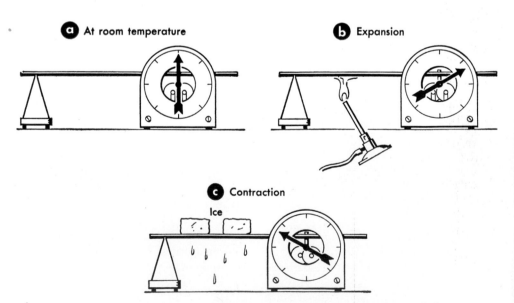

a At room temperature   **b** Expansion

c Contraction

Ice

Fig. 7–6. The metal rod expands when heated and contracts when cooled.

This is the Delaware Memorial two-mile-long suspension bridge. Discuss effects of expansion and contraction which occur with temperature changes in different parts of this bridge. Where would you expect to find expansion joints on this bridge? *(Engineering News Record)*

perature of 110°F. This represents a temperature range of 130°, and the engineer will have to provide some means of taking care of the expansion and contraction of the steel. His first problem is to determine just how much change in length he must provide for. If he finds from measurement of a sample that the coefficient of expansion of the steel he proposes to use is 0.0000067 per Fahrenheit degree, he then has all the information needed to calculate how much the bridge will change length.

SOLUTION: From the preceding equation

$$X = cL \, (t_2 - t_1)$$

In this problem

$c = 0.0000067$ per Fahrenheit degree

$L = 6,000$ ft

$t_2 - t_1 = 130$ Fahrenheit degrees

Hence

$$X = 0.0000067 \times 6,000 \times 130$$
$$= 5.23 \text{ ft}$$

Experience shows that the coefficient of linear expansion for a given material is far from constant. It may vary greatly when the material is heated or cooled over different ranges of temperature. For example, the average coefficient of linear expansion of commercial alu-

173

Material	Coefficient: change in length per unit length per centigrade degree
Fused quartz	0.000 000 5
Invar (36% nickel steel)	0.000 000 9
Diamond	0.000 001 18
Pyrex glass	0.000 003 6
Tungsten	0.000 004 3
Soft glass	0.000 008 5
Platinum	0.000 009
Steel	0.000 011
Soft iron	0.000 012
Copper	0.000 016 8
Commercial brass	0.000 019
Aluminum	0.000 024
Ice	0.000 051
Hard rubber	0.000 080
Celluloid	0.000 109
Cement and concrete	0.000 010–0.000 014

minum is 0.0000240 when heated from 20 to 100°C, but is 0.0000287 when heated from 20 to 600°C. This means that aluminum does not have the same rate of expansion at all temperatures. This is true of nearly all substances. The values given in Table 7–1 are for temperatures that range from 0 to 100°C, or less.

In most metals and other solids, the coefficient of linear expansion is the same for every one of the dimensions of a body, that is, every dimension expands at the same rate. Some crystals, such as quartz, expand at different rates along the different crystal axes. Woods expand from 5 to 25 times as fast across their fiber as they do parallel to it. The *diameter* of a beech log increases about 24 times as fast as its *length* when the temperature rises. The log gets thicker faster than it gets longer. But even in a beech log, the

174

change in its diameter for ordinary changes in temperature is exceedingly small.

When All Dimensions Expand

An interesting fact about expansion is demonstrated by the metal ring of Fig. 7–7. The hole in the ring is of such size that the ball cannot be pushed through it at room temperature. When the ring is heated, the ball can be passed through readily. The hole in the ring has enlarged, indicating that the *inside diameter of the ring has expanded*. This effect is not what a great many students expect to happen! Measurements show that the outside diameter, the width, and the thickness of the metal in the ring have all increased also. In short, *every dimension of the ring has increased*.

If the ring is cooled before the ball is removed, the ball will again be too large to withdraw through the hole. Every dimension of the ring contracts when it cools.

Allowances Made for Expansion

The forces that develop when solids are heated and not given room to expand are gigantic. A bar of steel only 1 in. square in cross section will exert a force of about 8 tons if heated from 0 to 50°C and not permitted to expand or bend. The length of the bar makes no difference in the force it can exert under these conditions, strange as it may seem.

Concrete roads are usually built in sections with expansion channels extending across the roadway between sections. These channels are filled with pitch to keep out dirt and water. In hot weather, the expanding concrete squeezes the pitch out of the channels so that it forms ridges across the road. In colder weather, the concrete contracts and the channels become wider.

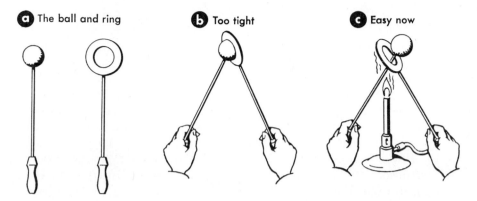

a The ball and ring   **b** Too tight   **c** Easy now

Fig. 7–7. All dimensions of the ring expand and contract with temperature.

The pitch packs into the channels again and the ridges disappear. Concrete roads sometimes buckle or explode in hot weather when adequate provision has not been made for expansion. Stadiums and other concrete structures are built with expansion joints between sections.

Steel beams and girders in buildings and bridges are sometimes joined together with *hot* rivets. When such rivets cool, they contract and pull the two pieces of metal together with great force.

Railroad rails fit together tightly at the joints in *hot* weather, but in cold weather there is a half inch or more between the ends of adjacent rails. Oval holes in the rails allow them to move endwise inside the plates that are used to bolt the rails together.

In long bridges, the change in length from winter to summer amounts to several feet, as shown in the example on p. 173. In designing the bridge, provision must be made to accommodate this change in order to prevent damage to the bridge and its piers.

In automobile engines, the pistons get hotter and expand more than the cylinders in which they run. For this reason, the cold pistons must have a little more clearance than they require when hot. More clearance is required for aluminum alloy (lynite) than for iron

In building a glass block section in a brick wall to admit light, an expansion strip set in asphalt emulsion is placed between the last course of blocks and the brick above. Clearance must be left between the last course of blocks and the expansion strip. (*Engineering News Record*)

175

pistons, because of the difference in their coefficients of linear expansion.

Boiling water poured into a cold fruit jar is likely to crack the jar. Water in a thin-walled glass beaker may actually be boiled by applying a flame without damage to the beaker. In the thick fruit jar, the inside surface of glass becomes hot and expands before the outside layer even becomes warm. This unequal expansion produces strains in the glass which cause the break. In the thin glass beaker there is more nearly uniform heating and uniform expansion. Less severe strains are set up in the thin glass and it is usually not so likely to break.

Pyrex glass has a coefficient of expansion only about one-third that of ordinary glass. This is one reason why Pyrex can be subjected to much greater changes in temperature without breaking. This is why Pyrex is used for baking dishes and cooking utensils. Fused quartz, which is clear like glass, is much better even than Pyrex for these purposes. A fused-quartz crucible can be heated red hot and plunged directly into cold water without breaking. Notice the coefficient of linear expansion of fused quartz in Table 7–1. Fused quartz is too expensive, however, for everyday use.

What Is Bimetal?

Figure 7–8 shows a metal bar made of a strip of iron and a strip of copper riveted or welded together. From Table 7–1 we can see that the coefficient of linear expansion of copper is about 1½ times that of iron, so the copper strip will expand and contract about 1½ times as much as the iron when their temperatures are changed by the same amount. For this reason, the *compound* bar in Fig. 7–8 bends when heated or cooled.

A metal bar made of two strips of different metals welded together is often called a *bimetal* bar. Bimetal is used in metal thermometers, and in thermostats for regulating the heating of rooms. Bimetal relays can be used to open or close any electric circuit we wish, and in this way many electric devices can be controlled by temperature changes.

▶**Do You Know?**

1. When the hot-air pipes of a furnace are heating, they often produce a

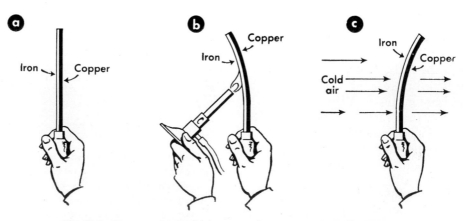

Fig. 7–8. How a compound bar responds to temperature changes.

cracking noise. What causes such noises?

2. When a glass stopper sticks in a bottle, it can sometimes be loosened by pouring warm water over the neck of the bottle. Why does this loosen the stopper?

3. Select two metals from Table 7–1 and sketch and label a bimetal bar made of these two metals. Indicate by an arrow which way the bimetal bar will bend when heated.

4. Does ice expand or contract when it is cooled below 0°C?

5. Why are high-grade surveyor's tape-lines made of Invar? See Table 7–1 for a clue to the answer.

6. Why are the rims of balance wheels of watches often made of bimetal?

7. Why is Invar advantageous for the pendulum rods of clocks and the balance wheels of watches?

8. Why are the wires of a fence likely to sag in summer and become tight in winter?

9. Why does the *volume* of a block of iron increase when it is heated?

10. If a rubber band, stretched by a weight hanging on it, is *heated* with a lighted match, does the band expand or contract? Try it.

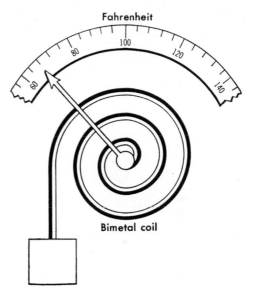

Fig. 7–9. The principle of a bimetal thermometer.

contracts when it is cooled. Second, the expansion and contraction are greater for water than for the metal of the tea-kettle or the metal jacket of the engine. The volumes of liquids in general expand when heated and contract when cooled, except in one interesting case that we shall examine. The change in volume for a given change in temperature is generally greater in liquids than in solids.

EXPANSION OF LIQUIDS

If you fill a teakettle level full of water and carefully place it on the stove to heat, water will overflow from the spout before it reaches the boiling temperature. If the radiator of your automobile engine is level full when the engine is hot, the water level will be down when cool.

These observations indicate two things. First, the *volume* of water expands when the water is heated and

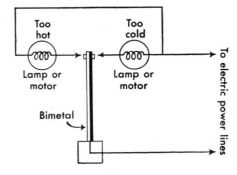

Fig. 7–10. In a thermostat a bimetal bar acts as a switch to open and close electric circuits.

177

Fig. 7–11. Water in a teakettle expands when heated.

Just as different solids have different coefficients of linear expansion, so different liquids expand in volume at different rates. Olive oil expands about $3\frac{1}{2}$ times as fast as water for ordinary temperature changes, turpentine 4 times as fast as water, and carbon tetrachloride more than 6 times as fast as water.

When a body of water is cooled from room temperature down to the point where it is just ready to freeze, its volume changes in a very unusual manner. Suppose we have a special water thermometer like that shown in Fig. 7–12. For most convincing results, this thermometer bulb and stem should be made of fused quartz, but Pyrex glass will be fairly satisfactory. If we gradually cool this water thermometer from room temperature to 4°C, the water column in the stem will continue to fall steadily. This is exactly what we would expect any liquid to do. However, if we continue to cool the thermometer gradually from 4 to 0°C, where the water is just ready to freeze, we observe a small but steady *rise* in the water column, indicating that the water in the bulb is now expanding. The expansion from 4 to 0°C is only 13 parts in 100,000 and is ordinarily quite difficult to observe without special

178

apparatus. This unexpected behavior is peculiar to water. No other common liquid shows this expansion on cooling.

Since a given body of water has its smallest volume at 4°C, 1 g of water occupies its smallest volume at this temperature. At this temperature we can pack more molecules of water into 1 cm³ of space than at any other temperature:

The maximum density of water occurs at 4°C.

It is fortunate that water reaches its maximum density at some temperature above freezing. When a still lake or pond cools to the point where it is about to freeze, the 4°C water settles to the bottom because it is more dense. The less dense water at 0°C collects at the surface and freezing begins at the top rather than at the bottom of the lake. Measurements show that the temperature at the bottom of deep lakes, such as Lake Superior, remains near 4°C the year around.

If water contracted regularly as other liquids do, the colder water would settle to the bottom and freezing would begin there. In all probability the lake would freeze up solid in the course of a few days of cold weather. In this case fish and other aquatic life would probably perish. Such freezing would greatly modify the climate in many parts of our country.

►Do You Know?

1. When a liquid is heated in a metal kettle, does the cubic capacity of the kettle increase or decrease?
2. Why would water not be a suitable liquid to use in place of mercury in a thermometer?
3. What would be the advantage of having the thermometer bulb in Fig. 7–12 made of fused quartz?
4. What principle is involved in the sinking of 4°C water to the bottom of a deep lake?
5. In the definition of the liter as the volume of 1 kg of water at 4°C, why is it necessary to specify the temperature of the water?
6. How could a solid freezing of lakes affect climate? In what areas would these effects be likely to be noticed?

TEMPERATURE EFFECTS IN GASES

A body of gas does not have a definite shape (as a solid) or a definite volume (as a liquid). A change in temperature therefore produces a special set of effects in a gas.

Gas Pressure and Temperature

Suppose the steel tank shown in Fig. 7–13a contains dry hydrogen gas at 0°C and a total pressure (not gage) of 273 lb/in.² Any other value of pressure would serve for this imaginary experiment, but we can simplify the calculations required by selecting 273 units as the pressure at 0°C. Careful measurements indicate that if the temperature of this gas were raised to 1°C, its pressure would become 274 lb/in.²· if its temperature were raised to 10°C, its pressure would become 283 lb/in.² Likewise if the gas were cooled to −1°C, its pressure would fall to 272 lb/in.² and if cooled to −10°C, its pressure would fall to 263

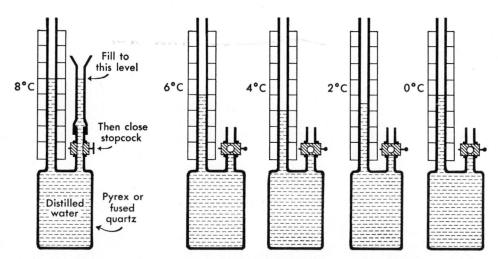

Fig. 7–12. If we had a thermometer like this, we might observe the peculiar behavior of water as it is cooled. The effect is exaggerated in the figure so that you can observe it.

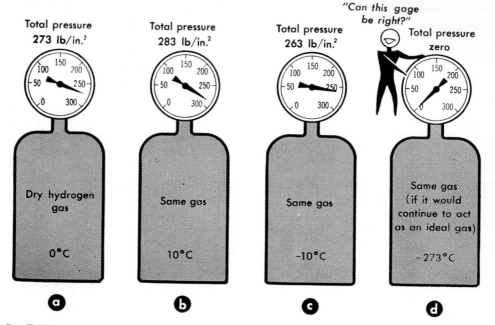

Fig. 7–13. What would happen to the pressure of a gas at −273°C? Its volume is supposed not to change as it is cooled.

lb/in.² In each case, *for every degree the temperature of the gas changes, its pressure changes 1/273 of the amount of pressure exerted by the gas at 0°C.* Experiments show that when the volume of *any* gas is kept constant, its pressure changes by this same fractional amount (1/273 of its pressure at 0°C) for each centigrade degree provided the gas is not near the point where it changes into a liquid (*liquefaction point*).

If we could reduce the temperature of the gas in the tank of Fig. 7–13 to −273°C and if this gas continued to behave in this manner all the way down to this low temperature, its pressure at this point *would become zero.* This is one of the reasons why −273°C is considered the *absolute zero* for temperature. We should observe in passing that no real gas actually behaves in this manner all the way down to absolute zero.

180

Absolute Temperatures

Temperatures counted from 273° below the centigrade zero are called *absolute temperatures.* A degree on this absolute scale is exactly the same as a degree on the centigrade scale. Absolute zero on the Fahrenheit scale is −459.4°F, as you could find by converting −273°C to Fahrenheit temperature. Temperatures counted in Fahrenheit degrees from 459.4° below the Fahrenheit zero are also *absolute temperatures.* Absolute Fahrenheit temperatures are less commonly used in our country than absolute centigrade temperatures. In the discussions that follow we shall use the term absolute temperature to refer to absolute *centigrade* temperature.

To change a centigrade temperature reading to the equivalent absolute temperature, we have only to shift the zero point to −273°C and count the degrees from this new zero. Thus 0°C is 273°A (absolute) and 100°C is 373°A.

Absolute temperature = centigrade temperature + 273°

There are no temperatures below absolute zero and hence no negative temperatures on the absolute scale.

The Pressure-Temperature Law

If we plot the pressure of the gas in the tank in Fig. 7–13 against its temperature and assume that the gas continues to behave in the same manner as its temperature approaches absolute zero, we obtain a graph like that shown in Fig. 7–14. You can check this graph from the information given in Fig. 7–13.

This graph is a straight line, passing through the origin (0,0) if we use *absolute* temperatures. Such a graph indicates a definite relationship.

The pressure of a gas at constant volume is directly proportional to its absolute temperature.

This relationship is often written

$$\frac{P_1}{P_2} = \frac{T_1}{T_2}$$

where P_1 and T_1 are the pressure and the absolute temperature at the start and P_2 and T_2 are the corresponding quantities when a change has occurred. This is one part of a general law known as *Charles's law* or the *law of Gay-Lussac.*

The Volume-Temperature Law

Suppose some dry hydrogen gas is placed in a metal cylinder with a close-fitting piston, as shown in Fig. 7–15. The piston should be designed to move up and down freely in the cylinder so that the pressure on the gas is constant. If the gas is heated or cooled, its volume will

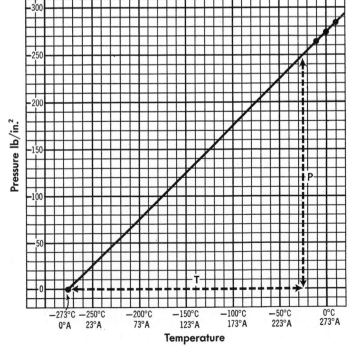

Fig. 7–14. How the gas pressure in Fig. 7–13 varies with temperature.

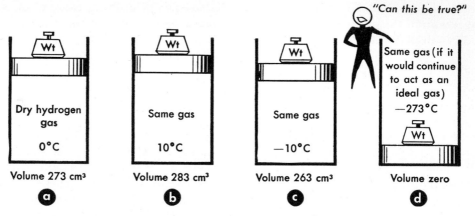

Fig. 7–15. What would happen to the volume of a gas at −273°C? Its pressure is supposed not to change as it is cooled.

change as indicated in Fig. 7–15. Careful measurements show that for every degree change in temperature, the volume changes 1/273 of the volume occupied by the gas at 0°C.

If the volume of this gas is plotted against its *absolute* temperature, a graph quite similar to that in Fig. 7–14 is obtained.

The volume of a gas at constant pressure is directly proportional to its absolute temperature.

Expressed in symbols,

$$\frac{V_1}{V_2} = \frac{T_1}{T_2}$$

where V_1 and T_1 are the original volume and absolute temperature of the gas and V_2 and T_2 are the corresponding quantities after the change in temperature and volume have occurred. This is the second part of Charles's or Gay-Lussac's law.

What Is an Ideal Gas?

An ideal gas is one that would behave exactly according to Charles's law all the way down to absolute zero, just as we

have assumed that the gas we have been considering might do.

For such a gas, two conditions are necessary: (1) its molecules must act like perfectly elastic balls when they collide and must not attract one another and (2) its molecules must be mere geometric points, with no volume of their own. If they could all be packed into a container like eggs in a basket, they would take up no space!

Of course, no actual gas molecules are like this. If they were, it would be perfectly reasonable that the volume of the gas should become zero when the molecules all settle down and are at rest at absolute zero. No real gas behaves like this ideal one at all temperatures. The molecules of a real gas have volume and may even have some motion at absolute zero. However, when a real gas is not near its liquefaction point, its molecules are relatively very far apart and exert practically no force on one another. Under this condition, any gas behaves almost like the ideal gas. This is why Charles's law holds for any gas that is not near its liquefaction point,

182

where its molecules begin to adhere to one another.

The General Gas Law

When a gas changes temperature, *both* its volume and its pressure may change. If this happens we have to use both Charles's law and Boyle's law (see page 69) to find its new volume and pressure. These two laws can be combined into one general law known as the *gas law*, which may be written

$$\frac{P_1 V_1}{T_1} = \frac{P_2 V_2}{T_2}$$

where P_1, V_1, and T_1 refer to the original pressure, volume, and absolute temperature, while P_2, V_2, and T_2 refer to the corresponding new values.

EXAMPLE: Suppose we collect 100 cm³ of hydrogen gas in a bottle at a pressure of 730 mm of mercury and a temperature of 24°C. What will be the volume of this gas when its temperature is reduced to 0°C and its pressure increased to 760 mm?

SOLUTION:

$P_1 = 730$ mm $\qquad V_1 = 100$ cm³
$P_2 = 760$ mm $\qquad V_2 = ?$
$\qquad\qquad T_1 = 24° + 273° = 297°$A
$\qquad\qquad T_2 = 0° + 273° = 273°$A

From the equation $\dfrac{P_1 V_1}{T_1} = \dfrac{P_2 V_2}{T_2}$

$$V_2 = \frac{P_1 V_1 T_2}{P_2 T_1}$$

$$= \frac{730 \times 100 \times 273}{760 \times 297}$$

$$= 88.3 \text{ cm}^3$$

►**Do You Know?**

1. What gases behave most nearly like the ideal gas, even at quite low temperatures?

2. Is any account taken of the expansion and contraction of the container of the gas in Fig. 7–13? Explain.

3. When air is compressed in a steel tank, which of the gas laws describes most nearly what happens to its volume, pressure, and temperature?

4. State the general gas law. What other laws are related to the general gas law?

5. What is meant by absolute temperature? Why is the absolute temperature scale useful in scientific measurement?

MEASURING TEMPERATURES

The molecules of a gas are in ceaseless random motion, according to the kinetic theory, as you will recall. Each molecule has its own mass and its own velocity at any particular time, so it has its own kinetic energy, $\frac{1}{2}mv^2$. A gas may consist of molecules that are all alike in mass, or it may be a mixture of molecules of different masses. In any body of gas there will be at any instant molecules with widely different velocities. So a gas will have molecules with a wide range of kinetic energies. To count the 28 billion billion molecules in 1 cm³, compute the kinetic energy of each one and find the *average* kinetic energy for one molecule by straightforward arithmetical means would be more than a superhuman task. Strange as it may seem, this is just what a thermometer does for us. According to the kinetic theory

Temperature of a gas is a measure of the average kinetic energy of molecules.

The temperature of liquids and solids, too, depends on the average kinetic energy of their molecules or other particles.

When we heat a body we merely prod its molecules so that, on the average,

183

Fig. 7–16. The velocity, kinetic energy, and temperature are about to rise! Is this a good analogy?

they move faster and have more kinetic energy. Faster moving gas molecules have more collisions per second with the walls of the container if they are confined in the same space, and hence the pressure they exert rises with temperature. Faster moving gas molecules will tend to get farther apart and still make as many collisions per second with the container wall, hence the volume of the gas expands with temperature if its pressure remains constant. At $-273°C$ the pressure of an ideal gas would become zero. This must mean that its molecules would no longer be in motion. The average kinetic energy of molecules at rest would be zero, since they would have no velocity. Their temperature would likewise be zero. This is why we consider $-273°C$ as *absolute zero*. More precise measurements indicate that absolute zero is a small fraction of a degree below $-273°C$. Temperatures within one or two thousandths of a degree of absolute zero have been reached in laboratories specializing in low-temperature work.

Mercury Thermometers

The common thermometer, consisting of a glass bulb and stem filled with 184

mercury, is familiar to nearly everyone. On warming, the mercury expands and pushes up into the very fine bore of the stem. On cooling, it contracts and the column shrinks down toward the bulb again. Mercury is especially suited for use in thermometers because it expands and contracts quite uniformly over the ordinary range of temperatures. This is not true for most common liquids. The space above the mercury column may be a vacuum, but in most thermometers designed to measure temperatures above $100°C$, this space is filled with some inert gas such as nitrogen. Usually the gas is under a pressure of several atmospheres. The size of the bulb and the diameter of the bore determine how far it is between degree marks on the thermometer stem.

Mercury freezes at $-38.9°C$, so the mercury thermometer cannot be used below about $-35°C$. At a pressure of 1 atmosphere, mercury boils at $357°C$, but its boiling point can be raised greatly by increasing the pressure on its surface. A mercury thermometer with the space above its column filled with nitrogen at a pressure of 20 atmospheres can be used for temperatures as high as $600°C$. Such a thermometer must be made of special glass, for ordinary thermometer glass will begin to soften before it reaches this temperature.

Low-temperature Thermometers

Liquid-in-glass thermometers can be used for temperatures much lower than the freezing point of mercury, if a suitable liquid is used. Ethyl alcohol, which freezes at about $-115°C$ and boils at $78.5°C$, is often used in low-temperature thermometers. A little coloring matter is generally added to the alcohol to make it easier to see the fine column. Other chemical substances, such as toluene and pentane, are also used in glass thermometers designed for low temperatures.

Two different types of electric thermometers are used to measure low temperatures. One of these is called a *resistance thermometer* and depends for its operation on the fact that the electric resistance of metal wire changes with temperature. Some resistance thermometers use a platinum wire, while others, designed to measure temperature within a few degrees of absolute zero, use phosphor bronze. The other type of electric thermometer is called a *thermocouple*. It consists of two wires of different metals, joined together end to end to form an electric circuit. When one of the *junctions* is at a different temperature than the other, a small electric voltage is set up in the circuit. The amount of this voltage, which can be measured with a suitable meter, depends on the *difference in temperature* of the two junctions. This type of thermometer can be used for temperatures well below −200°C. The magnetic properties of molecules are used to indicate temperatures that are within a degree of absolute zero.

High-temperature Thermometers

As we have seen, the mercurial thermometer is not suitable for temperatures above 600°C, even when especially constructed. The platinum resistance thermometer, mentioned previously, can be used for temperatures up to about 1500°C. Platinum melts at 1755°C. Different kinds of thermocouple thermometers can be used up to about the same limit, since one or both of the metals used for the couple melt at temperatures around 1800 to 2000°C.

For temperatures beyond the range of the thermocouple and the resistance thermometers, a special kind of thermometer, called a *pyrometer*, is used. Some pyrometers determine the temperature of a body by the color of its glow. A body at a "white heat" is hotter than one that is only red, and one that gives off a bluish glow is hotter still. Naturally these pyrometers are not very precise instruments and, fortunately, they do not need to be placed in a hot furnace to measure how hot it is! Other types of pyrometers measure the temperature of a glowing body by the amount and the wavelength of the energy it radiates. Instruments of this type are especially useful in measuring the temperature of distant objects like the sun, whose surface temperature is about 6000°C.

Table 7–2.   Some High and Low Temperatures

Boiling point of helium	−268.9°C
Melting point of hydrogen	−259.18°C
Boiling point of hydrogen	−252.8°C
Boiling point of liquid air	−192°C
Factory furnaces	(approx.) 1700°C
Carbon-arc furnace	3200°C
Oxyacetylene flame	3500°C
Iron-welding arc	6000°C
Sun, surface	6000°C
Other stars, maximum, surface	30000°C

A clinical or fever thermometer. *(The Taylor Instrument Companies)*

185

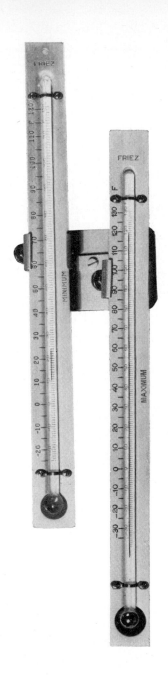

The maximum-minimum thermometer provides one method for keeping a record of highest and lowest temperatures reached over a period of time such as one day. *(Friez Instrument Division, Bendix Aviation Corporation)*

Special-purpose Thermometers

The *clinical thermometer*, used for measuring the temperature of the human body, is a mercury-in-glass instrument with some special features that make it more convenient. These thermometers are small and usually cover only a few more than 10 Fahrenheit degrees, extending at least from 96 to 106°F. The bore in the stem is very fine, which makes the mercury column a little hard to see. A constriction in the bore just above the bulb allows the mercury to flow past when it is being pushed out of the warmed bulb, but prevents its easy return, when the bulb cools again. For this reason, the thermometer may be removed from the mouth of the patient and carried to some other part of the room to be read. Before another temperature measurement can be made with the thermometer, however, the trapped mercury column must be shaken down past the constriction in the mercury tube into the bulb again.

►Do You Know?

1. Do you know the principle on which the thermometer on the oven of a cookstove works? Explain.
2. Why does the nurse or physician shake down a clinical thermometer before placing it in the patient's mouth?
3. For what different purposes have you used thermometers?
4. Explain the principle of the thermometer that indicates the temperature of the radiator solution in an automobile.
5. Explain how astronomers determine the temperature of the sun and stars.
6. Do you know any two metals that are used for thermocouples? What are they?

7. How does the maximum-minimum thermometer record temperatures.
8. How does a pyrometer measure temperature? Why are some pyrometer readings not entirely accurate? Where are pyrometers used?
9. What year-round Fahrenheit temperature would you expect to find at the bottom of a deep fresh-water lake? Find out whether your predicted temperature agrees with the measured temperature in any deep lake.

HIGHLIGHTS

Our sensation of temperature is unreliable. *Thermometers* are required to measure temperature.

Centigrade and *Fahrenheit* temperature scales are in common use.

The boiling point of water at 76 cm of mercury and the melting point of ice are the two *fixed points* of our present thermometer scales.

To convert from one scale to the other, $F = \frac{9}{5}C + 32°$ and $C = \frac{5}{9}(F - 32°)$.

Temperature produces changes in the size, characteristics, and physical properties of matter.

The *coefficient of linear expansion* of a solid is its change in length per unit length per degree.

$$c = \frac{X}{L(t_2 - t_1)}$$

This coefficient varies with the temperature range and other conditions.

Liquids, in general, *expand in volume* when heated.

Water contracts when heated from 0 to 4°C.

Water reaches its *maximum density* at 4°C.

The volume of a body of gas is directly proportional to its absolute temperature, if its pressure remains constant. $V_1/V_2 = T_1/T_2$

The pressure of a body of gas is directly proportional to its absolute temperature, if its volume remains constant. $P_1/P_2 = T_1/T_2$

The preceding two statements constitute *Charles's law.*

For any gas, in general, $P_1V_1/T_1 = P_2V_2/T_2$.

$-273°C$ is considered the *absolute zero* of temperature. Both the volume and the pressure of an *ideal* gas would disappear at this temperature.

Temperature is a measure of the *average kinetic energy* of molecules.

Special types of thermometers are used for different ranges of temperatures: liquid-in-glass for a few hundred degrees in the middle range; electric thermometers from very low to moderately high temperatures; pyrometers for high and very high temperatures.

PROBLEMS: GROUP A

1. What Fahrenheit temperature corresponds to each of the following: 20°C, 10°C, − 10°C, − 40°C, 6000°C?

2. What centigrade temperature corresponds to each of the following: 100°F, 150°F, 0°F, − 10°F, − 40°F?

3. What absolute temperature (centigrade) corresponds to each of the following: 72°F, 50°C, 98.6°F, 0°F, − 40°C?

4. What is the temperature reading of absolute zero on the Fahrenheit scale? Solve by converting − 273°C to F.

5. A nurse found that a patient had a temperature of 102°F. What would this temperature have been if she had used a centigrade thermometer?

6. The coefficient of expansion of steel is 0.000011 per centigrade degree. How much will a steel railroad rail 33 ft long expand when its temperature changes from − 10 to 30°C?

7. A brass rod is exactly 3 ft long at 20°C. What will be its length when heated to 50°C? See Table 7–1 for the value of c.

8. The melting point of one type of paraffin is 79°C. What is this temperature on the Fahrenheit scale? What is it on the absolute scale?

9. The boiling point of liquid oxygen is − 183°C. What is this temperature on the Fahrenheit scale? What is it on the absolute scale?

10. Tungsten melts at 3370°C and boils at 5900°C. What are these temperatures on the Fahrenheit scale? What are they on the absolute scale?

11. One form of hard solder melts at 188°C. What is this temperature on the Fahrenheit scale? What is it on the absolute scale?

12. A classroom is usually kept within the temperature range 70 to 74°F. Express this range in centigrade degrees.

13. How much does a 200-ft span of electric power wire (copper) expand in length when its temperature changes from 0 to 90°F?

14. How much does a 3-ft Invar rod expand in length when its temperature changes from 0 to 50°C?

15. Gas in a steel cylinder exerts a pressure of 50 lb/in.² when its temperature is 20°C. What will be the pressure of this gas if it is heated to 100°C? Neglect any change in the capacity of the cylinder.

GROUP B

1. A brass ball is 2 in. in diameter. How much will its diameter increase when the ball is heated from 0 to 100°C? See Table 7–1 for value of c.

2. How much does a 4,000-ft steel bridge change in length when its temperature changes from − 15 to 105°F?

3. An Invar steel rod is exactly 3 ft long at 20°C. How long will this rod become at 50°C?

4. A certain cylinder contains 2 ft³ of oxygen at a pressure of 1,500 lb/in.² To what volume will this gas expand if its pressure is reduced to one atmosphere (15 lb/in.²)? Assume that the temperature of the gas does not change.

5. How many cubic feet of gas under standard conditions (0°C and 760 mm pressure) are required to fill a balloon which is fully inflated to a volume of 3,000 ft³ at a pressure of 40 cm of mercury and a temperature of − 68°C?

6. A body of gas occupies 450 cm³ at a pressure of 740 mm of mercury and a

temperature of 25°C. What will be the volume of the gas under standard conditions (0°C and 760 mm pressure)?

7. What is the correction on a 100-ft steel tapeline at −10°C if it is exactly 100 ft long at 20°C?

8. If the coefficient of linear expansion of concrete is 0.000007 per Fahrenheit degree, how much will a 100-ft span of concrete highway increase in length when its temperature changes from 0 to 90°F?

9. A hard-rubber rod changes in length from 30.000 to 30.096 cm when its temperature changes from 0 to 50°C. What is the coefficient of linear expansion of this rubber?

10. Show by setting $F = C$ in the equation $F = \frac{9}{5}C + 32°$ and solving for C that the centigrade and the Fahrenheit temperature scales read the same at −40°.

11. A tungsten wire 100 cm long contracted 0.215 mm when it cooled from 50 to 0°C. What is the coefficient of linear expansion of this tungsten?

12. If the coefficient of volume expansion of mercury is 0.000182 per centigrade degree, what will be the volume of mercury in a bottle at 100°C when its volume is 500.00 cm³ at 20°C?

13. A volume of 500 cm³ of gas is collected in a chemistry experiment. Its pressure is 730 mm of mercury and its temperature 20°C. What would be its volume if its pressure were 760 mm and its temperature 0°C?

14. The rod in a pendulum in a clock is made of brass. Suppose the temperature of this rod changes from 0 to 30°C. Express the resulting change in length of the rod as a percentage of its original length. How would this change affect the operation of the clock?

15. The volume of a glass measuring flask is exactly 200 milliliters (ml) at 20°C. If the coefficient of volume (or cubical) expansion of the glass is 0.000011, how much will this flask be in error at 40°C?

16. The gas in a steel cylinder exerts a pressure of 250 lb/in.² when its temperature is 20°C. What will be the pressure of this gas if it is heated to 50°C? Neglect any change in the capacity of the cylinder.

THINGS TO DO

1. Read the temperature indicated by an outdoor thermometer once every hour during the day (on the hour, for example). Then plot these readings against the corresponding time of day and make a graph showing how outdoor temperature varied from hour to hour during this day.

2. Obtain an oven thermometer and measure the temperature inside the oven of a cookstove when baking or roasting meat. If the oven is fitted with a thermostat, compare the setting of the thermostat with the temperature indicated by the oven thermometer. What range of temperatures is used in baking and in roasting?

3. Obtain a suitable thermometer and measure the temperature on different shelves of an icebox or a mechanical refrigerator. What refrigerator temperature is recommended for keeping milk fresh? What temperature is recommended for keeping butter from spoiling?

4. If you live near a long bridge, try to get a picture of the arrangement used to permit expansion and contraction of the bridge with the changing seasons. Explain the operation of expansion sections of bridges.

Changes of State of Matter:
Measuring Heat Quantities

HEAT, A FORM OF ENERGY

Heat is one of the several different forms of energy. You should be careful not to confuse the amount of heat energy in a body of matter with its temperature.

A small particle of steel flying from a grinding wheel is often so hot that it sparks. Its temperature is high, perhaps 1500°C or more. A kettle of heating water begins to steam when its temperature reaches about 160°F. From which of these can we get more heat, the sparking particle of steel or the kettleful of steaming water? If you had to choose one or the other of these to take the chill off a tub of bath water, you would hardly hesitate to select the kettleful of

190

steaming water, even though its *temperature* is lower. Experience has taught us that the hot water will be more effective in warming the bath water, which is only another way of saying that the hot water yields the greater amount of heat.

What Is a Calorie?

Water is the standard substance used in setting up units for measuring heat. **One calorie is the amount of heat required to change the temperature of one gram of water through one centigrade degree.** When 1 g of water is heated through 1 centigrade degree, it must receive 1 calorie (cal) of heat energy from some other source. When 1 g of water is cooled through 1 centigrade degree, it must lose 1 cal of heat energy. The calorie is as definitely a unit of energy as are the erg and the joule.

The calorie is used in many fields of science for measuring heat. In biology, dietetics, and some areas of chemistry, a larger unit called the *kilocalorie* is used and designated a Calorie. A kilocalorie is 1,000 calories, and is the amount of heat required to change the temperature of *one kilogram* of water through one centigrade degree. The kilocalorie is often called a kilogram-calorie. It is also called a *large calorie* and a *greater calorie.* Usually the word kilocalorie is written out in full or abbreviated with a capital C (Cal) so that you cannot mistake it for the common calorie.

The British Thermal Unit

The British thermal unit is the amount of heat energy required to change the temperature of one pound of water through one Fahrenheit degree.

This is the unit of heat energy commonly used in the English system. It is abbreviated Btu and familiarly read B-T-U. The British thermal unit is much larger than the calorie. Since one pound is equivalent to 453.6 grams and one Fahrenheit degree is equivalent to $\frac{5}{9}$ of a centigrade degree, 1 Btu = $453.6 \times \frac{5}{9} = 252$ cal, about one-fourth of a kilocalorie. The Btu is used in different branches of engineering, especially in expressing the amount of heat energy obtained from coal, oil, and other fuels.

Quantity of Heat Energy

One calorie of heat energy will heat 1 g of water 1 centigrade degree, as we have just seen. To heat 1 g of water 2 degrees requires 2 cal and to heat 1 g of water 10 degrees requires 10 cal. So we

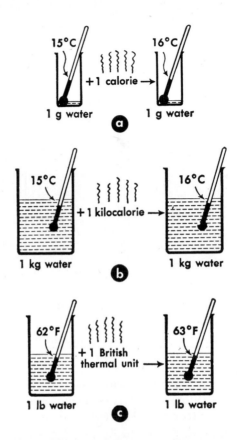

Fig. 8–1. The calorie, the kilocalorie, and the British thermal unit are units of heat energy.

say that *the number of calories required to heat a given body of water is directly proportional to the number of degrees its temperature changes.*

To heat 2 g of water 1 centigrade degree requires 2 cal, to heat 10 g the same amount requires 10 cal, and to heat 100 g this amount requires 100 cal. So again we may say that *the number of calories required to heat water a given number of degrees is directly proportional to the mass of the water heated.*

If we let m represent the mass of water to be heated, t_1 the temperature at which it starts, and t_2 the temperature it finally reaches, the temperature change

191

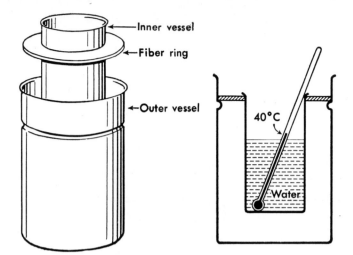

Fig. 8–2. Parts of a simple calorimeter.

of the water is $t_2 - t_1$ and the heat it takes on is

$$H = m \ (t_2 - t_1)$$

If m is expressed in grams and the temperatures in centigrade degrees, H will be in calories. If m is in pounds and the temperatures in Fahrenheit degrees, H will be in Btu's.

The same equation will serve to express the amount of heat given off by water when it cools. In this case, however, it is better to write $t_1 - t_2$ for the change in temperature, so that this difference may be a positive number.

What Is a Calorimeter?

A *calorimeter* is a device for measuring heat in calories or Btu's. A simple type of calorimeter consists of a metal vessel in which a certain weight of water, m, is placed. The heat lost or gained by this water during any series of events is easily computed by observing how much the temperature of the water changes and then applying the equation $H = m$ $(t_2 - t_1)$. In any actual measurement, allowance has to be made for the heat taken up or lost by the calorimeter itself.

192

In some cases, the heat taken on or given off by the thermometer has to be considered, too. You will no doubt learn how to measure heat if your laboratory is equipped with calorimeters.

▶Do You Know?

1. What does a thermometer measure? Explain.
2. We sometimes say that a refrigerator produces *cold*. How should this statement be interpreted in the light of our definition of heat?
3. In what units would we be likely to express the mass of water in the calorimeter in Fig. 8–2, if we were measuring heat in calories?
4. What kind of thermometer would we be likely to use with a calorimeter if we plan to measure heat in Btu's?
5. What kind of thermometer would we be likely to use when we wish to measure heat in calories? In kilocalories?
6. What are some of the laboratory applications of calorimeters? How do you think a calorimeter might be used to help measure calorie values of the foods you eat?

SPECIFIC HEAT

Water is the standard substance used in defining the units of heat, the calorie and the British thermal unit. Does one gram of mercury or oil or lead also give off one calorie of heat when it cools one centigrade degree?

Materials Absorb and Emit Heat

Suppose we have a lead ball that weighs 25 g, and an aluminum ball with the same mass. Because of the difference in their densities, the aluminum ball will have about four times the volume of the lead one. However, in matters concerning heat, we are interested in effects produced in *equal masses* of different materials, rather than in *equal volumes*.

Let us first heat the two balls in steam over boiling water until they become as hot throughout as the steam itself. Then let us quickly remove the two hot balls

from the boilers and drop them on a cake of ice as shown in Fig. 8–3. Ice will begin to melt under each ball at once. Melting will continue until the balls become just as cold as the ice. When this condition is reached, we may be surprised to find that the aluminum ball has melted several times as much ice as the lead one.

This shows that in cooling from the temperature of steam to that of ice, the 25-g aluminum ball gives off much more heat than the lead ball of equal mass. Materials differ in the amount of heat equal masses give off or take on when their temperatures are changed through the same range.

The number of calories required to change the temperature of *one gram* of a given substance *one centigrade degree* is called its *specific heat*. A gram of water requires one calorie to change its temperature one centigrade degree, so its

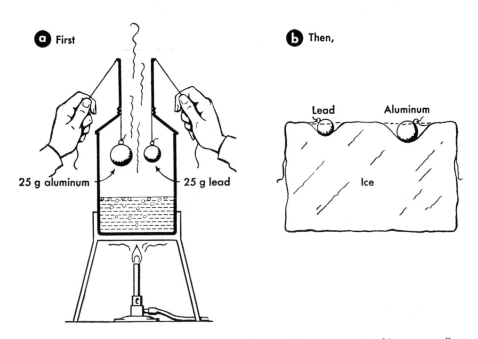

Fig. 8–3. Equal masses of aluminum and lead give up different amounts of heat on cooling.

Table 8–1. Specific Heats

Material	Specific heat, cal/g/°C
Gold	0.031
Platinum	0.032
Lead	0.032
Mercury	0.033
Silver	0.056
Copper	0.093
Zinc	0.095
Iron	0.115
Crown glass	0.162
Aluminum	0.22
Wood	0.42
Ice at −10°C	0.53
Water	1.00
Liquid ammonia	1.125

specific heat is one calorie per gram per degree. A gram of aluminum requires about 0.22 calorie to change its temperature one centigrade degree, so its specific heat is 0.22 calorie per gram per degree. Specific heats of some of the common substances are given in Table 8–1.

All specific heats have the same numerical value in both the metric and the English systems. For example, the specific heat of aluminum in the English system is 0.22 Btu/lb/°F, and in the metric system it is 0.22 cal/g/°C.

How Specific Heat Is Used

Suppose we wish to know the number of calories required to heat a 2-kg iron kettle from 20 to 100°C. The *change* in temperature, $t_2 - t_1$, is $100° - 20°$, which is 80 centigrade degrees. From Table 8–1 we find that the specific heat of iron is 0.115 cal/g/°C. This means that for each degree of change in temperature, each gram of the iron takes up 0.115 cal. For the 80° change in temperature, each

194

gram of the iron will take up 80×0.115 cal, and the 2,000 g (2 kg) of iron in the kettle will take up $2,000 \times 80 \times 0.115$ = 18,400 cal.

$$H = m\,(t_2 - t_1)\,S$$

where H is the amount of heat taken on or given off by a body whose mass is m and specific heat is S, when its temperature changes from t_1 to t_2 degrees.

From the relationship expressed in this equation we can compute how much heat is required to heat a steam radiator, a curling iron, or any other device from room temperature to its operating temperature, provided we can find out its mass and its specific heat.

Specific Heat of Water

Water has a very high specific heat. Its value of 1 cal/g/°C is exceeded only by that of liquid ammonia under pressure and by that of a few other uncommon substances. The average specific heat of rocks and soil is much less than that of water. As a consequence, land areas warm up and cool more rapidly than water areas in the same temperature zone. For this reason, land areas may experience sudden extreme changes in temperature, whereas water areas are less subject to such extremes. A large body of water, such as a lake or an ocean, tends to reduce extreme changes in temperature. Such bodies of water tend to hold back the advent of warm weather in the spring of the year, and at the same time prevent sudden drops of temperature below the freezing point.

In this way, the high specific heat of water plays an important role in the climate and economic life of many parts of our country. One of the requisites for successful fruit growing is the absence of killing frosts when the trees and vines are in bloom. The great inland lakes between the United States and Canada help to prevent such frosts in blossom time. This is one of the reasons for the fruit belts in northern Ohio and Pennsylvania and in southern Ontario along Lake Erie. It is likewise one of the reasons for the famous cherry orchards along Traverse Bay and the great fruit section in western Michigan along the Lake Michigan shore. The climate in the fruit-growing sections of Oregon and Washington is modified by the Pacific Ocean nearby.

▶**Do You Know?**

1. Do you know of any case in which heat flows from a colder to a hotter body? Explain.
2. Does 1 g of ice take on more or less heat than 1 g of water, when its temperature changes 1°C?
3. Will an iron and a glass container *of the same weight* take on the same amount of heat from an equal volume of hot coffee poured into them?
4. Plates made of silver and even of gold have been used in serving food at banquets. What are the advantages and disadvantages of such metal dinner plates?
5. Explain one everyday use of specific heat which you know about.

CHANGE IN STATE OF MATTER

As a general rule, the temperature of a body rises when the body receives heat and falls when the body loses heat. Under certain conditions, however, a body may take on or give off many calories of heat without affecting its temperature at all.

Water can be changed from a solid (ice) to a liquid and from a liquid to a gas (steam) by the application of heat alone. These transitions represent

A 100-ton Lectromelt furnace being tapped. This type of electric furnace produces the extremely high temperatures required to change metallic solids into liquids. These metallic liquids then are poured into molds and cooled to the solid state. The castings thus made are machine-finished for industrial use. (*Bituminous Coal Research, Inc.*)

195

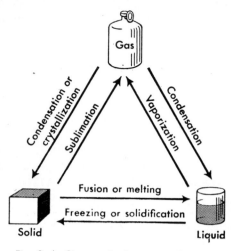

Fig. 8–4. Changes in the states of matter.

changes in the *state* of water. Many substances pass readily from one state to another under the action of heat. Figure 8–4 shows the names generally applied to the processes by which these transitions take place.

When Ice Melts

If you place the bulb of a thermometer on a piece of ice that is melting, you will find that its temperature is 0°C. If you test the ice water just as it comes from the melting ice, you will find that its

Table 8–2. Some Heats of Fusion and Melting Points

Substance	Melting point,°C	Heat of fusion, cal/g
Aluminum	658.7	76.8
Ammonia	−75.0	108.1
Copper	1083.0	42.0
Mercury	−39.0	2.8
Salt (sodium chloride)	804.3	124.0
Sulfur	119.0	13.2
Water	0	79.7

temperature, likewise, is 0°C. If there is no difference in temperature between ice and ice water, why does the ice melt at all?

Experience has shown that *ice can melt only when it receives heat.* Careful measurements with ice in a calorimeter show that every gram of ice at 0°C that melts to form ice water at the same temperature requires approximately 80 cal of heat to make the change. We express this in other words by saying that the *heat of fusion of water is 80 cal/g.* In the English system, this amounts to 144 Btu/lb. This same amount of heat is given up by every gram of water at 0°C that freezes into ice at the same temperature.

It is a strange phenomenon when approximately 80 cal of heat enter every gram of ice that melts and produce no observable rise in temperature! What becomes of this heat energy? Molecules in an ice crystal are more closely bound together than they are in the liquid state. To pull apart the molecules in the ice crystal in melting requires that work be done on them. This increases their potential energy. The 80 cal of heat represent the amount of work required to pull 1 g of ice molecules apart. The "hidden" or *latent* heat, as it is often called, is molecular energy that has changed from the kinetic to the potential form. This is why it fails to register on the thermometer, which is concerned only with the average *kinetic* energy of molecules. When water freezes, this molecular potential energy changes back to kinetic energy and the 80 cal/g reappears.

Notice that water has a comparatively high heat of fusion. Its value is exceeded by that of ammonia, salt, and a few other substances. When large bodies of water freeze, they yield great amounts of heat to the surrounding air. When they thaw again, they take up just as much heat from their surroundings. For these reasons, the high heat of fusion of water tends to prevent sudden extremes of temperature in the neighborhood of lakes and oceans, in much the same way that its high specific heat does.

Crystalline Substances

Ice, the metals, ordinary salt, and many other solid substances are built up of crystals. In crystals, molecules or atoms are arranged in a definite kind of pattern rather than tumbled together at random. Often crystals are large enough to be easily seen and recognized. You have probably seen six-sided snowflake crystals. *Crystalline* substances behave like water in that they have definite melting points where the solid and liquid exist side by side at the same temperature. Furthermore, they all have heats of fusion, even though their values differ widely from substance to substance.

Amorphous Substances

Have you ever tried to melt glass? It is not a crystalline substance and behaves in an entirely different way. As solid glass gets hotter, it begins to soften. Eventually it will flow like molasses or taffy. Some crystalline substances also become softer as they approach their melting point. However, with glass there is no definite temperature at which the material changes from a solid to a liquid, no temperature at which liquid and solid glass exist together. At no point does glass take on heat without changing its temperature. In other words, *glass has no definite melting point and no heat of fusion.* This behavior is characteristic of solids that are not crystalline. Such substances are described as *amorphous.*

Although sulfur is found in its crystalline form, it can be changed into an amorphous form by heating it until it melts and then cooling it slowly. Other substances exist in both forms. Plastic substances, like pitch, are generally amorphous.

Changes When Substances Solidify

When crystalline substances fuse or melt, the liquid generally occupies more volume than the solid from which it is formed. Such substances *expand on melting* and *contract on freezing or solidifying.* The density of the melting

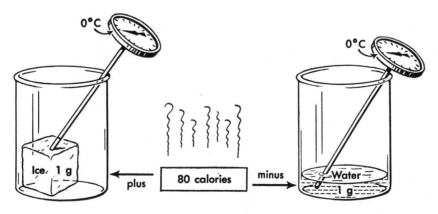

Fig. 8–5. The change from ice to ice water, or from ice water to ice.

solid is greater than that of the liquid surrounding it, hence the solid sinks in the liquid. Aluminum is a solid that behaves in this way. Its volume expands about 5 percent on melting and contracts a corresponding amount on solidifying.

Water is one of the outstanding exceptions to this general rule. Its volume *contracts* about 8.3 percent on melting. On freezing, the volume of the ice formed is about 9.1 percent greater than that of the water from which it comes. While these two percentages are different, they *represent corresponding changes in volume*. Ice floats because its density is less than that of water. This is very fortunate, because if ice settled to the bottom of lakes and streams, they would probably freeze solid in winter, even though water has its maximum density at 4°C.

Iron, type metal, and a few other substances expand on solidifying, just as water does. Such substances are suitable for casting in molds, since they tend to fill out the details of the mold when they solidify.

Water enclosed so that it cannot expand freely develops a tremendous expanding force on freezing. Cracked radiators on automobile engines and burst water pipes in cold weather bear evidence of the magnitude of this force. When water that has penetrated into the pores and crevices of rocks freezes, this expanding force cracks and crumbles the rock. Disintegration of rocks in this way is called *weathering.* Notice carefully that this increase in the volume of water occurs *when it changes from liquid to solid.* Ice itself contracts as it gets colder, just as other solids do.

Pressure and Melting Point

The melting point of ice is always so nearly the same under ordinary conditions that it has been chosen as one of the fixed points of the temperature scales. The melting point does change, however, when great pressure is applied to the solid ice. If the pressure is *increased* 1 atmosphere, the melting point is *lowered* about 0.0075 centigrade degree. A pressure of about 160 atmospheres is required to lower the melting point to −1°C. At a pressure of about 2,000 atmospheres, the melting point reaches −22°C.

Substances like ordinary ice, that expand on solidifying, have their melting points lowered by moderately increased pressure. On the other hand, substances like aluminum, that contract on solidifying, have their melting points raised by increased pressure.

Regelation

When two ice cubes at room temperature are pressed firmly together with sufficient force, they melt slightly at the points of contact because pressure lowers the melting point of ice. When this pressure is again relieved, the water at the points of contact freezes at once so that the cubes stick tightly together. This re-

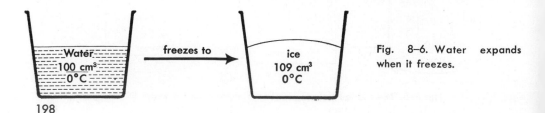

Fig. 8–6. Water expands when it freezes.

Fig. 8–7. Regelation in operation.

freezing of the water when the pressure is relieved is called *regelation*. A fine iron wire with weights attached to the ends can be arranged to pass slowly through a block of ice without breaking the block. Water from ice melted just ahead of the wire due to high pressure in this region passes around and refreezes behind the wire where the pressure is low. This cements the ice together again after the wire has passed.

Regelation accounts for the packing of snow when we make snowballs. If the snow is too cold, we cannot exert enough pressure to cause the particles in contact to melt and refreeze, so no balls can be formed.

Supercooling

Suppose we place some pure clean water in a test tube and insert the test tube in a freezing mixture of crushed ice and salt. Let us put a thermometer in the test tube so that we can observe the temperature of the water from time to time as our test progresses. If we are careful not to shake or jar the water, we can often get it to cool to as much as 8 or 9° below zero C without freezing. A sudden jar or a small crystal of ice dropped into the water in this condition will usually start ice to form. Then the freezing occurs with startling suddenness. The temperature of the water not yet frozen will rise to 0°C almost instantly, and will remain at this point until all of the water is frozen. Water cooled below the normal freezing temperature is said to be *supercooled*. Practically all crystalline substances can be supercooled under suitable conditions.

Lowering the Freezing Point

The freezing point of water can be lowered by dissolving salt or some other solid in it. How far the freezing point is lowered depends on the kind and amount of material dissolved in a unit volume of the water. By the addition of ordinary table salt in sufficient amounts, the freezing point of the solution can be lowered to about −21°C. Near this temperature, the solution freezes with salt and ice together in the solid. Sugar and many other solid substances dissolved in water likewise lower the freezing point.

Liquids such as denatured alcohol, methanol, ethylene glycol (Prestone), and glycerin, when mixed with water,

199

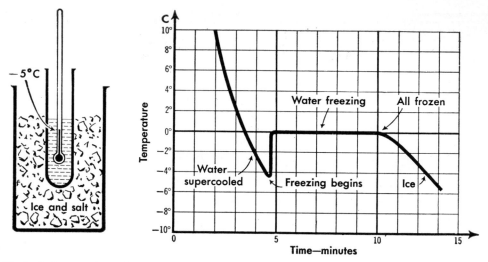

Fig. 8–8. Supercooling of water. The graph shows a typical rate at which water cools and changes to ice.

lower its freezing point. This is why these liquids are used in antifreeze solutions for radiators. A 50 percent solution of denatured alcohol—equal volumes of denatured alcohol and water—provides protection against freezing to −20°F. A 50 percent solution of some commercial antifreeze products is safe to −30°F.

Vaporization

The change of a liquid to a gas or vapor is called *vaporization*. Everyone is familiar with the fact that water on a street or sidewalk on a windy day soon dries up and disappears. Wet clothes hung on a line eventually become dry. In these cases, we say the water *evaporates*. Evaporation takes place only at the surface of a liquid and occurs at any temperature at which the liquid exists. *Boiling* is a more spectacular process of changing a liquid to a gas. In boiling, bubbles of vapor or gas form at the bottom and within the body of the liquid, rise to the surface, and burst. In a pure liquid, boiling takes place only at a definite temperature at a given pressure.

200

Vaporization may occur by either or both of these processes, evaporation and boiling.

Rate of Evaporation

The rate at which a liquid evaporates depends on several factors. Among them are the following:

1. The temperature of the liquid. At a higher temperature, the average kinetic energy of the molecules is greater and a larger share of the molecules striking the surface film from below in a given time have sufficient speed to break through and become gas. For this reason, the rate of evaporation increases as the temperature of the liquid is raised.

2. The extent of the surface. Since evaporation occurs only at the surface of a liquid, the larger this surface area, the more molecules will pass through to the gas state in a given time. The rate of evaporation increases with the surface area.

3. The rate at which escaped molecules are removed. If molecules that have already escaped from the liquid are not removed from the vicinity, many of them will find their way back into the liquid and be recaptured. These returning molecules will reduce the *net* rate at which molecules leave the liquid and hence slow down the rate of evaporation. A fan blowing a breeze across the surface of a liquid removes molecules that have passed into the gas state and in this way increases the net rate of evaporation. A vacuum pump that exhausts the space above the liquid hastens evaporation for much the same reason.

4. *The pressure on the surface of the liquid.* Air pressure on the surface of a liquid slows down evaporation. Liquids evaporate faster at lower pressures because molecules breaking through the surface of the liquid do not encounter so many other molecules to drive them back.

5. *The nature of the liquid.* At a given temperature, alcohol evaporates more readily than water and ether still more readily than alcohol. This is because less energy is required for an ether molecule to break through the surface of its liquid than is required for any other of these molecules to break through its respective liquid surface. A liquid that evaporates more readily is said to be more *volatile*.

Evaporation Produces Cooling

If you place a few drops of water on the back of your hand and blow across them, you will notice a sensation of coolness as the water evaporates. A few drops of alcohol, ether, or carbon tetrachloride seem much colder than water because these liquids evaporate much faster than water. If water in a porous cup or bag is placed in a breeze, it soon becomes much cooler than the surrounding air. This cooling effect is understood when we recall that it is always the fastest-moving molecules—those with the greatest kinetic energy—that are first to escape from the liquid by evaporation. The average kinetic energy of the molecules that remain in the liquid must be lowered by this continual loss of the faster molecules, unless additional energy is received from some outside source. This is only another way of saying that the temperature of the liquid must be lowered by evaporation, unless the liquid receives heat energy from the outside.

Heat of Vaporization

If cold water is placed in an open pan and heated steadily, its temperature will continue to rise until boiling begins. As the water becomes hot, air, dissolved in the cold water, will form in bubbles along the sides and bottom of the pan. The formation of these bubbles should not be confused with boiling. When the boiling temperature is reached, bubbles of steam will form on the bottom and throughout the body of the water. To keep the water boiling, we must continue to heat it. If we turn up the fire, the water will boil more vigorously but its temperature *will not rise any farther* as we can verify with a thermometer. *The heat we add to maintain boiling does not register on the thermometer.* It is used in pulling the molecules of water apart to give them the greater freedom required for the gas state. The potential energy of the molecules is increased in this way, but their average kinetic energy remains the same. **The amount of heat required to convert one gram of a liquid to a gas without changing its temperature is called its *heat of vaporization*.**

The heat of vaporization of water at 100°C is about 540 cal/g. This means that 540 cal is required to boil away 1 g of water, without changing its tempera-

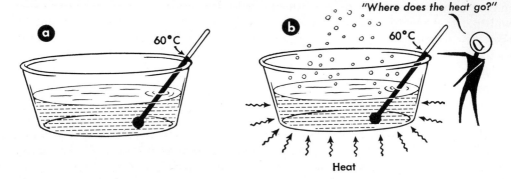

Fig. 8–9. When water evaporates.

ture at all. And, conversely, when 1 g of steam at 100°C condenses, it must give off 540 cal to become water at the same temperature. The heat of vaporization of water is much higher than that of any other common substance.

Suppose that evaporating water receives just enough heat from the outside to keep its temperature from changing while 1 g evaporates. This quantity of heat must represent the energy required to change this gram of water from a liquid to a gas, so it is equivalent to the heat of vaporization of water.

The heat of vaporization is generally greater when a liquid evaporates than when it boils. For example, at 10°C the heat of vaporization of water is about

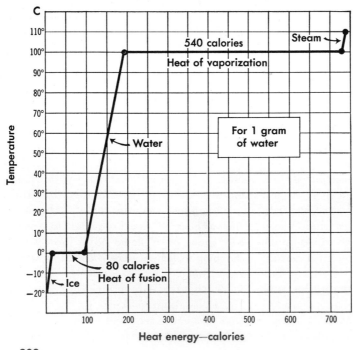

Fig. 8–10. Calories required when 1 g of water changes from ice to steam.

590 cal/g, at 50°C it is 574 cal/g, while at 100°C it is 540 cal/g. This must mean that it is harder for a molecule to break through the surface of water at the lower temperatures, as we might expect when we remember that the surface tension of water becomes higher as its temperature decreases.

Vapor Pressure

Suppose the air has been completely pumped out of the tank shown in Fig. 8–11a. Notice that the gage indicates *zero* pressure within the tank. Suppose we then open stopcock *A* and let some water into the tank. The gage will rise at first, but will eventually become stationary, indicating a steady pressure within the tank. If we heat the water from 20 to 40°C, the gage will rise still farther and become stationary again at a higher value of pressure.

The pressure within the tank is caused by water molecules that escape from the surface of the liquid (evaporate) and become gas or vapor. These vapor mole-

cules bombard not only the walls of the container and the gage, but the surface of the water as well. We believe that some of those that bombard the surface of the water are captured and become liquid again. When the pressure within the tank becomes stationary, the vapor is *saturated*. Then each square centimeter of the surface of the liquid captures as many molecules per second as escape from it.

We may imagine that there is a *pressure inside the liquid* which forces the escaping water molecules out through the surface of the liquid into the space of the tank. We cannot measure this internal vapor pressure directly, but by some method such as that shown in Fig. 8–11 we *can measure* the pressure of the saturated vapor that just balances this internal vapor pressure. Except when the vapor is saturated, the actual pressure exerted on the liquid by the vapor molecules above it is less than the vapor pressure of the liquid. In this event, more molecules escape from the liquid

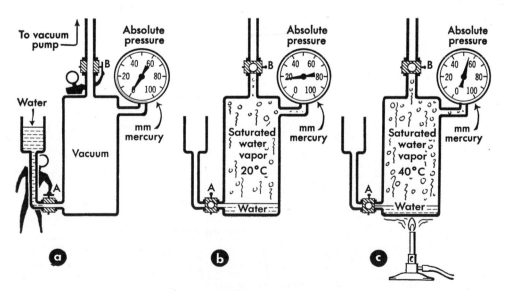

Fig. 8–11. Saturated vapor pressure.

Table 8–3. Pressure and Density of Saturated Water Vapor

Temperature, °C	Vapor pressure, mm of mercury	Vapor density, g/m³
0	4.6	4.9
5	6.5	6.8
10	9.2	9.4
15	12.8	12.8
20	17.5	17.3
25	23.7	23.0
30	31.7	30.4
35	42.0	39.6
40	55.2	51.1
45	71.7	65.6
50	92.3	83.2
55	117.9	104.6
60	149.2	130.5
65	187.4	161.5
70	233.6	198.4
75	289.0	242.1
80	355.1	293.8
85	433.5	354.1
90	525.8	424.1
95	634.0	505.0
100	760.0	598.0

pressure of the liquid becomes higher. The mass or weight of actual vapor molecules in a cubic centimeter or a cubic meter of space is called the *vapor density*. The density of *saturated vapor* also increases when the temperature becomes higher, as shown in Table 8–3.

Pressure and the Boiling Point

Notice in Table 8–3 that the vapor pressure of water is 760 mm of mercury (1 atmosphere) at 100°C. You already know that water boils at 100°C when the pressure on it is 760 mm of mercury. **A liquid boils when its internal vapor pressure equals the total external pressure on its surface.**

Water boils at a temperature above 100°C when the pressure on it is greater than 760 mm of mercury, and at a temperature below 100°C, when the pressure is less than this value. If the external pressure varies but slightly from 760 mm, the boiling point is changed about 0.037° for each millimeter change in pressure. The boiling point changes about one centigrade degree for each inch change in barometric pressure.

A method sometimes employed to determine the altitude of a location is "boiling the thermometer." The boiling point of water drops about one centigrade degree for each 900 ft of elevation. At an elevation of 9,000 ft, water boils at about 90°C. After observing the boiling point of water, the approximate elevation can be found. At high altitudes it is difficult or impossible to cook eggs or vegetables in an open vessel by boiling because of the low boiling point.

Boiling at Reduced Pressure

Figure 8–12 shows a method of demonstrating that water boils at a lower temperature when its pressure is reduced. Some water is placed in an open,

in a second than are captured, and the liquid continues to evaporate.

Even if there had been air in the tank at the start, the water would still have the same internal vapor pressure forcing its molecules to escape. The pressure due to the vapor molecules in the tank when saturation is reached would be just the same as if the air were not there. The presence of air molecules in the space above the liquid only slows down the rate of evaporation so that a longer time is required to reach saturation.

Water—and any other liquid, for that matter—has a definite internal vapor pressure at a given temperature. If the temperature is raised, the internal vapor

204

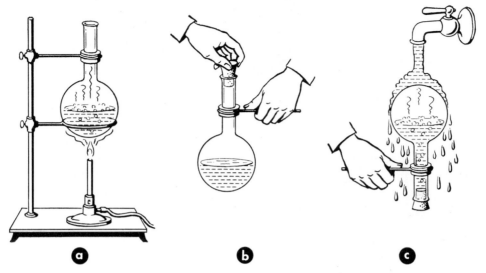

Fig. 8–12. Boiling water by cooling and condensing the vapor.

round-bottom flask and heated until it boils. A stopper is then inserted, the flask inverted and held under a stream of cold water. As steam in the flask condenses, the pressure on the hot water is reduced and boiling continues at the lower temperature. Often we can get water to boil in this way at temperatures not uncomfortable to the hands.

Water boiling at reduced temperature has to furnish its own heat of vaporization unless it receives this heat from some outside source. Water well insulated from outside heat sources will get colder and colder when we keep it boiling by continuing to reduce the pressure on it. With a suitable arrangement to pump away the air and water vapor, it is possible to boil water until it freezes into ice.

How a Pressure Cooker Works

A pressure cooker consists of a heavy-walled cooking vessel with a tight-fitting lid that is held in place with clamps. Steam generated in the cooker is kept in until the pressure rises to several pounds per square inch above atmospheric pressure. A safety valve releases the steam when the pressure reaches the value for which the valve is set. The increased pressure raises the boiling point of water

A pressure cooker. (Maid of Honor Canner, Sears, Roebuck and Company)

205

"No liquid yet?"

"Not a drop. Maybe we are not doing this right!"

Air

Fig. 8–13. Air cannot be liquefied by pressure unless its temperature is below −140°C.

and allows the food in the cooker to reach a temperature higher than 100°C, thus hastening the cooking process. If the pressure in the cooker is allowed to reach 15 lb/in.² (above atmospheric pressure) water can be heated to 121°C before it begins to boil. Pressure cookers are used extensively in canneries to cook and sterilize fruits and vegetables after they are packed in cans. Non-acid vegetables such as corn, beans, and peas require a temperature well above the normal boiling point of water for complete sterilization. Pressure cookers are often used by housewives for home canning and for speeding up home cooking.

A special steam pressure boiler, called an *autoclave*, is used in hospitals and laboratories for the rapid sterilization of utensils and instruments.

Compression of Gas to a Liquid

Everyone is familiar with the condensation of water vapor to form a liquid when it is cooled. Many gases can be liquefied by *compressing them at ordinary*

206

temperatures, if enough pressure is used. However, some gases cannot be liquefied at ordinary temperatures by merely squeezing the gas molecules together. It has been found that *no gas can be liquefied by compressing it, no matter how great the pressure, unless its temperature is below a certain critical value that is peculiar to that gas.* For example, sulfur dioxide cannot be liquefied by any amount of pressure unless its temperature is below 157°C. At this temperature a pressure of 78 atmospheres is required to squeeze the gas into a liquid. Carbon dioxide must be below 31°C to liquefy under pressure. If the temperature of a gas is lower than its *critical temperature*, less pressure is required to convert it to a liquid.

The reason why solid carbon dioxide—Dry Ice—forms no liquid when the solid sublimes is that a pressure of 1 atmosphere is not great enough to maintain the liquid at ordinary temperatures. If a pressure of 5.2 atmospheres or more were applied to the solid carbon dioxide and its vapor, the solid would then melt (at −56.6°C or less) and form a liquid, just as other crystalline substances ordinarily do.

►You Will Be Interested to Know

Scientists have not always known that all gases can be liquefied. They originally thought that many substances could exist only as gases. Some of the earliest experiments in changing gases to liquids were carried out by Michael Faraday, an English experimental physicist of the nineteenth century. Faraday succeeded in liquefying chlorine in 1823. He soon learned how to apply the same method—pressure and cooling—to a number of other gases which had never before been seen in the liquid state. But nitrogen, oxygen, air, hydrogen, and helium resisted all early efforts to change them to a liquid. For this reason, they were called "permanent" gases.

Dewar, an English physicist, first liquefied oxygen in 1891. He invented the Dewar flask (Thermos bottle) as a container for this new liquid. Linde liquefied air in 1895 and Dewar changed hydrogen to a liquid in 1898. Helium, the last and most stubborn of the so-called permanent gases, was finally changed to a liquid in 1908 by Heike Kamerlingh Onnes at the low-temperature laboratory at the University of Leyden in Holland. In recognition of his investigation into the properties of matter at very low temperatures, Kamerlingh Onnes in 1913 was awarded the Nobel prize in physics.

► **Do You Know?**

1. In which of the processes shown in Fig. 8–4 is heat energy released? In which of these processes is heat energy absorbed?
2. Why are the heat of fusion and the heat of vaporization often called *latent heats?*
3. A tub of water placed in a fruit cellar in cold weather may prevent the fruit from freezing. How is this possible?
4. The vapor pressure of ethyl alcohol is 760 mm of mercury at 78.3°C. At what temperature will this alcohol boil, if the pressure on it is exactly one atmosphere?
5. Why are *vacuum* pans used in evaporating water from the sirup in making sugar?
6. Make a list of five crystalline substances and five amorphous substances, other than those mentioned in the text.
7. Why does water evaporate more rapidly from the wide surface of a shallow pan than from the mouth of a narrow-necked bottle?
8. Why does blowing across the surface of a hot liquid tend to cool it quickly?
9. When potatoes have been brought to a boil, can they be cooked any faster by turning up the gas? Why?
10. Why can no liquid air be obtained by the method of Fig. 8–13?
11. What are Nobel prizes and how did these prizes originate? Who selects the winners of these prizes? Who was the latest winner of the Nobel prize in physics and why was he chosen?

HUMIDITY

Evaporation of water into the atmosphere is occurring continuously from the surface of all land and water. In addition, enormous amounts of water vapor enter the atmosphere through the leaves of trees, shrubs, and other vegetation. These molecules of water vapor mingle with those of the surrounding air. At any time and place, each cubic centimeter of the atmosphere contains a certain number of these water molecules. This number varies from time to time at any one place and from place to place at any given time. The mass or *weight* of these water molecules in a unit volume of the atmosphere is called the *humidity*. Sometimes we use the term *absolute* humidity to distinguish this from *relative* humidity. The humidity of the air may be 15 g/m^3 which means that the molecules of *water vapor alone* in 1 m^3 of that air weigh 15 g. The molecules of air also present in this cubic meter may weigh an additional 1,200 g.

Humidity may have any value from zero for perfectly dry air up to and including that of saturated vapor. In fact, under special conditions, the humidity of the atmosphere may at times even exceed the density of saturated vapor. In such a case, we speak of the air as *supersaturated*.

What Is Relative Humidity?

The atmosphere is usually not *fully* saturated with water vapor. Suppose, for example, that the humidity is measured and found to be 8.65 g/m³ when the air is at 20°C. Referring to Table 8–3, we see that saturated air at 20° has 17.3 g of water vapor per cubic meter. So, at the time of this test, the air is only $\frac{8.65}{17.3} \times 100\% = 50\%$ saturated. In other words, the *relative humidity* of the air at the time of the test is 50 percent.

Relative humidity =

$$\frac{\begin{array}{c}\text{density of water vapor} \\ \text{actually present in air}\end{array}}{\begin{array}{c}\text{density of water vapor} \\ \text{if air were saturated}\end{array}} \times 100\%$$

or

$$= \frac{\begin{array}{c}\text{pressure of water vapor} \\ \text{actually present in air}\end{array}}{\begin{array}{c}\text{pressure of water vapor} \\ \text{if air were saturated}\end{array}} \times 100\%$$

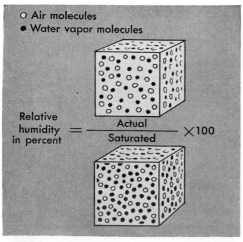

Importance of Relative Humidity

Relative humidity indicates the "dampness" of the air. The rate at which water evaporates is determined in part by the relative humidity of the surrounding atmosphere. With a high relative humidity, evaporation is slow, but with a low relative humidity, evaporation is much faster. It is chiefly for this reason that the relative humidity of the air in which we live has an important bearing on our health and comfort.

One way we lose heat from our bodies is through the evaporation of perspiration from the surface of our skin. The lower the relative humidity, the faster this evaporation and the faster we lose heat. The higher the relative humidity, the slower the evaporation and the slower we lose heat. On a warm humid day in summer, we may feel hot and uncomfortable, even though the actual temperature is not excessively high. "It's not the temperature, it's the humidity," is a common expression used to account for our discomfort when the relative humidity nears the 100 percent mark on a summer day. In winter, we bring cold air from outdoors and heat it for the rooms in which we live and work. Heating, in itself, does not change the *amount* of water vapor actually present in the air, but it does reduce the *relative humidity*. With the same amount of water vapor, the heated air is farther from saturation than the same cold air was. For this reason, water vapor generally has to be added to the heated air to bring its relative humidity up to a

Fig. 8–14. Relative humidity is the ratio of the actual amount of water per cubic meter of air to the amount per cubic meter necessary to produce saturation.

suitable value. This is why we have *humidifiers* in the hot-air furnaces used to heat our homes. It is also the reason for blowing steam into the heated air used in large buildings.

It has been found that a relative humidity of from 40 to 60 percent in heated rooms in winter is comfortable and healthful. If the humidity is too high, the air feels damp and clammy; if it is too low, it dries out the furniture as well as our skin. A low humidity in living quarters is supposed to contribute to the cause of colds and other respiratory diseases. A room with a low relative humidity in winter has to be kept several degrees warmer than one with moderate relative humidity, if the occupants are to feel comfortable, because the lower relative humidity speeds evaporation and cooling on our skin. Maintaining a suitable relative humidity is one way of saving fuel!

In many industries, such as the manufacture of paper and textile goods, it is essential that the relative humidity of the factory be maintained within proper limits at all times.

The Dew Point

Early in a quiet summer evening, drops of dew form on blades of grass and leaves of vegetation close to the earth. On a summer day, a glass of ice water soon acquires a film of minute water droplets on the outside. In winter, the window glass of an automobile often clouds over soon after occupants enter the car. In all these situations, warmer, moisture-laden air is cooled by contact with colder objects. When unsaturated air is cooled, it approaches its saturation point. When cooled below this point, some of its water vapor usually condenses into droplets of various sizes. *The temperature at which water begins to*

condense out of air is called the dew point. In all the cases cited above, the layer of air adjacent to the colder object is cooled to its dew point. The temperature of the dew point depends on the actual density of water vapor in the original air.

Determining Relative Humidity

The relative humidity of the air is determined with an instrument called a *hygrometer.* A common type of hygrometer consists of two ordinary thermometers, mounted side by side on the same frame. The bulb of one thermometer is dry, while that of the other thermometer is kept wet by means of a

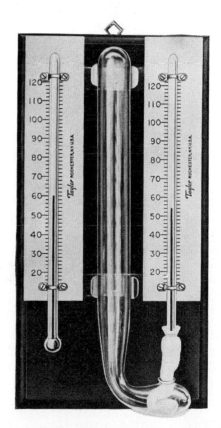

A wet- and dry-bulb type hygrometer used for determining relative humidity. (The Taylor Instrument Companies)

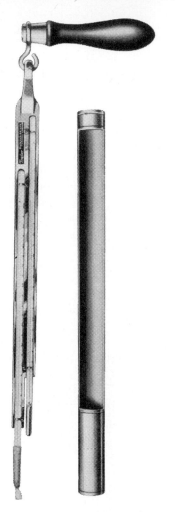

make sure that the layer of air next to the wet bulb is not more humid than the surrounding atmosphere in general, the wet-bulb thermometer is usually fanned for a few minutes before its reading is taken. After observing the readings of the two thermometers, we make use of a prepared chart or table to find the relative humidity. In one type of hygrometer, called a *sling psychrometer*, the two thermometers are whirled, mechanically or by hand, before the two readings are taken.

Another common type of hygrometer is based on the fact that a human hair tends to shorten as the relative humidity becomes less. Hairs for this purpose are first treated to remove the natural oil. A single hair or a bundle of hairs is arranged to move a pointer across a suitable dial as the hair changes length with relative humidity.

Condensation in the Atmosphere

When air is cooled to its dew point, water usually begins to condense out and the heat of vaporization is released to the surrounding air. Condensation may take one of several forms, depending on location and surrounding conditions. We shall now consider the most important forms of condensation in the atmosphere.

Clouds. Clouds consist of very small droplets of condensed water in suspension in the atmosphere above the earth. Some types of clouds are formed by bodies of warm, humid air rising and expanding in the regions of lower atmospheric pressure. When any gas expands without receiving heat from the outside, it cools. In this way, rising bodies of humid air cool below their dew point and clouds result. Other clouds are produced by the mixing of a mass of warm humid air with a colder one, causing the temperature of the warmer mass

A sling psychrometer, consisting of a wet-bulb and a dry-bulb thermometer, mounted together on a whirling frame, is also used for determining relative humidity. *(The Taylor Instrument Companies)*

cotton wick which dips into a reservoir of water. As water evaporates from the wick, the bulb is cooled and the thermometer reading drops. How far the wet-bulb thermometer reading falls below that of the dry-bulb thermometer depends on the rate of evaporation, which in turn depends on the relative humidity of the surrounding air. To

210

to fall below its dew point. Clouds take many interesting forms. The four main types are called *cirrus, stratus, cumulus,* and *nimbus.* Sometimes clouds consist of ice particles.

Fog. A fog is a cloud very close to the earth. It is usually formed by a quiet layer of humid air settling down on a cold surface layer near the earth, or by the layer close to the earth losing its heat by radiation. Occasionally a fog, too, consists of small ice particles rather than droplets of water.

Dew. In spring and summer, vegetation and other objects close to the earth lose heat by radiation very rapidly after sundown. On still nights, the layer of air in contact with these colder objects becomes chilled below its dew point and condensation in the form of dew is deposited on their surfaces. There is less likelihood of dew on a windy night, because the same air does not remain in contact with vegetation long enough to become chilled to its dew point. Contrary to the words of the poet, dew does not "fall," but forms directly on the surface where it is deposited.

Frost. Hoar or "white" frost is formed when air, whose dew point is 0°C or below, is cooled to this temperature by contact with objects close to the surface of the earth. White frost is not frozen dew.

Rain. When cooling and condensation occur very rapidly throughout a large body of upper air, many of the drops formed are too large to remain in suspension and fall as rain.

Hail. During thunderstorms, raindrops are sometimes caught by churning air currents and carried upward to colder regions where they freeze to ice. As they fall again through the warmer, humid cloud, they perhaps melt a little and collect additional condensation. If they are again whirled upward to the colder region, the freezing is repeated and the hailstone thus grows larger. This action may be repeated many times, resulting in concentric layers of ice about the core of the hailstone.

Sleet. Rain that freezes on the way down falls as sleet.

Snow. If the dew point in a mass of rising air is 0°C or below, snow crystals rather than water drops are formed when the temperature falls below this point.

Rain, hail, sleet, and snow are different forms of *precipitation.* Sometimes dew and frost also are considered forms of precipitation.

Droplets of condensation nearly always form around minute dust particles as nuclei. These finely divided particles seem to be sufficiently abundant in the air at all times.

Rainmaking

Can you imagine how convenient it might be for a farmer or a gardener if he could call up the local weather service and order a nice shower of rain over his fields when his crops need water? Picnickers and baseball fans in the neighborhood, however, might not appreciate

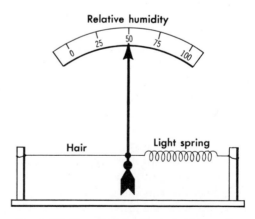

Fig. 8–15. The principle of a hair hygrometer.

the rain so much at the moment! Even though we can do very little to change the weather, nevertheless meteorologists and others have done considerable experimenting and have reported some success with rainmaking. The presence of heavy clouds or masses of moisture-laden (high humidity) air over the area seems to be necessary for a successful attempt at causing rain. Pellets of Dry Ice or other cooling agent are sprayed from an airplane into the mass of humid air. This may cool the air in the "seeded" cloud to its dew point or below. In some cases water condenses fast enough to form drops which fall as a shower of rain. Considerably more information and knowledge about clouds and the formation of rain are needed before this method of rainmaking becomes a reliable method of watering crops. If you continue with your work in physics you may be able to help solve this knotty problem of rainmaking.

►Do You Know?

1. In blossom time, fruit growers say there will be no frost as long as the dew point is well above 32°F. Why is this true?
2. Do you know of any local manufacturing processes in which the control of humidity is important? What are they?
3. What causes windows and walls to "sweat" in cold weather? How is "sweating" avoided?
4. What is a *hydrodeik?* How is it used?
5. How many "points" has a snowflake crystal?
6. If scientists ever succeed in fully solving the problem of rainmaking, what other problems do you think will arise from this discovery?
7. What weather proverbs do people in your community repeat? Discuss the

possible scientific basis for these proverbs. Weather proverbs that have survived for centuries are almost always based partly on facts. Why?

REFRIGERATION

We have already seen that we must remove heat energy from a body to lower its temperature. This is the fundamental principle involved in all methods of refrigeration. We have mentioned that a mixture of pulverized ice and salt will serve as a *freezing mixture* and produce a temperature below 0°C. The salt causes the ice to melt. The melting ice must get its heat of fusion largely from the remaining ice and from the surrounding ice water. The temperature of the entire mixture is thus lowered by the melting ice. How far the temperature can be lowered depends on the ratio of salt to ice in the mixture. The most effective proportions seem to be 1 part of salt to 3 parts of pulverized ice or snow. With this mixture, a temperature of about −21°C can be reached. Other substances may be used with ice for freezing mixtures. With 10 parts of calcium chloride to 7 parts of snow, a temperature of about −55°C can be reached. This is more than cold enough to freeze mercury solid. Gas from Dry Ice, solid carbon dioxide, bubbling in ether will produce a temperature of about −77°C.

A freezing mixture of salt and ice is used in making ice cream and other frozen food. Salt and calcium chloride are sometimes scattered on icy streets and sidewalks to lower the melting point to remove the ice.

A mechanical refrigerator of the type used in homes consists of four essential parts—the compressor, the radiator or condenser, the expansion valve, and the cooling coils. The compressor and the radiator must be outside the refrigeration compartment, while the expansion valve and the cooling coils form the freezing unit inside. A liquid with a low boiling point, so that it is easily condensed, is used for the refrigerant. Sulfur dioxide and a number of specially prepared organic liquids have been found well suited for refrigerants.

Gas from the evaporated refrigerant is taken in by the compressor and compressed. This heats the gas. The gas then passes into the radiator, where it is cooled and where it loses its heat of vaporization so that it changes into a liquid. From the radiator, the liquid under pressure goes to the expansion valve. Here it is sprayed through a needle-like opening into the cooling coils where the pressure is relatively low. The small droplets of liquid quickly evaporate and the gas expands. The heat of vaporization, as well as that required for expansion of the gas, comes from the space surrounding the cooling coils. This is how the inside of the refrigerator box and its contents are cooled. The expanded gas passes back into the compressor and the cycle is ready to start over again. These operations proceed continuously as long as the compressor runs. In effect, the compressor, through the agency of the refrigerant, takes heat from inside the refrigerator compartment and delivers it to the air outside the radiator, just as a vacuum pump takes air from a bell jar and delivers it to the atmosphere.

Deep-freeze units and home freezers work on the same general principle as mechanical refrigerators. One type of home refrigerator operates entirely from gas and has no mechanical pump or moving parts. Artificial-ice and cold-storage plants use refrigerating machines similar in principle to the mechanical type de-

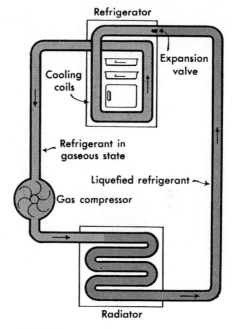

Fig. 8–16. The principle of a mechanical refrigerator.

signed for homes. In many industrial refrigeration plants, ammonia is used as the refrigerant. In some cases the evaporating liquid cools a surrounding brine solution, which in turn is pumped through pipes to the ice-freezing unit or the cold-storage room.

►**Do You Know?**

1. What is the advantage of stirring ice cream as it is freezing?
2. What are the names of some of the refrigerants used in modern home refrigerators?
3. Why do persons who work with liquid air have to take precautions against "burns"?
4. What are the four essential parts of a mechanical refrigerator? What function does each part serve?
5. Name three types of precipitation. Explain the conditions under which each form of precipitation occurs.

213

HIGHLIGHTS

Temperature is only one of several factors that determine the heat of any object.

A *calorie* is the amount of heat required to change the temperature of one gram of water one centigrade degree.

A *British thermal unit* (Btu) is the amount of heat required to change the temperature of one pound of water one Fahrenheit degree.

The *specific heat* of a substance is the number of calories required to change the temperature of one gram of the substance one centigrade degree. The specific heat of water is 1.

In melting, 1 g of ice must receive about 80 cal of heat that does not affect its temperature at all. This 80 cal/g is called the *heat of fusion* of water.

Crystalline substances have definite melting points and heats of fusion, while *amorphous substances* do not.

Water expands about 9 percent in volume as it freezes.

The melting point of ice is lowered by pressures less than about 2,000 atmospheres.

The rate of evaporation depends on temperature, surface area, rate of removal of escaped molecules, pressure, and nature of the liquid.

The heat of vaporization of a substance is the amount of heat required to convert one gram of that substance from a liquid to a gas without a change in temperature.

The heat of vaporization of water is 540 cal/g at the normal boiling point, but a little greater when vaporization occurs at a lower temperature.

The boiling point of a liquid is the temperature at which its internal vapor pressure just equals the atmospheric pressure on its surface.

The temperature of a gas must be below the *critical temperature* for that gas before the gas can be liquefied by compression alone.

Relative humidity is $\dfrac{\text{density of water vapor actually present in the air}}{\text{density of water vapor if air were saturated}} \times 100\%$.

The dew point is the temperature to which air must be cooled before condensation begins.

PROBLEMS: GROUP A

1. How many calories are required to heat 1 kg of water from 20 to 80°C?
2. How many Btu's are required to heat 2 lb of water from 40 to 160°F?
3. When 500 g of water cools from 50 to 0°C, how many calories are given up by this water? How many kilocalories are released in this change?

4. How many calories are required to heat a 2-kg block of aluminum from 20 to 200°C?
5. How many calories are released when 100 kg of ice water turns to ice?
6. How many calories are required to melt 22 lb (10 kg) of ice at 0°C?
7. How many calories are required to con-

214

vert 50 g of water into steam by boiling? (Pressure = 1 atmosphere.)

8. If the dew point in a room whose temperature is 25°C is found to be 10°C what is the relative humidity in that room?

9. How many calories of heat are required to heat a 2-kg aluminum kettle from 20 to 98°C?

10. An aluminum calorimeter cup weighs 50 g. How many calories of heat are required to raise the temperature of this cup 1 centigrade degree? This amount of heat is called the *water equivalent* of the calorimeter cup.

11. How many calories of heat are given off when 1 liter of water at 25°C cools to such an extent that one-fourth of the water freezes to ice?

12. How many calories of heat are released when 100 g of mercury changes from a liquid state to a solid state at the freezing temperature of mercury, which is −39°C?

13. How many calories of heat are required to melt 50 g of sulfur at its melting temperature of 119°C?

14. If the dew point of air is 5°C when the actual temperature of the air is 25°C, what is the relative humidity of this air?

15. If the dew point of air is 10°C, how many grams of water vapor are present in 25 m³ of this air? What is the pressure due to the actual water vapor in the air?

16. If the dew point is 0°C and the air temperature is 20°C, what is the relative humidity?

GROUP B

1. When a gallon of water (8.3 lb) cools from 210 to 32°F, how many Btu's are released?

2. How many Btu's are required to heat a 5-lb laundry iron from 60 to 215°F?

3. How many calories are required to melt 5 kg of snow and heat the snow water to 50°C?

4. When 2,000 g of steam at 100°C condense in a radiator and the resulting water cools to 80°C before leaving the radiator, how much heat is released?

5. If three melting ice cubes of 25 g each are dropped into 1 kg of water whose temperature is 80°C, what will be the final temperature of the water when the ice is all melted? Assume that the water is well stirred.

6. How much heat is released by 1 g of steam whose original temperature is 120°C when it has passed through all the changes necessary to convert it to a gram of ice with a temperature of −25°C? Take the specific heat of steam under these conditions as 0.48 and that of ice as 0.50.

7. If 500 g of water at 50°C is mixed with 100 g of water whose temperature is 10°C, what is the resulting temperature of the mixture?

8. If the relative humidity is 50 percent on a day when the temperature is 25°C, how many grams of water are present in each cubic meter of the air? What is the pressure due to the actual water vapor in the air at this time?

9. If the relative humidity is 40 percent when the air temperature is 20°C, what is the dew point?

10. If the relative humidity is 70 percent when the air temperature is 25°C, what is the dew point?

11. How many Btu's of heat are released when 50 lb of water at 32°F changes to ice?

12. How many Btu's of heat are released

when steam at 212°F condenses to form 50 lb of water at the same temperature?

13. If a 10-kg block of ice at 0°C is placed in 100 kg of water at 80°C, what will be the temperature of the mixture when all of the ice has melted? Assume that no heat enters or escapes from the water from outside.

14. How many Btu's of heat are required to heat a 2-lb iron frying pan from 60 to 250°F?

15. A 50-g iron ball is placed in a furnace until it reaches the same temperature as the furnace. The ball is then quickly removed and dropped into water in a calorimeter. If the total equivalent of water and calorimeter is 200 g of water, and the temperature of the water rises from 20 to 30°C when the water and ball reach the same temperature, what is the temperature of the furnace?

16. In an experiment, live steam is blown through 100 g of water whose temperature at the start is 10°C. Some of the steam condenses and gives up its heat of vaporization to the water. Suppose that the temperature of the water rises to 40°C when 5 g of steam has condensed. Compute the heat of vaporization of water from these data. Assume that no heat enters or escapes from the water from outside.

THINGS TO DO

1. Obtain a block of ice and pass a wire through it without breaking it. See Fig. 8–7. The action is speeded if heavy weights and small wire are used. Explain results. Would this experiment work better in warm weather or cold weather?

2. Place drops of ink and ice cubes in cold water in a glass and dry the outside of the glass. Set the glass in a warm humid place until beads of moisture form on the outside. Wipe off some of this mois-ture with a piece of cleansing tissue or with your handkerchief. Do you find any color of ink on the cleansing tissue? Explain.

3. Obtain a canvas water bag or a porous cup (without glazing). Put water at room temperature in the bag or cup and read a thermometer placed in the water. Set the bag or cup in the stream of air from an electric fan. Read the thermometer from time to time. Explain results.

9.

Transfer of Heat:
Methods of Transfer

CONDUCTION OF HEAT

If you hold a short piece of iron rod in the flame of a bunsen burner you will soon discover that the end in your hand gets heat energy from the flame. In this case, the iron rod *conducts* heat and we speak of the process as *conduction*. If you hold your hand above a hot stove or radiator you can often feel a stream of warm air rising past your hand. This air carries heat energy from the stove to remote parts of the room. We speak of this process as *convection*. If you stand in a cold room in front of an open fire you can feel the heat from the fire, even though the air itself remains cold. In this case, heat energy is transferred from the fire to you by still a different process, called *radiation*. We shall now explore how these three processes—conduction, convection, and radiation—play an important part in your daily living.

Some Good Conductors of Heat

Conduction can take place only through matter, that is, only when particles are present. Experiments show that conduction does not occur through a vacuum. Not all forms of matter are equally good conductors of heat. Many solids, especially the metals, are good conductors; liquids and gases, in general, are poor conductors.

The metals are not all equally good conductors of heat. This can be shown

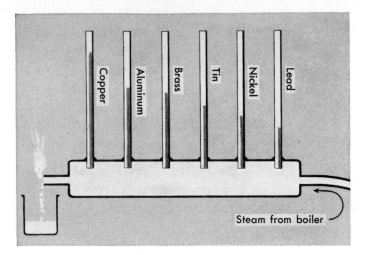

Fig. 9–1. Copper is the best conductor of heat in this group of metals.

Steam from boiler

with the apparatus illustrated in Fig. 9–1, in which rods of different metals are pushed through stoppers into a metal box. Steam from a boiler is passed through this box. The rods are all coated with a special paint which is *red* at room temperature but changes to *gray* at

Table 9–1. Thermal Conductivities of Some Metals

[Calories transmitted per second through a plate 1 cm² in area and 1 cm thick when the difference in temperature is 1 centigrade degree.]

Material	Conductivity
Silver	1.006
Copper	0.918
Gold	0.700
Aluminum	0.480
Zinc	0.265
Brass	0.260
Iron	0.161
Tin	0.155
Nickel	0.142
Lead	0.083

about 72°C. As heat is conducted from the steam along the rod, the gray band extends farther and farther up the rod. In Fig. 9–1, it can be seen that the gray band is longest on the copper rod and shortest on the lead rod. This indicates that copper is the best conductor of heat in this set of metals and lead the poorest.

Accurate measurements show that some of the better-known metals rank as heat conductors, as shown in Table 9–1. The number in the second column is the value that has been found for the *thermal conductivity* of the metal. Thermal conductivity refers to the rate at which the metal can conduct heat. We may use this number to compute the *relative* heat-conducting ability of any two metals. For example, the thermal conductivity of silver (from the table) is 1.006, while that of aluminum is 0.480. We may then say that silver is 1.006/0.480 or 2.1 times as good a conductor of heat as aluminum. In the same way, aluminum is 0.480/0.161 or 3 times as good a conductor of heat as iron.

If a device or appliance is to conduct heat quickly and effectively, it must be made of good heat-conducting material.

For this reason, cooking utensils, stoves, laundry irons, soldering irons, and the fins of radiators are made of metals which are good conductors. A wire screen, often used by chemistry students when they want to boil water in a glass beaker, is a good conductor of heat. This is why the screen can transfer heat quickly from the hottest part of the flame to the outer cooler parts. The whole bottom of the beaker is thus heated almost uniformly and the danger of cracking it is reduced.

Thermal Insulators

Almost all other materials are poorer conductors of heat than the metals. Under ordinary conditions, many materials conduct so slowly that relatively little heat passes through them in a given time. Such materials are called *thermal insulators*. The thermal conductivities of a few materials which are *very poor conductors* or *very good insulators* are shown in Table 9–2. From this table, the thermal conductivity of paper is 0.0003 while that of window glass is 0.0025. Hence, under similar conditions, window glass is 0.0025/0.0003, or 8.3 times as *good a conductor* of heat as paper. We may also say that paper is 8.3 times as *good a thermal insulator* as window glass.

Thermal insulators are used whenever we wish to retard the transfer of heat. For this reason materials such as asbestos paper and asbestos fiber are used extensively to cover steam, hot-water, and hot-air pipes. Insulating material is placed in the walls of houses and other buildings to reduce the rate of transfer of heat through them. Cork or some similar material is placed in the walls of refrigerator boxes to provide thermal insulation. The handles of cooking utensils are commonly made of insulating material to prevent them from becoming too hot to touch. A blanket of snow pro-

Table 9–2. Thermal Conductivities of Some Good Insulators

[Calories transmitted per second through a plate 1 cm² in area and 1 cm thick when the difference in temperature is 1 centigrade degree.]

Material	Conductivity
Ice	0.0022–0.005
Glass (window)	0.0025
Water at 20°C	0.00143
Asbestos paper	0.0006
Snow (compact)	0.0005
Leather (cowhide)	0.00042
Soil (dry)	0.00033
Paper	0.0003
Asbestos fiber	0.00019
Cork	0.00013–0.00072
Sawdust	0.00012
Silk	0.000095
Felt (wool)	0.000087
Air at 0°C	0.0000568

tects grass roots and other vegetation from damage during very cold weather because snow is a good thermal insulator. In localities where sawdust is plentiful and inexpensive, the walls of storage houses for natural ice are sometimes

Some modern cooking utensils are made with copper bottoms. Copper is one of the best conductors of heat. (*Revere Ware, Revere Copper and Brass, Inc.*)

219

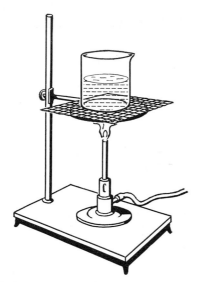

Fig. 9–2. A wire screen used over a bunsen flame to protect the glass beaker.

Heat Conduction through Glass

Have you any idea how fast heat will escape by conduction through a window-pane? You would quite naturally expect that the amount of heat that gets through in a minute would depend on the area of the pane and its thickness. You may realize that the amount of heat that escapes also depends on the difference in temperature between the two sides of the pane. *More heat will pass through a windowpane in a minute when* (1) the area of the pane is greater, (2) the thickness of the pane is less, (3) the thermal conductivity of the glass is higher, and (4) the difference in temperature between the inside and the outside face of the glass is greater.

Calculations show that more than 1000 calories will escape each minute by conduction through a windowpane which is ⅛ in. thick, 10 in. wide, and 12 in. long, when the inside of the glass is 5 Fahrenheit degrees warmer than the outside.

filled with sawdust. Ice may be stored in sawdust for extended periods at temperatures above the freezing point of water. What are some of the reasons why sawdust is an excellent thermal insulator?

Fiberglas insulating form boards being placed in the roof of a school building. Gypsum was later poured over these form boards to provide an economical, lightweight, noncombustible roof which has low heat transmission and excellent sound absorption.

Some Poor Conductors

Table 9–2 indicates that both water and air are very poor conductors of heat. Most gases are even poorer conductors than air and many of the common liquids are poorer conductors than water. In many cases, the transfer of heat through a fluid involves both conduction and convection, so that it is not always easy to separate one effect from the other. We can demonstrate that water is a poor conductor by means of the simple apparatus shown in Fig. 9–3. A piece of ice of suitable size is placed in a test tube and held at the bottom by a coiled spring that fits snugly inside the tube. The tube is then filled with water and held over a bunsen burner so that the flame strikes the tube above the ice level. The water can be boiled without melting the ice, showing that relatively little heat is conducted downward through the water. The very poor conducting ability of water explains *in part* why the water in a deep lake does not become uniformly heated during a hot summer.

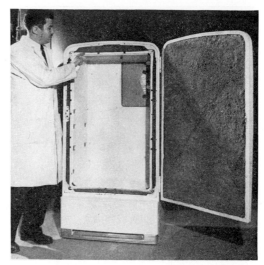

The dark material on the back of the door and between the walls of this refrigerator is plastic foam insulation. This material is designed to prevent the passage of heat through the walls of the refrigerator. (*Westinghouse Electric Corporation*)

How Heat Is Conducted

Recall from the kinetic theory that matter is made up of atoms and molecules and that these particles are in continu-

Large store and office windows are usually made of very thick glass for strength. This thick glass also reduces the rate of heat conduction through the windows. Sometimes such windows are made of several sheets of glass with dead air spaces between them to reduce the rate of conduction. In such windows, radiation is the chief method of heat transfer.

221

Fig. 9–3. The water in the test tube may be boiled without melting the ice.

With this picture in mind, it is easy to understand why solids, whose particles are relatively close together, should be better heat conductors than liquids and gases, whose particles are farther apart and less likely to collide. This picture also suggests why porous solids with many air cells or pockets should be good insulators.

You would think it strange if you were to see a ball rolling uphill without any help from outside. It would be equally strange to find heat energy moving from a place of lower temperature to one of higher temperature, without outside help. The natural highways for heat are all one-way.

Heat energy moves from regions of higher temperature to regions of lower temperature.

ous motion. The higher the temperature of a given body, the greater the average speed of its particles. Neighboring particles collide frequently and rebound one from the other. When a faster-moving particle collides head-on with a slower-moving neighbor, the neighbor rebounds with the greater speed. This is similar to what happens when a faster-moving billiard ball collides head-on with a slower-moving or stationary one. In such a collision, kinetic energy is passed along from one ball to the other. In the same way, collisions of the faster-moving particles in the hotter part of a metal rod with their slower-moving neighbors speed up these neighbors. The newly speeded-up particles in turn collide with their slower-moving neighbors farther along the rod and speed them up also. In this way increased particle speed and, hence, heat energy is passed along from particle to particle from the hot end of the rod toward the cooler end.

222

▶Do You Know?

1. Are there any advantages in a *copper* bottom on a teakettle? What are they?
2. A package of ice cream wrapped in heavy paper does not melt as rapidly as an unwrapped one. Why?
3. Persons who work on cold concrete floors often stand on pads of paper or similar material. What are the advantages of the pads?
4. Will insulating material placed in the walls of a building keep out heat in the summer? Explain.
5. Sometimes windowpanes are made of two sheets of glass cemented together with a "dead" air space between them. What is the purpose of this type of construction?
6. Why does relatively little heat escape by *conduction* from the filament of an electric lamp?
7. What are the advantages of insulating the walls of the oven of a cooking stove? What materials are suitable

for this insulation? What thermal insulator cannot be used?

8. What are the advantages of making the tip of a soldering iron of copper?

9. A silver teaspoon placed in a drinking glass before boiling water is poured into the glass is said to prevent it from cracking. What is the scientific basis for this statement?

10. It was said of a certain king that he was probably never served a really hot meal. His dishes and table service were made of pure gold. Could this fact account for his cold food? How?

11. How is convection avoided in the experiment shown in Fig. 9–3?

12. What is the principle of the Davy safety lamp once used by miners?

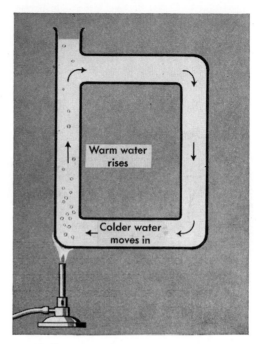

Fig. 9–4. Tracing convection currents in water.

CONVECTION OF HEAT

Convection is another important method by which heat energy is transferred from one place to another.

We can trace the progress of a *convection* current in water in the apparatus shown in Fig. 9–4. A glass tube, bent in the form of a rectangle, is filled with water through the opening at the top. A few crystals of potassium permanganate are dropped in through the same opening while the tube is held so that the crystals fall directly down to the bottom of the tube. The glass tube is then heated with a bunsen burner. As the crystals dissolve, they color the water purple and make it easy to see the flow of the convection current around the tube.

Convection Currents in Air

We can watch the progress of the convection currents in air in the apparatus shown in Fig. 9–5. Suppose we

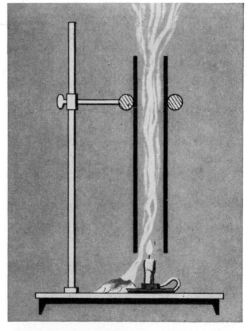

Fig. 9–5. Tracing convection currents in air. Smoke acts as the tracer.

A sailplane in flight. Sailplanes soar on thermals and rising air currents without using engines. A record flight of 227 miles has been made with a sailplane of the type shown. Altitudes over 30,000 ft have been reached. The top cruising speed is about 75 mph. (*Schweizer Aircraft Corporation*)

set a lighted candle directly under the lower end of the glass tube. Then let us put a piece of thin cotton cloth (cheesecloth) near the candle and light the cloth so that it burns slowly. Smoke from the burning cloth can be seen carried up the glass tube by the convection current that rises above the candle flame.

This experiment illustrates the principle that is chiefly responsible for the *natural* draft in chimneys and smokestacks. The furnaces in some factories have *forced* draft; motor-driven fans built into the bases of the smokestacks force the smoke and fumes up the stack and thus provide draft for the furnaces. Is forced draft commonly used in chimneys of home heating systems?

Can We See Heat?

We can sometimes see a wavy pulsating pattern in the air above a hot stove. A similar effect often appears over metal roofs, railroad tracks, pavements, and even rocks and sand on hot calm sunny days in summer. Many people who see these wavy patterns mistakenly believe that they are "seeing heat." In reality, this wavelike appearance is only one of the *effects* of convection currents. The rising currents cause irregular layers of different densities to form in the air. Rays of light coming from objects beyond the rising air are bent slightly more in passing through the denser layers than in passing through the less dense ones.

This causes a wavy appearance in objects viewed through the rising air, in the same way that a windowpane of irregular thickness causes a wavy distortion of objects seen through it.

Causes of Convection Currents

When a portion of a liquid or a gas is heated, that portion generally expands and becomes less dense. A less dense portion within a body of fluid may be thought of as displacing its own volume of the surrounding more dense fluid. In accordance with Archimedes' principle, the less dense portion will then tend to rise and float on the more dense part. Hence, when a body of liquid or gas is heated so that some parts get hotter than others, the hotter portions tend to rise and the cooler portions tend to settle downward, thus setting up currents.

Convection currents bring about the transference of heat by the circulation or movement of the heated parts of a liquid or a gas.

Convection Currents Heat Houses

Convection currents are commonly used in hot-air heating systems in houses and other buildings. Figure 9–6 shows the path of a convection current of heated air from the furnace through the hot-air pipe to the room of a house. The returning current of cold air through its pipe back to the furnace is also shown. The return pipe must be properly installed for most efficient operation. Sometimes the return pipe is omitted entirely. In this case, the heated air must be allowed to escape after it reaches the room and is cooled. Cold air must flow into the furnace from the basement or

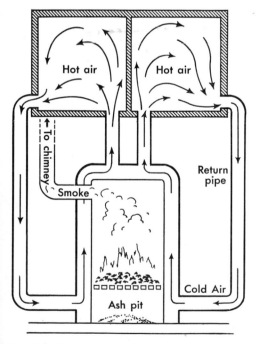

Fig. 9–6. How a house is heated by convection currents from a hot-air furnace.

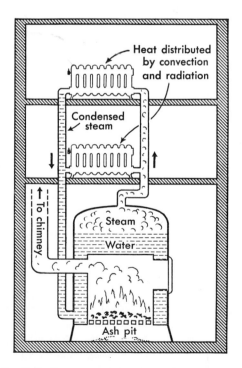

Fig. 9–7. How a steam-heating system operates.

225

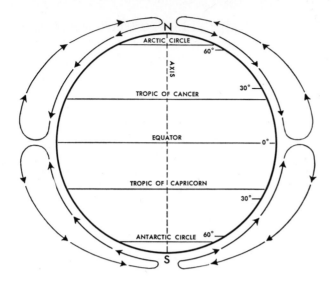

Fig. 9–8. Convection currents in the atmosphere would be like this if the surface temperature of the earth increased at a uniform rate from the poles to the equator and if the earth did not rotate on its axis.

from outside. Some hot-air heating systems do not rely on convection alone but use a motor-driven fan to force the heated air up the hot-air pipes or ducts.

Some home heating systems use steam or hot water to transfer heat from the furnace to the rooms. The experiment on convection currents in water demonstrates the principle of such systems.

Figure 9–7 shows the plan of a steam-heating system installed in a house.

Why Winds Blow

We know that the earth's surface and the adjacent layer of atmosphere are hotter in regions near the equator than at either pole. If we consider this fact alone, we would at first expect to find a huge

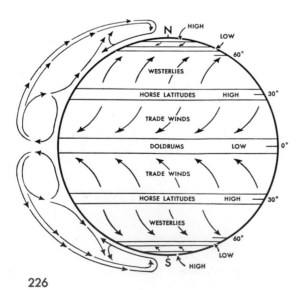

Fig. 9–9. Wind belts and belts of permanently high and low pressure. Arrows indicate directions of principal winds. Highly diagrammatic; actually the belts shift north and south with the seasons, and their positions are modified by the continents. (From Fundamentals of Physical Science, Krauskopf, McGraw-Hill, 1953)

convection system in the earth's atmosphere. In this pattern there would be a general upflow of warm air in regions near the equator. This rising air would expand, cool, and spread out at high altitudes toward the poles. It would settle down over the polar regions, from which it would return along the surface to the equatorial region. Thus we who live in the northern hemisphere would have a constant wind from the north, while people in the southern hemisphere would have a corresponding wind from the south.

Three major factors operate to modify the simple atmospheric convection pattern of air currents over the earth: (1) The rotation of the earth on its axis deflects the surface air currents, (2) the water and land areas of the earth do not heat (or cool) at the same rate, and (3) local topographical features such as mountains, hills, valleys, plains, and deserts result in unequal heating of land areas, even though these areas may be the same distance from the equator.

In addition to these permanent factors temporary and purely local conditions cause modifications in the surface winds.

▶**Do You Know?**

1. Chimneys do not work well when cold and damp. Why?
2. Chimneys sometimes draw better on windy days. Why?
3. What are meant by doldrums, horse latitudes, and prevailing westerlies?
4. Certain well-defined currents that flow through the oceans are probably caused in part by convection. Find the names of several of these currents and trace their approximate paths.
5. What is the basic reason why winds blow? What may cause wind to change in direction suddenly?

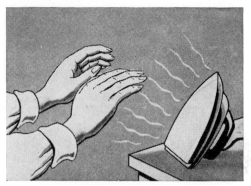

Fig. 9–10. Radiation from the hot laundry iron is absorbed by the hands and becomes heat.

RADIATION OF HEAT

Conduction and *convection* are processes which transfer heat energy at slow speeds over relatively short distances. *Radiation* is a high-speed process which may transfer heat energy over great distances.

Any source of heat, such as the sun, a hot laundry iron, or even a pan of hot water, is constantly changing ordinary heat energy into a new form, called *radiant energy*. Visible light is also a form of radiant energy, but we are interested at this point in the invisible kind called *infrared radiation*. Infrared rays cause heat and make up most of the radiant energy from bodies not hot enough to glow with visible light.

Radiant energy has special properties that enable it to break away from its place of origin and speed onward through space. When it encounters a body of matter, such as the hand in Fig. 9–10, part of the energy is stopped or *absorbed* by the matter. When radiant energy is absorbed, it is converted back into ordinary heat (movement of molecules) again and raises the temperature of the absorbing body. It is for this reason that you feel warm when rays from the sun strike you.

227

Rate of Heat Radiation

Ordinary heat is changed into radiant energy chiefly at the *surface* of a hot body. Three major factors determine how much heat is changed over in 1 sec: (1) The area of the radiating surface. The number of calories radiated per second is doubled when the radiating surface is made twice as great and other conditions are kept the same: the rate of radiating heat is directly proportional to the area of the radiating surface. (2) The temperature of the radiating surface. The rate of radiating increases with an increase in temperature. (3) The nature of the radiating surface. Some kinds of surfaces are much better radiators than others.

Good Radiators

Study the apparatus shown in Fig. 9–11. The essential part is a hollow metal cube, each of whose six faces has a different kind of surface. One is rough black, another is polished copper, a third

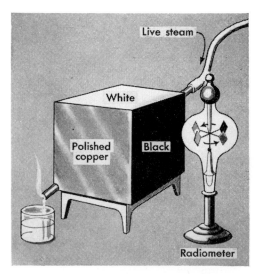

Fig. 9–11. Different kinds of surfaces have different abilities to radiate heat.

is painted smooth white, and so on. Steam from the boiler passes through the hollow cube and heats all the surfaces to the same temperature. Radiation from the faces may be detected by means of a *radiometer*, a device which consists of four small well-balanced vanes in the form of a cross, mounted in a glass bulb from which part of the air has been removed. Radiant energy falling on the vanes causes them to rotate; the more energy per second the vanes receive, the faster they move. If we set the radiometer close to the cube and at the same distance from each face in turn, we can see that the vanes move faster when opposite some faces than when opposite others. This indicates that the faces have different radiating abilities. From this experiment, we can usually show that (1) rough surfaces are better radiators than smooth ones, (2) black surfaces are better radiators than white ones, and (3) highly polished mirrorlike surfaces are very poor radiators.

Uses for Good Radiators

In situations where we wish to lose heat energy rapidly, large surfaces with good radiating properties are employed. A steam or hot-water radiator in a heating system is designed to have as much surface as practicable and its surface is usually rough. From the standpoint of radiating efficiency, it would probably be better not to paint the radiator, or at least to paint it black, but other considerations usually induce us to paint it a color which blends with its surroundings. The radiators in the cooling systems of gasoline and other internal combustion engines are constructed with fins to increase the radiating area and are usually designed with good radiating surfaces.

Uses for Poor Radiators

Poor radiators are used in situations where we wish to retard the loss of heat. A well-known example of this use occurs in the Thermos or vacuum bottle, whose construction is shown in Fig. 9–12. The bottle has double glass or steel walls with a vacuum space between. Removing the air from the space between the walls blocks the transfer of heat by convection. Losses by conduction can occur only at the neck of the bottle where the two walls join, and through the stopper. Silvering the inside walls makes them very poor radiators. By these means, the transfer of heat through the walls is reduced to a minimum and the bottle will keep liquids hot or cold for many hours.

One type of building paper designed for thermal insulation in the walls of a building has a shiny metallic surface. It is claimed to be very effective in preventing the escape of heat by radiation.

Speed of Radiant Energy

We have mentioned that radiant energy breaks loose from the radiator and travels rapidly away through space. All forms of radiant energy have been found to travel through space with the same speed. This speed has been measured experimentally and found to be about 186,000 miles/sec, or 3×10^{10} cm/sec. The speed through the atmosphere is only slightly less than that through empty space. This is such a tremendous speed compared with those with which we ordinarily deal that we have difficulty in imagining it. The sun is some 93 million miles from the earth. Infrared radiation, which produces heat, reaches us just a little more than 8 min after it leaves the sun. If radiation could follow such a route, it would pass completely around the earth about 7½ times

in 1 *second*. You can see that the length of time required for infrared radiation from a fireplace to reach the most remote corner of a room which it heats is so small that it is negligible for all practical purposes.

Infrared Shadows

Infrared radiation travels along straight-line paths called rays. It does not bend around corners readily, and in this respect it differs from convection and conduction, which have little difficulty following winding routes. For this reason, objects in the path of infrared rays cast shadows, just as they do with visible light. Of course, the infrared shadows are invisible. You can easily detect the shadow cast by a piece of paper or other screen held between an open fire and your face. With the screen in place, you no longer feel the radiant heat from the fire on your face.

Infrared rays can be focused by a lens and reflected by a mirror just as visible

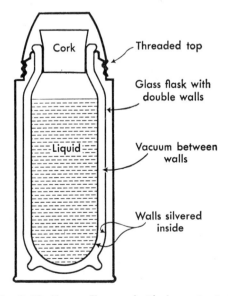

Fig. 9–12. How a Thermos bottle is constructed.

Cork

Threaded top

Glass flask with double walls

Liquid

Vacuum between walls

Walls silvered inside

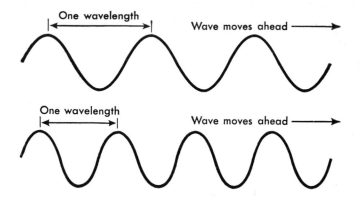

Fig. 9–13. A wavelength in one wave may differ from a wavelength in another wave.

light rays can. These effects will be considered in a later unit when we study light.

Infrared Wavelengths

Waves and wavelengths have become commonplace ideas in this age of radio. However, we often fail to recognize that these same ideas and terms belong to infrared radiation, too. In common with radio, infrared and visible light act like waves as they travel through space. Figure 9–13 shows a simple wave and indicates what is meant by a *wavelength*. Wavelengths may be expressed in any convenient units of length, but the metric units, such as meter and centimeter, are generally used for this purpose.

Infrared rays are shorter in wavelength than the shortest radio wave, and longer than the longest wavelengths of visible light, the ones that produce the color red. Figure 9–14 shows radio, infrared, and visible light arranged according to wavelengths. Such an arrangement is called a *spectrum*. The shortest infrared waves are radiated mostly by very hot bodies, and the longer ones by cooler bodies. For example, a hot glowing piece of iron radiates strongly the wavelengths just beyond visible light, while a piece of iron that is just warm to the touch

230

radiates chiefly the longer infrared waves.

Good Absorbers

The principal method of detecting radiant energy is by intercepting and absorbing it. But not all of the radiant energy that strikes a body is necessarily absorbed. When radiation falls on a body, any one or more of three possibilities may occur: (1) The rays may be reflected by the body as a mirror reflects light, (2) the rays may pass right on through the body, and (3) the rays may be absorbed by the body. Usually several of these processes occur together. For example, a part of the radiation from the sun may be reflected by a sheet of paper, a part may possibly pass through the sheet, and still another part may be absorbed and reconverted into ordinary heat. With a better absorber, a larger share of the energy that falls on the body is absorbed and converted into ordinary heat. Absorption may occur at the surface or in the interior of a body. Rays with longer wavelengths are more likely to be absorbed at the surface, while the shorter wavelengths penetrate deeper into the body before they are reconverted to heat.

Surfaces that are good radiators are

likewise good absorbers. So, as a rule, a rough surface is a better absorber than a smooth one, a black surface better than a white one. Good reflectors are poor absorbers since a greater part of the energy that falls on the surface is reflected and little is left to be absorbed. Shiny polished surfaces do not absorb well.

Suppose we place a piece of black cloth and a piece of white cloth side by side on snow in strong winter sunlight. After an hour or so we may find that considerable snow has melted under the black cloth while almost none at all has melted under the white one. A thermometer would indicate that the black cloth becomes warmer than the white one. The black cloth is a better absorber of radiant energy than the white cloth. For a similar reason, black asphalt pavements become hotter than concrete on a hot summer day.

The Hothouse Problem

Materials, such as glass, which allow the visible rays and the short infrared rays to pass through readily, often reflect or absorb longer rays completely. In a hothouse, the short rays from the sun pass in readily through the glass walls and roof and are absorbed by the earth and vegetation inside. The earth and vegetation become warm and they,

too, become radiators. Their radiations are of very long wavelength and do not easily pass through the glass. So the hothouse acts as a trap for radiant energy from the sun. For this reason, the temperature within the hothouse becomes considerably higher than that outside.

Harnessing Infrared Rays

Paints that formerly required hours to dry can now be dried in a few minutes by infrared rays. Fruits and vegetables can be dehydrated quickly with these rays. An infrared baking machine has been invented that is said to bake more quickly and more uniformly than the ordinary oven process. Infrared lamps are used for killing larvae in tobacco-processing plants and weevils in grains and cereals. Similar lamps are used for certain types of medical treatment.

Infrared rays have been used in cooking food ever since the practice of cooking began. Meats and other foods broiled over an open fire are cooked almost entirely by infrared radiation. An electric toaster for bread and rolls operates chiefly because of the infrared radiation it produces.

Photographic plates are made which are sensitive to certain parts of the infrared. With these plates photographs can be taken in the dark and through haze and fog. Such photographs often reveal

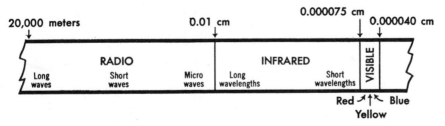

Fig. 9–14. A spectrum showing the wavelengths and relative positions of radio waves, infrared radiations, and visible light.

Fig. 9–15. A hothouse acts as a trap for radiant energy from the sun.

details that are invisible to the eye, and do not appear in photographs made in ordinary light. For this reason, infrared photographs were used in warfare to show up camouflage and discover concealed gun emplacements. This type of photography is useful in crime detection since infrared often brings out stains and marks that cannot be detected with ordinary light. The genuineness of documents and paintings can often be tested by means of infrared photographs because they reveal differences in paints and inks.

Beams of infrared rays are sometimes used to operate photoelectric alarm systems to protect factories and offices from intruders. When the invisible infrared beam directed on the photoelectric cell is interrupted by anyone moving into its path, the alarm system operates to summon police or guards to the spot.

►**Do You Know?**

1. Why does infrared radiation cast shadows?
2. Is there any reason, aside from appearance, why the outside surface of an electric toaster should be polished and shiny?
3. The bulb of a glass thermometer is

The photo on the right was taken by using infrared radiation only; the photo on the left was taken in ordinary daylight. (*Eastman Kodak Company*)

first blackened with soot. It is then hung side by side with an unblackened thermometer in the beam from an infrared lamp. Which thermometer will have the higher reading? Why?

4. Would you expect black or white clothing to be warmer in the summer? Why? In the winter? Why?

5. A closed automobile standing in the sun becomes much warmer inside than the surrounding air. Why?

6. Infrared rays heat window glass only slightly on passing through. Why?

7. On a sunny winter day, snow on a black asphalt pavement may melt while that on a nearby concrete pavement remains frozen. Why?

8. Can infrared photographs be taken with an ordinary camera if a suitable plate or film is used? Explain.

9. Vacuum bottles are often of one-pint or one-quart capacity. You may have seen a vacuum bottle of one-gallon capacity. What difficulties might occur in manufacturing larger vacuum bottles? What is the smallest vacuum bottle you have seen?

HIGHLIGHTS

Heat energy is moved from one place to another by *conduction, convection,* and *radiation.*

Energy can be moved only *from a higher to a lower temperature* by these methods.

Conduction occurs chiefly *in solids;* liquids and gases are very poor conductors of heat; metals are the best conductors.

Any very poor conductor is called a thermal *insulator.* Thermal insulators are used to retard or block the flow of heat by conduction.

Conduction occurs because of the collision of adjacent molecules or other particles.

Conduction is the slowest of the three methods of transferring heat.

Convection currents flow in liquids and gases, but not in solids. They are caused by unequal heating of the fluid.

Winds are huge convection currents in the atmosphere.

The pattern of atmospheric convection currents is modified by (1) the rotation of the earth, (2) the non-uniform distribution of land and water, and (3) local topography and vegetation.

In *radiation,* ordinary heat energy of a material body is converted into *radiant energy,* which is largely *infrared* or *invisible light.*

Infrared rays have *wavelengths* between those of radio and those of visible light.

Infrared waves travel through space about 186,000 miles/sec, or 3×10^{10} cm/sec.

The shortest infrared rays are radiated profusely by very hot bodies; the longer ones mainly by cooler bodies.

The rate of radiation depends on (1) the area, (2) the temperature, and (3) the nature of the radiating surface.

Rough surfaces are better radiators than smooth ones. Black surfaces are better radiators than white ones. Polished, mirrorlike surfaces are very poor radiators.

Good radiators are also good *absorbers*.

Radiant energy must be absorbed to convert it back into heat again.

Infrared radiation has many everyday and industrial uses.

THINGS TO DO

1. To demonstrate the principle of a coffee percolator, obtain a 500-ml glass beaker and a glass funnel small enough that its top fits easily into the beaker. Set the funnel top down in the beaker on two pieces of small glass rod or strips of metal on the bottom of the beaker to hold up the funnel. Pour water into the beaker until the level is up to where the stem of the funnel begins. Then place the beaker over a burner and heat until the water boils. Explain what happens.

2. Wrap single layers of paper tightly around a *wooden* roller and a metal pipe. Hold each separately above the flame of a bunsen burner for a few minutes. Observe what happens to each. Account for the difference in the two cases.

3. Close the windows of an automobile on a warm sunny day and leave it in the direct sunlight. After an hour or more measure the temperature outside the car and inside. Explain the temperature readings.

4. On a bright winter day with snow on the ground, lay a piece of *white* wool cloth and a piece of *black* wool cloth side by side on the snow in direct sunlight. After an hour look under the pieces of cloth. Explain what you observe.

10.

Transformation of Heat:
Heat Does Work

MECHANICAL EQUIVALENT OF HEAT

If you apply the brakes on a moving automobile, it slows down and loses kinetic energy while the brake drums get hot. If you pound, drill, or grind a piece of metal, it gets warm. If you churn or stir a liquid rapidly, its temperature rises a little. If you pump up a tire with a hand pump, the air in the tire gets warm. In every one of these operations, you do mechanical work, mechanical energy is used, and heat appears. In each case mechanical energy is *transformed* into heat energy. Such transformation of mechanical energy into heat energy offers both advantages and disadvantages in everyday living. Name some of each.

Joules in a Calorie

The number of joules of mechanical energy that is used up to produce a calorie of heat was determined quite accurately in 1849 from a series of careful experiments by a Scottish scientist, James Prescott Joule. He built a special kind of calorimeter with an arrangement for using mechanical work to churn the water in it. The more the water was churned the more mechanical energy was used up and the warmer the water became.

Joule's experiments have been checked a number of times since with the most accurate and improved equipment. Accepted values of the *mechanical equiva-*

235

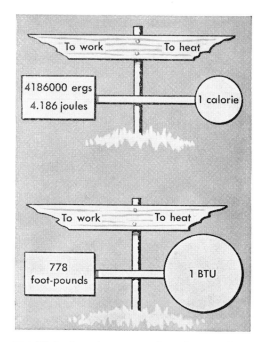

Fig. 10–1. From heat to work: joules to calories and foot-pounds to British thermal units.

lent of heat at the present time are the following:

1 cal = 41,860,000 ergs = 4.186 joules
1 Btu = 778 ft-lb

Joule's results were only slightly lower than these values.

Heat of Combustion

Heat energy may be transformed into mechanical energy. An engine derives power from the heat produced by *burning* fuel, that is, from *combustion*. To find out how much heat a pound of coal can produce when completely burned, a sample of the fuel is carefully prepared and burned inside a special calorimeter. The amount of heat produced is then calculated in the usual way from the rise in temperature of the water along with other data. The value thus obtained, reduced to the basis of a

236

pound or a gram, is called the *heat of combustion* of the fuel. Different fuels have different heats of combustion, as indicated in Table 10–1, and even different samples of the same fuel often yield quite different values.

Large users of coal, such as manufacturers and electric-power companies, usually make regular analyses of the coal they receive to determine its heat of combustion and its sulfur and ash content. In fact, buyers often specify in their purchasing contracts the Btu limits of the fuel they will accept.

Energy in a Gallon of Gasoline

A gallon of water weighs 8.33 lb. The specific gravity of gasoline shown in Table 10–1 is 0.739. So a gallon of gasoline weighs

$$0.739 \times 8.33 \text{ lb} = 6.16 \text{ lb}$$

The heat of combustion of gasoline shown in Table 10–1 is 20,750 Btu/lb. By completely burning 1 gal, we should obtain

$$6.16 \times 20,750 = 127,820 \text{ Btu}$$

Each Btu is capable of doing 778 ft-lb of mechanical work, so 1 gal of gasoline is capable of doing

$$127,820 \times 778 = 99,400,000 \text{ ft-lb}$$

This is enough work to lift a 3,000-lb automobile more than 6 miles vertically upward, an incredible amount of work from such a small quantity of liquid. Another example of the energy of gasoline is shown in the photograph on page 115.

Fuel for One Horsepower

Suppose we could have an ideal engine capable of changing *all* the heat from its burning fuel into mechanical energy. If this imaginary engine burned coal whose heat of combustion is 12,000 Btu/lb, how many pounds would it have to burn each minute to develop 1 hp?

$$1 \text{ hp} = 33,000 \text{ ft-lb/min}$$

1 lb of coal completely burned yields 12,000 Btu or

$$12,000 \times 778 = 9,336,000 \text{ ft-lb}$$

Therefore the number of pounds of this coal that must be burned per minute to produce 1 hp is

$$\frac{33,000}{9,336,000} = 0.00354 \text{ lb}$$

This is equivalent to about 0.2 lb/hr or 1 lb in 5 hr. An engine would have to be 100 percent efficient to convert *all* the heat of combustion into mechanical energy, as the ideal engine above is assumed to do. No practical engine can now approach this figure. Efficiencies of 30 to 35 percent are high for any type of heat engine.

Counting Your Calories

A major part of the food we eat is ultimately oxidized in our tissues and converted into heat and mechanical energy, much as fuel is burned in an engine. Our food thus serves as fuel for our bodies. For this reason, dieticians and biologists often rate our foods in terms of their *fuel value*, so many Calories per 100 g. The Calories used here are kilocalories, equivalent to 1000 of the ordinary calories that we have used before. To determine the fuel value of a food, a sample is prepared and completely burned in a special calorimeter, resembling that used for solid fuels. Experiments show that equivalent amounts of energy are released whether the food is burned in a calorimeter or digested in the human body.

Table 10–1. Heat of Combustion of Fuels

Coal	Heat of combustion, Btu/lb
Semibituminous	12,500–14,500
Bituminous (soft)	10,000–14,000
Anthracite (hard)	11,000–12,000
Cannel	10,500–11,500
Lignite	5,500– 6,000

Petroleum derivatives	Specific gravity at 60°F	Heat of combustion, Btu/lb
Gasoline	0.739	20,750
Kerosene	0.819	19,810
Crude oil (Oklahoma)	0.869	19,502
Furnace oil	0.896	19,025
Fuel oil (California)	0.955	18,835

Gases	Heat of combustion at 60°F and a pressure of 30 in. of mercury, Btu/ft³
Natural gas (West Virginia)	1,700–2,200
Natural gas (northern Ohio)	950–1,050
Coal gas	550–650
Coke-oven gas	500–600

The value of 3000 Calories has been accepted as a standard daily requirement for an average adult. During periods of war and famine, many people have existed on much less than half this standard requirement. Table 10–2 shows the fuel or Calorie value of some foods.

▶You Will Be Interested to Know

At the end of the eighteenth century scientists had not yet come to realize that heat is a form of energy. To explain what they knew about heat they built up a theory that heat was a kind of invisi-

237

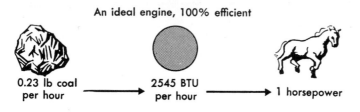

An ideal engine, 100% efficient

0.23 lb coal per hour → 2545 BTU per hour → 1 horsepower

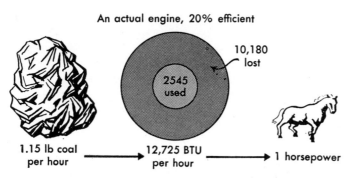

An actual engine, 20% efficient

10,180 lost

2545 used

1.15 lb coal per hour → 12,725 BTU per hour → 1 horsepower

Fig. 10–2. Rate of fuel consumption to furnish one horsepower, for an ideal engine (100% efficient) and for an actual engine that is only 20% efficient.

ble, weightless fluid, which they called *caloric*. Caloric was supposed to flow through a piece of metal much like a liquid flows through a pipe. Caloric could be poured from one body to another just as water can be poured from one beaker to another.

Benjamin Thompson (later Count Rumford) was one of the first to chal-

Table 10–2. Fuel Value of Some Foods

Food	Fuel value, kilocalories per 100 g
Butter	794
Sugar, granulated	410
Lean ham, smoked	274
White bread, wheat	266
Cream	201
Beefsteak, round	184
Egg, plain	159
White potatoes, boiled	97
Milk, whole	71.6
Cabbage	31.9

lenge this ancient theory. Thompson was born in 1753 at Woburn, Massachusetts. During the Revolutionary War period he served first with the Colonial Army but later left that service, went to England, and joined the British Army. He began his scientific work in England, but when peace was again restored, he went to Germany, where he became minister of war and rendered other services to the King of Bavaria. When the King conferred a title on him and he was allowed to choose, he elected to be called Count Rumford, after the name of his former estate near Concord, New Hampshire. While observing the boring of brass cannon in the arsenal at Munich, Rumford noticed how hot both cannon and chips became during the drilling. He became doubtful of the old caloric theory. Accordingly, he began a series of careful experiments, which he reported in 1798. These tests convinced him that the heat came not from released caloric, but from "motion," that is from mechanical energy expended in drilling.

1. Would you expect to get more heat by burning 1 ft³ of coal gas or 1 ft³ of natural gas in a properly adjusted burner?
2. The heat of combustion of hard coal is not much different from that of soft coal. Why would you expect to get more heat from burning a scuttleful of hard coal than from an equal volume of soft coal?
3. The diet of people who live in cold regions is largely meats, while that of people in warm countries consists more of vegetables. Can you suggest some reasons for this difference?
4. Define the term *calorie*. What is the difference between kilocalorie and calorie?
5. Explain the large difference between the work output which is theoretically possible from burning a gallon of gasoline and the work output which is obtained in practice when 1 gal of gasoline is burned.
6. Explain the meaning of the term *horsepower*.
7. Define the term *heat of combustion*.

TYPES OF HEAT ENGINES

A *heat engine* is a device for changing heat energy into mechanical energy.

A steam engine derives its power from steam fed into it. This steam is generated in a boiler, in the firebox of which coal, oil, or other fuel is burned. The boiler is not a part of the engine proper and may even be located some distance from it. Because the fuel is burned outside the engine itself, this type of engine is called an *external-combustion engine*. All engines that operate from steam are external-combustion engines. A few experimental external-combustion engines that use mercury instead of water and mercury vapor instead of steam have been built and operated successfully, but the high cost of mercury and mechanical difficulties seem to make such engines impractical for most purposes.

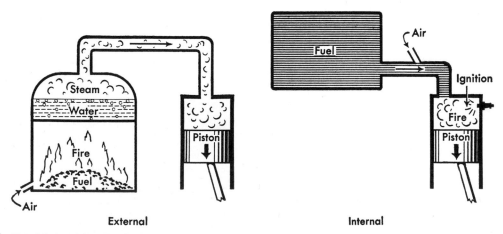

External   Internal

Fig. 10–3. The basic difference between external- and internal-combustion engines depends on where the fuel is burned.

239

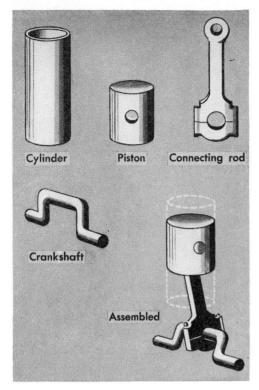

Fig. 10–4. Cylinder, piston, connecting rod, and crankshaft of an internal-combustion engine.

The Internal-combustion Engine

An automobile engine derives its power from gasoline vapor and air drawn directly into the cylinders. The gasoline vapor, that is, the fuel, is burned inside the cylinders of the engine. Because the fuel is burned *inside* the engine itself, this type of engine is called an *internal-combustion* engine. The hot gases produced by the combustion of the fuel serve the same purpose in this type of engine as steam serves in the external-combustion type. Automobile, aircraft, and diesel are important types of internal-combustion engines. Marine, stationary, and other internal-combustion engines are usually modifications of one or another of these three types.

240

The Reciprocating Engine

The ordinary steam engine and the automobile engine are *reciprocating engines*. The four chief parts of such engines are (1) the cylinder, (2) the piston, (3) the connecting rod, and (4) the crankshaft, shown in Fig. 10–4. The cylindrical metal piston fits snugly inside the metal cylinder, but is free to slide back and forth. In the automobile engine one end of the straight metal connecting rod is attached to the piston by means of a pin. The other end is attached to an oiled bearing on the crank. The crank is the offset portion of the crankshaft. The two ends of the crankshaft are mounted in bearings. In operation, the piston is *forced* up and down or back and forth. The connecting rod-crankshaft assembly changes this to-and-fro motion of the piston into rotary motion of the shaft. The crankshaft delivers power to the machine to which it is connected. The term *reciprocating* refers to the to-and-fro motion of the piston.

The Turbine Engine

Many steam engines and some internal-combustion engines operate on the turbine principle. A turbine resembles a pinwheel or a wind wheel in its action. The principal parts of a steam turbine are a wheel of special design mounted on a shaft to form the *rotor* and a set of nozzles to direct steam at high speed against the curved blades of the wheel, as shown in Fig. 10–5. The curved blades deflect the jets of steam. This produces a reaction force on the blades and sets up a torque to turn the rotor. The rotor turns constantly in one direction rather than with a to-and-fro motion. The shaft of the rotor is usually connected directly to the machine which it drives and to which it delivers power.

1. Why would it be desirable to use mercury vapor instead of steam in an external-combustion engine?
2. When were external-combustion engines used in automobiles? What fuels did they burn?
3. For what purposes are *water* turbines used?
4. Could gasoline or oil be used as a fuel in an external-combustion engine? Explain.
5. What is meant by a *prime mover?*
6. Were there any steam engines before the ones Watt built? If so, can you find out how they operated? For what were they used?
7. What effect did the introduction of the steam engine have on the way people lived and the kind of work they did?

How a Steam Turbine Works

We have already considered the fundamental principle of the steam turbine. The high-speed steam from the nozzles strikes the first row of blades on the rotor, is deflected, and *expands* in the process. In order to use the energy that still remains in the steam, a set of stationary deflection vanes is mounted inside the housing, just opposite the row of movable blades on the rotor. These stationary vanes catch the steam and direct it back against a second row of curved blades on the rotor, as shown in Fig. 10–7. With additional alternate sets of stationary vanes and rows of rotor blades, the steam passing through the turbine is expanded a number of times. In this way a large portion of the available energy in the steam is converted into mechanical work.

Reciprocating Steam Engine

In addition to a cylinder, a piston, a connecting rod, and a crankshaft, an actual engine needs valves to regulate the flow of intake and exhaust steam and a mechanism for operating these valves at the proper time. Examine the *double-action* reciprocating steam engine shown in Fig. 10–6 to see what takes place within the cylinder.

You may think at first that this engine works like a double-action force pump operated backward, with steam rather than water forced into the device to drive it. But a closer examination will reveal that an outstanding feature of the steam engine is the *expanding* of steam in the cylinder during the work stroke. The more the steam is expanded, the lower its pressure and temperature at the end of the stroke, and the more mechanical energy it gives to the engine.

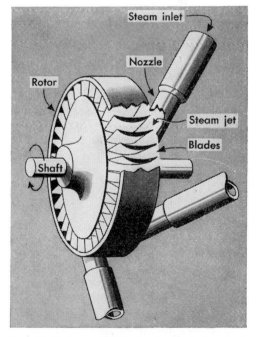

Fig. 10–5. A simplified diagram of the shaft, rotor, and nozzles of a steam turbine.

Steam inlet

Nozzle

Rotor

Steam jet

Blades

Shaft

241

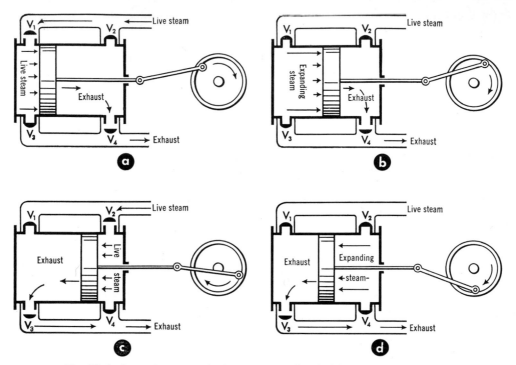

Fig. 10–6. Successive stages in the operation of a double-action steam engine.

Some Uses of Steam Turbines

The steam turbine is essentially a high-speed machine; it does not operate efficiently at slow shaft speeds. It runs in one direction only and cannot be reversed as a reciprocating engine can. Because its fundamental motion is rotary rather than reciprocating, it is less likely to produce vibration. A turbine is smaller and more convenient to mount than a reciprocating engine of equal power. One of the chief uses for turbines is in driving electric generators in power plants, on shipboard, and on some types of locomotives. Some ships use steam turbines with reduction gears to drive their propeller shafts directly. Turbines are generally more simple in construction and more efficient in operation than any type of reciprocating engine. Turbines seem likely to be widely used in the future.

242

Efficiency of Steam Engines

The efficiency of a steam engine may mean any one of several things. The input power may be computed from the heat of combustion of the fuel used in the boiler and the rate at which it is burned. The output generally means the mechanical power delivered by the engine to the machine which it drives. The ratio $\dfrac{\text{power output}}{\text{power input}}$ then gives the overall efficiency of the power plant, including both boiler and engine. On this basis, the efficiency of a steam locomotive is of the order of 8 to 12 percent. Stationary power plants using reciprocating engines have efficiencies of 15 to 20 percent, while plants using turbines and condensers have efficiencies that reach about 35 percent. The development of more efficient types of engines would do much to conserve our reserve supply of fuels.

The efficiency of an engine is increased when more work units are taken from the steam used, that is, when the steam is expanded farther. This is the reason why *multiple* expansion is used in steam turbines. This is also the reason why the intake of live steam is limited to a small fraction of the stroke in a reciprocating engine. Compound reciprocating engines have two cylinders connected to the same crankshaft. The exhaust of the smaller cylinder serves as the intake of the larger one, so that the steam is expanded once in each cylinder. This double expansion of the steam promotes higher efficiency.

▶Do You Know?

1. Why does scale result from hard water used in a hot-water heater? Explain.
2. Does new water have to be injected into a boiler which receives the hot water from a condenser? Explain.
3. Is salt water suitable for use in a boiler? Why?
4. In a steam engine, why is the intake valve closed before the end of the stroke?
5. Where are the cylinder and the steam chest on a railroad locomotive usually located?
6. How is the speed of a reciprocating steam engine regulated?
7. How is the speed of a steam turbine regulated?

POWER FROM GASOLINE AND OIL

The internal-combustion engine has now virtually replaced the steam engine for transportation on land and water, and is also used for transportation by air.

An internal-combustion engine requires *fuel*, *air*, and *ignition* for its operation. For service, it must also have oil for lubrication and a means of cooling to carry away excess heat. To supply these needs, an engine has four auxiliary systems: (1) a fuel-air system, (2) an ignition system, (3) a cooling system, and (4) a lubrication system.

The engine we use in automobiles and trucks has 4, 6, or 8 cylinders, although it could have any convenient number. The pistons of these cylinders are all connected to the same crankshaft, although each one may be connected to a different crank. They are mounted "in line," in a "V," or in some other arrangement to form the assembled engine. Each cylinder operates like every other one and is a *unit engine* in itself. When we understand how one of these unit engines works, we know how all operate.

How a Unit Engine Works

A single-unit engine (cylinder) at four different stages in its operation is shown in Fig. 10–8. The top end of the cylinder is closed with a heavy metal plate called the *cylinder head*. The hollowed-out under part of the head plate forms the *compression chamber*, a space just above the end of the cylinder

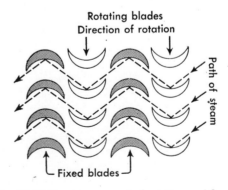

Fig. 10–7. The arrangement of rotating and fixed blades and the path of expanding steam in a steam turbine.

into which the piston cannot reach. The *poppet valves* are mounted in the head. The intake valve *I* connects the compression chamber with the *intake manifold*, a pipe from the *carburetor* through which the fuel-air mixture enters the cylinder. The exhaust valve *E* connects the compression chamber to the *exhaust manifold*, a pipe through which the burned gas leaves the cylinder. In some engines the valves and manifold connections are placed at the side of the cylinder, rather than in the head. The valves are opened and closed by a mechanism operated from the crankshaft. A *spark plug*, with two points separated by a small air gap,

is shown in the side of the cylinder. The points, which extend through into the compression chamber, are connected into an electric circuit which is part of the *ignition* system. When the system operates, a hot spark jumps between the two points and *ignites* the mixture of fuel and air.

Notice the positions of the intake and the exhaust valves during each of the strokes shown in Fig. 10–8. At the end of the exhaust stroke, the unit engine is ready to start all over again on a new intake of fuel. The four strokes, *intake*, *compression*, *power*, and *exhaust*, constitute one cycle in the operation of this

View of one of the world's largest single-shaft turbogenerators at Philadelphia Electric Company's Richmond station. This unit has a capacity of 165,000 kilowatts with a running speed of 1,800 rpm. (*Philadelphia Electric Company*)

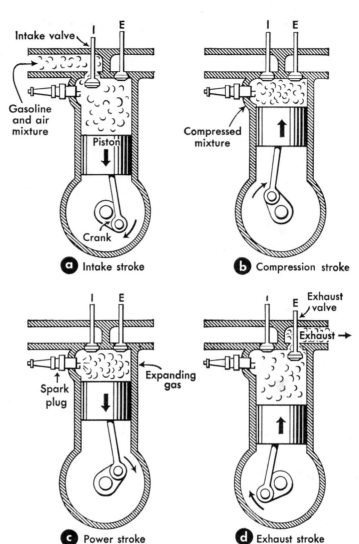

Intake valve

Gasoline and air mixture

Piston

Crank

a Intake stroke

Compressed mixture

b Compression stroke

Spark plug

Expanding gas

c Power stroke

Exhaust valve

Exhaust →

d Exhaust stroke

Fig. 10–8. Operation of the four-stroke cycle in a gasoline engine.

kind of engine. Hence, this is called a *four-stroke cycle*, but we usually shorten this term and speak of a *four-cycle engine*. The four-stroke cycle is also called an *Otto cycle* after the man who first built a successful engine of this type. The crankshaft makes two complete turns for every cycle and power is delivered to the crankshaft during only one of the four strokes. We should

never confuse the term four-cycle with the number of cylinders that an engine may have.

Two-cycle engines, which have only two strokes in a cycle, are sometimes used in outboard motors and small marine engines. Two-cycle diesel engines are quite common. Explain possible advantages and disadvantages of a two-stroke cycle engine.

What the Carburetor Does

The carburetor prepares the liquid fuel for combustion (burning) within the cylinders. Theoretically 15 lb of air should be mixed with 1 lb of vaporized gasoline (a 15 to 1 mixture ratio) for proper combustion, but gasoline will burn with mixture ratios from 18 to 1 (very lean) to 8 to 1 (very rich). The carburetor receives the liquid fuel from the fuel pump, vaporizes it, and mixes it with air by spraying the liquid through a fine nozzle into the stream of air on its way to the cylinder. Figure 10–9 shows some details of a carburetor.

Why Engines Knock

Suppose that the volume of mixture taken into the cylinder during the intake stroke is 60 in.³ and that at the end of the compression stroke this is squeezed into 10 in.³ in the compression chamber. In this case, the *compression ratio* is 60 to 10 or 6 to 1. The higher the compression ratio in an engine, the more power is obtained from the fuel and the higher the efficiency of the engine. If the mixture is compressed to 140 lb/in.² before ignition, it will produce *more than twice as much power* as it would if it were compressed to only 100 lb/in.² A common value of compression ratio in present-day automobile engines is 6½ or 7 to 1.

You may ask why engineers do not design the engine with a higher compression ratio, 10 to 1, for example. If the compression is too high for the gasoline used, it burns too rapidly and unevenly, causing detonation or *knock* in the engine. *Tetraethyllead* added to gasoline slows down its burning rate and permits the use of higher compression without knocking. Gasolines with *higher percentages of octane* have the same effect. It seems probable that future engines will have higher compression ratios when higher-octane gasoline becomes available for general use.

Aircraft Engines

The gasoline engines used in aircraft operate on the same four-stroke cycle as automobile engines. Differences in design occur because of the difference in conditions under which the engines are used. The aircraft engine must lift itself as well as the plane and its load; every pound that can be taken from the engine adds a pound to the pay load. The *pound-per-horsepower* rating of an aircraft engine is, therefore, important. An aircraft engine must operate in any position, whereas an automobile engine has chiefly one operating position. Furthermore, the aircraft engine must operate not only on the ground, but at high altitudes where both air pressure and temperature are low. So the aircraft engine must adjust itself to variations in temperature and air pressure.

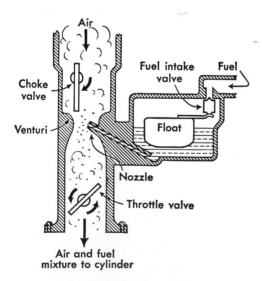

Fig. 10–9. A carburetor vaporizes liquid gasoline and mixes it with air.

Some points of difference between aircraft and automobile engines are:

1. Parts of an aircraft engine are often smaller than the corresponding parts on an automobile engine of equal power. Many parts are made of light aluminum and magnesium alloys, rather than steel. The workmanship and finish on aircraft engine parts are of the highest order.

2. The cylinder arrangement and mounting are often quite different. X-type, radial, and double-radial engines are commonly used in aircraft.

3. Many aircraft engines are air-cooled, although some have liquid cooling systems similar to those in automobile engines.

4. Dual ignition systems with *two spark plugs* in each cylinder are used in aircraft engines to insure positive ignition and cause the mixture to burn better.

5. An injection-type carburetor with the liquid fuel *forced* into the air stream is used in aircraft engines.

6. A *supercharger* or a *turbosupercharger* is often added to an aircraft engine, especially for high-altitude flying. These devices compress the air before it is mixed with gasoline and enters the cylinder. This boosts the pressure within the cylinder and is equivalent to increasing the compression ratio. It would cause knocking with ordinary motor gasoline, but 100-octane gasoline, developed primarily for this purpose, enables the engine to operate at the higher compression and develop much more power than it could without the supercharger. On the ground, this enables a plane to take off faster and with a heavier load. At high altitudes, the supercharger is necessary to provide enough air to burn the fuel properly.

How a Diesel Engine Works

The diesel engine, named for its inventor, Rudolf Diesel (1858–1913), is an internal combustion engine designed to burn oil or other liquid fuels. The early diesels were cumbersome, low-speed engines whose uses were limited, but the later high-speed engines develop more power in a smaller cylinder. Both two-cycle and four-cycle types are used in the locomotives of streamlined trains, to power trucks and ships, and to drive electric generators in portable and stationary power plants.

A diesel engine requires *fuel, air,* and *ignition* for its operation, just as a gasoline engine does. It also must have a cooling system and a lubricating system. Two outstanding features of the diesel are that it has *no spark plugs* and *no carburetor*. On the intake stroke in the four-cycle type, air alone is drawn into the cylinder. On the compression stroke this air is compressed to a very high

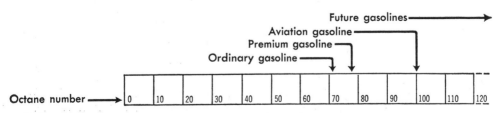

Fig. 10–10. The octane scale.

A three-unit diesel-electric locomotive used for fast through passenger service. This locomotive weighs over 465 tons and is rated at 6,000 hp. *(The Pennsylvania Railroad)*

pressure, ranging from about 250 to 600 lb/in.^{2} in different engines. Under such high compression the air gets hot, reaching temperatures well over 1000°F. Near the end of the compression stroke, a stream of liquid fuel is sprayed under high pressure into the compression chamber. It ignites at once in the very hot air, without the aid of a spark, and the power stroke follows.

Modern engineering has reduced the weight of the diesel engine from about 250 lb/hp in the early models to 10 or even 5 lb/hp. The efficiency of this engine is higher than that of the ordinary gasoline engine partly because of the much higher compression ratio, which is commonly more than 16 to 1 and which reaches 40 to 1 in some models of diesel engines. These factors, along with the lower cost of fuel, make diesel engines economical for operating modern trains, trucks, and buses.

248

Power for Rockets

Have you ever watched a skyrocket take off and zoom upward through the air at a fireworks display? If so, you have witnessed the operation of one type of modern reaction engine. As the fuel and oxidizing agent in the tube of the rocket burn, they develop a large volume of intensely heated gas. The heat causes the gas to expand rapidly and shoot backwards at high speed through the tube. The reaction force pushes the rocket forward along its upward path.

Rockets differ from other types of reaction engines in that they carry not only their own fuel, but also their own supply of oxygen to burn the fuel. Some rockets, like the skyrocket, are designed to burn *solid fuel* and obtain the required oxygen from oxidizing chemicals mixed with the fuel. Other rockets are designed to use liquid fuels, such as alcohol, and carry liquid oxygen to supply the oxygen gas needed to burn the fuel. The combustion occurs at explosive speeds in rockets that use solid fuel and there is very little that can be done to control the process once it has started. In liquid-fuel rockets, combustion generally occurs in a separate chamber into which the fuel and oxygen are fed. In this case the rate of fuel flow can be set so that the fuel supply is not all used up in an instant. This is one reason why long-range rockets are usually designed to use liquid fuel.

Since rockets are not dependent on the atmosphere for the supply of oxygen to burn their fuel, their range is not limited to heights of 10 miles or less as are other types of engines. Rockets could travel through outer space where there is no air just as well as or even better than through the air. Rockets are sometimes equipped so that a second explosion occurs after the rocket has reached a certain height. This second explosion causes the lighter forward compartment of the rocket to break away from the main body and proceed at a much higher speed. A rocket of this type has reached a height of more than 200 miles.

Jet Propulsion

Airplanes designed for very high speeds and some guided missiles are powered with a type of reaction engine called a *jet engine*. The plane or missile is *pushed* along by the reaction force set up by a high-speed jet of hot gases pro-

Boeing YB-52 Stratofortress in flight. (*Air Force photo, Washington, D.C.*)

249

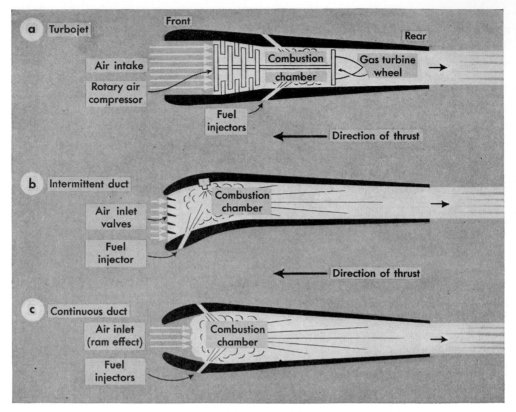

Fig. 10–11. Three types of jet engines; (a) turbojet; (b) intermittent jet; (c) continuous duct, or ram-jet.

duced by combustion of the fuel. The plane is *jet-propelled*—there is no need for a propeller of the conventional type.

Several types of successful jet engines have been developed. Among the best known are the *turbojet*, the *intermittent-duct*, and the *continuous-duct* or *ram-jet*. Figure 10–11 shows the general principle of each of these types.

In the *turbojet* engine of Fig. 10–11a, air enters the front end of the engine tube, is compressed as it passes through the rotary compressor and enters the combustion chamber at high pressure. Liquid fuel is sprayed under high pressure into this compressed air and the

mixture is ignited. The very hot gases produced by combustion pass through the vanes of a gas turbine wheel and are ejected from the tube through a jet at the rear. The ejected gases thus exert a forward thrust on the plane or missile. The turbine wheel which is set into rotation by the passing gas, drives the air compressor. This type of power plant has only one moving part and that is within the engine itself. It has no gears, no reciprocating pistons, no valves, no crankshaft, and no cooling system. It can be started while the plane is parked on the field and can be used on the take-off.

Both the *intermittent-duct* and the *continuous-duct types* of engine have no air compressors, so they can be operated only after a plane equipped with them has reached a speed of 150 mph or more.

The *intermittent-duct type* shown in Fig. 10–11*b* has a set of vanelike valves on the air inlet. When the plane or missile is moving fast enough, these vanes are opened automatically by the air pressure on them to admit a charge of air. This air is pushed into the combustion chamber and compressed by the air that follows it. Fuel is sprayed into the compressed air and ignited. The rapid combustion that occurs sets up pressures that close the inlet valves momentarily and push the hot gases out the rear jet. When the internal pressure drops, the inlet valves automatically open again and let in a new charge of air. The operation then repeats itself and power is delivered to the plane or missile in a series of pulses.

The *continuous-duct* or *ram-jet type*, shown in Fig. 10–11*c*, is open at both ends and has provisions for injecting fuel and for ignition. This type of engine will not operate until it is moving through the air at high speed. The engine then gives a steady push to the plane or missile to which it is attached.

▶**Do You Know?**

1. Why do automobile engines have more than one cylinder?
2. Does the spark ever occur *before* the piston reaches the top of the compression stroke? Explain.
3. What is meant by advancing the spark? Retarding the spark?
4. What is the octane rating of ordinary motor gasoline?
5. What kind of fuel do jet motors burn?
6. How are diesel engines started?
7. How does the miles-per-gallon rating of a jet engine compare with the fuel consumption of a conventional airplane engine?
8. Why are superchargers needed at high altitudes?

HIGHLIGHTS

Mechanical energy is *transformed* into heat by friction, compression, and pounding.

Joule first found experimentally the value of the *mechanical equivalent* of heat. The best accepted values now are 4.186 joules/cal, and 778 ft-lb/Btu.

Each kind of fuel has its own characteristic value for *heat of combustion*.

Foods have characteristic *fuel values*.

Heat engines are *internal-* or *external-combustion, reciprocating, turbine*, and *reaction* types.

Steam *expands and cools* as it does work in the cylinder of a reciprocating engine.

Steam turbines are used chiefly to drive electric generators.

An *internal-combustion* engine requires *fuel, air*, and *ignition*.

The four strokes in the cycle of a *four-cycle engine* are *intake, compression, power*, and *exhaust*.

In a *two-cycle engine* every downstroke is a *power* stroke.

A *carburetor* vaporizes liquid fuel and mixes it with the proper proportion of air.

Gasoline requires a theoretical air-gasoline *mixture ratio* of 15 to 1, but will burn with any ratio between 18 to 1 and 8 to 1.

Knocking is caused by uneven and too rapid burning of the fuel mixture.

High-octane gasoline reduces knocking.

Aircraft engines differ in design from automobile engines chiefly because aircraft engines operate under different conditions. In aircraft the *weight per unit of power* is very important.

A *supercharger* or a *turbocharger* compresses air before it enters the cylinder of an aircraft engine.

Diesel engines burn fuel oil. A *fuel injector* is used in place of a carburetor.

Diesel engines have no sparkplugs. *Ignition is automatic*, caused by the high temperature generated in compressing the air in the cylinder.

Jet engines, used on high-speed planes, are a kind of *internal-combustion* engine. They operate on the reaction principle expressed in Newton's third law of motion.

Rockets are propelled by reaction forces.

PROBLEMS: GROUP A

1. What is the fuel value of 1 lb of sugar? See Table 10–2.

2. What is the fuel value of 1 lb of butter? See Table 10–2.

3. How many calories may be obtained from the complete combustion of 1 gal of gasoline?

4. If the efficiency of a gasoline engine is 30 percent, how many foot-pounds of work can it do while burning 1 gal of gasoline?

5. How many calories of heat energy are required to do 75,000 joules of mechanical work, if the transformation is 100 percent efficient?

6. How many kilocalories of heat energy come from the complete oxidation of 1 lb of beefsteak? See Table 10–2.

7. How many kilocalories of heat can be obtained from the complete oxidation of 1 gal of whole milk? A gallon of milk weighs approximately 8.58 lb.

8. How many cubic feet of natural gas (1,200 Btu/ft^3) must be burned to do 2,800,800 ft-lb of mechanical work, if the heat is fully utilized?

9. How many Btu's of heat will be produced by the complete burning of 15 lb of cannel coal (11,000 Btu/lb)?

10. If an internal-combustion engine has a compression ratio of 8 to 1, what is the approximate pressure of the air-fuel mixture in the cylinder just before it is ignited?

11. Assume that burning a pound of coal produces 15,000 Btu's. If this energy were used in lifting coal up from a mine 200 ft deep, how many tons of coal would be raised from the mine for each ton of coal burned if the engine and hoist were only 10 percent efficient?

12. Assume 1 lb of gasoline burned gives 21,000 Btu's. How many ft-lb of work does this represent?

1. What is the fuel value of a 12-oz loaf of white bread?
2. How many calories may be obtained from the complete combustion of 1 lb of soft coal, whose heat of combustion is 11,000 Btu/lb?
3. If the volume within the cylinder and compression chamber of a diesel engine is 250 in.³ when the piston is at one end of its stroke and 12.5 in.³ when the piston is at the other end of its stroke, what is the compression ratio of the engine?
4. How many Btu's of heat are required to do 100,000 ft-lb of mechanical work if the transformation is only 20 percent efficient?
5. What is the over-all efficiency of a power plant which burns coal at the rate of 1 lb/hr to produce 1 hp? Assume the coal yields 12,000 Btu/lb.
6. How many Btu's of heat can be obtained by burning 50 gal of furnace oil which weighs 7.47 lb/gal?

7. If the engines of a jet airplane burn 1 gal (7.96 lb) of fuel oil per second, how many foot-pounds of mechanical work per minute can these engines do, assuming that all heat energy could be converted to mechanical energy? What horsepower would this rate of working represent?
8. How much water could be heated from 60°F to boiling (212°F) by burning 1 ft³ of natural gas (1,500 Btu/ft³), if all the heat energy could be utilized in heating the water?
9. How many joules of energy come from the complete oxidation of 1 lb (453.6 g) of beefsteak? See Table 10–2.
10. How many joules of energy may be obtained from the complete oxidation of 1 lb of white bread? See Table 10–2.
11. If a diesel engine burns 10 gal (79.6 lb) of fuel oil, whose heat of combustion is 18,800 Btu/lb, in doing 3.2 × 10⁸ ft-lb of mechanical work, what is the over-all mechanical efficiency of the engine?

THINGS TO DO

1. Find information in your school library on Newcomen's atmospheric engine. Write a report to be read in class on the operation of this engine.
2. Discuss with your classmates how a rocket could be steered after it has left the earth's atmosphere.
3. Consult managers of service stations to find out the octane rating of the different kinds of gasoline sold in your community. What advantages does each type have as a motor fuel?

4. What is the heat of combustion (Btu/ft³) of fuel gas used in your community? The manager of the utility company from which people buy fuel gas can probably help you find the answer.
5. What are the compression ratios in the engines of different makes and models of automobiles sold in your area? Consult automobile dealers. What are advantages of different compression ratios? What changes in compression ratios would you expect to be made in the future?

Unit **3.**

Sound in Our World

PREVIEW

Sound is probably as old as the earth. The prehistoric animals that were here before the appearance of man may have used sounds to give warning of danger or to strike terror among their victims or enemies. Thus, man was not the first living thing to communicate through the use of sound. It is likely that thousands of years were required to develop even the most rudimentary forms of speech and still more thousands of years must have elapsed before a language adequate for communication was evolved. In this unit you will be exploring not a newly discovered world, but one of very ancient origin.

Through practice and training people have learned how to use the sounds of speech and music fluently and skillfully to express their ideas and emotions. Little or no scientific knowledge of sound is needed to do this. However, when we wish to control sound, to find ways to suppress it, or to find new ways to use it, we must have scientific laws and principles. Our modern uses of sound, such as in public-address systems, recorders, and record players, are based on carefully established physical principles.

Many noises or unwanted sounds are produced in our modern world. Reducing or eliminating such sounds is an important problem that has been only partially solved. You will have an opportunity to investigate some of these problems and the physical laws and principles of sound in this unit.

11.

Sounds and Sound Waves:
Sound Energy

THE WAVE NATURE OF SOUND

Have you ever tried to imagine what our world would be like if there were no sound? If you have seen a "silent" movie you have had a glimpse of a small section of a *soundless* world. On the silent screen, the actors may move their lips, but no words come forth; a dog may rush out and bark silently at an automobile that goes whizzing by without a sound; lightning may flash brilliantly, but there is no peal of thunder. Without sound, our world would be as strange and unnatural as the silent movie. We could have no sermons, no lectures, no music, no radio, and none of us could possibly be on "speaking terms" with one another!

Our schools, if any, would surely be different than those of today. Sound enables us to communicate our ideas quickly to others. Sound sometimes brings us warning of danger. Sound is the medium from which artists mold and fashion beautiful symphonies and operas. In these and other ways sound plays a very important role in our everyday lives.

What Causes Sound?

To most of us, sound is something we can hear. When we hear a sound, we usually want to know where it comes from and what causes it. When a drummer strikes the head of a bass drum, the stretched drumhead vibrates rapidly

256

in and out. If we are nearby, we may hear the characteristic booming sound of the drum. If the drummer then touches the vibrating drumhead and stops the vibration, the sound at once disappears. Thus, we know from what we observe that the vibrating drumhead is the source of the sound we heard. Stretched strings, wires, rods, plates, air columns, in fact any body or part of a body that can vibrate may become a source of sound.

The source of every sound is a vibrating body.

What Is Sound?

The vibrating drumhead in our example pushes the surrounding air ahead of it every time it moves outward. The air in turn tends to follow the drumhead every time it moves inward. On the outward motion, the air close to the drum head is bunched or compressed a little. This *compression* seems to move ahead through the air and is followed by another compression on the next outward swing of the drumhead. This second compression in turn moves ahead and is followed on the next outward swing by a third. In this way compressions move through the air in a regular succession

away from the drumhead as long as it continues to vibrate. Between the compressions are regions where the air is slightly thinner than normal. These regions are called *rarefactions*. We call this regular bunching of the air into compressions and rarefactions a sound wave. Figure 11–1 represents a sound wave moving away from the vibrating drumhead.

When a sound wave of sufficient strength reaches our ears, it stimulates their mechanism and we hear the sound. The energy required to stimulate our ears must come from the sound wave which in turn receives it from the vibrating drumhead. The air serves merely as a medium through which the wave travels and energy is transferred. Even if we were not there to hear, sound waves would still be produced by the drumhead when it vibrates.

Sound is a form of energy that travels in waves away from a vibrating source through the surrounding medium.

Different Kinds of Waves

Waves on the ocean or a lake are familiar to nearly everyone. You may have watched such water waves move

Fig. 11–1. A vibrating body is a source of sound.

past a small boat or other floating object. As the wave passes, the boat is raised and lowered without moving ahead. A water wave represents a different type of motion than the sound wave we have discussed. The infrared waves that we discussed when we were considering how heat travels are of still a different type. But even though these waves are all different, they have several properties in common.

We usually assume that the medium through which the wave moves is made up of very small but distinct particles. We may not always be able to say just what these particles are, whether they are individual molecules or groups of molecules. Each of these particles vibrates as the wave passes along. In a very simple wave, the motion of these particles is simple harmonic motion, similar to the motion of the pendulum discussed in Chapter 4. Waves in general are divided into two chief elementary classes, *transverse* and *longitudinal*, depending on how the particles vibrate. In transverse waves, the individual particles vibrate along paths that are perpendicular to the direction the wave moves; in longitudinal waves, the individual particles vibrate along paths that are parallel to the direction the wave moves.

Sound waves are longitudinal waves. Infrared and light waves are transverse waves, as also are radio waves. In water waves, the particles of water move around circular or elliptical paths.

Some Important Parts of Waves

To understand how waves behave, we shall need to become familiar with some of the terms commonly used in describing them. In a transverse wave, the top of the wave (A in Fig. 11–2) is a *crest;* the bottom of the wave (B in Fig. 11–2) is a *trough.* In an advancing wave, crests and troughs appear to move ahead in regular succession, like troops marching in formation. The velocity or speed with which any one crest moves ahead is called the *velocity of the wave.*

In a longitudinal wave, a region where the particles are bunched together (A in Fig. 11–3) is a *compression* or *condensation;* a region where the particles are thinned out (B in Fig. 11–3) is a *rarefaction,* as we have already seen. In an advancing longitudinal wave, compressions and rarefactions follow one another at regular intervals as they appear to move ahead. The velocity or speed with which any one compression moves ahead is the *velocity of the wave.* This is true for sound waves in air, water, and other materials.

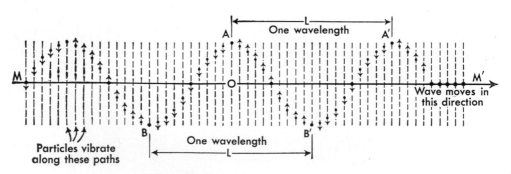

Fig. 11–2. A transverse wave.

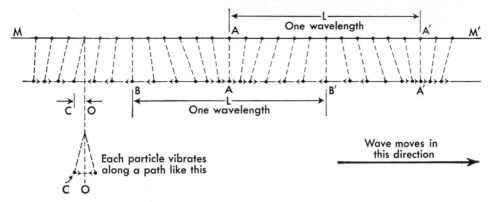

Fig. 11–3. A longitudinal wave.

Amplitude of a Wave

If there were no wave, the particles in Fig. 11–2 would be at rest along the line MM', so MM' marks their *position of rest*. When a transverse wave comes along, each individual particle vibrates *up and down* about its position of rest, while the wave moves forward to the right. The figure shows the positions of different particles in the wave at a particular instant. Notice that the particles are not all at the same relative position in their vibrations at this instant. The position of a particle in its cycle of vibration is called its *phase*. The particles then do not all have the same phase. As we go along the wave to the right, each particle lags behind its neighbor before it. This lagging in phase is what makes the wave appear to move ahead.

The *amplitude* of the wave shown in Fig. 11–2 is the distance OA. This is the maximum distance any particle of the medium moves from its position of rest and is half the height of the wave, if we measure height from the level of a trough to that of a crest. Amplitude may be expressed in centimeters, inches, or any other convenient unit of length.

If there were no wave in Fig. 11–3, the particles would be at rest in positions along MM'. When a longitudinal wave comes along, each individual particle vibrates *back and forth* while the wave moves forward parallel to this motion. Again, the particles are not all at the same relative position in their vibrations at a given instant. Each one lags behind its neighbor before it. This lagging in phase is again the reason why the wave appears to move ahead.

The amplitude of the longitudinal wave shown in Fig. 11–3 is the distance OC, which is the *maximum* distance any particle moves from its position of rest. It is important to know the amplitude of a wave when we are interested in the amount of energy the wave is carrying.

Wavelength

Another important thing to know about a wave is how closely the crests or the compressions are spaced. This spacing is called the *wavelength*. A wavelength is the linear distance between two adjacent crests (AA'), or two adjacent troughs (BB') in the transverse wave of Fig. 11–2, or two adjacent compressions (AA') or two adjacent rarefactions (BB')

259

in the longitudinal wave of Fig. 11–3.

Wavelengths are expressed in meters, centimeters, feet, inches, or other convenient units of length. The wavelength of a given sound wave may be 60 cm while the wavelength of a given radio wave may be 600 m.

Frequency

The *frequency of a vibrating body*, such as the drumhead in Fig. 11–1, is the number of complete vibrations the body makes in one second. During each vibration, the body sends one compression and one rarefaction moving out into the surrounding air. The *frequency of the sound wave* in the air is the number of compressions that move past a given point in a second. This must correspond to the number of compressions generated in one second by the vibrating body, so we may say that the frequency of the sound wave is the same as that of the vibrating body that produces it.

Each particle along the path of the wave must vibrate at the same frequency in order that there may be a wave. One compression and one rarefaction pass a given position while the particle there makes one complete vibration. Thus if the cone of a loudspeaker is vibrating 500 times per second each particle along the sound wave will also vibrate 500 times per second. Furthermore, if you could see this sound wave and could count fast enough you would observe 500 compressions and 500 rarefactions moving past your eye every second!

Frequency is sometimes expressed in *vibrations per second* and sometimes in *cycles per second* (cps). These are two different ways of saying the same thing. Two hundred vibrations per second is also 200 cps. Often we omit the "per second" and say simply 200 cycles. Kilocycles and megacycles per second are used for higher frequencies.

Wavelength, Frequency, Velocity

A tuning fork is a simple and convenient device for producing a particular sound. When struck with a rubber hammer, the prongs of the fork vibrate in and out, setting up sound waves in the surrounding air, as indicated in Fig. 11–4. Let us focus our attention on the right-hand prong. It starts a new compression into the surrounding air each

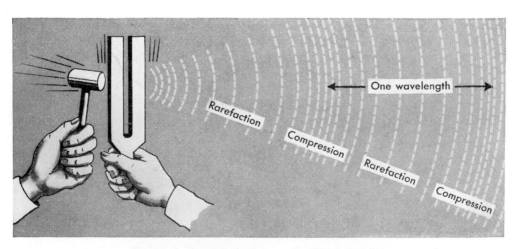

Fig. 11–4. Sound wave from a vibrating tuning fork.

time it moves to the right. In the mean-time, the preceding compression must have moved ahead *1 whole wavelength.* Thus when the prong has made 10 complete vibrations the first compression will have moved ahead 10 whole wave-lengths. If the prong makes f vibrations in one second, then the first compression will have to move ahead f whole wave-lengths in this time. The distance the first compression moves ahead in 1 sec is the velocity v of the wave. If we let L represent one wavelength, then we may write the following law:

Velocity = frequency $\times$ wavelength

or

$$v \quad = \quad f \quad \times \quad L$$

This is a fundamental relationship that holds for all kinds of waves.

EXAMPLE 1: When the velocity of sound is 1,100 ft/sec, what is the wavelength of the fundamental sound wave given off by a whistle vibrating at 200 cps?

SOLUTION:
Given: $v = 1{,}100$ ft/sec and $f = 200$ cps
To find: L
Since $v = f \times L$,

$$L = v/f = \frac{1{,}100 \text{ ft/sec}}{200 \text{ cps}}$$

$$= 5.5 \text{ ft}$$

Notice that *cycles* does not appear in the answer. You might expect the answer to be 5.5 ft/cycle but the "per cycle" is omitted by general agreement.

EXAMPLE 2: When the velocity of sound is 1,100 ft/sec, what is the frequency of a tuning fork which produces a sound wave whose wavelength is 2.75 ft?

SOLUTION:
Given: $v = 1{,}100$ ft/sec
$\qquad L = 2.75$ ft
To find: f
Since $v = f \times L$,

$$f = v/L = \frac{1{,}100 \text{ ft/sec}}{2.75 \text{ ft}}$$

$$= 400 \text{ cps}$$

Speed of Sound

Have you ever watched a batter hit a ball when you were some distance away, perhaps in an outfield bleacher? Did you notice that you heard the crack of the bat against the ball a short time *after* you saw the hit? This interval is the time required for sound to travel from home plate to where you were; the light rays which enabled you to see the batted ball traveled to you in practically no time. In a column of marchers in a parade led by a band, those farther back are apt to be out of step with those near the band, even though they all keep step with the music as *they hear it.* This is but another illustration that sound waves require time to travel. *The speed of sound in air at 0°C is 1,087 ft/sec or 331.4 m/sec.*

Measurements also show that the speed of sound in air increases somewhat when the air becomes warmer. This increase amounts to about 0.6 m or 2 ft/sec for each additional centigrade degree if the temperature is within about 25 degrees of 0°C. At 20°C the speed of sound in air is thus $1{,}087 + (20 \times 2) = 1{,}127$ ft/sec. Ordinary changes in air pressure have little or no effect on the speed of sound. Even on high mountains, where atmospheric pressure is quite low, the speed of sound is about the same as in air at the same temperature at sea level.

If you have ever held your head under water while someone nearby struck two

261

Table 11–1. Speed of Sound in Various Materials

Material	Temperature, °C	Speed, ft/sec	Speed, m/sec
Carbon dioxide	0	846	258
Air	0	1,087	331.4
Cork	..	1,640	500
Lead	20	4,026	1,227
Hydrogen	0	4,165	1,270
Fresh water	4	4,700	1,420
Sea water	3–17	4,760–4,960	1,453–1,511
Copper	20	11,670	3,560
Brick	..	11,980	3,652
Aluminum	..	16,740	5,104
Iron	20	16,820	5,130

stones together *under water*, you know from experience that sound waves travel through water. You may have stood by a railroad track and heard the sound of an approaching train through the steel rails. Sound waves can travel through solids and liquids as well as through gases. The speed of sound, however, differs greatly in different materials. In Table 11–1 you will notice that the speed in water is nearly five times that in air.

What Are Supersonic Speeds?

The speed of sound in air at 0°C is about 741 mph. It is a little more than this at temperatures above zero and a little less for temperatures below zero. When airplanes approach the speed of sound, they encounter special difficulties which make them unstable and hard to control. At speeds higher than that of sound many of these difficulties disappear. Planes equipped with jet engines have been driven at speeds considerably greater than 750 mph. Speeds greater

than the speed of sound are called *supersonic* speeds. Supersonic wind tunnels have been developed for testing the performance of materials and model airplanes at supersonic speeds.

►You Will Be Interested to Know

Underwater sounds are used to detect and locate submarines and torpedoes, as well as surface craft. Torpedoes and underwater mines have been designed to explode when certain underwater sounds strike them. Special types of microphones are required for use under water. Records on disks or tape can be made of underwater sounds. When such records are made in ocean water and later played back, strange sounds are often heard. Some of these sounds have been traced to fish and other marine animals. Croakers make a noise that sounds like blowing out air. Some fish make sounds that resemble the grinding of teeth. Others seem to carry on a continual chatter among themselves, loud and rapid when frightened or excited, gentle and slow almost like a purr, when at rest. Shrimp have proved to be noisy creatures.

Can Sound Go through a Vacuum?

We have seen that sound waves can travel through gases, liquids, and solids —all three states of matter. Can sound waves also travel through space where there are no particles at all, as infrared waves do? The answer is indicated by a simple experiment. Suppose we have a special bell jar with two electric wires passing through its tight-fitting stopper, as shown in Fig. 11–5. If we connect an electric bell to the wires inside the jar and a suitable electric battery to the outside wires, the bell will begin to ring. Then if we place the bell jar with the bell suspended in it on the plate of a

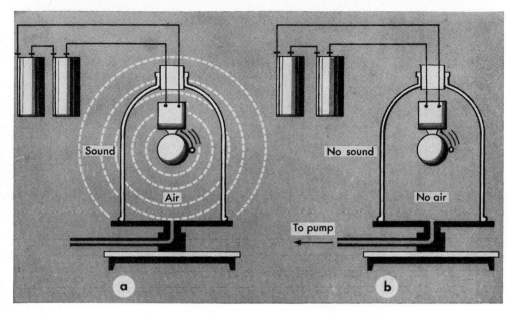

Fig. 11–5. Sound does not travel through a vacuum.

vacuum pump, as shown in Fig. 11–5a, we shall usually have no difficulty hearing the sound of the ringing bell. However, if we pump as much air as possible out of the jar, the sound from the bell will almost or entirely disappear. Then if we let air back into the bell jar we shall be able to hear the sound if the bell is still ringing. It is reasonable to conclude from this experiment that sound is unable to travel through the space from the bell to the walls of the jar when this space has no air in it. *A medium that contains particles of matter is required for the transmission of sound.*

►**Do You Know?**

1. Astronomers find no evidence of an atmosphere on the moon. Could a rocket crashing into the surface of the moon produce sound? Why?
2. The number you can count slowly after seeing a lightning flash before hearing the thunder, divided by 5, is approximately the number of miles to the lightning. How can you prove this statement?
3. Why does oil stop the squeaking of a door or gate hinge?
4. Do higher or lower frequency sounds have longer wavelengths?
5. Air speeds comparable to the speed of sound are sometimes expressed in *Mach numbers*. The speed of sound is Mach 1. What is the Mach number for a speed that is 3/4 that of sound? What speed corresponds to "Mach 1.2?"

CHARACTERISTICS OF SOUND

The song of a canary is easily distinguished from the call of a crow. A note struck on a piano is different from one sounded on a violin. Have you ever paused to think *why* sounds are different? Fundamentally two sounds may differ because (1) one is higher or lower in

263

pitch than the other, (2) one is louder or softer than the other, or (3) one has a different tone quality than the other. These are the chief characteristics that enable us to distinguish one sound from another. All these characteristics depend somewhat on the physiological and psychological make-up of the listener. Many persons have difficulty determining which of two sounds is higher in pitch, if the sounds occur separately. Highly trained musicians, on the other hand, can recognize very small differences in pitch. A sound that seems loud to one person may seem faint to another who is hard of hearing. One person may like the tone quality of a given sound, while another may find it quite unpleasant. This is why we usually refer to this set of sound characteristics as *psychological*.

Pitch, loudness, and tone quality are the chief psychological characteristics of sound.

Upon What Does Pitch Depend?

Figure 11–6 shows a siren disk with several circular rows of holes. The disk is mounted on a rotator so that it can be turned at different speeds. A jet of air blown through one row of holes is inter-rupted at a frequency corresponding to the number of holes that pass through the jet in a second. This produces a sound of the same frequency. If we spin the siren disk faster, the number of holes that pass through the jet per second will be increased. This action will increase the frequency of the sound produced correspondingly. At the same time we should notice that the pitch of the sound appears to rise.

The pitch of a sound depends primarily on the frequency of the vibrating source.

Pitch is often affected by intensity and waveform, but to a much lesser extent than by frequency.

Frequency can be measured and expressed in cycles, or vibrations, per second. It does not depend on any peculiarity of the hearing mechanism of the listener; in fact, it does not depend on the listener at all.

Upon What Does Loudness Depend?

The harder the drummer strikes the bass drum, the louder the sound coming from it. The drumhead must vibrate with a greater swing to produce a loud sound than it does to produce a faint sound. This greater swing of the drum-

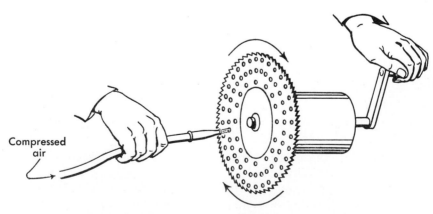

Fig. 11–6. A siren disk and air jet can produce sounds.

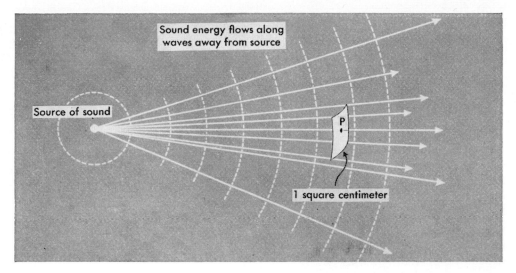

Fig. 11–7. The intensity at point P is the amount of sound energy per second flowing through a square centimeter at that point.

head sets up sound waves of greater amplitude. In doing this, the drumhead *gives more energy per second* to the sound wave. The sound wave in turn delivers more energy per second to our ears. This is why the sound seems louder. Let us substitute for the listening ear a square centimeter of surface perpendicular to the wave direction. This, of course, is several times as large as the ordinary human eardrum. If we place the square centimeter at a given position directly facing the waves, as shown in Fig. 11–7, a certain amount of energy will pass through it each second. The amount of energy per second which passes through the square centimeter is a measure of the *intensity* of the sound wave.

The intensity of a sound is also a quantity that can be measured. It does not depend on peculiarities of the ear of the listener. It may be expressed in ergs per second per square centimeter, or in watts (joules per second) per square centimeter.

The loudness of a given sound depends chiefly on the intensity of the sound wave at the ear of the listener.

If two sounds have the same intensity but different frequencies, they may not seem equally loud to a listener. Some people hear certain frequencies better than they hear other frequencies. Young people usually hear more of the higher frequencies than do older people. Thus the relative loudness of two different sounds may depend to some extent on their frequencies, as well as on their intensities. Loudness also depends somewhat on the *form* of the sound wave that reaches the listener's ear.

Making Sound Waves Visible

Many methods have been used in the past to make sound waves visible. The most convenient method today involves apparatus that is a bit complicated, but with which you may already have some acquaintance. A *microphone* is used to pick up the sound wave and convert its energy into a corresponding wave of electric voltage. An *amplifier* similar to a part of your radio, is used to amplify the voltage wave, that is, to add energy to it. The amplified voltage wave is then used to control the up-and-down motion of a focused beam of electrons in a cathode-ray tube, similar to the tube on which you watch the image on a television set. Control circuits cause the electron beam to sweep horizontally across the field at the same time the voltage wave is moving it up and down. Where the beam of electrons strikes the screen of the tube, the screen material glows green or blue or some other color, depending on the material. In this way the electron beam seems to trace out the sound wave on the screen of the tube. The original *longitudinal* sound wave is changed in the process to a corresponding *transverse* wave.

The cathode-ray tube, amplifier, and necessary control circuits are usually built together into one instrument called a *cathode-ray oscilloscope*. An oscilloscope connected to a suitable microphone can in this way make a sound wave visible.

A vibrating tuning fork set near the microphone produces a picture on the screen shown in Fig. 11–8.

An oscilloscope is a useful device for studying the relation of pitch to frequency and of loudness to intensity as well as the relation of tone quality to *waveform*, that is, the form of the sound wave.

Tone Quality

A vibrating tuning fork produces a sound-wave picture on the oscilloscope that is smooth and regular, as shown in Fig. 11–8. Students of trigonometry will recognize this as a sine or cosine curve. Figure 11–10 shows pictures of a musical tone and of static. The wave picture of the musical tone repeats itself but is not smooth like that of the tuning fork. You would have no difficulty recognizing the difference in these two sounds, even though they have the same intensity and the same frequency. The difference is one of tone quality.

Tone quality depends chiefly on the form of the sound wave—waveform.

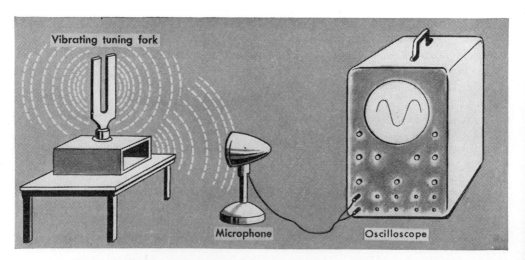

Fig. 11–8. A microphone and an oscilloscope can make a sound wave visible.

Pictures of sounds as displayed on the screen of an oscilloscope.

Sound of a dropped coin striking the floor, spinning on its edge, and gradually teetering to a full stop.

The sound produced when a cork is pulled out of a bottle consists of a single line which varies up and down and gradually gets smaller as the sound fades out.

Sound from a burning match. When the match is struck, it first bursts into a sputtering flame and then settles down to a steady rate of combustion.

A picture of a human cough, as it appears on the oscilloscope screen.

Which of these sounds are clearly noises? (Instrument Division, Allen B. Du Mont Laboratories, Inc.)

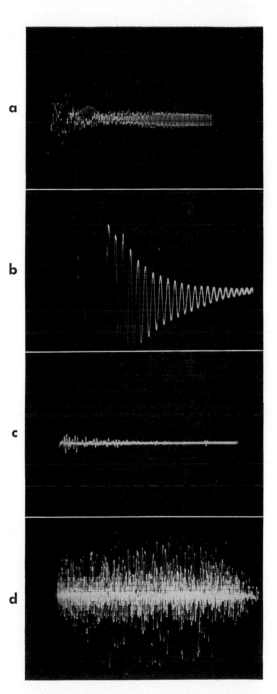

Sound without a Listener

Frequency, intensity, and waveform are measurable physical properties of sound waves. They do not depend on any peculiarities of an individual listener's ear. They do not depend on the presence or absence of a listener. In physics and engineering, we commonly regard these physical effects as sound. It will, therefore, be quite consistent to consider as sound all vibrations of this type, whether or not anyone can or does hear them.

Figure 11–9 shows how the psychological and physical characteristics of sound are related.

Why Waveforms Differ

The sound from a vibrating tuning fork, viewed on the screen of an oscilloscope, has a smooth regular waveform similar to Fig. 11–8. Sounds from musical instruments, the voice, and other sources generally have waveforms that are less smooth. Some may be even more complicated than those of Fig. 11–10. When these sounds are analyzed, the waves from the tuning fork are found to consist of a *single frequency,* whereas those with the more irregular waveforms have *several frequencies at once.* For this reason, the sound from a tuning fork is often called a *pure tone,* while that from a violin is a *complex* tone or sound.

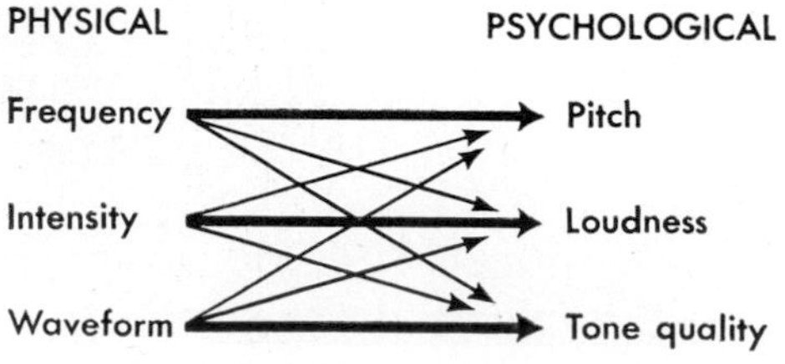

PHYSICAL   PSYCHOLOGICAL

Frequency → Pitch

Intensity → Loudness

Waveform → Tone quality

Fig. 11–9. The relation of physical to psychological characteristics of sound.

268

The lowest frequency present in a complex sound is called the *fundamental;* frequencies higher than the fundamental are *overtone frequencies.* If the fundamental frequency in the sound from a vibrating string is 300 cps, the overtone frequencies are 600, 900, 1,200, . . . cps. In this case, the overtone frequencies are *exact* multiples of the fundamental and are called *harmonic frequencies* or simply *harmonics.* In our illustration, 300 cps is the fundamental frequency, 600 cps is the *second* harmonic frequency and 900 cps is the *third* harmonic frequency. Notice that the first harmonic frequency is the fundamental.

In many complex sounds, overtone frequencies occur that are *not exact* multiples of the fundamental. This is true of the sound from cymbals for example. There is no special name for these inexact overtone frequencies.

The waveform of a complex sound depends on the particular overtone frequencies present, their relative amplitudes, and where each one is in its vibration when they start. The tone quality of a complex sound depends chiefly on the overtone frequencies present and on their relative prominence.

When Is a Sound a Noise?

The boom of a drum, the pure tone of a tuning fork, the song of a canary, and even the harsh call of a crow, when heard singly, are more or less pleasing to the ear. All these sounds have definite pitch, loudness, and tone quality. Viewed on an oscilloscope, each one shows a waveform that *repeats itself regularly.* Under suitable conditions, we would call these sounds *musical tones.*

Sounds such as static on your radio and the clatter of busy typewriters are much more complicated. It is difficult to assign definite pitch and tone quality to them. Viewed on an oscilloscope, such sounds show waveforms that are exceedingly irregular and in general *do not repeat themselves*. We call such sounds *noises*. Often, however, we call any disturbing sound a noise, whether its waveform repeats itself regularly or not. In this sense, even musical tones that we do not like or do not want are noises.

The difference between a musical tone and a noise can be demonstrated with the apparatus of Fig. 11–6. Some siren disks are provided with a circular row of unequally spaced holes. In any event, unequal spacing can easily be obtained by plugging some of the holes in an equally spaced row with wax. When the disk is rotated and the air jet directed on the equally spaced holes, we hear a musical tone; when the jet is directed on the unequally spaced holes, we hear a noise.

Decibels of Sound

We express temperature in degrees above or below a certain reference temperature which we agree to call zero. The zeros we use in the Fahrenheit and the centigrade scales are not points without temperature but merely temperatures from which we begin to count. We use a somewhat similar system to express the relative intensity of a sound. This relative intensity is called the *sound level*.

To construct a scale for sound level, we must first have some intensity from which to count, a sound level zero. The reference intensity generally used for zero level is 10^{-16} watt/cm². This represents quite a low intensity. A person with normal or slightly better hearing can just hear a 1,000-cps tone at this zero level of intensity. At a compression in a sound wave the pressure is momentarily increased, and at a rarefaction it is de-

creased. For a sound in air at zero level, the increase in pressure is only about 0.0002 dyne/cm². When we compare this with normal atmospheric pressure of more than 1,000,000 dyne/cm², we can easily see that such a sound wave does not disturb the air very much!

The levels of sounds of different intensities are expressed in *decibels* above or below this zero. The decibel is not an ordinary unit like the centimeter or the pound, but rather is a special kind of ratio.

You will be able to see from the decibel scale in Table 11–2 how intensity and sound level are related. *Multiplying* the intensity by 10 at any point in the scale raises the sound level 10 decibels. If the intensity of noise in a broadcasting studio is 10 times the reference intensity, then the sound level in the studio is 10 decibels above zero, or simply 10 decibels. If the intensity of noise in a private office is 100 times the reference intensity, then the sound level in the office is 20 decibels. The intensity in the office is just 10 times that in the studio and the sound level is 10 decibels higher than in the studio. If the intensity of noise in a residence is 1,000 times the reference intensity, the sound level there is 30 decibels. This is 10 decibels higher than the level in the office and 20 decibels higher than in the studio. Doubling the

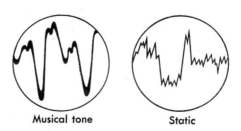

Musical tone   Static

Fig. 11–10. Oscillograms of a musical tone and noise.

Table 11-2. An Intensity and Decibel Scale for Sound

Decibels	Relative energy	
120	1,000,000,000,000	Threshold of painful feeling
110	100,000,000,000	Thunder, unmuffled airplane engine
100	10,000,000,000	Boiler factory, in subway car
90	1,000,000,000	Noise in untreated airplane cabin, elevated trains from street
80	100,000,000	Noisiest street corner in New York, large public address system
70	10,000,000	Average machine shop, interior of electric interurban train
60	1,000,000	Average factory, full volume home radio, average busy street
50	100,000	Church bells at 1200 ft., average store, moderate restaurant clatter
40	10,000	Average office, quiet automobile, ordinary school classroom
30	1,000	Public library, average residence, quiet office
20	100	Office acoustically treated, rustling paper, average whisper
10	10	Quiet church, underground vault, broadcasting studio
0	1	Threshold of audibility

intensity of sound at any point along the scale always raises the sound level about 3 decibels. Sounds whose intensities are less than the reference intensity have levels that are negative or below zero. Thus a sound whose intensity is 10^{-17} watt/cm² has a level -10 decibels.

Why Faraway Sounds Are Fainter

You know from experience that as you move farther away from a vibrating body the sound you hear from it gets fainter and fainter. This means that the intensity of the sound wave *decreases* with distance from the source. If the vibrating body gives off sound energy equally well in all directions, if there is no absorption of the sound, and if there are no nearby objects that reflect the sound, the following is true:

The intensity of sound at any point is inversely proportional to the square of the distance from the source to that point.

Expressed in symbols,

$$\frac{I_1}{I_2} = \frac{D_2{}^2}{D_1{}^2}$$

where I_1 is the intensity of the sound at a point whose distance from the source is D_1 and I_2 is the intensity at a point whose distance is D_2. The intensity of the sound of a whistle at a point 200 ft from the whistle is only one-fourth as great as it is at a point 100 ft from the whistle. Can you show from Fig. 11–11 why this is true? This is the same type of law as that for gravitational force. Because of reflections, wind, absorption, and other effects, actual sounds rarely follow this law exactly.

270

1. How could you use a microphone and an oscilloscope to show that the loudness of a sound depends chiefly on the amplitude of the sound wave?
2. How could you use the same apparatus to show that the pitch of a sound depends chiefly on its frequency?
3. Why do we not commonly speak of the *first* harmonic frequency?
4. "Noise consists of sounds that we don't like, made by the other fellow." Is this a reasonable definition of noise? Explain.
5. Why is a scratching sound always a noise?

THE BEHAVIOR OF SOUND WAVES

In hilly or mountainous country, it is a common experience to shout a few syllables and have them come bounding back to your ears perhaps a second or more later. The effect is almost as if some mimic on a distant cliff or hill were shouting your words right back at you. Often the returning syllables are nearly as clear and distinct as the original ones. This returning sound is an *echo*. Echoes are produced by reflection of sound waves from an obstacle with a relatively smooth surface in much the same way that light is reflected from a mirror. Sound waves are reflected whenever they come to a boundary of the medium in which they are traveling.

The reflected sound must be at least one-tenth of a second behind the original sound in reaching your ear to produce a distinct echo. In one-tenth of a second sound travels about 110 ft. If you make the original sound yourself, then the reflecting surface must be at least 55 ft (110 ft there and back) from you to produce a distinct echo. The effect is more pronounced when the reflecting surface is farther than 55 ft away.

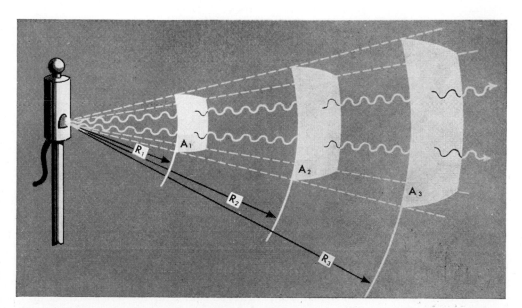

Fig. 11–11. The intensity of sound decreases with distance. At the greater distance the same amount of energy is distributed over a larger area.

Fig. 11–12. An echo is a sound wave reflected back from a large object such as a hill or cliff.

Making Use of Echoes

In waters along high and rocky coasts, navigators often make use of echoes to estimate the distance to shore, especially at night or in foggy weather. A whistle or bell is sounded on the ship and the time required for the echo to return observed. Knowing the speed of sound, the navigator can make a quick estimate of his distance from shore. Icebergs in ship lanes have been located in the same way. Radar, the radio echo method, may supplant the sound echo method for most navigational purposes.

The depth of water is often measured by acoustic "sounding." A projector near the bottom of a vessel sends a pulse of sound waves downward through the water. These waves are reflected at the bottom and returned to the vessel as an echo. Instruments measure the interval of time between the original sound and the echo. Then, from the speed of sound in water, the depth of the water can easily be computed. The instruments are usually designed to make this computation and are calibrated to read the water depth directly from a dial. A similar echo-system, called *sonar*, has been used for locating submerged submarines and other underwater bodies.

Engineers and geophysicists use an echo method to find the depth of oil-bearing strata in the earth. A charge of explosive placed in a hole at the surface sets up waves in the earth when the charge explodes. These waves are reflected from underlying rock strata. By measuring the time required for the echo to return and knowing the speed of sound in the earth, engineers can easily compute the distance down to the layer of rock.

Bats are believed to use an echo method to enable them to avoid walls and other obstacles when they fly in the dark. The sounds they produce are too high in frequency for human ears to hear.

Mirrors for Sound

In early New England churches, a sounding board was often placed back of the high pulpit to reflect the voice of the preacher down on the congregation. Today band shells are built with smooth curved walls back of the players to reflect the sound out to the audience. Curved surfaces tend to concentrate and focus sound waves, just as we shall find curved mirrors focus light waves. Large curved sound mirrors are often set up in laboratories and science museums to demonstrate that sound waves can be

272

focused. Under proper conditions, a faint sound, such as the tick of a watch, produced at the focus of one mirror can be heard distinctly at the focus of the other mirror, but not at points in between.

A "whispering gallery" was unintentionally built into our National Capitol at Washington, D.C. If a person standing at a certain spot on the floor of Statuary Hall speaks softly, he can be heard by another person standing on another particular spot some distance away, but not by persons elsewhere in the hall. The curved undersurface of the Capitol dome acts as an excellent mirror that focuses the sound waves. A similar effect occurs in the Mormon Tabernacle at Salt Lake City, Utah.

The Doppler Effect

Have you ever observed closely the sound from the horn of a passing automobile? As the automobile is approaching, the pitch of the sound seems higher than normal. As it passes and begins to move away from you, the pitch seems suddenly to fall below normal. If you were in an automobile rapidly approaching a ringing bell, you would again notice that the pitch of the bell seems higher

The domed ceiling of Statuary Hall in our National Capitol at Washington acts as an excellent curved mirror for focusing sound waves.

than normal. As you pass and move away from the ringing bell, its pitch seems to fall.

When the distance between you and the source is growing less, the number of compressions that reach your ear in a second is actually greater than the number produced by the source of sound because each successive one has a shorter distance to travel. It is for this reason the apparent pitch is higher than normal. For a similar reason, the apparent frequency is less than the actual frequency, and the pitch seems lower than normal, when the distance between you and the source is increasing.

When the distance between the source of sound and the listener is decreasing, the apparent frequency is more than the actual frequency; when the distance is increasing, the apparent frequency is less than the actual frequency.

This seeming change in frequency is known as the *Doppler effect*. It provides an important method of determining whether a source of sound is approaching or moving away, and how

Fig. 11–13. A playground swing illustrates resonance.

274

fast. The same principle applies also to light waves and to radio waves.

Resonance

Almost everyone has pushed a playground swing with a child in it. To swing high, that is to build up a large amplitude, we must apply a push at just the right time in each swing or cycle. In other words, our pushes must be in step with or *synchronized* with the motion of the swing.

A similar effect occurs in sound. Suppose two tuning forks are placed near each other and are adjusted so that, when struck, they will vibrate at exactly the same frequency. If we strike one fork with a rubber hammer and then stop it with the hand, we will usually hear the other fork giving out sound. Sound waves from the struck fork give little pushes to the second fork at just the right time in each cycle to set it into vibration and build up considerable amplitude, much as we do with the swing. The second fork receives energy through the air from the first one by means of the interlinking sound wave. In the same way, you can often set some of the strings of a piano into vibration if you hold off the damper and sing into the case. Vibrations set up in this way are often called *sympathetic* vibrations. The general phenomenon is called *resonance*. **Any system that can vibrate freely will be set into motion by waves whose frequency is the same as the resonant frequency of that system.**

This principle has widespread application in other fields, as well as in sound. Undesired vibration of parts of machines is often due to resonance. Resonance in electric circuits enables you to tune in and separate stations on your radio. In some cases, even atoms and electrons appear to resonate.

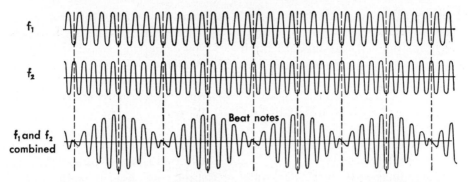

f₁

f₂

f₁ and f₂ combined

Beat notes

Fig. 11–14. Two sound waves of slightly different frequencies combine to produce beats.

Counting the Beats

Attach a piece of wax or a light clamp to one prong of one of the resonating tuning forks discussed on p. 274 and strike the fork with a rubber hammer. The pitch of its sound will be very slightly lower, indicating that its vibration rate has been lowered by *loading* it in this way. Striking the first fork will no longer set the second fork into vibration; they are no longer resonant. If we strike both forks together or in quick succession, we usually hear a single tone that seems to swell and die away in loudness alternately. We say that the two sounds *beat* together. One swell and one ebb constitute one *beat*.

The two sound waves with slightly different frequencies have to travel simultaneously through the same air to our ears. A particle of air which has to transmit several sound waves at the same time must have a complicated motion indeed! When the two waves meet at the particle so that they are *in phase*, both at a compression, for example, they work together and the particle vibrates with a larger amplitude. When they meet *in opposite phase*, one at a compression and the other at a rarefaction, for example, they work against each other and

the particle vibrates with a smaller amplitude, or with no amplitude at all. When the waves are in phase at our ears, we hear a louder sound; when they are out of phase we hear a weaker sound or none at all. But because the waves have different frequencies, they cannot stay in phase at any one particle for long. *They will come into phase again each time one wave gains a whole vibration on the other.* The number of times they come into phase in a second is, therefore, the same as the *difference in their frequencies.* This difference in frequencies corresponds to the number of beats we hear. **The number of beats per second corresponds to the difference in frequency of two sound waves.**

If one fork vibrates 256 times and the other 260 times per second, the number of beats produced per second when both are vibrating together is $260 - 256 = 4$. If the forks could be adjusted so that their frequencies became more nearly equal, their beat rate would become slower and slower. When they reach "zero beat," their frequencies would be exactly the same and they would again be *in resonance*. The disappearance of beats furnishes one very good means of telling when two vibrating bodies have exactly the same vibration rates. Organ and piano tuners use the "zero beat" method to determine when a pipe or string is in tune with a standard pitch pipe.

►**Do You Know?**

1. Can you hear an echo from a distant hill even when you are several hundred feet from the person who makes the sound? Explain.
2. Can buildings with large flat walls produce echoes? Explain.
3. If indicating instruments were used that respond to sound more rapidly than the human ear, could echoes be detected from surfaces closer than 55 ft? Explain.
4. Can you tell by the Doppler effect whether an airplane is coming toward you or moving away? How?
5. Would the Doppler effect be more apparent with jet-engine planes or with slower-moving cargo planes? Why?
6. Why do some sections of an automobile fender or body sometimes vibrate vigorously at a certain engine speed but not at higher or lower speeds?
7. When beats are present, does the sound always disappear entirely at an ebb? Explain.
8. Do rifle bullets generally travel at supersonic speeds? Explain.

HIGHLIGHTS

The *source* of every sound is a *vibrating* body.

Sound is a form of *energy* that travels in *waves* away from a vibrating source through the surrounding medium, usually air.

The chief types of waves are *transverse* and *longitudinal*. Transverse waves have *crests* and *troughs;* longitudinal waves have *compressions*, or *condensations*, and *rarefactions*.

The particles vibrate in a plane *perpendicular* to the path of a *transverse* wave; they vibrate in a plane *parallel* to the path of a *longitudinal* wave.

Sound waves are longitudinal.

The *amplitude* of a wave is the maximum distance any particle moves from its position of rest. Amplitudes are expressed in millimeters, centimeters, or other units of length.

A *wavelength* is the distance between two adjacent crests or two adjacent compressions.

Wavelengths are expressed in meters, centimeters, feet, or other units of length.

The *frequency* of a sound wave is the same as the frequency of the vibrating body that produces it. Frequency is expressed in *cycles* (per second), *kilocycles*, and *megacycles*.

Velocity of a wave = frequency × wavelength, or $v = f \times L$.

The speed (or velocity) of sound in air at 0°C is *1,087 ft/sec*. This speed increases with a rise in temperature.

The speed of sound in water is nearly five times that in air.

Supersonic speeds are speeds faster than that of sound.

Sound waves cannot travel through a vacuum but require a material medium.

Pitch, loudness, and *tone quality* are the chief *psychological* characteristics of sound.

Frequency, intensity, and *waveform* are the chief *physical* characteristics of sound.

Pitch depends chiefly on frequency, loudness on intensity, and tone quality on waveform.

The intensity of a sound wave is expressed in watts per square centimeter; sound level is expressed in decibels above or below zero.

The *fundamental* is the lowest frequency in a complex sound wave; higher frequencies are *overtone frequencies*. Overtone frequencies that are exact multiples of the fundamental are *harmonics*. The second harmonic frequency is twice the fundamental frequency.

The number of overtone frequencies and their relative prominence determine tone quality.

Musical tones have waveforms that repeat themselves periodically. One type of noise has very irregular nonperiodic waveforms.

In an ideal case, the intensity of a sound is *inversely proportional* to the *square* of the distance from the source.

Echoes are produced by *reflection* of sound waves.

Sound waves can be *focused* by curved reflecting surfaces.

The Doppler effect: When the distance between the source and the listener is *decreasing,* the apparent frequency is *greater* than the actual frequency; when the distance is *increasing,* the apparent frequency is *less* than the actual frequency.

Sympathetic vibrations are set up by resonance.

Principle of resonance: Any body that can vibrate freely can be set into vibration by waves whose frequency is the same as its resonant frequency.

Beats are produced by the *interference* of two sound waves that have nearly but not quite the same frequency.

The *beat rate* is equal to the *difference* in the frequencies of the interfering sound waves.

PROBLEMS: GROUP A

1. When the velocity of sound is 1,100 ft/sec, what is the frequency of a sound whose wavelength is 2 ft?

2. When a tuning fork whose frequency is 440 cps produces a sound whose wavelength is 2.56 ft, what is the speed of sound?

3. What is the speed of sound in air at 25°C? Express your answer in both feet per second and meters per second.

4. What is the frequency of the fourth harmonic of a 250-cps vibration?

5. If you hear a ringing church bell and then go three times as far from it, how will its intensity there compare with the first intensity? Assume that this sound obeys the inverse-square law.

6. How far away is a wall from which an echo returns in 3 sec? The temperature of the air at the time is 28°C.

7. One tuning fork has a frequency of 440 cps while another has a frequency of 435 cps. How many beats per second will be produced when both forks are struck simultaneously?

8. An observer noticed that the flash of distant fireworks occurred 23 sec before he heard the sound. If the speed of sound was 1,125 ft/sec at the time, how many miles was the observer from the fireworks?

9. When the speed of sound is 1,100 ft/sec, what is the frequency of an organ-pipe tone whose wavelength (in air) is 55 ft?

10. If a sound whose frequency is 4,000 cps produces a wavelength of 8.6 cm in air, what is the speed of sound?

11. One tuning fork has a frequency of 440 cps and another has a frequency of 446 cps. How many beats per second will be observed when both forks are set into vibration at the same time?

12. A boy observes an echo from a distant cliff of a sharp sound that he produces. If 4 seconds elapse between the beginning of the sound and the echo, how far away is the cliff?

13. What is the frequency of the third harmonic of a fundamental tone whose frequency is 330 cps?

14. What is the frequency of a sound in air whose wavelength is 5.0 cm when the speed of sound is 345 m/sec?

15. In attempting to tune two strings to unison by ear, a musician observed two beats per second when the strings were vibrating at the same time. One string was known to have a frequency of 420 cps. What was the vibration rate of the other string? Give two possible answers.

16. If, on a quiet day, you can see the condensed steam issuing from a whistle 3.5 sec before you hear the sound, how far are you from the whistle? Assume that the speed of sound is 1,125 ft/sec.

GROUP B

1. What is the speed of sound in air, expressed in centimeters per second, when the temperature is 20°C?

2. What is the speed of sound in water when a quartz plate in the water vibrating at 25,000 cps produces sound waves whose wavelength is 5.80 cm?

3. By what number must the intensity of a given sound be multiplied to raise the sound level 60 decibels?

4. What is the frequency of the eighth harmonic of a 250-cps vibration?

5. A student tuned in WWV and received a steady tone whose frequency is exactly 440 cps. At the same time he struck the A key above middle C on a nearby piano and observed three beats per second. What was the actual frequency of the A key? Why are there two possible answers to this question?

6. A navigator estimated 5 sec between the sound of a whistle on shipboard and the return of the echo from a cliff on shore. The thermometer outdoors indicated 20°C. What was the approximate distance from ship to shore?

7. In making an acoustic sounding on shipboard, the operator found that the echo returned from the bottom of the sea in 4.5 sec. The average temperature of the water was assumed to be 17°C. What was the depth of the water?

8. What is the speed of sound in air at 0°F? Express your answer in feet per second.

9. By what number must the intensity of

a given sound be multiplied to raise the sound level 30 decibels?

10. A navigator measured an interval of 4 sec between the reception of the direct sound from a siren on shipboard and the return sound from an iceberg. The temperature of the surrounding air was 0°F. What was the approximate distance from the ship to the iceberg?

11. How long will it take sound to travel ½ mile in fresh water at 4°C?

12. If the wavelength of a given sound in air at 0°C is 20 cm, what will it be in carbon dioxide at the same temperature?

13. The speed of sound in hydrogen gas is how many times as great as its speed in air? Both air and hydrogen are at 0°C.

14. The speed of sound in copper is how many times as great as its speed in lead? Both lead and copper are assumed to be at 20°C.

THINGS TO DO

1. Drop a button or other object into water in a bathtub and watch the progress of the waves produced. Explain what happens when the waves strike the sides of the tub and the curved ends of the tub.

2. Set up traveling waves in a rope. Obtain a ¼-in. clothesline, 25 ft or more in length. Stretch the rope loosely on a smooth floor, such as the floor of a corridor in your school. Hold one end of this rope in your hand and try to produce regularly repeated *horizontal* waves in it parallel to the floor. Discuss the velocity and the wavelength of different trials.

3. Obtain two empty tin cans with their tops cut out. Punch a small hole at the center of the bottom of each can. From the outside of each can, insert the ends of a piece of cotton string 10 ft or more long in these holes and tie large knots in the ends of the string so that it will not pull out easily. Stretch the string in a straight line so that it is supported by the tin cans and does not touch anything else. Each can should now act as a transmitter when you talk into it and a receiver when you put your ear to it. How far can you make a tin-can telephone work?

4. Demonstrate how beats are produced. If you play a portable musical instrument, sound a note on it (A, for example) and at the same time strike the key of a piano that produces the same note. Explain.

Applications of Acoustics:
Control of Sound

HOW WE HEAR

That branch of science which deals especially with the production and hearing of sounds is often called *acoustics*.

Our ears are intricate devices, even though they look simple from the outside. The *outer ear*, which we see, aids us somewhat in receiving sound energy. The real hearing mechanism is in the *middle ear* and the *inner ear*, deep in the bony structure of the head. We shall use the simplified drawing, Fig. 12–1, to help us understand how the ear works. We must keep in mind that this drawing does not show the relative size, shape, and position of the parts.

280

The real hearing mechanism begins at the middle ear, at the end of the tube leading into the head from the outer ear. Across the end of this tube is stretched a delicate elastic membrane, the *eardrum*, or *tympanum*. The eardrum closes this tube completely from the outside. Sound waves coming into the tube from the outer ear force the eardrum to vibrate with them.

The vibrations of the eardrum are transferred across the middle ear by a lever system made up of three small bones, the *hammer*, the *anvil*, and the *stirrup*. The mechanical advantage of this lever system is slightly greater than one. The hammer is attached to the eardrum and the stirrup works into the *oval window*, an opening into the bony cavity of the inner ear.

The inner ear consists of a heavy-walled structure shaped something like a snail shell and is filled with a liquid. This structure has two openings to the middle ear, the oval window which is closed by the base of the stirrup and the round window just below the first, which is closed by an elastic membrane. The stirrup moving in and out with the sound vibrations pushes on the liquid. The liquid is practically incompressible, so the membrane over the round window has to stretch outward and inward to allow the stirrup to move. This sets the liquid in the inner ear in vibratory motion. The auditory nerve ends in fine hairlike structures located on the partition in the inner ear and extending into the liquid. Motion of the liquid stimulates these nerve ends and we have a sensation of hearing. The three small semicircular canals concerned with equilibrium are part of the inner ear. They are not shown in Fig. 12–1.

How Good Are Your Ears?

The eardrum is quite small, perhaps 5 mm or less in diameter. Very little energy is needed to force it to vibrate. If you have "normal" hearing you can probably just hear a sound whose level is zero decibels and frequency 1,000 cps. Figure 12–2 shows curves of equal loudness for different frequencies. These curves are average values obtained by testing a great many persons who were supposed to have normal hearing. The curve marked 0 shows the level of sound at different frequencies that could just be heard by a person whose ears behave like these average curves. This curve is sometimes called the *threshold of hearing*. These curves indicate that the normal ear is most sensitive to sounds in the frequency range 3,000 to 4,000 cps.

The curve marked 120 is also marked "feeling." Sounds at these levels can be felt as well as heard. They are painfully loud. Not only do they hurt your ears, but you can actually feel the vibrations in other parts of your body.

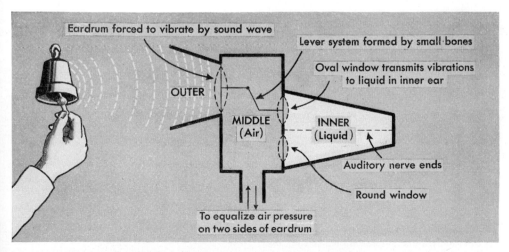

Fig. 12–1. A functional diagram of the arrangement and operation of the parts of the ear. This resembles a real ear only in principle.

Vibrations We Cannot Hear

Have you ever seen a whistle that when blown made little or no sound you could hear yet served to call back a roving dog? The sound waves set up by such whistles have frequencies too high for human ears, even though the dog seems to hear them well. The flying bat, too, makes sounds with frequencies too high for us to hear. You will notice in Fig. 12–2 that all the loudness curves stop at about 20,000 cps. Most persons cannot hear frequencies higher than this and many persons cannot hear frequencies that are even as high as 15,000 cps. The upper limit of audibility is, therefore, taken as 20,000 cps.

There are many vibrations and waves with frequencies above our upper limit of audibility. These are called *ultrasonic* vibrations. Ultrasonic frequencies extend well up in the range of megacycles.

The operator in this photograph is using an *audiometer* to test the hearing of the girl at the right. A graph showing how sensitive a person's hearing is at different frequencies can be made from the results of such a hearing test. (*Sonotone Corporation*)

282

You will notice also that the loudness curves of Fig. 12–2 stop suddenly at about 25 cps at the low-frequency end. Vibrations with frequencies lower than this are difficult or impossible to hear. Some investigators set the lower limit of audibility at 16 cps, but there is a question whether any one can actually hear fundamental frequencies as low as 16 cps. The lower limit of audibility is probably near 20 cps. Vibrations with frequencies lower than we can hear are called *subsonic*.

Some Uses for Ultrasonic Waves

Plates and bars cut from a quartz crystal and placed in a suitable electronic circuit can be made to vibrate at ultrasonic frequencies. Nickel and special alloy rods can also be used to generate ultrasonic frequencies. These vibrators can give considerable power to the waves they set up in the surrounding air or liquid. Such underwater ultrasonic waves and their echoes are used in the *sonar* system used for locating submarines and other craft under water. Ultrasonic waves are used in an echo method in testing metal shafts and castings for flaws. The axles of locomotives and railroad cars, for example, can be examined quickly for possible cracks and flaws by this method. These very-high-frequency waves are used to break up fat globules and *homogenize* milk. They are used also to destroy bacteria.

▶Do You Know?

1. The Eustachian tube extends from the middle ear to the throat. How does this tube aid in hearing?
2. Why is it difficult to hear when you get water in your ears?
3. If you ever had your hearing range tested, how high in frequency can you hear?

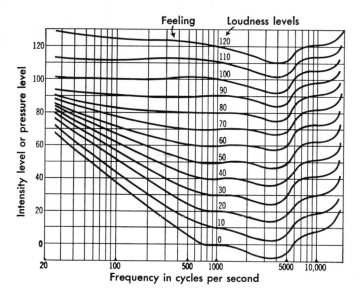

Fig. 12–2. Curves of equal loudness.

Feeling **Loudness levels**

Intensity level or pressure level

Frequency in cycles per second

4. Why is it difficult for a person who uses a hearing aid to determine the directions from which various sounds come?
5. Explain the meaning of the terms *subsonic* and *ultrasonic.*
6. Define the term *acoustics.*

SOUND AND MUSICAL SCALES

You may be surprised to learn that music has a certain physical and mathematical basis. If you strike a tuning fork whose frequency is 256 cps and another whose frequency is 512 cps at the same time, you will probably like the combination of these tones, as most people do. You may be able to recognize the *musical interval* between these tones as an *octave.* A fork whose frequency is 220 cps sounded with one whose frequency is 440 cps would also give a pleasing combination. The musical interval between these two tones is also an octave. There are an unlimited number of pairs of tones whose interval is an octave.

If the fundamental frequency of one tone is exactly twice that of another tone, the musical interval between them is an octave. The octave is the frame within which musical scales are built.

Musical Intervals

A musical interval is the *ratio* of two fundamental frequencies, never their difference. Thus the musical interval between two tuning forks in the preceding paragraph is $512/256 = 2/1$. It is never $512 - 256 = 256$. We already know that the ratio $2/1$ represents an octave. Other intervals also have names. Table 12–1 shows the names of some common musical intervals.

Tones That Clash

While each of two tones may be musical and pleasing by itself, this is no assurance that their combination will also be pleasing. Two tones that are an *octave* apart combine to produce the most pleasing effect. Such tones are *harmonious* or *consonant.* Tones that are a *fifth* apart are only slightly less

283

Table 12–1. Frequency Ratios of Common Intervals

Interval	Frequency ratio
Unison	1/1
Octave	2/1
Fifth	3/2
Fourth	4/3
Major third	5/4
Minor third	6/5
Major tone	9/8
Minor tone	10/9
Semitone	16/15

harmonious. When the frequency ratio is the ratio of two small whole numbers, the two notes are harmonious.

When a tuning fork whose frequency is 288 cps is sounded with one whose frequency is 256 cps (D and C on the musical scale) their combined effect is unpleasant. These two tones clash; they are *discordant*. It has been found that discord depends chiefly on the beat rate between the two tones. When their frequencies are almost alike, there are only a few beats per second and the two tones sound pretty well together. Conditions begin to change when the beat rate reaches 8 or 10 per second, and their combined effect becomes more discordant. When the beat rate reaches 70 or more per second, tones in the middle octave (256 to 512 cps) begin to become harmonious again. For this range of frequencies, the most disagreeable beat rate is about 32 per second.

The Diatonic Scale

A musical *scale* consists of a series of eight notes or tones arranged in a definite way so that the interval from the lowest

284

to the highest is an octave. The term *octave* refers to the number eight. The diatonic scale uses each letter of the tonal alphabet once: C, D, E, F, G, A, B, (C'). This uses just the white keys of the piano. Table 12–2 shows the notes of an octave of the diatonic scale as they are written in music.

C is the keynote or *tonic* for the octave shown. The scale notes are indicated by the letters C, D, E . . . in the first row. C' is an octave higher than C. The vocal names for these notes, do, re, me . . . are given in the second row.

The third row indicates the *relative*, but not the actual, vibration rates of the different notes in the diatonic scale. These are the *smallest whole numbers* that can be used to express this relationship. The fourth row shows the ratio of the vibration rate of any note to that of the keynote C. These ratios are easily found from the ratio numbers in the row above. For example, the ratio number of G is 36 and that of C is 24. The ratio of the vibration rate of G to that of C is therefore 36/24 = 3/2. The other ratios are found in the same way. These ratios are really the musical interval between the different notes and the keynote C.

The ratio for C' is 2. This indicates that it is an octave above C, as we already know. The ratio of G is 3/2; we know that this interval is a fifth. G is the fifth note above C, if we count both C and G. This may seem to you an odd way of counting! The ratio of F is 4/3. This is the interval called a *fourth*, because F is the fourth note from C.

The fifth row shows the musical intervals between successive notes. Three of these intervals are major tones with ratios 9/8; two are minor tones with ratios 10/9, and two are semitones with ratios 16/15.

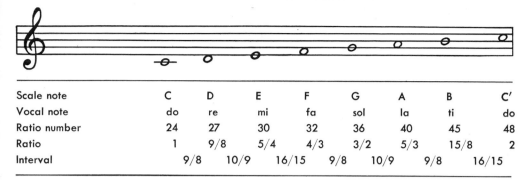

Table 12–2. The Diatonic Scale

Scale note	C	D	E	F	G	A	B	C'
Vocal note	do	re	mi	fa	sol	la	ti	do
Ratio number	24	27	30	32	36	40	45	48
Ratio	1	9/8	5/4	4/3	3/2	5/3	15/8	2
Interval		9/8	10/9	16/15	9/8	10/9	9/8	16/15

Standard Pitch

Although the numbers 24, 27 . . . 48 are not the actual frequencies of the different notes, they are convenient to use in computing the actual frequencies. First we must decide on a definite reference pitch. Let us start with an actual vibration rate of 256 cps for middle C. We find from the table that the ratio number of C is 24 and that of the next note, D, is 27. Then the vibration rate of D must be $27/24 \times 256 = 288$ cps. In the same way, the vibration rate of E must be $30/24 \times 256 = 320$ cps. Table 12–3 shows the vibration rates of all the notes of the octave starting from the reference pitch corresponding to 256 cps for C.

For frequencies of the corresponding notes in the next lower octave, divide the frequencies in Table 12–3 by 2. For frequencies of the corresponding notes in the next *higher* octave, multiply the frequencies in Table 12–3 by 2.

A pitch of 256 cps for C is commonly used for laboratory work, but present-day musicians tend to use a higher pitch. Musicians usually base the scale on the note A; orchestra players tune their instruments to A of the oboe, or to a standard A fork or bar.

In standard pitch, A has a frequency of 440 cps.

Suppose we wish to compute the vibration rate of C for standard pitch with A as the base. The ratio number of A is 40 and that of C is 24. The vibration rate of C must therefore be $24/40 \times 440 = 264$ cps. The vibration rates for standard pitch shown in Table 12–3 were computed in this way.

►You Will Be Interested to Know

In the years from 1880 to date the pitch actually used by bands and orchestras has varied all the way from A = 423 to A = 548 cps. In 1883 the Boston Symphony Orchestra adopted A = 435 as its standard. In 1891 the

Table 12–3. Frequencies of Laboratory and Standard Pitches

Scale note	C	D	E	F	G	A	B	C'
Ratio number	24	27	30	32	36	40	45	48
Frequency: laboratory pitch	256	288	320	341	387	427	480	512
Frequency: standard pitch	264	297	330	352	396	440	495	528

American Piano Manufacturers Association adopted the same standard, A = 435, and called it International Pitch. In 1918 the American Federation of Musicians adopted A = 440; this standard was later adopted by the Music Industries Chamber of Commerce of the United States. Practically all orchestras and musical instrument makers today adjust their instruments to 440 cps for A. This exact frequency is now broadcast by radio from the National Bureau of Standards.

You can usually receive standard pitch on your short-wave radio, if you live within range of the National Bureau of Standards Radio Station WWV, located at Beltsville, Maryland. This radio station transmits a standard A tone, 440 cps, during alternate 5-min periods on a number of short-wave frequencies, including 2.5, 5, and 10 megacycles per second. The schedule is modified from time to time. When you tune in WWV you will hear the steady tone of standard A, along with faint ticks to mark seconds. When reception is good, it is interesting to check a piano or other musical instrument against this very precise standard A, which varies from 440 cps by less than 0.000009 cps! Strike the A key of the piano (the A above middle C) while you are receiving standard A on the radio and count the beats.

A Scale with Many Notes

Music is not all written or played in the key of C. If the keynote is D, several new notes with frequencies not shown in Table 12–3 are required to maintain the same diatonic intervals from the keynote. To provide for every possible keynote, the octave would have to include at least 53 different notes, each with its own frequency. A singer or a

286

violinist might be able to distinguish fairly well between so many notes, but a pianist would face an impossible task with 53 keys on each of the seven octaves on the keyboard.

An Equal-tempered Scale

Students acquainted with music know that a much simpler scale with only 13 notes in an octave is used on a piano. This is the *equal-tempered scale* obtained by modifying the diatonic scale in the following way:

1. Each of three *major tones* in the diatonic scale is replaced by a *whole tone*.
2. Each of the *two minor tones* is replaced also by a whole tone.
3. Each of the two *semitones* is replaced by a *half tone*.

All whole tones represent the same interval and a half tone is just half this interval.

An 8-note octave modified in this way would have intervals arranged as follows:

$$C \longrightarrow D \longrightarrow E \rightarrow F \longrightarrow G \longrightarrow A \longrightarrow B \rightarrow C'$$

Each of the whole tones, such as that from C to D, is then subdivided into two half-tone intervals. This introduces 5 new notes, called *flats* and *sharps*, into the octave, making 13 notes in all. This 13-note octave is shown in the following diagram:

In this equal-tempered scale, C-sharp (C♯) and D-flat (D♭) are the same note. The interval between successive notes can no longer be expressed as the ratio of simple whole numbers. Since there are now 12 equal intervals in 1 octave, it

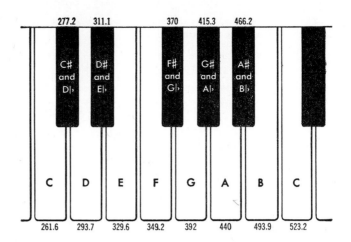

Fig. 12–3. One octave of the keyboard of a piano showing the vibration rates corresponding to the different keys.

follows that each interval must be the *twelfth root of* 2. This turns out to be 1.0595. Thus the frequency of each one of the 13 notes is about 6 per cent higher than that of the note just preceding it. Table 12–4 shows how the frequencies of different notes compare on the diatonic and the equal-tempered scales.

►**Do You Know?**

1. Do musicians ever actually use the diatonic scale? Explain.
2. Are E-flat and D-sharp always the same note on all musical scales?
3. What is the name of the musical interval from C to E?
4. What is the difference between laboratory pitch and standard pitch? Has the note C the same frequency in lab-

oratory pitch as in standard pitch? Explain.
5. Explain the meaning of the term *octave*.
6. How can you tell when two tones are discordant?
7. How many notes are there in one octave of the equal-tempered scale?

MUSICAL INSTRUMENTS

The art of using sound in speech and music developed long before the science of sound. Musical instruments have generally been built and developed by trial and error. Very few have been designed and blueprinted in the same way that a house or a bridge is designed before it is built.

Table 12–4.   Notes and Frequencies

Scale note	C	C#D♭	D	D#E♭	E	F	F#G♭	G	G#A♭	A	A#B♭	B	C'
Frequency in diatonic scale (A = 440 cps)	264		297		330	352		396		**440**		495	528
Frequency in equal-tempered scale (A = 440 cps)	261.6	277.2	293.7	311.1	329.6	349.2	370	392	415.3	**440**	466.2	493.9	523.2

Classes of Musical Instruments

Do you play a musical instrument? If so, do you know the physical principle on which your instrument is based? To which of the following general classes does it belong?

1. Stringed instruments, like the violin, cello, double bass, guitar, harp, and piano.
2. Wind instruments, like the French horn, bugle, trombone, flute, saxophone, and pipe organ.
3. Percussion instruments, like the bass drum, kettle drum, and cymbals.

In the stringed instruments, the primary vibrating body is a stretched wire or string. This may be set into vibration by (1) bowing, as on the violin; (2) plucking, as on the harp; or (3) striking with a soft hammer, as on the piano. The vibrating string forces the body of the instrument to vibrate with it. In some cases the string also sets air cavities in the instrument into vibration. This is how a stringed instrument acquires its own characteristic tone quality.

The principal vibrating body in practically all wind instruments is a column or a body of air. This air is set into vibration by resonance with other bodies that vibrate, such as (1) a vibrating reed, as in the clarinet and saxophone; (2) the lips of the player, as in the bugle;

or (3) an air jet blowing against an edge or lip, as in the pipe organ.

Percussion instruments are set into vibration by striking with some form of stick or hammer.

Standing Waves

If your instructor or a classmate will blow a clear high-pitched whistle steadily in your classroom, you may be able to observe a peculiar effect. By moving your head a short distance to the right or left you can make the sound seem louder or make it almost disappear. This is caused by the interference of sound waves, traveling in opposite directions through the air in the room. Since the direct waves and those reflected from the walls all have the same frequency they combine to produce a type of wave that seems to stand still. Such waves are called *standing* or *stationary* waves. Standing waves are generally caused by reflection. These waves are important in all kinds of vibration.

It is easy to set up and see standing waves in a rope fastened to a post or wall, as shown in Fig. 12–4. After a few trials you will discover that the speed of your hand, together with the tension you apply to the rope, determines whether a particular rope will vibrate in one, two, or three *segments*. These waves on the rope appear to stand still, although the

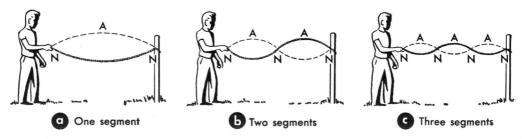

(a) One segment   (b) Two segments   (c) Three segments

Fig. 12–4. Standing waves may be set up in a rope.

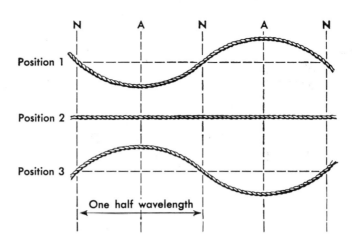

N A N A N

Position 1

Position 2

Position 3

One half wavelength

Fig. 12–5. Successive positions of a rope vibrating in two segments.

particles of the rope are surely vibrating. At some points along the rope, the amplitude of vibration is large, while at other points, the amplitude is nearly zero. The points such as those marked A in Fig. 12–4 have greatest amplitude. These points are *antinodes* or *loops*. The points such as N in Fig. 12–4 have minimum amplitude. These points are *nodes*. Standing waves with nodes and antinodes are formed by longitudinal waves as well as by transverse waves.

A Standing Wave in Slow Motion

Producing a standing wave on a rope by hand soon becomes tiresome. Mechanical devices driven by motors can be arranged to apply the same kind of motion as the moving hand. We can see the vibration of the rope in slow motion if we illuminate it with a light that is interrupted at nearly the same frequency as that of the moving rope. The rope then will appear to pass successively through the positions shown in Fig. 12–5. You can see from the figure that it is only a *half-wavelength* from one node to the next.

When we can make a wave appear to stand still and can locate its nodes and antinodes, it is easy to measure its

wavelength with a ruler or meter stick. The distance between two successive nodes or two successive antinodes in a standing wave is a half-wavelength.

What Is a Stroboscope?

An instrument for producing interrupted light and for varying the number of interruptions per second is called a *stroboscope*. A simple stroboscope can be made by sending light from a projector through suitable holes in a rotating disk. If the disk is mounted on a variable-speed rotator, the speed of interruption can be varied. With light from this device, rotating or vibrating motions appear slowed down, stopped, or even reversed, while the actual vibrations continue at full speed ahead! So the stroboscope is a useful device in studying vibrating motion.

How Strings Vibrate

If a violin string is plucked, it will vibrate with a standing wave along the string. This vibration can be verified with a suitable stroboscope. The end points of the string must always be nodes because the ends are fastened so that they cannot vibrate. The simplest way for the string to vibrate is in a single seg-

289

Fig. 12–6. A simple form of laboratory stroboscope.

ment with a node at each end and an antinode in the middle. The length of the string is then just a *half-wavelength* for the vibration wave along the string. This is the *fundamental* frequency, the lowest frequency at which the given string can vibrate.

There are other ways in which the string can vibrate and still have a node at each end. Figure 12–7*b* shows the string vibrating in two segments, with a node at the mid-point. The length of the string is a whole wavelength for this vibration. The frequency of the sound produced when the string vibrates in two segments is *twice* the fundamental frequency of the string. In Fig. 12–7*c*, the string is vibrating in three segments, with a wavelength and a half on the string. The frequency of the sound produced in this case is three times the fundamental frequency.

A string of a musical instrument usually vibrates at its fundamental and one or more of its other possible frequencies *at the same time*. Overtones in the sound from a string are produced by these multiple modes of vibration. You

290

can show this by plucking a string a short distance from one end and then touching the mid-point lightly with the edge of a card. The strong fundamental tone will be damped out by the card, and you will hear for a moment the first overtone an octave higher than the fundamental. **The first overtone of a vibrating string has a frequency twice that of the fundamental; the second overtone has a frequency three times that of the fundamental. Any number of overtones is possible.**

Violin and Piano

We have already seen that the tone quality of a musical sound depends upon the particular overtone frequencies that accompany the fundamental, and on their relative amplitudes. In stringed instruments, the overtones produced and their amplitudes depend on (1) whether the string is excited by bowing, plucking, or striking; (2) the force applied in exciting the string; and (3) the place along the string where this force is applied.

The wood in the body of a violin and the air cavity enclosed by it are forced to vibrate by the vibrating strings. These parts respond better to some overtone frequencies than to others and thus accentuate particular overtones. Differences in materials, structural design, and the methods of exciting the strings are responsible for the difference in tone quality of A on the violin and A on the piano.

The Laws of Vibrating Strings

The light E string of a violin vibrates faster than the heavy G string. The frequency of any string changes when the violinist tunes it by adjusting its tension. The frequency changes also when he changes the length of a string in playing. Thus all the factors that control the vibration rate of a string are represented in the violin and its use.

Careful measurements show that (1) a string 100 cm long will vibrate with a fundamental frequency just half that of a similar string 50 cm long under the same tension, (2) a string under a tension of 4 kg will vibrate at a fundamental frequency twice that of a similar string in which the tension is 1 kg, and (3) a string with a mass of 16 mg/cm of length will vibrate at a fundamental frequency half that of a string whose mass is 4 mg/cm if both strings have the same length and the same tension.

From these cases we may conclude that the fundamental frequency of a vibrating string is (1) *inversely* proportional to its length, (2) *directly* proportional to the *square root* of its tension, and (3) *inversely* proportional to the *square root* of its mass per unit length. These relations can be expressed in a single equation

$$f = \frac{1}{2L}\sqrt{\frac{T}{m}}$$

in which f will come out in cycles per second when L, the length of the string, is expressed in centimeters; T, the tension, in dynes; and m, the mass per unit length, in grams per centimeter.

How Closed Air Columns Vibrate

Suppose we hold a vibrating tuning fork above the open end of a glass tube, set up as shown in Fig. 12–8. If we start with the tube nearly filled and lower the water level slowly, we soon find a level at which the sound from the fork seems to swell up and become much louder. A small adjustment one way or the other from this level will cause the sound to die down again. At this particular length the air column inside the tube vibrates in resonance with the tuning fork. If we make the air column about 3 times as long, we may find another resonance point. A third resonance point occurs at about 5 times the original length. The first resonance point is easiest to locate because the increase in loudness is most marked at this point.

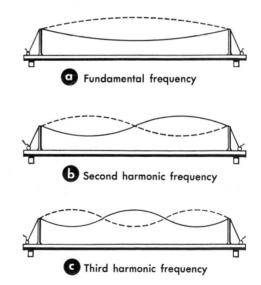

ⓐ Fundamental frequency

ⓑ Second harmonic frequency

ⓒ Third harmonic frequency

Fig. 12–7. A string vibrating at different frequencies.

291

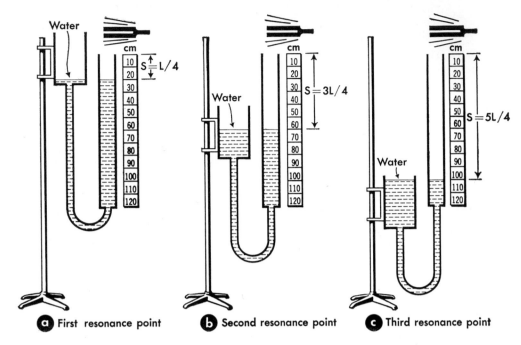

Fig. 12–8. Resonance points in an air column closed at one end.

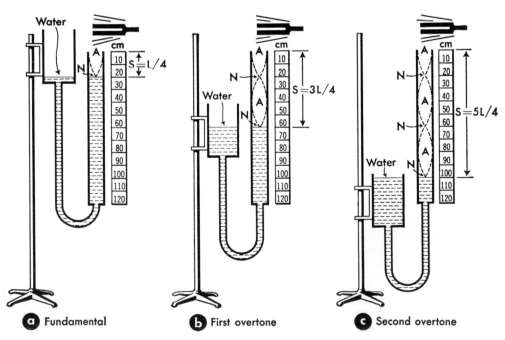

Fig. 12–9. Standing waves in the resonant air columns of Fig. 12–8. Nodes are indicated by N and antinodes by A.

Standing Waves in Closed Air Columns

A standing wave is set up inside the tube when the air column of Fig. 12–8a vibrates in resonance. The air particles that touch the water cannot vibrate up and down, hence the lower end of the standing wave must *always be a node*. The upper end open to the air outside must *always be an antinode*. The simplest pattern of nodes and antinodes that can satisfy these conditions is shown in Fig. 12–9a. The air column in Fig. 12–8a is vibrating in this pattern. The length of the air column is a *quarter-wavelength* of the sound wave traveling down and back in the tube. If we let S represent the length of this air column and v the velocity of the sound wave in the tube, the wavelength of the sound is $L = 4S$ and the frequency is given by the basic equation

$$f = \frac{v}{L} = \frac{v}{4S}$$

If we know the velocity of sound in the tube and can measure the length of the air column which will resonate with a given tuning fork, we can use this equation to compute the frequency of the fork. If the velocity of sound is 33,000 cm/sec and the length of the air column that will resonate with a given fork is 33 cm, the frequency of the fork is

$$f = \frac{v}{4S} = \frac{33,000 \text{ cm/sec}}{4 \times 33 \text{ cm}} = 250 \text{ cps}$$

Figure 12–9b shows the standing wave in the air column at the second resonance point. The length of the column is now *three* quarter-wavelengths. The frequency is 3 times the fundamental frequency for an air column of this length. The length of the air column in Fig. 12–9c is *five* quarter-wavelengths. The frequency is 5 times the funda-mental for an air column of the same length. There are other resonance points for the tuning fork and the air column of Fig. 12–8, but in each case the length of the air column is an *odd number* of quarter-wavelengths. The frequency will be an *odd number* times the fundamental frequency for an air column of the same length in each case.

An air column may vibrate with several of these possible standing-wave patterns at the same time. In doing so, it may give out its fundamental and over-tone frequencies. *The first overtone fre-quency of an air column closed at one end and open at the other is 3 times the funda-mental; the second overtone frequency is 5 times the fundamental; the third overtone frequency is 7 times the fundamental.*

The *first* overtone in this case is the *third* harmonic frequency. It is a twelfth rather than an octave above the funda-mental. The *second* overtone is the *fifth* harmonic, and the *third* overtone is the *seventh* harmonic frequency.

How Open Air Columns Vibrate

Figure 12–10 shows a glass tube with a telescoping sleeve for varying its length. If we hold a vibrating tuning fork at the end of such a tube and adjust its length properly, we shall find that the air column in this open tube can also be set into vibration by resonance. For the first resonance point with the same tuning fork, the length of the open air column will be *twice* the length found for a closed column. The second reso-nance point occurs when the open air column is about twice its first length; The third resonance point requires an air column about 3 times its first length. Additional resonance points may be found, but with more difficulty. For these, the length of the air column is 4, 5, and so on, times its first length.

293

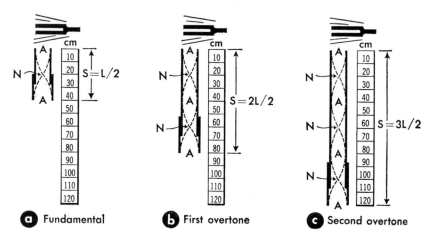

(a) Fundamental   (b) First overtone   (c) Second overtone

Fig. 12–10. Standing waves in a resonating air column open at both ends. Nodes are indicated by N and antinodes by A.

Standing Waves in Open Columns

The standing wave set up in an open tube when the air column vibrates must have an antinode at each end. The simplest pattern of nodes and antinodes to satisfy this condition is shown in Fig. 12–10a. Here the length of the column is a half-wavelength. The column is vibrating at its fundamental frequency. If f represents this frequency, v the velocity of the sound wave in the tube, and S the length of the air column, the wavelength of the sound is $L = 2S$ and the fundamental frequency

$$f = \frac{v}{L} = \frac{v}{2S}$$

Figure 12–10b shows the standing wave for the second resonance point. The length of the tube is now two half-wavelengths. The frequency of this vibration is *twice* that of the fundamental for an air column of the same length. In Fig. 12–10c the length of the tube is three half-wavelengths and the frequency is 3 times the fundamental for that tube.

Open air columns may also vibrate with several of these standing-wave patterns at the same time. For this reason, they give out fundamental and overtone frequencies. *The first overtone frequency of an air column open at both ends is 2 times the fundamental; the second overtone frequency is 3 times the fundamental; the third overtone is 4 times the fundamental.*

In this case, the *first* overtone is the *second* harmonic frequency, the *second*

Table 12–5. Fundamentals and Overtones of Open and Closed Air Columns

Velocity of sound: 33,000 cm/sec
Length of columns: 33 cm

Frequency	One end closed, frequency, cps	Both ends open, frequency, cps
Fundamental	250	500
First overtone	750	1,000
Second overtone	1,250	1,500
Third overtone	1,750	2,000

overtone is the *third* harmonic frequency, and the *third* overtone is the *fourth* harmonic frequency. The first overtone is one octave above the fundamental.

Table 12–5 summarizes the important differences in the way open and closed air columns vibrate. These values are for an open and a closed column, each 33 cm in length. The velocity of sound inside the tube is assumed to be 33,000 cm/sec.

Air Columns in Wind Instruments

Wind instruments like the pipe organ use air columns in pipes of fixed length. Each pipe then produces a single fundamental tone. The bugle, too, has an air column of a fixed length. Its fundamental frequency is about 66 cps and the notes it produces are all harmonics of this frequency. The bugler selects the overtone he wants by setting his lips to vibrate at about that frequency.

Instruments like the flute have valves that open and close holes along the tube. When a valve is opened, the air column must vibrate with an antinode at that point. Thus, opening different valves produces different fundamentals and overtones.

In the trombone and other instruments of this class, different notes are produced by changing the length of the air column by means of the slide. The slide is moved in for the high notes and moved out for the low notes.

How Plates Vibrate

The vibration of a stretched membrane such as a drumhead or a metal plate such as a cymbal is much more complicated than the cases just considered. Standing waves are produced on the vibrating body, but the nodes are lines rather than points, and the antinodes are areas of the plate. It is often hard to tell which, if any, is the *fundamental* frequency of a vibrating plate. Overtones occur with frequencies which are not exact multiples of the main frequency. Often the overtones of bells and chimes are quite discordant, even though their main tones may be harmonious. For this reason, the bells in a carillon are generally struck one at a time.

Making a Standing Wave Visible

Perhaps you are now interested in seeing the nodes and antinodes in an actual sound wave. Kundt's apparatus, shown in Fig. 12–11, enables you to do this. The steel or brass rod is made to vibrate endwise by stroking it vigorously with a cloth sprinkled with powdered rosin. If you adjust the length of the glass tube just right by moving the piston back and forth, the sound wave within the tube will make the fine cork dust dance and vibrate. The dust will pile up into easily seen ridges at the antinodes of the standing wave, and

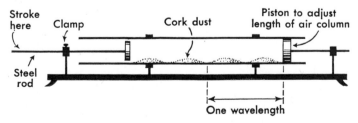

Fig. 12–11. Standing waves shown by cork dust in a Kundt's tube.

scarcely move at all at the nodes. The wavelength of the sound can be measured with a ruler, since the distance from one node to the next is a half-wavelength. Then if the frequency of the vibrating rod is known, the velocity of sound in the tube can be computed; or if the velocity of sound is known, the frequency of the vibrating rod and the sound can be computed from the general wave equation

$$v = f \times L$$

▶Do You Know?

1. Why would you expect a given low note to have a different tone quality if produced by an open pipe than it would have if produced by a pipe closed at one end?
2. Why does a violinist rub rosin on the strings of his bow?
3. Why does a piano need to be tuned from time to time?
4. In a motion picture, the wheels of an automobile often appear to stop and then turn backward before the automobile comes to a dead stop. What is the cause of this effect?
5. Why does one's voice sound different when one has a head cold?
6. If the temperature of the room rises, will the pitch of organ pipes rise or fall?
7. If an organ pipe were filled with hydrogen and blown, would the frequency of its fundamental tone be higher or lower than for air?

THE ACOUSTICS OF ROOMS

Is it easy to hear everywhere in your school auditorium or assembly room? Some rooms are much better for hearing than others. We now know that the reasons for differences in the acoustic

properties of rooms are entirely physical.

One cause for poor acoustics in some rooms is the reflection of sound waves from large unbroken areas of wall or ceiling. These reflections cause standing waves in the room. At a given point in the room, there may be a node for some frequencies and an antinode for others. As a result the sound which the listener hears is distorted and hard to understand. This effect may be much more pronounced at some places in the room than at others. It is likely to occur in rooms with curved walls and high curved ceilings. To prevent standing waves, it would be better to avoid large unbroken wall surfaces, if possible. Choosing the best proportions for the height, length, and width of the room also helps to keep this effect at a minimum.

Reverberation

Have you ever tried to speak or sing in a room that is too "alive"? Every syllable that you speak in such a room seems to drag out and have a "tail" on it. This effect is *reverberation* and is caused by reflection. The energy in a sound wave must die away before we cease to hear the sound. When sound waves are outdoors, the energy simply flows along the wave away into space. Sound waves in a room, however, may rebound time after time from the walls and other surfaces. Some sound energy is lost by *absorption* at each rebound. If the energy lost is a large fraction of the energy in the original sound wave, the sound will die down quickly to a level that we cannot hear. If the absorption is a small fraction of the energy in the original sound wave, the sound may last for seconds. *The number of seconds required for a sound which is suddenly interrupted to die down 60 decibels below its original level is the reverberation time of*

The General Assembly Hall, United Nations, N.Y., is an example of an auditorium designed to provide the best possible acoustics. (*United Nations*)

a room. The reverberation time of a room is also the time required to absorb 999,999/1,000,000 of the sound energy in the room after the source actually stops giving out sound.

For best hearing conditions, the reverberation time of classrooms and small auditoriums should be from 1 to 2 sec, depending on size. If the reverberation time is much over these values, it is difficult to speak in the room because of the way sounds "slap back" at the speaker. If the reverberation time is much lower than these values, the speaker has to exert extra effort to be heard. Such a room seems "dead" and unnatural. Musicians sometimes like a room with somewhat higher reverberation time than that best suited for speaking. Broadcasting studios are usually designed to have reverberation times lower than are required for good hearing in rooms of the same size.

How Sound Is Absorbed

When a sound wave strikes a surface, some of its energy is reflected and some passes through the surface into the material behind it. The part that passes through the surface is usually absorbed and changed into heat before it goes far. A hard smooth plaster wall is a good reflector and a poor absorber; a carpet with heavy nap is a poor reflector and a good absorber. Good reflectors are poor absorbers and poor reflectors are good absorbers.

Many rooms are noisy because they

297

Broadcasting studio, radio station KORO, Seattle, Washington. The curved forms built into the walls and ceilings illustrate one method that has been used to break up reflections, reduce reverberation time, and improve the acoustic characteristics of studios.

have high reverberation times. One way of reducing noise is by increasing the total absorption in the room. This may be done by the use of heavy rugs or carpet on the floor, by hanging heavy curtains, and by covering the walls and ceiling with special sound-absorbing materials. In some cases, a special acoustic plaster is used to increase absorption. In other cases, special forms of porous fiber sheets, with or without small holes, are used to cover the ceiling. Sometimes the walls also are covered with similar material. Telephone booths, offices, cafeterias, ballrooms, auditoriums, classrooms, and corridors are generally "sound-treated" by one of these methods to reduce the noise level by many decibels.

►You Will Be Interested to Know

Prior to about 1900 all new music halls, large lecture rooms, and auditoriums were modeled after older structures in which listeners had found it easy to hear. Sometimes the new room turned out to be good for hearing but often it was very poor. No one seemed to know exactly why two rooms of practically the same design should be so strikingly different acoustically. Many schemes for improving a poor room were tried, including the stringing of wires and the placing of vases. None of these seemed to make it much easier to hear in the room.

Sanders Theatre in Cambridge, Massachusetts, was an excellent auditorium for hearing. The lecture room in the Fogg Art Museum at Harvard University was modeled after Sanders Theatre, but turned out to be an exceedingly poor room in which to hear. Wallace C. Sabine, then a teacher in the Department of Physics at Harvard, was asked to investigate the cause of the difficulty and find out what could be done about it. This started him on a series of experimental studies of the acoustics of rooms which continued for some 25 years. In the course of these studies, he developed the theory of room reverberation, absorption of sound energy, and the formulas for reverberation time. The pioneer work of Professor Sabine in this field formed the basis for the present-day science of architectural acoustics. Although it is now possible to design an auditorium for good hearing, there is still much to be learned about the behavior and control of sound in rooms. Many persons find problems in acoustics interesting. You, too, may become interested in such problems and wish to help in finding their answers.

▶**Do You Know?**

1. Are any rooms in your school building "sound-treated" to reduce noise? If so, what method is used?
2. Why is it easier to speak in a large room when it is filled with people than when it is empty?
3. Why does your voice sound unnatural and "hollow" in a room without furniture, rugs, or curtains?
4. Why is it easier for scientists to make acoustical measurements and study the effects of sound in rooms today than it was for Professor Sabine in the early 1900's?
5. Explain the meaning of the term *reverberation*.

AMPLIFIERS AND SOUND RECORDING

New and improved methods for measuring, controlling, preserving, and using sound energy were made possible by the invention and development of the electron tube, discussed in Chapter 18.

A microscope makes a very small

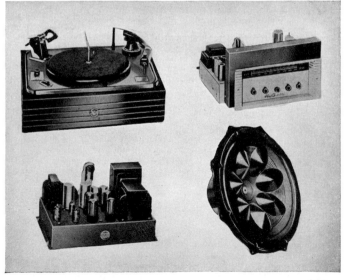

High-fidelity sound-reproducing equipment designed to reproduce music and voice with a high degree of naturalness. The apparatus consists of a three-speed automatic record changer (*upper left*), an AM and FM radio tuner (*upper right*), a 20-watt high-fidelity amplifier (*lower left*), and a special loudspeaker (*lower right*). (*Radio Corporation of America*)

object look larger. Do you know how we can make a faint sound louder? To do this, we need to *amplify* it by increasing the energy in the sound waves. Many of you know from experience that a *loudspeaker* system will amplify sounds many times. The *microphone* of a loudspeaker system converts sound waves into electric waves, just as it does when attached to an oscilloscope. The *electronic amplifier* adds energy to these electric waves and builds them up to a higher level. The *loudspeaker* converts these electric waves into sound waves again. Thus, with public-address equipment, an announcer speaking at an ordinary level can be heard easily by thousands.

Sound Tracks

When you listen to a phonograph record, do you realize that the originals of the sounds you hear may have been made years before? These original sounds have been preserved on the

UNILATERAL
VARIABLE AREA

SINGLE
VARIABLE DENSITY

BILATERAL
VARIABLE AREA

Sound on film. Three different methods of recording the sound. (*Westrex Corporation*)

300

record for your later enjoyment, just as a scene from last summer's vacation may have been preserved on a photograph. There are several ways of recording and preserving sounds.

In sound motion pictures, photographs are taken of fluctuations in light that correspond to the original sound waves. These sound-wave photographs are then printed on the sound track of the film, at the side of the pictures. The photograph on this page shows three types of sound tracks on motion-picture films.

When the film is projected, a strong light is focused on the sound track. This light shines through the track into a *photoelectric cell* on the opposite side. The amount of light reaching the cell depends on the amount of clear area under the sound wave curve in the variable-area type of sound track. In the variable-density type, the amount of light getting through depends on the density of the sound track. As the film moves, the amount of light reaching the cell varies in accordance with the original sound. The photoelectric cell controls an amplifier and a loudspeaker, which reproduces the original sound.

Recording

Records for phonographs are made in a different way. The original sound waves are picked up by a microphone, amplified, and used to drive a sharp cutting needle called a *stylus*. The original record is made on a soft wax plate, which is rotated by a turntable. The stylus touches the moving wax plate and engraves wavy grooves which correspond to the original sound waves. In *lateral* recording the waves are back and forth across the groove. In *vertical* recording, the waves are up and down like hills and valleys in the bottom of the groove.

A coating of metal is deposited electrically on the wax plate, after the grooves have been cut in it. The metal fills out all of the minute details in the grooves cut by the stylus. When the metal plate is separated from the wax, it has on its face all the wavy grooves as ridges. This *master* plate is then backed with more metal to strengthen it and is used to make *pressings* in softened shellac or plastic disks. You get one of these pressings when you buy a phonograph record.

In playing a record, the little waves in the grooves set up a mechanical vibration of the *needle*. These vibrations are converted into electric waves by the *pickup*. The electric waves are amplified and used to operate a loudspeaker, which converts them into sound.

Recordings are made with the turntable turning 78, 45, or 33⅓ rpm. If the playback turntable goes a little faster than the original recording speed, the pitch of all sounds will be raised. If the playback speed is slower than the recording speed, all pitches will be flattened. If you could run the turntable backward, you would get sound that no one could understand.

Recording in Plastic Materials

When only one copy of a sound recording is needed, it is more convenient to make the record directly on a plastic-coated disk, which can be played back immediately without processing. A vibrating stylus cuts the grooves and engraves the waves in the plastic just as in the soft wax. The record is ready to play back as soon as cut. Many recordings used in broadcast stations are made this way. Copies are made by playing the first record and recording the sounds from it on a second record. Records of this type may be used several times.

Recording on Wire and Tape

Sounds can be recorded on fine steel wire. Sound waves are used with a microphone and amplifier to set up magnetic fields in the wire as it is drawn rapidly across a recording head. The wire becomes magnetized in patterns corresponding to the original sound waves. When the magnetized wire is again pulled across the same recording head, connected to control an amplifier and loudspeaker, sounds corresponding to the originals are produced. Enough wire to record for an hour or more can be placed on one spool.

Special tape made of plastic ribbon or similar material and filled with fine particles of iron is often used in much the same way as wire for recording sound. A durable, anti-curl magnetic tape that does not shrink, stretch, or dry out under abnormal climatic conditions is sometimes used for this purpose.

This inspector is using precise optical instruments to check the centering of a new 45-rpm record. Even microscopic divergence from true centering would result in tonal distortion. (*Radio Corporation of America*)

▶**Do You Know?**

1. Have you ever seen a home recording machine? If so, on what principle did it work?
2. Can variable-area and variable-density sound tracks be used on the same sound movie machine without adjustment? Explain.
3. Explain the difference between a lateral recording and a vertical recording.
4. Name three methods by which sound may be recorded and reproduced. Explain the differences between the methods.
5. Explain the effect which is obtained when a phonograph record is played at a higher rate of speed than that for which it was intended.

HIGHLIGHTS

Sounds of the *same intensity* but of *different frequencies* may not sound equally loud.

The *lower limit of audibility* is about 20 cps; the *upper limit* is about 20,000 cps.

Ultrasonic vibrations have frequencies too high to hear. *Subsonic* vibrations have frequencies too low to hear.

Two tones in the range of the middle octave are *discordant* if their beat rate falls between about 10 and 70 beats per second.

An *octave* is the musical interval between two tones when the frequency of one is just twice that of the other.

The *diatonic scale* has eight notes in an octave, with three different kinds of intervals between successive notes.

The set of smallest whole numbers that can express the relative frequencies of the notes in an octave of the diatonic scale is
$$24—27—30—32—36—40—45—48$$

For *standard pitch*, A has a frequency of 440 cps; for *laboratory pitch*, C has a frequency of 256 cps.

In the *equal-tempered* scale, each of the 12 intervals is $\sqrt[12]{2} = 1.0595$.

Musical instruments are classified as (1) stringed, (2) wind, and (3) percussion.

Standing waves are set up by *reflection* and *interference* of sound waves.

The distance between *two successive nodes* or *two successive antinodes* in a standing wave is a *half-wavelength*.

Strings vibrate in one and in several segments simultaneously.

Vibrating strings produce a fundamental and several overtone frequencies. The overtone frequencies are 2, 3, 4 . . . times the fundamental. The fundamental frequency is given by

$$f = \frac{1}{2L}\sqrt{\frac{T}{m}}$$

Closed air columns resonate when the length of the tube is ¼, ¾, ⁵⁄₄ . . . of a wavelength.

Closed air columns vibrate at a fundamental and overtone frequencies, which are 3, 5, 7 . . . times the fundamental.

Open air columns resonate when the length of the tube is ½, ²⁄₂, ³⁄₂ . . . of a wavelength.

Open air columns vibrate at a fundamental and overtone frequencies, which are 2, 3, 4 . . . times the fundamental.

Plates and stretched diaphragms vibrate in complicated patterns, with overtone frequencies that are *not exact multiples* of the main frequency.

Reverberation time is the number of seconds required for the sound level in a room to fall 60 decibels after the source of sound has suddenly stopped.

Standing waves and high reverberation time make some rooms poor for hearing.

The *optimum reverberation time* in an ordinary room is from 1 to 2 sec, depending on the size of the room.

Amplifiers and *loudspeakers* are required to intensify sounds.

Sounds can be recorded (1) on sound tracks on motion-picture film, (2) on wax for a master and pressings for copies, (3) on plastic-covered disks for instantaneous playback, and (4) on magnetic wire or tape.

PROBLEMS: GROUP A

1. What is the frequency of a tone an octave below C = 264 cps?
2. What is the frequency of a tone a fifth above A = 440 cps?
3. If the vibration rate of A on the diatonic scale is taken as 435 cps, what must be the vibration rate of C?
4. What is the frequency of the third overtone of a string whose fundamental is 132 cps?
5. What is the frequency of the second overtone of an air column closed at one end whose fundamental is 128 cps?
6. What is the frequency of the second overtone of an open air column whose fundamental frequency is 128 cps?
7. What is the length of an air column *open at both ends* that will resonate at its fundamental frequency of 512 cps when the speed of sound is 335 m/sec?
8. What is the length of an air column *closed at one end* which will resonate at its fundamental frequency of 512 cps when the speed of sound is 335 m/sec?
9. Would you expect to hear a sound whose wavelength in air is 6 mm? Explain the basis for your answer.
10. Would you expect to hear a sound whose wavelength in air is 34.5 m? Explain the basis for your answer.
11. What is the frequency of a tone two octaves above standard A (440 cps)?
12. What is the frequency of a tone two octaves below standard A (440 cps)?
13. What is the musical interval, expressed as a ratio, between A and C of the diatonic scale?
14. What is the musical interval, expressed as a ratio, between A and C′ of the diatonic scale?
15. What is the approximate length of an

open organ pipe which can produce a fundamental frequency of 100 cps?

16. What is the approximate length of an organ pipe, *closed at one end*, which can produce a fundamental frequency of 100 cps? Of 200 cps?

17. What is the approximate length of an organ pipe, *closed at one end*, which can produce a fundamental frequency of 300 cps? Of 600 cps?

GROUP B

1. If the vibration rate of C on the diatonic scale is taken as 259 cps, what must be the vibration rate of A?

2. Compute the fundamental frequency of a string whose length is 100 cm, tension 25,000,000 dynes, and mass 0.01 g/cm.

3. If the distance from one node to the eighth one beyond it in a Kundt's tube is 32 cm and the velocity of sound is 340 m/sec, what is the frequency of the sound made by the vibrating rod?

4. If the first resonance point in the apparatus of Fig. 12–8 is 20 cm from the top of the tube and the second one is 60.35 cm from the top, when a fork whose frequency is 440 cps is used, what is the speed of sound in the tube?

5. If the distance in air between two successive nodes in a standing wave originating from a 2,000-cps whistle is 9 cm, what is the velocity of sound in this air?

6. What is the approximate length of an organ pipe, *closed at one end*, which can produce a first-overtone frequency of 264 cps?

7. What is the approximate length of an *open* organ pipe which can produce a first-overtone frequency of 264 cps?

8. What is the difference between the fifth *harmonic* and the fifth *overtone* of an organ pipe closed at one end whose fundamental frequency is 130 cps?

9. A given string under a tension of 3 kg can vibrate at a fundamental frequency of 180 cps. What must the tension in the same string become in order that it will vibrate at a fundamental frequency of 360 cps? Its length is not changed.

10. A string 80 cm long under a given tension can vibrate at a fundamental frequency of 180 cps. How long must this string be made in order that it will vibrate at a fundamental frequency of 540 cps? Its tension is not changed.

THINGS TO DO

1. Arrange for the use of a tape recorder to record your voice and the voices of your classmates. Your own voice will probably sound quite unnatural to you when you play it back from the tape. Why is this true?

2. Partially fill several water glasses with water. Strike the edge of a glass gently with a spoon or fork handle and observe the pitch of the tone produced. You can produce a different pitch by adjusting the amount of water in a given glass. Try to adjust the water levels so that the glasses produce a chord.

3. Obtain an ultrasonic whistle and see if you can produce a sound with it whose frequency is too high for most human ears but within the range of a dog's ears. Find out, if possible, what frequency the whistle produces.

4. Make a classified list of the instruments actually used in your school orchestra or band. Put the names of all stringed instruments in one list, all wood winds in another list, and so on.
5. Collect and mount samples of different types of acoustic absorbing building materials used to reduce reverberation time in rooms and auditoriums. A builders' supply company in your community may be willing to contribute some of these samples.

Unit 4.

Electricity in Our World

PREVIEW

Electricity has done much to change the way people work and play and live. In less than 100 years, electricity has been developed from a mere experimental curiosity into one of the most convenient and widely used forms of energy in the world. Almost every industry, business, and home uses electricity in some form today.

The story of matter and energy in this unit turns to electrons, those tiny particles of which electricity is composed. Electrons are responsible for small electric sparks and mighty flashes of lightning. The flow of electrons through a wire causes a lamp to glow, a motor to run, or an iron to heat. The motion of electrons conveys telephone conversations and telegraph messages over wires. Electrons, properly directed, produce waves for transmitting radio, television, and radar signals. Our huge radio, television, and electric-power industries are thus built on effects produced by electrons.

Electrons are normally parts of all atoms. Chemistry is concerned with atoms and their combinations, so electrons play an important role in chemistry. Many of the effects involving electrons are both physical and chemical in nature. The realm of electrons is thus a borderland between physics and chemistry. This unit will take you into the border zone where physics and chemistry overlap.

13.

Static Electricity:
Electrostatic Laws

FRICTION AND ELECTRIC CHARGES

When you run a rubber comb through
your hair on a dry winter day, you can
often hear a faint crackling noise. Your
hair, if dry, may at the same time appear
to stand on end. After several strokes,
you may notice that the comb can attract to itself small bits of lint, paper, or
other light material. These new properties acquired by your hair and the comb
are caused by *electricity*. We say that
both the comb and your hair have been
charged or *electrified* by friction. We very
often speak of the electricity that
accumulates on the comb or on your
hair as an *electric charge*. So when we
speak of electric charges in the discus-

308

sions that follow we shall always be
thinking of accumulations of electricity.
Electric charges that are produced by
friction, such as those on your hair and
the comb, are often called *static electricity*.
There are, however, other ways of
accumulating static electricity, as will
be shown later in this chapter.

Static Electricity

Many different materials, when rubbed
together, will produce static electric
charges. If you rub a rod of hard rubber
with a piece of fur, the rod becomes
charged and will attract small bits of
paper. Under favorable conditions you
can hear the faint crackling noise of
small sparks as you continue the rubbing.

If you hold the charged rod near the antenna connection of your radio, you can often produce in the radio an effect similar to that of a severe "static" storm in the atmosphere.

A clean glass rod rubbed vigorously with a piece of silk or rayon usually acquires an electric charge.
When a body of any kind of material is rubbed with another kind of material we may expect the friction between them to produce electric charges.
The amount of charge may be small, however, and in some cases the charge may escape before we can detect its presence. In warm, humid weather, the charges produced on rubber and glass disappear so fast that it is often impossible to perform the experiments and tests that we are about to investigate. A *dry* atmosphere is much more favorable for producing and holding electric charges on a body.

Tests for Electric Charges

The simplest test we can make to determine whether a body is charged or not is that shown in Figs. 13–1 and 13–2. If the particles of cork dust leap up and cling to the body brought near them we may conclude that the body has an electric charge on it. If we have a number of tests to make, however, it may be more convenient to use an instrument called an *electroscope*. One of the simplest types of electroscope is made of a light, dry, pith ball suspended by a silk thread, as shown in Fig. 13–3.

You will notice that when we bring a hard-rubber rod that has just been rubbed vigorously with fur near the pith ball, the ball *is attracted*. If the ball makes contact with the charged rod for a moment, it will usually spring away and thereafter be repelled by the rod. Part of the electric charge originally on the hard-rubber rod is shared with the pith ball during the moment of contact. We say the pith ball has become charged by *contact* with another charged body. Notice that this is another method by which bodies may acquire an electric charge.

The attraction of the pith ball, *with contact followed by repulsion*, is a conclusive test that the hard-rubber rod is charged. A similar test can be applied to a glass rod or to any other body that

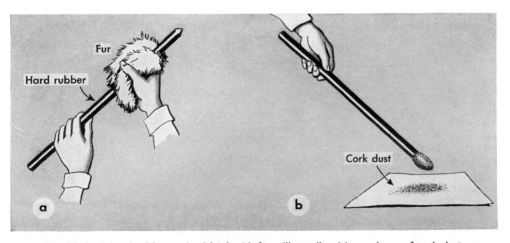

Fig. 13–1. A hard-rubber rod rubbed with fur will usually pick up pieces of cork dust.

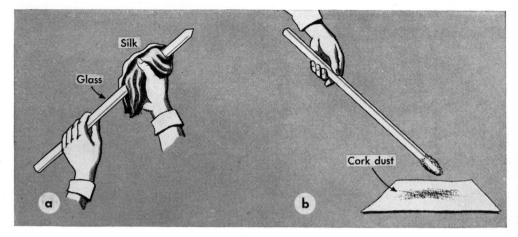

Fig. 13–2. A glass rod rubbed with silk will usually pick up pieces of cork dust.

we may wish to investigate for electric charge. Of course, if any charge is present, it must be great enough to operate the pith ball before we can detect it in this way.

Two Kinds of Electric Charges

Suppose we charge a pith ball by contact with a charged rubber rod, as shown in Fig. 13–4. Then when we bring the rod near the pith ball, it will be definitely *repelled*. Suppose we now bring up a glass rod that has just been rubbed vigorously with a silk cloth. It may at first astonish you to see that the pith ball is *attracted* strongly to this rod. If we allow the pith ball to touch the glass rod for a moment, we may find that the ball again springs away and thereafter is *repelled* by the glass rod. It we test again with the hard rubber rod, we may find that the ball is now *attracted* to it.

The charge on the hard rubber does not act the same as that on the glass rod.

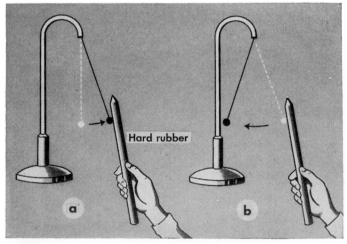

Fig. 13–3. The pith ball is first attracted by the charged rubber rod and after contact is later repelled by it.

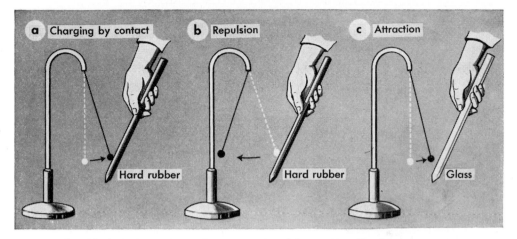

Fig. 13–4. Bodies with like charges repel and those with unlike charges attract.

One attracts the pith ball when the other repels it. This is why we are sure there are *two different kinds* of electric charge. Benjamin Franklin named these two kinds of charge nearly 200 years ago. He called the charge produced on glass when it is rubbed with silk a *positive* charge and that produced on rubber when it is rubbed with fur a *negative* charge. We still use these names and often use the symbol + to designate a positive charge and the symbol − to designate a negative charge.

Attraction and Repulsion

The experimental facts shown in Fig. 13–4 lead to this general conclusion:
Bodies with like charges repel and those with unlike charges attract.
This is one of the fundamental laws of electricity.

Sources of Charges

An abundance of experimental evidence has enabled scientists to build up a fairly adequate picture of what electricity seems to be and how it behaves. This picture constitutes the *electron theory of matter*. In preceding units, we

have learned that all matter is built up of very small elementary units called *atoms*. Small as these atoms are, we must look *inside them* for a rational explanation of electricity and its effects. Present evidence indicates that each atom is made up of a central *nucleus*, which is positively charged, surrounded by one or more very minute *negatively charged* particles called *electrons*. *These electrons are the fundamental units of negative electric charge.* The electrons are attracted to the nucleus of the atom and are generally believed to revolve around the nucleus. Sometimes scientists call these particles of negative electricity *negative electrons*, to distinguish them clearly from a more recently discovered atomic particle called a *positron* or *positive electron*. In this book we shall follow the custom of calling these *negative electrons* simply *electrons*.

The atoms of different chemical elements all have different numbers of electrons. A hydrogen atom is the simplest atom of all. It normally has only 1 electron revolving around its nucleus. Neon atoms normally have 10 electrons. Uranium, the heaviest and

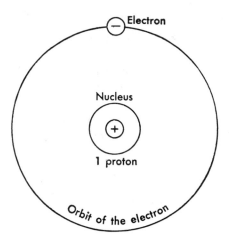

Fig. 13–5. Model of a hydrogen atom.

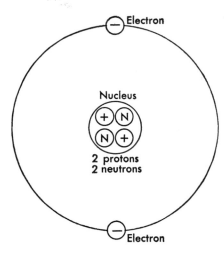

Fig. 13–6. Model of a helium atom.

most complicated *natural* element, normally has 92 electrons. The type of simple atom model shown in Figs. 13–5, 13–6, and 13–7 is only one of a number of such models that scientists have invented to explain the things they have discovered about atoms.

Even though an atom is so small that it cannot be seen with the most powerful microscope, its nucleus and electrons are much smaller still. And small as the nucleus of an atom is, scientists have found ways of exploring inside these nuclei. These explorations have uncovered some strange and interesting information about how nuclei are constructed. Nuclei seem to be built from smaller elementary units, of which there are at least two kinds. One of these is called the *proton;* the other is the *neutron.* The proton is a relatively heavy unit. Its mass is about 1,836 times that of the much lighter electron. The *proton possesses a fundamental unit of positive electric charge.* Its *positive* charge is just equal in magnitude to the *negative* charge of an electron. The other fundamental unit in the nucleus, the neutron,

is electrically neutral, that is, it has no electric charge, as its name implies. Its mass is nearly the same as that of a proton, so it, too, is many times as heavy as an electron.

Under normal conditions, the number of electrons attached to an atom is just equal to the number of protons in its nucleus. So the atom as a whole has as many units of negative electric charge as it has units of positive charge. At a little distance from an atom, the force of attraction or repulsion due to its electrons will, therefore, just balance the force of repulsion or attraction due to the protons in its nucleus. Under this condition, the atom, for all practical purposes, appears to be without any charge at all, that is, it is *neutral.*

Suppose an atom should somehow lose one or more of its electrons. It would then possess more protons than electrons, and so would appear to have a net *positive charge.* When a great many of the atoms of a body, such as a glass rod, *lose electrons,* the body as a whole appears to have a *net positive charge.* This positive charge of the body is merely the sum of

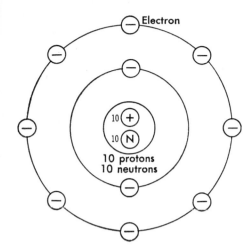

Fig. 13–7. Model of a neon atom.

the net unit positive charges of those of its atoms which have lost electrons.

To place a positive charge on a body, we must remove some of its electrons.

Suppose an atom should somehow capture and hold prisoner one or more extra electrons. The atom would then possess more electrons than protons and would appear to have a *net negative charge*. If this happens to many of the atoms of a body, the body as a whole will appear to have a *net negative* charge. As before, this charge on the body is the sum of the net negative charges of all its atoms which have gained electrons.

To place a negative charge on a body, we must transfer electrons to it.

You may wonder whether an atom cannot lose or capture *protons*, just as well as electrons. This does not seem to happen under ordinary circumstances. The protons are an integral part of the nucleus of an atom and are not dislodged by any of the processes we are now considering. In Chapter 23 we shall investigate processes involving single protons.

You must now realize that positive and negative electric charges in the form of protons and electrons are fundamental constituents of all matter. We do not *create* the charges on hard rubber and glass by friction. All we do is transfer electrons to or from the body that we charge.

A positive charge means a net deficiency of electrons. A negative charge means a net surplus of electrons.

►You Will Be Interested to Know

Thales of Miletus, one of the Seven Wise Men of ancient Greece, who lived about 600 B.C., knew that amber rubbed with fur would attract to itself bits of light material such as straw and lint. It is not certain whether he discovered this effect himself or whether he got information about it from some earlier, unknown discoverer.

Our words *electric, electricity,* and *electron* come directly from *ēlektron*, the Greek word for amber. The electron as a fundamental unit of electricity (electric charge) was first identified by Sir J. J. Thomson of Cambridge, England, about 1897.

Charged rubber rod

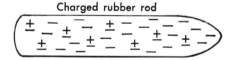

Charged glass rod

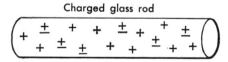

— represents excess electrons

+ represents atoms which have lost electrons

± represents atoms which have their normal number of electrons

Fig. 13–8. A charged rubber rod has an excess of electrons; a charged glass rod has a deficiency of electrons.

313

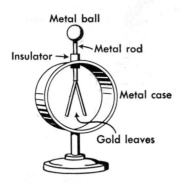

Fig. 13–9. A gold-leaf electroscope.

A Gold-leaf Electroscope

When we need a more sensitive kind of electroscope, we often use one made from gold or aluminum foil, such as the one shown in Fig. 13–9. A narrow strip of the foil is attached to a metal rod and suspended to form two leaves that hang downward. The metal rod usually has a metal ball on the upper end. The rod is *insulated* from the metal or glass case which is placed around it to protect the leaves from air currents and mechanical injury. The *insulator* is generally a plug or stopper of amber, hard rubber, sulfur, or other material through which electrons cannot easily pass.

Suppose we touch the metal ball of an electroscope with a hard-rubber rod that has just been rubbed with fur. Some of the excess electrons on the hard rubber will pass over to the metal ball while they are in contact. Many of these electrons will not remain long on the ball, however, but will quickly distribute themselves throughout the metal rod and the gold leaves, because these are *conductors* of electricity. The two leaves thus receive electric charges of the same kind or sign (negative in this example) so they repel each other and spread apart or *diverge*, as shown in Fig. 13–10. If we had touched the electroscope with a charged glass rod, the leaves would also diverge. Can you explain why?

Types of Electric Charges

Figure 13–10 shows what happens when we bring a charged rubber rod (negative) *near* the ball of this negatively charged electroscope. You may be surprised to notice that the leaves spread farther apart while the charged

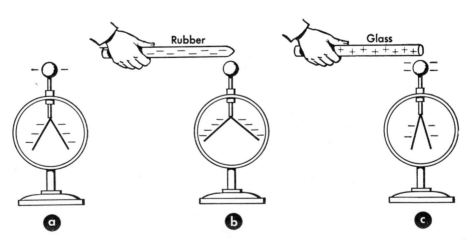

Fig. 13–10. Using a *negatively* charged electroscope to test for an electric charge and its sign. For symbols, see Fig. 13–8.

314

rod is in the vicinity of the ball, but resume their former positions again when the rod is removed. Any *negatively charged body* brought near the ball of this negatively charged electroscope will cause the leaves to diverge in this same manner. So the *diverging leaves* become an excellent indicator that the body brought near the electroscope is *negatively charged*.

If we bring up a glass rod that has just been rubbed vigorously with silk, the leaves of the negatively charged electroscope will fall and may collapse entirely. You will naturally expect then that *collapsing leaves* indicate that the body near the electroscope is *charged positively*. This is usually the case unless the leaves collapse only a little bit. An uncharged metal rod held in the hand can cause a *slight* collapse of the leaves. So if the leaves fall *only a small amount*, we are not quite sure whether the body near the electroscope has a small positive charge or no charge at all. What happens when we start with the electroscope charged positively is shown in Fig. 13–11. Study Figs. 13–10 and 13–11.

If the leaves of a charged electroscope spread still farther apart when we bring a test body near the ball, the test body has a charge which is of the same sign as that of the electroscope.

How to Ground a Charge

If you have an opportunity to work with an electroscope, you will want to be sure that the instrument is fully discharged before starting on a new test. You will soon discover that the simplest way to make the leaves collapse and discharge the electroscope is to *touch the ball with your finger*, or with a wire or metal rod held in your hand. If the instrument has a metal case, it may be well to touch both the ball and the metal case at the same time. Under some circumstances it may be necessary for you to touch a water pipe or a steam radiator with your other hand at the same time. We say that the electric charge that was on the electroscope is *grounded* in this way. You do not have to make a direct connection to the earth to ground a *small* electric charge. Your body will sometimes act as a ground.

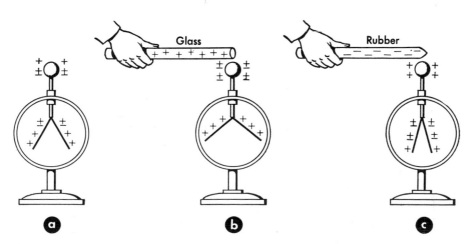

Fig. 13–11. Using a *positively* charged electroscope to test for an electric charge and its sign. For symbols, see Fig. 13–8.

The Size of an Electric Charge

If we stroke a glass rod *once* with a silk cloth, the glass rod may lose only a few electrons and thus acquire a positive charge. If we rub another glass rod vigorously several times with a silk cloth, that rod may lose a great many electrons. The second rod could make the leaves of the electroscope in Fig. 13–11 diverge more than the first rod. We say that the second rod is charged *more strongly* than the first one. We mean that it possesses a larger charge, a larger *quantity of electricity*. The size or magnitude of an electric charge depends on the number of electrons lost or gained. The first glass rod may have a positive charge corresponding to the loss of 10,000 electrons while the second rod may have a positive charge corresponding to the loss of 100,000,000 electrons. When we use the electron as the unit for expressing the size or quantity of an electric charge, we usually have to deal with very large numbers. So for everyday purposes we generally use a much larger unit called the *coulomb*. A coulomb is equivalent to about 6.25×10^{18} electrons.

Charges Produced by Friction

Where does a hard-rubber rod get the electrons it captures when rubbed with fur? We know now that these electrons must be *rubbed off* the fur. This ought to leave the fur with an excess of positive charge, one excess proton for each electron rubbed off. Can we detect a positive charge on the fur with our gold-leaf electroscope? Figure 13–13 shows how we can test the fur for charge. We must wrap the fur around an insulating rod (glass or rubber will do) before we rub the rubber rod with it; if we hold the fur directly in our hands, it will soon pick up electrons from our body and any positive charges that it may acquire by friction will be neutralized by these electrons. Figure 13–13 shows what happens when we successfully test the fur after rubbing it on the hard-rubber rod. The *fur does acquire a positive charge*, as we should expect. A similar test would show that the silk cloth used to rub glass acquires a negative charge. These tests do not prove that the amount of charge on each is equal to that on its companion body. More careful and exact measure-

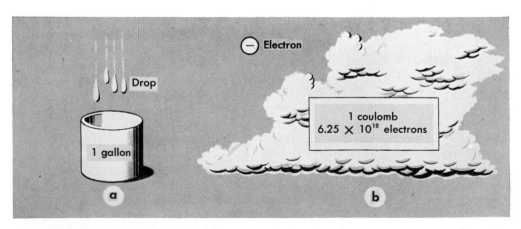

Fig. 13–12. We may measure the quantity of water in drops or gallons; we may measure the quantity of electricity in electrons or *coulombs*.

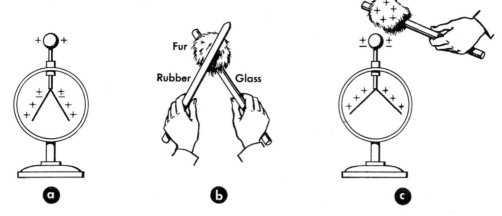

Fig. 13–13. Testing fur for charge. Fur acquires a positive charge when rubbed on a hard-rubber rod. What charge does the hard-rubber rod acquire? See Fig. 13–8 for symbols.

ments than we can make in this way are necessary to show that the size of the charge on the fur is equal to that on the hard rubber.

►You Will Be Interested to Know

For more than 2,000 years after the discovery that rubbed amber will attract small particles, almost nothing new was found out about electricity. Sir William Gilbert, court physician to Queen Elizabeth I of England, became intensely interested in electric phenomena and soon discovered that a great many substances other than amber can be charged by friction. In 1600 he published a book in Latin called *De Magnete* in which he reported many interesting facts and experiments dealing with electricity and magnetism.

The first book dealing exclusively with electricity was written by Robert Boyle (famous for Boyle's law) and was published at Oxford, England, in 1676. Boyle discovered that electric attraction does occur in a vacuum and that the pull on the charged body is equal to the pull it exerts on the attracted body.

►Do You Know?

1. What happens to the leaves when an electroscope receives a positive charge?
2. What becomes of the electrons originally on a charged electroscope when the instrument is discharged by grounding?
3. Where do the electrons required to discharge a positively charged electroscope come from when you touch the metal ball?
4. A toy rubber balloon after being rubbed with a wool cloth will sometimes stick to a dry wall. Why?
5. What are the steps necessary to place a positive charge on an electroscope? A negative charge?

CONDUCTORS AND INSULATORS

Electrons can apparently move about quite freely in some materials while they seem to be bound in position in other materials.

Look carefully at what takes place in Fig. 13–14. When we touch the charged

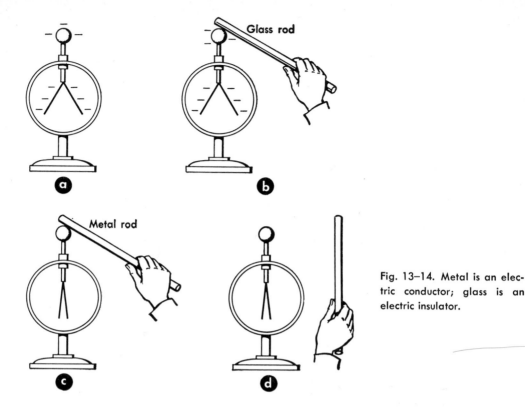

Glass rod

Metal rod

Fig. 13–14. Metal is an electric conductor; glass is an electric insulator.

electroscope with an uncharged glass rod, nothing much happens to the leaves. When we touch the electroscope with a metal rod held in the hand, the leaves at once collapse and remain collapsed after we remove the rod. Obviously the metal rod acts differently from the glass rod; it allows electrons to pass through from the electroscope to the body while the glass rod blocks the electrons. Any material like the metal in the rod which allows electrons to move freely through it is called an electric *conductor*. Any material like the glass rod which does not allow electrons to move freely through it is called an electric *nonconductor* or *insulator*.

In the gold-leaf electroscope of Fig. 13–9, the ball, rod, and leaves are all good conductors so that electrons can move freely from the ball to the leaves

and vice versa. The rod is insulated from the case by means of a plug of amber, rubber, sulfur, or other similar material. Since these are all good insulators, they will prevent the interchange of electrons between the rod and the metal case.

In hot, humid weather a charged electroscope often loses its charge very rapidly. The loss of charge is usually caused by the formation of a thin film of moisture on the surface of the insulator. A film of moisture is a very poor insulator and allows electrons to leak across it much more readily than amber, rubber, or sulfur. Thus the charge escapes in a short time. This explains why it is almost impossible to develop a charge on any body by friction when the surrounding atmosphere is very humid.

318

Our own bodies are fairly good conductors of electricity. The materials on which we develop charges by friction and which retain their charges for some time are all good insulators. This is why we do not discharge them completely whenever we touch them with our hands, just as we can discharge a charged electroscope.

Dry gases are generally good insulators. Some liquids are good insulators, others are good conductors. Many solids are excellent insulators, but some, especially the metals, are very good conductors. The best conductor of the metals is *silver*, followed closely by copper, gold, and aluminum in order.

A great many substances are neither good insulators nor good conductors. There is probably no *perfect* conductor of electricity, although some metals at very low temperatures are nearly perfect conductors. There is also no perfect insulator under all conditions.

Charging by Induction

There is an interesting and convenient method of *charging a body* without friction and without contact with another charged body. This is a kind of

Table 13–1. Electric Insulators and Conductors

Good insulators	Good conductors
Amber	Any metal
Bakelite and most plastics	Electrolytes (ionized liquids)
Cotton (dry)	Carbon
Glass	Earth (damp)
Mica	
Paraffin	
Porcelain	
Rosin	
Sealing wax	
Sulfur	
Oils	
Shellac and lacquers	
Air (dry)	
Vacuum	

"remote control" method that works only with conductors. We find this method especially useful for charging an electroscope. Suppose we have a metal cylinder mounted on an insulating stand, as shown in Fig. 13–15. Now suppose we bring a well-charged rubber rod near one end of the metal cylinder. If the charge on the rubber rod is great enough and if the rod is close enough to

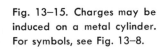

Fig. 13–15. Charges may be induced on a metal cylinder. For symbols, see Fig. 13–8.

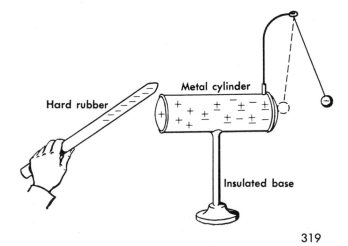

Hard rubber

Metal cylinder

Insulated base

319

the cylinder, a pith ball at the remote end may indicate the presence of an electric charge there.

A test with an electroscope will show that there is a negative charge at the remote end of this metal cylinder and a positive charge at the end nearer the rubber rod. *The induced charge at the end nearer the rod is of opposite sign and that at the remote end is of the same sign as the inducing charge.*

Why do these charges occur? In a metal, which is a good conductor, some electrons are easily separated from their atoms and require but little force to cause them to move from one part of a body to another. Because like charges repel, electrons move away from the end of the cylinder next to the charged rubber rod, leaving an excess of protons (a positive charge) at this end. The repelled electrons accumulate near the remote end of the cylinder, as far away from the charged rod as they can conveniently go. This is how the remote end acquires the negative charge shown in Fig. 13–15.

If we remove the charged rubber rod from the vicinity and again test the metal cylinder with an electroscope, we shall find it uncharged (neutral) not only at the ends but at every other point. There is no longer any repelling force to push the free electrons toward the remote end of the cylinder, so they return to the regions from which they escaped, spreading uniformly through the material. *Electric charges of opposite signs appear at the two ends of the metal cylinder only when the charged rod is near.*

There is an effective way to trap the

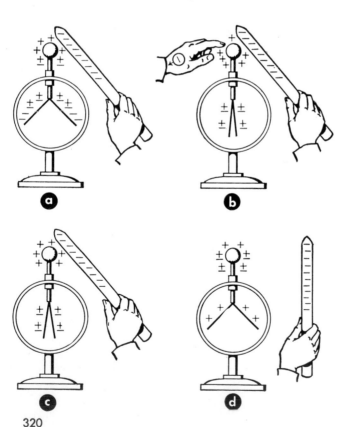

Fig. 13–16. Charging an electroscope by induction. For symbols, see Fig. 13–8.

Fig. 13–17. A Wimshurst electrostatic machine.

repelled electrons so that they cannot return when the charged rod is removed. Suppose we touch the metal cylinder with a finger and then remove the finger *before* we take away the charged rod. It does not make much difference where we touch the metal cylinder; *any place will do as well as the remote end*. If we test sample charges taken from the cylinder after we have trapped the electrons, we will find a positive charge not only at the ends but at every other point on the cylinder. A charge produced in this way is called an *induced* charge. We say that the cylinder is charged by *induction*. You will recall that this is a *third* way to charge a body.

An induced charge is always opposite in sign to the inducing charge.

Generating Large Charges

When we want to have a larger electric charge than we can get with the simple devices that we have used so far, we generally rely on an *electrostatic machine* for generating the charge. A great many different types of static machines have been designed and built since the days of Sir William Gilbert. Every one of them utilizes one or more of the methods listed above for building up the charge. A type now often seen in high-school laboratories is called a *Wimshurst machine*. This machine, shown in Fig. 13–17, was invented by James Wimshurst in England in 1878.

When the disks are rotated in opposite directions, a positive charge accumulates on one knob and a negative charge on the other. When the charges become sufficiently great, a spark may jump between the knobs and discharge the machine.

Very large and powerful electrostatic generators are now used in atom smashing experiments and to operate X-ray tubes that produce some of the most intense penetrating rays. These machines are usually patterned after the Van de Graaff generator, invented in 1931 by Dr. Robert J. Van de Graaff of Massachusetts Institute of Technology.

►Do You Know?

1. What is a proof plane? How could you make one?
2. If you scuff your feet across a rug or carpet on a dry winter day you can often get a spark to jump from your finger when you touch a door knob or other piece of metal. What causes the spark?
3. What is the source of the very large charge which is generated on a Wimshurst electrostatic machine?
4. Try to explain why an induced charge is always opposite in sign to the inducing charge.
5. Why does an electrostatic charge disappear more rapidly in hot, humid weather than in cold, dry weather?
6. Define the terms *electric conductor* and *electric insulator*.

POINTS DISCHARGE A CONDUCTOR

When large numbers of electrons are crowded together into a small space, enormous electric forces are set up in that vicinity. The electric forces that arise from the concentration of electrons are not easy to control.

In favorable weather it is easy to build up an electric charge large enough to cause a spark to jump a gap of several centimeters between the knobs of an electrostatic machine. If the knobs are separated so far that no spark can jump, then the charges may remain on the machine for a considerable time before they become completely neutralized. If one knob is fitted with sharp points as shown in Fig. 13–18, we find it almost impossible to build up charges strong enough to cause a spark, regardless of how close we bring the knobs. The charges generated by the machine seem to become neutralized as fast as they are generated. Why do the charges vanish so rapidly? We must look to the surrounding air for the answer.

When we charge a body that has sharp edges and points, the net charge per unit area is much greater at the points than at the flatter parts of the body. We sometimes say that the charge is denser and more crowded at sharp points. This causes very strong forces of attraction and repulsion for other charges in the neighborhood. When these forces become great enough, they may tear electrons from neutral atoms of the sur-

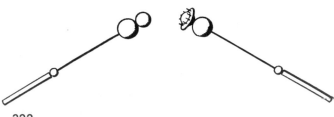

Fig. 13–18. A metal ring fitted with sharp points and hung on one knob of a static machine can prevent sparks between the knobs.

rounding air. This leaves the atoms of air with a net positive charge and leaves the dislodged electrons free to move independently. Usually these free electrons soon join other neutral atoms in the air, which then become negatively charged. Charged atoms are called *ions*. Air which contains large numbers of ions is said to be *ionized*.

Air ions are strongly attracted by the charged metal points in Fig. 13–18 and when they come into contact an exchange of electrons takes place so that a part of the charge on the points as well as that on the ion is neutralized. Ions whose charge is of the same sign as that on the points are repelled and move swiftly away. These ions or similar ions are attracted by the opposite knob of the machine. When they make contact, they neutralize part of the charge on this knob. If this process occurs as rapidly as the static machine develops electric charges, it becomes impossible to build up any charges on the machine. *The original charge on the sharp-pointed conductor is, in effect, transferred to the surrounding air.*

Ionized air is a good conductor of electricity.

The air always has a few ions and a few free electrons per cubic centimeter present in it. These, of course, do not need sharp points to start their discharging action. They will neutralize some of the charge on any body to which they are attracted and touch, regardless of the shape of its surface. So even the air is never a *perfect insulator*. This is one reason why it is impossible to keep an electroscope charged indefinitely, even in a very dry atmosphere.

Corona Discharge

The transfer of electric charge from the sharp points into the air by the method just described is called a *brush* *discharge* or *corona discharge*. It is a different process from the *spark* discharge that you observe when a spark passes between the knobs of the electrostatic machine. A brush discharge is often accompanied by a luminous purplish-blue haze which can be seen at a number of points about an electrostatic machine operated in a darkened room. This faint bluish light frequently takes the form of streamers that diverge from a sharp point like the bristles of a paint brush. When this type of discharge occurs from the side surface of a cylinder or wire, a luminous band or ring appears to surround the wire like a halo. This form of the discharge is commonly called *corona* (crown).

Corona discharge is usually silent, but may be accompanied by a soft hissing noise that is quite distinct from the sharp crack of a spark. Corona and other forms of leakage from high-voltage transmission lines are sources of considerable power loss and often cause serious interference with radio reception in the immediate neighborhood, especially in wet weather.

Putting Corona to Work

Smoke and fumes consist of very fine particles of solid matter in suspension in the air. A Cottrell precipitator is a device for removing this suspended solid matter. In this system, the smoke-filled air is charged with electricity obtained from a corona discharge. The particles of solid matter become electrically charged when some of the charged ions of air strike them. These charged particles are then removed by attracting them to a screen or net which is kept charged with electricity of the opposite sign from that of the particles. Commercial precipitators do not rely on electrostatic generators to keep the corona discharge go-

323

ing; they employ high-voltage transformers to accomplish the same result.

Precipitators are effective in reducing the smoke nuisance in large industrial areas. They are used also in smelters and portland cement plants to remove objectionable and dangerous fumes from the stacks. Sometimes the solid materials recovered by this method have considerable industrial and economic value. In the melting of gold, fine particles of the metal can be recovered from the fumes rising from the molten metal. These precipitators can remove from 90 to 99 percent of the suspended solid matter from smoke and fumes.

►Do You Know?

1. Have you ever heard of St. Elmo's fire? How is this effect related to static electricity?
2. How does a Cottrell precipitator or similar device for smoke reduction operate?
3. What did Dr. Cottrell do with the proceeds from the patent on his precipitator? (Consult an encyclopedia.)
4. Explain how a sharp point may give off an electrostatic charge more rapidly than a rounded surface.
5. Explain the meaning of the term *corona discharge*. What are two disadvantages of corona discharges?

LIGHTNING AND GROUNDING CHARGES

We have already considered how to ground an electroscope and how to ground your body. Why does a charged body lose its charge when we connect it through a conductor to the earth?

The earth is a good conductor of electricity, so electrons are easy to dislodge from it. Because of its enormous size, the earth acts as a gigantic store-house, from which we can withdraw and return electrons with the greatest of ease. The supply of electrons in the earth never becomes low, and space is never lacking for storing those that are returned. When we connect a positively charged body to the earth through a conductor such as a wire or a water pipe, electrons move out from the earth through the conductor to make up the deficiency on the body. In this way the positive charge on the body is neutralized and the body is discharged. When we connect a negatively charged body to the earth through a conductor, electrons flow from the body through the conductor back into the earth, and thus neutralize the charge on the body. The total number of electrons withdrawn from the earth in a period of time is approximately equal to the number returned, when we consider the exchanges that occur all over the earth. For this reason, the net charge of the earth does not change appreciably.

In a similar manner, the metal frame of an automobile acts as a *ground* for a radio receiver in a car. The metal structure of an airplane acts as a ground for both the radio transmitter and the receiver, even though the plane is far above the earth. So you can see that not all so-called grounds are directly connected to the earth.

Attendants at toll bridges and on toll highways often receive severe electric shocks when they collect money from the occupants of passing automobiles. In suitable weather, wind and road friction build up quite a large electric charge on the car. When the attendant reaches for the coin or touches the car, he becomes the immediate *ground* for this charge. Repeated shocks from this source are annoying if not actually dangerous. For this reason short wires are often set vertically in the ground in the approach to the tollgate. When the car touches the wires, any charge it may have is grounded before the attendant is reached. Sometimes similar safety devices are installed in the approach to parking lots.

Belts used to drive machinery often develop large electric charges by friction. Although the metal machinery itself is usually grounded, this does not remove the charge from the belt. Sparks from a charged belt may be a real fire hazard in some factories. Workmen sometimes receive severe electric shocks when they approach large belts in operation. In the manufacture of paper, electric charges often accumulate on the sheet of paper as it passes over the rolls of the drying and finishing machines. Special means are employed to discharge moving belts and sheets of paper in order to reduce the risk of shock and injury to workmen.

What Is Lightning?

Many early scientists believed that lightning was an explosion of large volumes of gas that in some unexplained way had accumulated in the upper regions of the atmosphere. Since the days of Benjamin Franklin and his famous kite, however, men have known that lightning is a grand display of electricity much like the spark that jumps between the knobs of the electrostatic machine. Lightning may jump from one cloud to another, or from a cloud to the earth. A bolt of lightning is nature's way of grounding huge electric charges in the atmosphere.

Each of the countless little droplets that make up a cloud becomes charged by friction with air, by induction, and perhaps by capturing ions from the surrounding atmosphere. It is known that in a typical thundercloud a huge current of swiftly moving air sweeps upward in

Lightning appears as a single jagged stroke hitting the Empire State Building in the lower part of the picture. The true picture of a lightning stroke may show a series of flashes as shown in the upper part of the picture, taken with a General Electric high-speed camera. The film in this camera was moved at a rapid rate while the exposure was made. (*General Electric Company*)

the cloud as through a chimney. This updraft encounters falling raindrops and by friction literally pulls them apart into smaller droplets. Some of these droplets are swept upward with the rising air current, while others fall to the earth as rain or remain to form the base of the cloud. The droplets carried upward are usually *positively charged*. Those at the base of the cloud are usually *negatively charged*. When the total electric charge in any one region of the cloud becomes great enough, a flash of lightning from that region to another is likely to occur. Present evidence seems to indicate that most lightning strokes to the earth occur from negatively charged cloud bases. Many of the flashes that we see during a thunderstorm occur be-

325

Fig. 13–19. A charge of opposite sign is induced in the earth, trees, and buildings under a strongly charged cloud.

tween two clouds or between different parts of the same cloud.

Lightning Rods

Benjamin Franklin is credited with the invention of the *lightning rod* used to protect farm houses, barns, and other buildings from the danger of lightning strokes. Figure 13–19 shows how lightning rods are intended to work. A large electric charge is induced in the earth immediately under a charged cloud. This induced charge crowds up into trees, buildings, and everything else that may

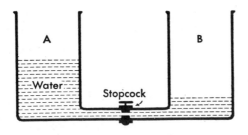

Fig. 13–20. A difference in water level causes water to flow from tank A to tank B when the stopcock is opened.

project above the ground surface. Projecting structures present a somewhat shorter path so that a flash of lightning to the earth usually passes through them, often doing much damage and sometimes starting fires. Franklin's invention consists of several metal rods extending vertically upward from the building. Each rod has one or more sharp metal points at its tip. The base of the rod must be connected as directly as possible to the earth by means of a heavy wire or cable. The wire must be well grounded to be effective. Whenever possible, it is fastened to sheets of metal buried in damp soil.

Lightning rods are intended to serve two purposes: (1) to cause the charge induced in the earth to escape through a brush discharge at the sharp points and thus neutralize the charge in the cloud before a stroke can occur; and (2) to provide a good conductor to the earth when a stroke does occur, so that the discharge will pass through the wire rather than the building.

What Is Voltage?

You probably have heard persons who handle electricity speak of high voltage and low voltage. Do you know what they mean by these terms?

Look at the simple water system shown in Fig. 13–20. We all know from experience that water will flow from tank A to tank B as soon as the stopcock is opened. Water will continue to flow in this direction as long as the *water level* in A is higher than that in B. The greater the *difference in water levels* the faster the water will flow.

Now look at the heat system shown in Fig. 13–21. Again we all know from experience that heat energy will flow from the hot iron through the copper bar to melt some of the ice, if the bar makes contact with both the iron and the ice. We say the heat flows because there is a *difference in temperature* between the iron and the ice. The greater this difference in temperature, the faster the heat will flow, as we have seen in an earlier unit.

Now look at the electric system shown in Fig. 13–22. When we hold the wire by its insulating handle and touch it to both spheres at the same time, we establish a continuous path over which electrons can move freely. The excess electrons on the sphere at the left are repelled by their neighbors. As a result these electrons flow over the easy path in the wire to the uncharged sphere at the right. A condition similar to the *difference in water level* and the *difference in temperature* must exist in this system to cause the electrons to move

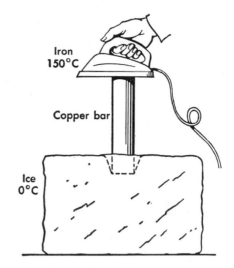

Fig. 13–21. A *difference in temperature* causes heat to flow from the iron to the ice.

A 15,000,000-volt bolt of man-made lightning leaps 50 ft between two impulse generators in the General Electric Company's high-voltage laboratory. This is the longest distance yet attained with man-made lightning. (*General Electric Company*)

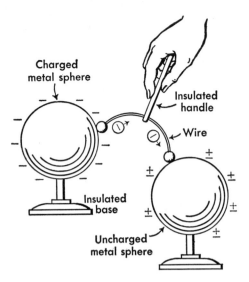

Fig. 13–22. A *difference in potential* causes electrons to flow through the wire from the charged to the uncharged sphere.

from one place to another. We call this condition a *difference in potential*. The greater this difference in electric potential, the greater the flow of electrons through the wire.

We can measure the *difference in water level* in the two tanks and express it in feet or even in pounds per square inch, if we wish to convert it to *difference in pressure*. We can measure the *difference in temperature* between the iron and the ice and express it in degrees. We can likewise measure the *difference in potential* between the two spheres. We usually express this difference in potential in *volts* (named for the Italian scientist Volta). We often refer to the difference in electric potential between any two points as *voltage*.

Electricity of Lightning

A flash of lightning between a cloud and the earth can occur only when there is a difference in potential between them. This difference in potential or voltage is

difficult or impossible to measure directly, but scientists estimate that it may range from 200,000,000 to 1,000,-000,000 volts. The voltage developed between the knobs of the ordinary laboratory electrostatic machine is roughly 50,000 volts while that between the wires of your electric lamp is commonly 115 volts. You can see by comparison how gigantic the voltage of a thundercloud may be.

The amount or quantity of the electric charge involved in a stroke of lightning reaching the earth varies considerably from stroke to stroke. From experimental records that have been obtained, it appears that from 0.1 to 200 coulombs may be contained in a single stroke. Undoubtedly some strokes may have more quantity than this and probably there are smaller ones, too.

The amount of *electric energy* associated with a charged cloud, however, is not great by present-day standards. A 10-coulomb charge at a difference of potential of 200,000,000 volts represents in round numbers 500 kilowatthours (kwh) in terms of the electric energy we buy from the power company. This is probably as great as the *average* lightning stroke to earth. If this energy could all be harnessed, stored, and put to work when needed, it would supply the needs of one typical modern home for perhaps five or six months. It would supply the demand of a moderate-sized city for only a few minutes. If all the strokes of lightning during a thunderstorm could be completely harnessed the electric energy from this source would scarcely supply the needs of such a city even during the course of the storm. At many of the large electric power plants of the country the cost of generating an equivalent amount of electric energy is less than $2.

1. Why are lightning rods not commonly used on houses in a town or city?
2. Why is the charge induced in the ground (Fig. 13–19) opposite in sign from that in the cloud?
3. Buildings equipped with lightning rods are sometimes struck by lightning. Explain how this is possible.
4. Does lightning ever strike broad surfaces, such as the earth or the water in a lake or ocean? Why?
5. Why does lightning often "run in" on telephone or other wires attached to a house?
6. Does lightning ever "strike twice in the same place"? Explain your answer.

CAPACITORS STORE CHARGES

One day in January, 1746, Professor Pieter van Musschenbroek and a student at the University of Leyden in Holland, were working at the electric machine attempting to charge some water in a flask. They had a wire extending through a stopper into the water. This wire was connected to one knob of the machine while the student held the flask in his hand. After the machine had been running for a few minutes the student reached over to disconnect the wire and received a stunning shock from the effects of which he did not fully recover for two days! Professor van Musschenbroek, reporting this astonishing incident to a friend in Paris, wrote that he "would not take such a shock for all the Kingdom of France." Thus, by accident, was discovered the famous *Leyden jar*, the earliest form of electric capacitor.

The Leyden Jar

If you look at an electrostatic machine, you will probably notice two glass vessels attached to the knobs in some way. These are Leyden jars used to store electric charge. Such a jar consists of a glass vessel with a metal coating part way up, both inside and out. A metal knob is electrically connected to the inside coating. Figure 13–23 shows the essential parts of a Leyden jar.

Figure 13–24a shows how you can charge a Leyden jar from an electrostatic machine. The glass jar and outside coating make it possible to store a much larger *quantity* of electricity than could

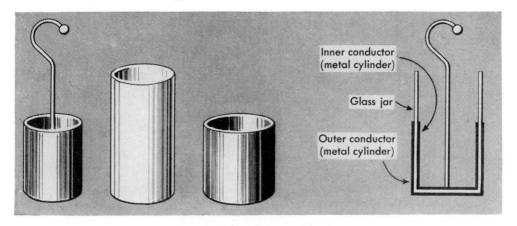

Inner conductor (metal cylinder)

Glass jar

Outer conductor (metal cylinder)

Fig. 13–23. Parts of a Leyden jar.

be stored on the inside coating if it were alone. Figure 13–24b shows how you can safely discharge a charged Leyden jar. The size of the spark you obtain is some indication of the quantity of electricity that was stored on the Leyden jar.

An Electric Capacitor

Any device like a Leyden jar that stores up electric charge is called an electric *capacitor* or *condenser*. A capacitor consists essentially of two conducting plates, usually metal, separated by an insulator called a *dielectric*. The dielectric used in a Leyden jar is glass, but mica, paraffined paper, oil, wax, air, and other dielectrics are used in other types of capacitors.

When a capacitor is charged, a difference in potential exists between its metal plates. This is why a spark jumps when you touch one plate with a wire and bring the other end of the wire near the other plate. Charging a capacitor is somewhat like filling a tank with compressed air. The more pressure you apply, the more air you can put in the tank. You cannot increase the pressure indefinitely, however, or the tank will explode. In the same way, the more voltage you apply the more coulombs of charge you can store on a given capacitor. However, if you apply too high a voltage, the dielectric will break down and a spark will pass through it from one metal plate to the other. Then the charge on the capacitor vanishes.

Electric capacitors are made in different forms and used for a great many purposes. Radio transmitters and receivers contain many capacitors. Telephone lines employ electric capacitors. Capacitors serve an important purpose on some power lines. The photograph on the facing page shows several sizes of commercial capacitors that operate efficiently in a wide range of temperatures.

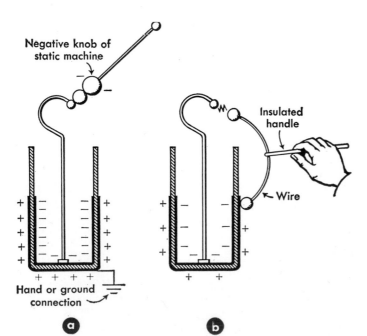

Fig. 13–24. How to charge and discharge a Leyden jar.

Capacitors designed for use in electric power distribution. These Inerteen capacitors can be operated at temperatures from −40 to 104° F without loss in operating efficiency. (*Westinghouse Electric Corporation*)

Capacitance and the Farad

The electric size of a capacitor is called its *capacitance*. The unit used in measuring capacitance is the *farad*. The farad is much too large electrically for most purposes, so we use *microfarads* and *micromicrofarads* to express the capacitance of ordinary capacitors.

1,000,000 microfarads = 1 farad
1,000,000 micromicrofarads = 1 microfarad

Variable air capacitors used for tuning radio sets commonly have a capacitance of about 350 micromicrofarads.

►Do You Know?

1. Why do the 50,000 or more volts generated by a small electrostatic machine not produce fatal shocks, while shocks from a 110-volt power line can sometimes prove fatal?
2. Does the electrical size of a capacitor (in microfarads) necessarily have any direct relation to its physical size (in inches)?
3. What are some devices that use electric capacitors? How does the automobile engine use a capacitor?
4. Define the terms *farad, microfarad,* and *micromicrofarad.*
5. What is meant by a variable capacitor?
6. Define the term *dielectric.* Name three materials commonly used as dielectrics.
7. How is electricity stored in a Leyden jar?
8. What is capacitance? What unit is used to measure capacitance?
9. From your study of static electricity in this chapter, when is an object neutral? Positively charged? Negatively charged?
10. Explain how a lightning rod may protect a building from being struck by lightning.
11. Explain what happens when thunder is heard following a flash of lightning.
12. Make a drawing to show how a negative electric charge is distributed on a single metal sphere.
13. If two adjacent metal spheres are negatively charged, how are their charges distributed?

HIGHLIGHTS

A *positive* charge is developed on glass rubbed with silk; a *negative* charge is developed on hard rubber rubbed with fur or wool.

Bodies with *like charges repel;* those with *unlike charges attract.*

The *electron* is the unit of *negative* electric charge, the *proton* is the unit of *positive* electric charge; *neutrons* have no electric charge.

An *electroscope* is used to test for electric charge.

A *coulomb* is a unit of electric charge or quantity. There are 6.25×10^{18} electrons in one coulomb.

Electric *conductors* transmit electrons; electric *insulators* block the flow of electrons.

Bodies may be charged by friction, by contact, and by induction.

Electric charges are readily transferred to the surrounding air through sharp points. The discharge at points is called a *brush* discharge or a *corona* discharge.

Electric charges may be *grounded* to your body, to the frame of a machine, or directly to the earth.

Lightning is a huge electric discharge.

A *difference in potential* or *voltage* causes electrons to move from place to place through a conductor.

Electric capacitors are used to store up electric charge.

The *capacitance* of a capacitor is a measure of its electric size.

The *farad, microfarad,* and *micromicrofarad* are used to express capacitance.

THINGS TO DO

1. Rub an inflated toy balloon with a piece of wool cloth and touch the balloon to a wall. Can you make it stick to the wall? Explain. Try rubbing the wall instead of the balloon with the cloth, and see if you can make the balloon stick. Explain.

2. Try combing your hair near the antenna wire of an operating radio. If the weather is right and your hair is dry you can often set up "man-made static" that resembles the noise from a severe electric storm. Why is a rubber comb better for this experiment than a metal comb?

3. Make an electroscope of your own. Secure a clear-glass pint jar with a metal screw cap or lid. Punch or drill a ½-in. hole through the center of the metal lid. Obtain a straight piece of bare copper wire, No. 14 or larger, about 3 in. long. Bend this wire about ½ in. from one end to form a right-angle hook. Heat some sealing wax and fill the hole in the lid with it. Before the hot wax sets, push the straight end of the wire up through the wax until the bent hook is about 1 in. below the face of the lid. Cut metal foil

from a package of chewing gum into a strip about $\frac{1}{4}$ in. wide and 3 in. long. Fold this strip lengthwise so that you have a double strip $1\frac{1}{2}$ in. long. Place the folded strip over the hook on the wire. A little shellac on the wire will help hold the leaves in place. Then put the lid on the jar. Test the sign of the charge which collects on your body when you scuff your feet across a rug with a thick nap. Test the sign of the electric charge you acquire when you slide across plastic seat covers in an automobile. Remember that experiments with static electricity work best in dry weather.

4. Obtain a heavy rubber band or a strip of rubber from an old inner tube. Stretch this rubber and see if you can charge an electroscope with it by touching the stretched rubber to the knob of the electroscope. This is another dry-weather experiment, but if you are successful in charging the electroscope, determine what kind of charge you have obtained from the stretched rubber. Then discharge the stretched rubber by pulling it across a water or gas pipe, being careful to keep the rubber dry. Then allow the rubber to contract to its original size and test it again for electric charge. If it is charged, what is the sign of the charge now on it?

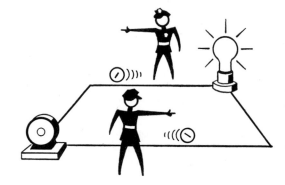

14.

Electric Circuits:
The Flow of Electrons

THE ELECTRIC CIRCUIT

It is necessary to provide a suitable path or highway over which electrons can travel if they are to do the many tasks that electricity is called on to perform.

Electrons *at rest* or in helter-skelter motion in all directions do no useful work, such as operating an electric lamp or running a motor. It is only when electrons move along through a conductor that they can deliver energy to do work. A stream of electrons moving in this way is called an *electric current.* The stream of electrons moving through the filament of an electric lamp is an electric current. Electrons moving through the wires of a motor constitute

the electric current through it. In the diagrams of this book, we shall use the symbol ⊙➔ to indicate the direction of motion of electrons through wires and circuits.

What Is an Ampere?

The size of an electric current *depends on the number of electrons that flow past a given point in the conductor in a second.* We could use one electron per second as a unit for electric current. If we did this, however, we would need very large numbers to express the size of ordinary currents, such as that through the filament of a lamp. So we commonly use a very much larger unit, one coulomb per second. This unit of current is so important

334

that it has been given a special name, the *ampere* (amp). The electric current in a wire is one ampere when one coulomb (6.25×10^{18} electrons) flows past a given point in the wire in one second. There is a current of about 0.5 amp through the filament of a 110-volt 60-watt electric lamp when it is lighted. There is a current of 4 to 10 amp through an electric laundry iron when it is in use.

When we want to measure very small currents we find it convenient to use *milliamperes* (ma) and *microamperes*.

$$1 \text{ amp} = 1{,}000 \text{ ma}$$
$$= 1{,}000{,}000 \text{ microamperes}$$
$$1 \text{ ma} = 1{,}000 \text{ microamperes}$$

The current through parts of a radio tube may be 2 ma, while the current through a photoelectric cell may be only 50 microamperes.

An electric instrument called an *ammeter* is used to measure electric current in amperes. *Milliammeters* and *microammeters* are used to measure very small electric currents.

An Electric Circuit

A single dry cell connected to a switch and a small flashlight bulb by means of wires, as shown in Fig. 14–2, forms a simple electric circuit. When the circuit is *closed* by closing the switch, the light will glow steadily, indicating a current through the filament. In a circuit like this, there is a completely closed path of electrical conductors around which the electrons can flow.

Electrons in a Circuit

There are many occasions when scientists are faced with the difficult task of trying to explain some structure or operation which we cannot see or experience directly. This was the case when we were studying how atoms are constructed. To make the atom understandable scientists have designed models which fit as nearly as possible the evidence we have about atoms. These models are not atoms and may not even be like atoms in every respect, but they help us understand the relation of things we cannot see with our eyes. When we study electrons and their motions in circuits, we are again dealing with things unseen. A kind of model made up of things we can see and with which most of us are already familiar often helps us understand the ideas and principles involved in an electric current. This is the purpose of the comparison in the paragraphs that follow. There is a close similarity between what happens in a closed water system and what happens in an electric circuit. A comparison of the

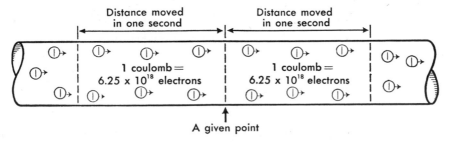

Fig. 14–1. The electric current is one ampere when one coulomb or 6.25×10^{18} electrons move past a given point in one second. The actual motion of electrons is more complicated than what is shown here.

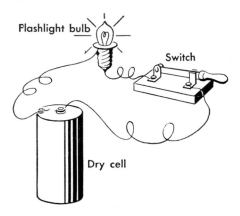

Flashlight bulb

Switch

Dry cell

Fig. 14–2. The dry cell, wires, closed switch, and light bulb form an electric *circuit.*

is connected by wires to a small electric motor M. Any other device that uses electric energy, such as a lamp, a toaster, or a laundry iron, could be substituted for the motor. The battery, connecting wires, and motor contain electrons free to move, much as the pipes are filled with water. When the circuit is closed, the battery sets these electrons in motion through the wires and motor back to the battery again, much as the pump sets the water in motion. Thus the battery corresponds to the pump, the electric motor to the water motor and the wires to the connecting pipes.

Electromotive Force

A dry cell has an outside zinc can and a central terminal. This terminal is at the end of a carbon rod which extends into the cell. Chemical action within the cell results in removing electrons from the carbon rod and placing an excess of electrons on the zinc can. In this way the carbon rod becomes positively charged, and the zinc can becomes negatively charged. This is why we label the zinc terminal $(-)$ and the carbon terminal $(+)$. When the zinc can is connected to the carbon rod through an

two may help you understand the electric circuit better.

Figure 14–3 represents a closed water system, completely filled with water. A centrifugal pump P, pressure gages G_1 and G_2, and a water motor WM are connected by pipes as shown. When the pump is driven by an engine or motor, it sets the water in motion, circulating through the pipes and motor back to the intake of the pump again.

Figure 14–4 represents the corresponding electric circuit. An electric battery E

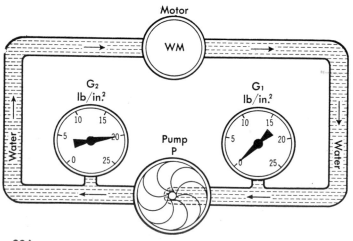

Fig. 14–3. A closed water system.

external circuit of wires and a lamp, electrons at once start to flow through the wires from the zinc toward the carbon. As soon as some electrons leave the zinc, replacements are, in effect, rushed up from the interior of the cell to take their place. When some electrons arrive at the carbon rod, they are, in effect, removed at once to the interior of the cell. A dry cell thus is able to replenish continuously the electrons that flow away from its negative terminal. A body charged by friction has no way of replenishing its charge once it has been discharged. This is why we get a steady

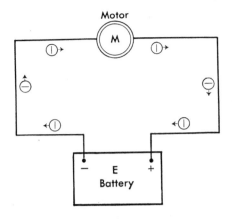

Fig. 14–4. A closed electric circuit, analogous to the closed water system of Fig. 14–3.

SOME HELPFUL PARALLELS

Water system	Electric circuit
1. The pump develops a *difference in pressure* which sets the water in motion and produces a water current.	1. The battery develops a *difference in potential* (voltage) which sets the electrons in motion and produces an electric current.
2. The pump does not manufacture or create water. As much water flows into the pump each second as flows out. The current of water into the pump is as large as the current out.	2. The battery does not manufacture or create electrons. As many electrons flow into the battery each second as flow out. The electric current into the battery is as large as the current out.
3. The water motor does not use up or destroy water. As much water flows out of the motor each second as flows in. The water current out of the motor is as large as the current in.	3. The electric motor does not use up or destroy electrons. As many electrons flow out of the motor each second as flow in. The electric current out of the motor is as large as the current in.
4. The water current at any instant is the same at all points along the system. As much water flows past any one point in a second as flows past any other point.	4. The electric current at any instant is the same in all parts of the circuit. As many electrons flow past any one point in a second as flow past any other point.
5. *Friction* in the pipes, the motor, and the water itself opposes the flow of water and limits the size of the current.	5. *Resistance* in the wires and motor interferes with the flow of electrons and limits the size of the electric current.

Cutaway view showing the positions of the individual dry cells in a 45-volt B battery. Note that the 1.5-volt cells in this battery are rectangular in shape. (*Burgess Battery Company*)

electric current from a battery but only a single pulse of current from a discharging capacitor.

The chemical action within the dry cell generates an *electromotive force* (emf). The emf produces the difference

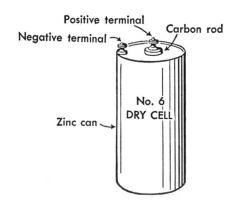

Fig. 14–5. External parts of a dry cell.

in potential in a circuit which sets the electrons in motion and produces the current. The size of the emf is expressed by the difference in potential it can produce between the $(-)$ and $(+)$ terminals of the cell, when the cell is not connected to an external circuit.

The practical unit of emf is the *volt*. The emf of a single new dry cell is about 1.5 volts. The emf of a single storage cell is about 2 volts. The emf of the generator in an automobile is approximately 8 volts. Thermocouples, certain crystals, and a type of photoelectric cell are also sources of small but important electromotive forces.

Electromotive force may usually be measured with a suitable type of voltmeter. Millivoltmeters are used in measuring small electromotive forces.

What Resistance Does

Frictional forces retard the flow of water through a pipe, and *resistance* retards the flow of electrons through a wire or other conductor. The electrons within a conductor are not entirely free to move but are restrained by the attraction of the atoms among which they must move. A good conductor of a given size has a low resistance, a poor conductor has a higher resistance, while a good insulator of the same size has an exceedingly high resistance.

The unit of resistance is the *ohm*. The resistance of an electric laundry iron is 15 to 25 ohms; that of a 60-watt light bulb (hot) is about 240 ohms. Very high resistances are usually expressed in *megohms*. One megohm is 1,000,000 ohms. Some *resistors* used in radio and electronic circuits have resistances of several megohms.

We often use the Greek letter omega Ω as an abbreviation for ohms. Thus 240 ohms may be written 240 Ω. You will see

	Water		Electricity		
	Water		**Electricity**		
	Unit		Unit		Symbol
Pressure or potential	Pound per square inch		Volt		E
Quantity	Gallon or cubic foot		Electron or coulomb		Q
Current	Gallon per minute or cubic foot per minute		1 coulomb per second = 1 ampere		I
Friction or resistance	No simple unit		Ohm		R

why the letter O would be a poor abbreviation if you will write it in place of the Ω following the 240.

The above chart shows the corresponding units for water and electricity.

Circuit Diagrams

There are several different ways of representing an electric circuit. One way is by means of a photograph or a scale drawing showing each part and the connecting wires just as they appear in the actual circuit. When the circuit extends over a considerable area, this method is impractical or even impossible. When there are many parts, the diagram may become very confusing. A second way is to use a pictorial diagram, such as Fig. 14–2, in which each part of the actual circuit is represented by a recognizable drawing of the original. The pictorial diagram does not necessarily show the parts or the connecting wires in their actual positions. A simpler device is a "schematic" diagram in which the parts of the circuit are represented

A Few Symbols Commonly Used in Circuit Diagrams

Description	Symbol	Description	Symbol
Battery (one cell)	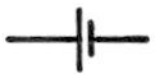	Wires crossed, not connected	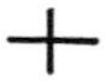
Battery, series (several cells)	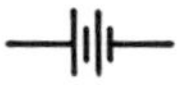	Wires crossed, connected	
Ammeter		Voltmeter	
Galvanometer		Fuse	
Resistor (fixed)		Rheostat or variable resistor	
Switch, single-pole single-throw		Switch, single-pole double-throw	
Switch, double-pole single-throw		Switch, double-pole double-throw	
Motor, direct current		Generator, direct current	

339

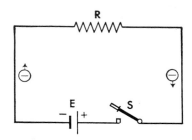

Fig. 14–6. A schematic circuit diagram.

by conventional symbols and the connecting wires by straight lines with square corners. Figure 14–6 is a schematic diagram of the circuit of Fig. 14–2. We shall use schematic circuit diagrams in this book because of their simplicity and convenience in drawing. You should be able to follow these diagrams as soon as you learn a few of the conventional symbols.

Ohm's Law

Serious damage may result from connecting a source of emf into a circuit which is not adequate to carry the required current. For this reason, it is important that we know how large the

current will be before we connect a circuit. There is a way of obtaining this information in most cases.

The amount of current in the electric circuit of Fig. 14–4 depends on two factors: (1) the size of the electromotive force (in volts) and (2) the amount of resistance in the circuit (in ohms). The way in which these two factors affect the amount of current in a circuit is shown in Fig. 14–7.

By comparing Fig. 14–7a with 14–7b, you can see that *doubling the emf doubles the current*. By comparing Fig. 14–7b with 14–7c, you can see that *doubling the resistance halves the current*. These two effects are combined in *Ohm's law*, which may be expressed in the following ways:

The current through a circuit is directly proportional to the electromotive force and inversely proportional to the resistance in the circuit.

$$I = \frac{E}{R} \qquad \text{Amperes} = \frac{\text{volts}}{\text{ohms}}$$

$$E = IR \qquad \text{Volts} = \text{amperes} \times \text{ohms}$$

$$R = \frac{E}{I} \qquad \text{Ohms} = \frac{\text{volts}}{\text{amperes}}$$

Unit	Use	Pioneer in Electricity and Some of His Contributions
Volt	Potential	Alessandro Volta (1745–1827)—Italian
		The electric battery
Coulomb	Quantity	Charles Augustin de Coulomb (1736–1806)—French
		Laws of attraction and repulsion of charged and magnetized bodies
Ampere	Current	André-Marie Ampère (1775–1836)—French
		Relation between currents and magnetic fields
Ohm	Resistance	Georg Simon Ohm (1787–1854)—German
		Ohm's law
Farad	Capacitance	Michael Faraday (1791–1867)—English
		Lines of force—the generator principle
Henry	Inductance	Joseph Henry (1797–1878)—American
		First secretary Smithsonian Institution
		Principle of induction

EXAMPLE: What is the value of the resistance in the circuit of Fig. 14–7a?

SOLUTION: By Ohm's law

$$\text{Ohms} = \frac{\text{volts}}{\text{amperes}} \quad \text{or} \quad R = \frac{E}{I}$$

From Fig. 14–7a

$E = 1.5$ volts   and $I = 0.1$ amp

Hence

$$R = \frac{1.5 \text{ volts}}{0.1 \text{ amp}} = 15 \text{ ohms}$$

This is the value shown in Fig. 14–7a.

►You Will Be Interested to Know

The electrical units were all named for pioneers in the science of electricity, men who made significant contributions to our present knowledge of the subject.

►Do You Know?

1. Why is electric voltage sometimes called *electric pressure?*
2. Is it correct to say that a power plant manufactures electricity? Explain.
3. Some persons believe that an electric lamp uses up electric current. Is this true? Why?
4. Is it true that there is as much current in the service wire leading away from your house as in the wire coming in? Explain.
5. A sign
   DANGER   1,000,000   OHMS
   appeared in a physics classroom. What is wrong with it?
6. What is an *open* circuit?
7. What is a *short* circuit?
8. What is a *grounded* circuit?
9. Which common household appliances may be called *resistors?*
10. What is an ampere?
11. State Ohm's law and give formula.

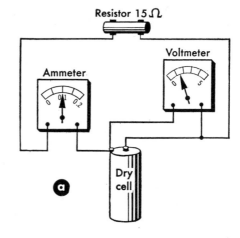

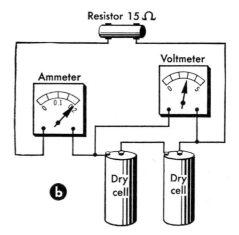

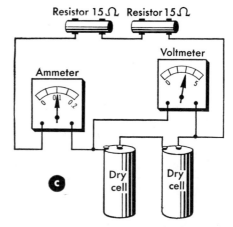

Fig. 14–7. How voltage and resistance affect the amount of current.

341

SERIES AND PARALLEL CIRCUITS

Some highways are located so that you have to travel first over one and then over the other to reach your destination. These highways are *in series*. Other highways are laid out so that you can choose one or the other to travel to your destination. These highways are *in parallel*.

What Is a Series Circuit?

In the circuit of Fig. 14–8a, the three resistors R_1, R_2, and R_3 are connected in *series*. They provide only one route by which electrons can move around the circuit. The stream of electrons that flows through one resistor must flow through all the others. The ammeter A_2 will indicate just as many amperes as the ammeter A_1. The electric current is the same through all three resistors. *Resistors do not use up electric current.*

You can see that a series arrangement would not be satisfactory for house lights. If a switch is opened anywhere in the circuit, all the lights will go out together. If a filament burns out or if one lamp is removed from the socket, all go out. In spite of this inconvenience, the bulbs in some strings of Christmas-tree lights are connected in series. Street lights are sometimes connected in series but usually with an arrangement to maintain the circuit even if one light burns out. The heaters of several or all of the tubes in some radio sets are connected in series. Many other important uses for this arrangement occur.

Voltages in a Series Circuit

You will observe that a current of 2 amp is assumed to exist in every part of the circuit in Fig. 14–8a. By Ohm's law, the difference in potential across the 5-ohm resistor R_1 must then be

$$E_1 = IR_1 = 2 \text{ amp} \times 5 \text{ ohms} = 10 \text{ volts}$$

The difference in potential across the 2-ohm resistor R_2 must be

$$E_2 = IR_2 = 2 \text{ amp} \times 2 \text{ ohms} = 4 \text{ volts}$$

The difference in potential across the 9-ohm resistor must be

$$E_3 = IR_3 = 2 \text{ amp} \times 9 \text{ ohms} = 18 \text{ volts}$$

The ammeters and the connecting wires generally have very low resistances. In most cases it is safe to assume that any differences in potential that occur across them will be so small that they can be neglected. This may not be true, however, in every electric circuit.

Notice that 10 volts + 4 volts + 18 volts = 32 volts, which is the difference in potential established by the battery.

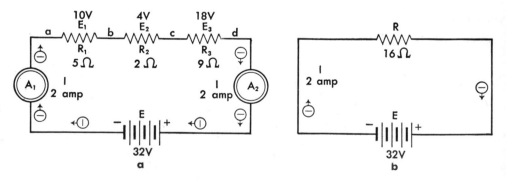

Fig. 14–8. A series circuit and the equivalent simple circuit.

In other words, $E = E_1 + E_2 + E_3$.
In a series circuit the sum of all the differences in potential across individual resistors is equal to the difference in potential set up by the battery or other source of emf.

Resistance in a Series Circuit

To see how a complicated circuit works, we usually try to reduce it to a simple *equivalent circuit*. Figure 14–8*b* shows the equivalent circuit of Fig. 14–8*a*. In the equivalent circuit, the emf and the current it sets up are the same as in the original circuit. However, one single resistor R takes the place of the three resistors R_1, R_2, and R_3. To describe the equivalent circuit completely, we need to find the size of the resistor R in terms of the original three resistances.

In the equivalent circuit,

$$R = \frac{E}{I} = \frac{32 \text{ volts}}{2 \text{ amp}} = 16 \text{ ohms}$$

In the original circuit $R_1 + R_2 + R_3 = 5$ ohms $+ 2$ ohms $+ 9$ ohms $= 16$ ohms. Thus it is evident that $R = R_1 + R_2 + R_3$ in these two circuits. This relation is always true for series resistors.
The equivalent resistance of several resistors in series is the sum of their separate resistances.
The amount of current in a circuit does not depend on the *order* in which series resistors are connected.

What Is a Rheostat?

A *rheostat* is a variable resistor placed in series with other parts of a circuit to regulate and control the amount of current through them. The resistance of a rheostat can be varied by some arrangement such as a movable arm or a sliding contact. Figure 14–9 shows schematically a rheostat R_1 connected in series with a resistor R_2. The battery furnishes a fixed voltage E in the circuit.

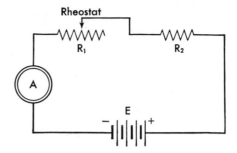

Fig. 14–9. A *rheostat* is used to control the amount of current in a circuit.

The current is

$$I = \frac{E}{R_1 + R_2} \quad \text{(amp)}$$

By changing R_1, the rheostat resistance, we can increase or decrease the current. The *largest* current will be obtained when the resistance of the rheostat is *minimum* and the *smallest* current when the resistance is *maximum*.

In a case in which it is not necessary to *vary* the size of the current, a fixed resistor may be used in place of the rheostat.

EXAMPLE: In Fig. 14–9, suppose E is a 6-volt battery and R_2 is a lamp whose resistance is 20 ohms. The lamp requires 0.25 amp to operate. How large must R_1 be?

SOLUTION: The *equivalent* circuit resistance can be found by Ohm's law.

$$R = \frac{E}{I} = \frac{6 \text{ volts}}{0.25 \text{ amp}} = 24 \text{ ohms}$$

But in a series circuit $R = R_1 + R_2$. R_2 is given as 20 ohms, so

$$R_1 = R - R_2 = 24 \text{ ohms} - 20 \text{ ohms}$$
$$= 4 \text{ ohms}$$

A suitable 4-ohm resistor should be used for R_1 under the conditions of this problem.

343

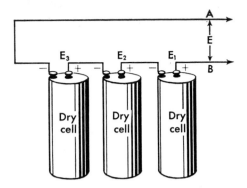

Fig. 14–10. Dry cells connected in series to form a battery.

Rheostats are used to dim lights on some automobiles. Some theater lighting circuits use rheostats for controlling house and stage lights. In some electric motor circuits, rheostats are used during starting and for speed control. Radio sets and other electronic devices use rheostats for a number of different purposes.

Emf's in Series

Dry cells are connected in series when the $(-)$ zinc terminal of one is connected to the $(+)$ carbon terminal of the next one, as shown in Fig. 14–10. The schematic symbol for cells connected in series is shown at E in Fig. 14–9. The corresponding arrangement of pumps in a water circuit is shown in Fig. 14–11.

From this figure you can see that each pump boosts the pressure above that of its predecessor. The total pressure produced by the battery of pumps is equal to the sum of those produced by the individual pumps. In the series circuit of Fig. 14–10, each cell contributes its share to increase the difference in potential between the points A and B so that the over-all emf of the battery is

$$E = E_1 + E_2 + E_3 \text{ (volts)}$$

In a series circuit the equivalent emf is the sum of the emf's of the separate units.

When we connect emf's in series, the electric current has the same value in all the units, so we can draw no more current from the battery than the maximum that *one cell* can furnish. The series arrangement is used to increase the available emf, not the maximum permissible current. Thus generators are often connected in series to obtain higher voltage than one alone can produce. The cells of a storage battery are connected in series for the same reason. Dry cells are commonly connected in series to form radio batteries.

Internal Resistance

Figure 14–12 shows a single dry cell connected in series with a rheostat and a small resistor. An ammeter to indicate

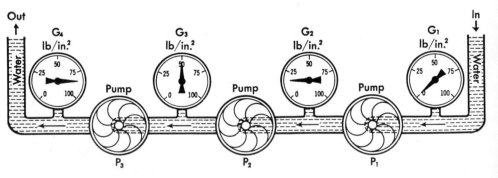

Fig. 14–11. Water analogy of cells connected in series.

current and a voltmeter to measure the voltage across the terminals of the cell are also shown. When the current is small, less than 0.1 amp, for example, the voltmeter will read about 1.5 volts, But if we increase the current *momentarily* to several amperes, the voltmeter will indicate less than 1.5 volts. The voltage will decrease as the current is increased, as shown in the graph of Fig. 14–13. The voltmeter reading in this case is called the *terminal voltage* of the cell.

Every source of emf acts as if it had a resistance associated with it. We designate this resistance by r and call it the *internal resistance* of the device. We cannot separate this internal resistance from the source of emf; when we place a voltmeter across the terminals of a cell to measure its voltage, we must measure the voltage across the emf and the internal resistance combined. Figure 14–14 shows the schematic diagram of the circuit of Fig. 14–12, with the internal resistance of the cell included. When the internal resistance is very small and the current is not large, the terminal voltage is practically the same as the emf of the cell. This is the condition we assume when we omit the internal resistance from our circuit diagrams. When the internal resistance is large, even a small current will reduce the terminal voltage below the emf. For this reason, a voltmeter, which takes a small current to operate, does not measure the true emf of a device which has a high internal resistance.

The internal resistance of a new dry cell is usually less than 0.05 ohm. The internal resistance of a dry cell increases slowly as the cell ages. The internal resistance of a single storage cell is about 0.005 ohm. Generators have internal resistance from a small fraction of an ohm up to several ohms.

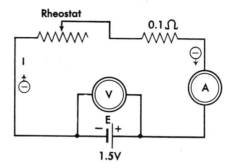

Fig. 14–12. Schematic diagram of a circuit for showing the effect of internal resistance of a dry cell.

When cells are connected in series to form a battery, the equivalent internal resistance of the battery is

$$r = r_1 + r_2 + r_3 + \ldots \text{(ohms)}$$

What Is a Parallel Circuit?

Figure 14–15 shows two water motors connected in *parallel*. The main stream of water comes to the point a and *divides*, one part going through WM_1 and the other through WM_2. At point b these two streams reunite to form the main stream again. The difference in pressure from a to b is just the same, whether the water goes over one route or the other. Why is this true?

Figure 14–16a shows a corresponding electric circuit with the resistors R_1 and R_2 in *parallel*. The main current divides

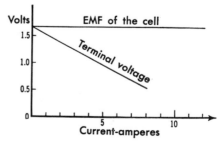

Fig. 14–13. The terminal voltage of a dry cell decreases as more current is drawn from the cell.

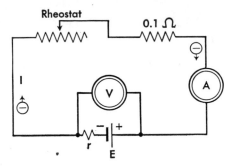

Fig. 14–14. The same circuit as in Fig. 14–12, modified to indicate the internal resistance of the cell.

at a, part going through each resistor. The two branch currents reunite at b to form the main current again. You can see that if the current I_1 through the R_1 branch is 2 amp and the current I_2 through R_2 is 3 amp, the main current must be 5 amp.

$$I = I_1 + I_2 + I_3 + \ldots \text{(amp)}$$

In a parallel circuit the main current is equal to the sum of the branch currents.

You can also see that if the voltage E_1 across R_1 is 6 volts, that across R_2 must likewise be 6 volts, because the difference

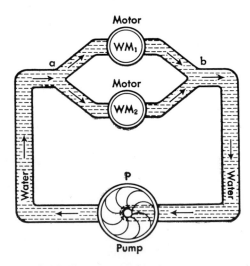

Fig. 14–15. The two water motors are connected in parallel.

in potential between a and b is the same over each branch, just as the difference in water pressure from a to b is the same over each branch in Fig. 14–15. In general,

$$E = E_1 = E_2 = E_3 = \ldots \text{(volts)}$$

Parallel circuits are also called *multiple* and *divided* circuits. The branches are sometimes called *legs*. A circuit may have any number of parallel branches. All our house lights and household appliances, such as the electric iron, toaster, refrigerator, vacuum sweeper, and radio, are operated in parallel.

Equivalent Resistance

The circuit of Fig. 14–16b is equivalent to that of Fig. 14–16a, if the value of R is properly chosen. The same emf—6 volts—is used in each circuit. The same current—5 amp—is maintained by the battery in each case. Our problem is to determine how R must be related to R_1 and R_2.

In the parallel circuit of Fig. 14–16a

$$I_1 = \frac{6 \text{ volts}}{3 \text{ ohms}} = 2 \text{ amp} \quad \text{or} \quad I_1 = \frac{E}{R_1}$$

$$I_2 = \frac{6 \text{ volts}}{2 \text{ ohms}} = 3 \text{ amp} \quad \text{or} \quad I_2 = \frac{E}{R_2}$$

$$I = I_1 + I_2 = 2 \text{ amp} + 3 \text{ amp} = 5 \text{ amp}$$

or

$$I = \frac{E}{R_1} + \frac{E}{R_2} = E\left(\frac{1}{R_1} + \frac{1}{R_2}\right) \text{ amp}$$

In the equivalent circuit, Fig. 14–16b,

$$I = \frac{E}{R} = E\frac{1}{R}$$

Since E and I are the same in both circuits, it follows that

$$\frac{1}{R} = \frac{1}{R_1} + \frac{1}{R_2}$$

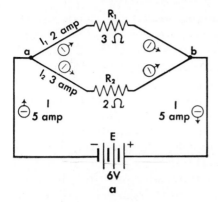
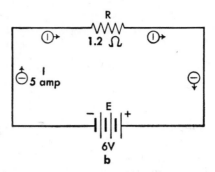

Fig. 14–16. The resistors R_1 and R_2 are connected in parallel in the circuit at the left. The equivalent simple circuit is shown at the right.

When solved for R, this equation gives

$$R = \frac{R_1 R_2}{R_1 + R_2}$$

So in the circuit of Fig. 14–16a

$$R = \frac{3 \times 2}{3 + 2} = 1.2 \text{ ohms}$$

And in the equivalent circuit of Fig. 14–16b

$$R = \frac{6 \text{ volts}}{5 \text{ amp}} = 1.2 \text{ ohms}$$

The equivalent resistance of two resistors in parallel is the product of their separate resistances divided by their sum.

Notice that the equivalent resistance with which we have been dealing is that of a circuit with *two* parallel branches. In case there are more than two branches, the above equation for the equivalent resistance R becomes

$$1/R = 1/R_1 + 1/R_2 + 1/R_3 + \ldots$$

For *two* resistances in parallel, (1) when the two parallel resistors have *equal* resistances, their equivalent resistance is *half* that of either one; (2) the equivalent resistance is always less than that of the smaller resistor; (3) when one resistor is small and the other large, the equivalent

resistance is only slightly less than that of the smaller one; and (4) when the resistance in either branch is increased, the equivalent resistance is increased.

You can check these statements by assigning any convenient numbers to R_1 and R_2 and solving the equation above for R.

Emf's in Parallel

Figure 14–17 shows three dry cells connected in parallel. All the (−) zinc terminals are connected together to form the negative terminal of the assembled battery. All the (+) carbon terminals are connected to form the positive terminal of the battery. Figure 14–18 shows how these cells may be represented in a circuit diagram. Figure 14–19 is a corresponding arrangement of water

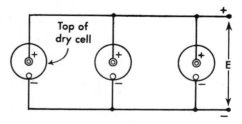

Fig. 14–17. A battery of three dry cells connected in parallel.

347

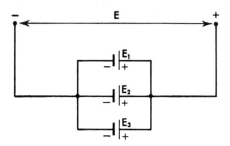

Fig. 14–18. A schematic method of representing cells in parallel.

pumps. You can see that these three pumps all take in water at the same pressure. They must all give out water at the same pressure also, for if one gave out water at a higher pressure than the other two, then water would flow backward through the low-pressure pumps. In other words, the three pumps must be

operated so that each produces the *same difference in pressure*. This difference in pressure is the same as that which a single pump alone could produce, if the pumps are equally effective. The three pumps can, however, handle a much larger volume of water than a single pump can handle.

In the same way, the three cells in Fig. 14–17 must produce the *same difference in potential*, if current is not to flow backward through one or more of them. The emf of the battery is the same as that of a single cell.

$$E = E_1 = E_2 = E_3 \text{ (volts)}$$

The three cells in parallel can, however, furnish more current than a single cell alone can furnish.

The internal resistances of cells arranged in parallel are also in parallel. The internal resistance of a battery made up of similar cells in parallel is less than that of a single cell.

$$\frac{1}{r} = \frac{1}{r_1} + \frac{1}{r_2} + \frac{1}{r_3}$$

Cells are connected in parallel in batteries designed to furnish more current than one cell alone can furnish. One type of 1.5-volt dry battery consists of four 1.5-volt cells in parallel. Electric generators are usually connected in parallel when a large current is needed. Sometimes series-parallel arrangements such as those shown in Fig. 14–20 are used to increase both the voltage and the current that the battery can furnish.

▶**Do You Know?**

1. Is the switch on a desk lamp in series or in parallel with the lamp?
2. What does the switch do in a circuit to turn off the lamp?
3. How many Christmas-tree lights are

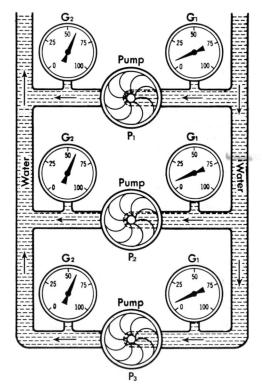

Fig. 14–19. Three water pumps connected in parallel.

commonly used in a series string? Why?

4. What are the advantages of parallel wiring for Christmas-tree lights? The disadvantages?

5. Does the ordinary electric light bulb of higher wattage rating require more or less voltage to operate than one of lower rating? More or less current?

6. Are automobile lights connected in series or in parallel? How can you tell?

7. Are the cells in a flashlight in series or in parallel? How many cells are commonly used?

8. How many cells are in an automobile battery? How are they connected?

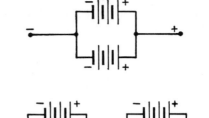

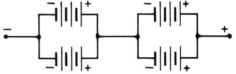

Fig. 14–20. Series-parallel arrangements of cells.

MEASURING ELECTRICITY

Rugged, reliable, and sensitive instruments are used to measure the electrical quantities, current, voltage, and resistance.

We have already seen that electric current is measured with an instrument called an *ammeter*. If the meter is designed to measure *direct current*—the kind we have been discussing—one of its two terminals is usually marked with a (+) sign and the other with a (−) sign. In almost every case the electric current that an ammeter measures must actually pass through the instrument, so this meter must be connected *in series* with the circuit in which it is to measure the current. Electrons must flow through the meter from its (−) to its (+) terminal to cause its pointer to swing upscale. The meter must have its (−) terminal connected with the (−) terminal of the battery or other source of emf, as shown in Fig. 14–21. If the connections are reversed, the pointer will move off-scale (backward) until it strikes the bumper post.

The ammeter should have only a very small resistance, so that it will not change the current appreciably in a circuit into which it is inserted. For this reason, we must be careful to see that there is always enough other resistance in the circuit to limit the current to a value that the meter can safely carry.

A single-range ammeter for direct current. The mirror back of the pointer makes it easier to read the meter correctly. (*Weston Electrical Instrument Corporation*)

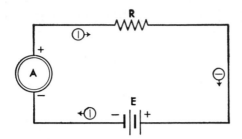

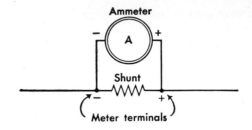

Fig. 14–21. How an ammeter should be connected to measure the current in a circuit.

Fig. 14–22. A shunt is used with an ammeter to extend its range.

Excessive current generally ruins an ammeter.

The range of an ammeter is the number of amperes required to move its pointer completely across the scale. The range can be increased by use of a *shunt,* as shown in Fig. 14–22. A shunt is simply a parallel route for current around the meter. A major portion of the main current goes through the shunt; a small, definite fraction of the current goes through the meter. If it takes 1 amp for a full-scale reading of the meter alone,

it may require 10 amp for a full-scale reading when a particular shunt is used. Of these 10 amp, 9 then go through the shunt and only 1 through the meter itself. Some ammeters have several shunts built into the meter case and so have several ranges. Each range may have its own scale marked on the dial.

How Voltage Is Measured

One way of measuring voltage is by means of a voltmeter, as we have seen. A voltmeter looks much like an ammeter. It is intended to be connected *between two points of a circuit* without opening the circuit, as shown in Fig. 14–23. The voltmeter is thus connected in parallel with the portion of the circuit across which the voltage is to be measured. Connecting the voltmeter must not change appreciably the voltage it is to measure, so the meter must have a high resistance. One type of laboratory meter has 100 ohms per volt. When the range of a meter of this type is 150 volts, its resistance is $150 \times 100 = 15,000$ ohms. A meter of this type with a range of 3 volts has a resistance of only 300 ohms. Test voltmeters used in radio and electronic work often have resistances of 1,000, 10,000, or 20,000 ohms per volt.

If a voltmeter is designed to measure direct voltages, such as we have discussed, one of its two terminals is usually

A triple-range DC voltmeter. (*Weston Electrical Instrument Corporation*)

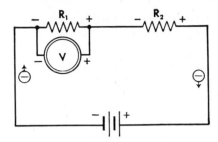

Fig. 14–23. How a voltmeter should be connected to measure the voltage across the resistor R_1.

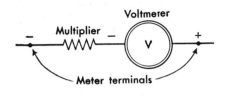

Fig. 14–24. A multiplier is used with a voltmeter to extend its range.

marked $(-)$ and the other $(+)$. The $(-)$ terminal of the meter must be connected with the $(-)$ terminal of the battery or emf. If the leads are reversed, the pointer will move off-scale (backward), just as the pointer of an ammeter does. This makes a voltmeter very useful for determining the *polarity* of a battery or points along a circuit. By polarity we mean which of two points (poles) is positive and which negative with respect to the other.

The range of a voltmeter may be extended by means of a series resistor called a *multiplier*, as shown in Fig. 14–24. The full-scale reading of the meter alone may be 15 volts. With the multiplier, 150 volts may be required to move the pointer to full-scale, 135 volts across the multiplier, and 15 across the meter. Some voltmeters have several multipliers built into the meter case, and so have several ranges. Each range may have its own scale marked on the dial.

How Resistance Is Measured

A voltmeter and ammeter may be used to measure resistance. When a resistor is connected into a circuit in which there is a current, the ammeter may be used to measure the current I through the resistor; the voltmeter to measure the voltage E across the resistor. From the two meter readings, the resist-

ance of the resistor may be calculated by Ohm's law, $R = E/I$. This is a practical method of making a rough measurement of resistance.

An ohmmeter may be used to measure resistance. The internal circuit of a simple type of ohmmeter is shown in Fig. 14–25. The meter contains a battery E, a rheostat R_1, a fixed resistor R_2, and a

This instrument can be used to measure resistance, voltage, and current. (*The Triplett Electrical Instrument Company, Bluffton, Ohio*)

351

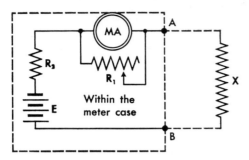

Fig. 14–25. Circuit diagram for one type of ohmmeter.

sensitive milliammeter or microammeter *MA*. These parts are all mounted inside the case of the ohmmeter. The instrument must be set or adjusted each time before using it. To do this, the terminals *A* and *B* are *short-circuited* by touching the leads from the terminals together, and the rheostat, R_1, adjusted so that the pointer stands at the top of the scale. The short circuit is then removed and the resistor *X* which we wish to measure is connected between the points *A* and *B*. The pointer will now stand at a position farther downscale because there is less current. The higher the resistance of *X*, the less current and the farther downscale the pointer will be. An ohm scale is marked on the dial so that the value of *X* in ohms can be read directly from the position of the pointer.

A multimeter is a milliammeter, voltmeter, and ohmmeter all in one case.

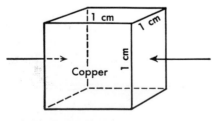

Fig. 14–26. Resistivity is the resistance between opposite faces of a cube of the material 1 cm on an edge.

CONDUCTORS AND RESISTANCE

The resistance of an electric circuit may be thought of as the difficulty electrons have in moving through that circuit. Two quantities—voltage and resistance—determine the size of an electric current. Only one of these—resistance—depends on the conductors which make up the circuit. The resistance of any conductor depends on its length. *The resistance of a conductor is directly proportional to its length.*

The resistance of a conductor depends on its cross section. *The resistance of a conductor is inversely proportional to its cross-section area.*

The resistance of a conductor depends on its material. A conductor made of copper has less resistance than a conductor of the same size made of aluminum or iron.

These three effects can be combined into one equation:

$$R = K\frac{L}{A}$$

where R = the resistance of the conductor
L = length
A = cross-section area
K = the resistivity of the material of which the conductor is made

When L is expressed in centimeters and A in square centimeters K is the resistance in ohms between the opposite faces of a cube of the material 1 cm on an edge. Practical electricians prefer to express L in feet and A in circular mils. Then K becomes the *mil-foot resistance* of the material. The mil-foot resistance is the resistance in ohms of a unit wire 1 ft long and 1 mil (0.001 in.) in diameter. The mil-foot resistance of standard copper is 10.4 ohms. That of other materials is shown in Table 14–1. The resistance of a wire may then be expressed as

$$R_{\text{ohms}} = K_{\text{mil-foot resistance}} \times \frac{\text{length in feet}}{(\text{diameter in mils})^2}$$

You may not be acquainted with circular units of area. They are much more convenient to use to describe round wires than the ordinary square units. The area of a circle in square units is $A = \pi d^2/4$. In circular units, the area of a circle is simply $A = d^2$; thus the area of a circle 100 mils in diameter is $A = 100 \times 100 = 10,000$ circular mils.

Temperature and Resistivity

The resistance of the tungsten filament of an electric lamp when hot is about 4 times as great as when cold. The resistance of a copper telephone wire is greater in summer than in winter. *The resistivity of all pure metals increases with a rise in temperature.*

Carbon, once used extensively for the filaments of lamps, acts differently. The hot resistance of a carbon filament lamp is much less than its cold resistance. *The resistivity of carbon decreases with a rise in temperature.*

The conductors of electric heating devices, such as laundry irons and toasters, are made of an *alloy* rather than a pure metal. The resistivity of an alloy, as a general rule, (1) is higher than that of the pure metals that form the alloy and (2) changes less rapidly with changes in temperature than that of the pure metals. The resistivity of some alloys increases and that of others decreases as their temperature rises. For some alloys, the change in resistivity in the ordinary range of temperatures (*e.g.*, 0 to 36°C) is exceedingly small or even zero. This is the characteristic which makes manganin

Table 14–1. Resistivity of Metals

Metal	Resistivity at 20°C, ohm-centimeters	Mil-foot resistance at 20°C, ohms
Silver	1.59×10^{-6}	9.6
Annealed copper	1.724×10^{-6}	10.4
Hard-drawn copper	1.771×10^{-6}	10.7
Gold	2.44×10^{-6}	14.7
Aluminum	2.824×10^{-6}	17.0
Tungsten	5.6×10^{-6}	33.8
Brass	7×10^{-6}	42.1
Platinum	10.0×10^{-6}	60.2
Iron, pure	10.0×10^{-6}	60.2
Tin	11.5×10^{-6}	69.1
German silver	33×10^{-6}	199
Monel metal	42×10^{-6}	253
Manganin	44×10^{-6}	264
Constantan	49×10^{-6}	295
Nichrome	100×10^{-6}	602

especially well adapted for use in resistance coils which are to serve as standards.

Why Insulate?

Conductors of a circuit that can possibly make contact with one another require an insulating covering to prevent *short-circuiting.* Conductors that can touch pipes, metal frames, or other conducting material need insulation to pre-

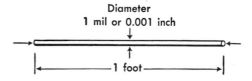

Fig. 14–27. Mil-foot resistance is the resistance in ohms between the opposite ends of a unit wire, which is 1 mil in diameter and 1 ft long. The mil-foot resistance of copper is 10.4 ohms.

353

vent *grounding*. These are the reasons why the wires installed in a house have a covering of plastic or rubber compound and fabric. The connecting cords for lamps and electric appliances require adequate insulation to prevent shocks to the operator and fires resulting from short circuits. A cord should be repaired or replaced when it shows signs of wear or broken insulation. The cords for toasters, irons, and heaters require large wires and special insulation.

Oil and gasoline cause rubber insulation to deteriorate. Synthetic insulating material is required when conductors are exposed to oil. Moisture ruins the insulating property of cotton and other fabric insulations. In the interest of safety, electric wires and appliances should be kept free from oil and moisture.

►Do You Know?

1. Why is an ammeter likely to be burned out if you connect it in parallel as you would a voltmeter?

2. Would a shunt enable you to make a 10-amp meter become a 1-amp meter? Explain.

3. Would a multiplier enable you to *reduce* the range of a voltmeter? Explain.

4. What are the advantages of a rough, black insulating coating on the outsides of resistors which become heated?

5. Show why the area of a circle in circular units is d^2. This is a problem in geometry.

6. Which four metals in Table 14–1 are the best conductors?

7. Where is carbon used as a conductor in present-day circuits?

8. Why is nichrome wire used in the coils of electric heaters?

9. Why do the cords of electric toasters usually have asbestos wrapping under the fabric covering?

10. Why should electric switches, outlets, and appliances be placed out of reach of a person in a bathtub?

HIGHLIGHTS

An *electric current* is a stream of electrons moving through a conductor.

The *ampere* is the unit of electric current. One ampere is one coulomb per second.

An *electric circuit* is a closed path of conductors through which electrons can flow.

An *electromotive force* (emf) is necessary to set electrons in motion in a circuit.

The size of an electromotive force is expressed in *volts*. Batteries and generators are the chief sources of electromotive force.

Resistance retards the flow of electrons and limits the size of the current.

The unit of resistance is the *ohm*.

Ohm's law: The current is directly proportional to the emf and inversely proportional to the resistance in a circuit.

$$\text{Amperes} = \frac{\text{volts}}{\text{ohms}} \qquad I = \frac{E}{R}$$

Two common ways of connecting resistors and emf's are in *series* or in *parallel*.

The *equivalent resistance* of several resistors in series is the sum of their separate resistances. $R = R_1 + R_2 + R_3 + \ldots$

A *rheostat* is a variable resistor used to regulate and control current.

The equivalent emf of a battery made up of cells in series is $E = E_1 + E_2 + E_3 + \ldots$.

Any source of emf has an *internal resistance* r associated with it. This internal resistance forms part of the equivalent resistance of the circuit.

In a parallel circuit, the voltage drop across one branch is the same as that across every other branch.

The equivalent resistance of two resistors in parallel is the product of their separate resistances divided by their sum.

$$R = \frac{R_1 R_2}{R_1 + R_2}$$

The emf of several similar cells in parallel is equal to that of one of them.

$$E = E_1 = E_2 = E_3 = \ldots$$

Electric current is measured with an *ammeter*. The *range* of an ammeter may be extended by means of a *shunt*.

Electric voltage is measured with a *voltmeter*. The range of a voltmeter may be extended by means of a *multiplier*.

Resistance may be measured by the voltmeter-ammeter method or by an ohmmeter.

The resistance of a conductor depends on its length, its cross-section area, and its material. $R = K L/A$

K is the *resistivity* of the material of which the conductor is made. Practical electricians commonly express the length in feet, the cross-section area in *circular mils*, and K as the *mil-foot resistance* of the material.

$$R_{\text{ohms}} = K_{\text{mil-foot resistance}} \times \frac{\text{length in feet}}{(\text{diameter in mils})^2}$$

PROBLEMS: GROUP A

Draw circuit diagrams wherever possible.

1. What is the value of the current in a 75-ohm lamp? Assume 110 volts.
2. What is the resistance (hot) of a radio dial light which requires 0.15 amp at 6.3 volts to operate?
3. How many volts are required to send 0.25 amp through 10 ohms resistance?
4. The resistance of a voltmeter is 15,000 ohms. What is the value of the current in this meter when a difference in potential of 15 volts is applied between its terminals?
5. An electric toaster takes 4 amp from a 110-volt line. What is the resistance of the toaster?

6. What is the value of the current in a 1,000-ohm resistor when a difference in potential of 10 volts is applied to its terminals?

7. How much current flows through a 500-ohm resistor when the difference in potential across its terminals is 100 volts?

8. What is the equivalent resistance of 10 ohms and 25 ohms in series? In parallel?

9. What is the total emf of five 1.5-volt dry cells connected in series? In parallel?

10. An electric iron has a resistance of 20 ohms and a toaster 30 ohms. What is their equivalent resistance when connected in parallel?

11. What is the value of the current in the iron and toaster of Problem 10 when the line voltage is 110 volts?

12. An ammeter has a resistance of 0.01 ohm and carries a current of 10 amp. What is the voltage across the ammeter?

13. Draw a schematic diagram of a circuit consisting of a battery of four 2-volt cells, a 5-ohm resistor, an 8-ohm resistor, a 12-ohm resistor, and a single-pole single-throw switch, all connected in series.

14. Redraw the circuit of Problem 13, putting in an ammeter to measure the current through the resistors and a voltmeter to measure the voltage across the 12-ohm resistor.

15. What is the equivalent resistance of two 250-ohm lamps in parallel? What would be the equivalent resistance of five such lamps in parallel?

16. How many volts will be required to set up a current of 0.15 amp through a lamp whose resistance is 40 ohms?

17. How many new dry cells (1.5 volts each) must be connected in series to make a 15-volt battery?

18. How many new dry cells (1.5 volts each) must be connected in series to make a 45-volt B battery?

19. A certain electric laundry iron has a resistance of 12 ohms. How many amperes of current will flow through it when it is connected to a 120-volt electric service line?

20. If the maximum current a dry cell should furnish continuously is 0.15 amp, how many dry cells should be used to furnish a continuous current of 0.75 amp? How should these dry cells be connected?

21. No. 20 copper wire has a resistance of 10.15 ohms per 1,000 ft. What is the resistance of 250 ft of this wire?

22. No. 12 copper wire has a resistance of 1.59 ohms per 1,000 ft. How many feet of this wire would be required to make a resistance of 5.3 ohms?

23. What is the voltage across a 50-ohm resistor which is carrying a current of 0.15 amp?

24. An electric iron draws 10 amp, an electric toaster draws 5 amp, and an electric refrigerator draws 3 amp from a 120-volt service line. The three appliances are connected in parallel. If all three are operating at the same time, will a 15-amp fuse be adequate to carry the load? Give the reason for your answer.

25. An electric lamp requires 3 amp of current at 120 volts for its operation. What is the equivalent resistance of three of these lamps connected in parallel?

26. Make a list of all the resistances which it would be possible to obtain by combining three separate resistors of 2, 4, and 6 ohms, respectively. Use all three resistors in each combination which you make.

27. Five dry cells of 1.5 volts emf each have internal resistance of 0.2, 0.3, 0.4, 0.5, and 12 ohms, respectively. When connected in series, what current will these five cells furnish through 10 ohms resistance? What current would they furnish if short-circuited?

GROUP B

1. What is the value of the current in milliamperes in a 1-megohm resistor when the difference in potential between its terminals is 100 volts?

2. What is the internal resistance of a dry cell whose emf is 1.58 volts and which sets up a current of 1 amp through a 1.5-ohm resistor?

3. How much series resistance must be used with a 1.50-volt dry cell whose internal resistance is 0.1 ohm in order that the current may be limited to 5 amp?

4. Eight similar Christmas-tree lights are connected in series. What is the voltage across each light when the line voltage is 115 volts?

5. Two resistors, one of 20 ohms and one of 30 ohms, are connected in series across a 100-volt line. What is the voltage across each resistor?

6. Each of the connecting wires of a motor has a resistance of 0.1 ohm. The motor takes 20 amp of current. If a potential difference of 110 volts is applied to the connecting wires, what is the voltage across the terminals of the motor?

7. An electric generator has an emf of 8 volts and an internal resistance of 0.02 ohm. What is its terminal voltage when it is furnishing a current of 20 amp?

8. Draw a schematic diagram of a circuit consisting of a battery made up of two dry cells in series, and a 20-ohm resistor and a 10-ohm resistor in parallel. Put a single-pole single-throw switch in each parallel branch.

9. Redraw the circuit diagram of Problem 8, putting in two ammeters, one to measure the current in each branch, and a voltmeter to measure the terminal voltage of the battery.

10. Suppose you need 50 ohms and have the following assortment of resistors available: a 10-ohm, a 100-ohm, a 75-ohm, a 60-ohm, and two 250-ohm resistors. What is the nearest value to 50 ohms you can obtain by combining these resistors, and what combination would you use?

11. A conductor known to have a resistance of 5 ohms is connected to a 1.5-volt dry cell. Would it be safe to connect a 1-amp ammeter in this circuit? Why?

12. Draw a schematic diagram of a circuit which has four dry cells in parallel connected to a 12-ohm resistor and a 5-ohm resistor in parallel.

13. Compute the current in the circuit of Problem 12 when each dry cell has an emf of 1.5 volts.

14. A dry cell has an emf of 1.58 volts and an internal resistance of 0.079 ohm. What is the maximum current this cell can furnish when short-circuited? On short circuit, the external resistance is assumed to be zero.

15. The heaters of four radio tubes are connected in parallel. Each heater requires 0.3 amp of current at 6.3 volts. How much current must the transformer that supplies these heaters furnish?

16. A single cell of a storage battery has an emf of 2 volts and an internal resistance of 0.01 ohm. A certain 10-amp ammeter has a resistance of 0.01 ohm. Would it be safe to connect this ammeter directly across the terminals of the storage cell? Give the reason for your answer.

17. A 40-watt lamp requires 0.3 amp of current at 120 volts, while a 60-watt lamp requires 0.5 amp at 120 volts. If a 40-watt lamp and a 60-watt lamp are connected in series across a 120-volt line, how many amperes of current will flow through each lamp?

18. The diameter of No. 10 wire is 102 mils. The mil-foot resistance of alumi-

num is 17.0 ohms. What is the resistance of 500 ft of No. 10 aluminum wire?

19. The diameter of No. 18 wire is 40.3 mils. The mil-foot resistance of nichrome is 602 ohms. What is the resistance of 75 ft of No. 18 nichrome wire?

20. A type of voltmeter is designed to have a resistance of 20,000 ohms per volt of full-scale range. If the range used is 10 volts (full scale) and the meter reads 6 volts, how many milliamperes of current are passing through the meter?

THINGS TO DO

1. Collect, mount, and label samples of different sizes of wire. The size of copper wire is designated by a number from the Brown & Sharpe (B & S) wire gage. Find in your school or local library a table showing this gage.

2. Collect, mount, and label samples of resistors used in radio and electronic work. The color code explaining the significance of the color bands on these resistors can be found in radio and electronic handbooks.

3. Collect and label as many different kinds of electric lamps as you can. Lamps used in flashlights, pilot lamps used in radios, automobile lamps, as well as incandescent and fluorescent lamps used in homes, offices, shops, and factories would be suitable for this collection.

4. If you have a 2- or 3-cell flashlight available, turn it on and observe the brightness of the light. Then remove and reverse one of the cells, being sure that the cell makes good contact with the other cell and with the housing connection. Turn the flashlight on again and observe the lamp. Explain why the brightness of the lamp is now different.

5. Collect, mount, and label samples of electric wires with different types of insulation. The simplest practical insulation is a coat of enamel or a layer of woven cotton threads. Much heavier insulation is needed for high-voltage wires.

15.

Electric Currents:
Heating and Chemical Effects

POWER AND HEAT FROM ELECTRICITY

Heat is one of the unavoidable by-products of every electric current. "From kilowatthours to calories" is the transformation electrical energy undergoes in the electric toaster and the electric range on which food is cooked.

What Is Electrical Energy?

Let us examine again the water circuit of Fig. 14–3. There the motor gets energy from the water to enable it to run and do work. The water must, therefore, lose energy in passing through the motor. The amount of energy delivered to the motor by the water depends on two factors: (1) the total mass of water passing through the motor and (2) the fall in pressure across it.

You know that when a stream of electrons flows through a resistor, such as the element of an electric heater, heat energy appears and the resistor gets hot. The resistor must take from the moving electrons as much energy as that of the heat produced. Thus *electrical energy is converted into heat energy* by a resistor. The amount of electrical energy lost by the stream of electrons and converted into heat likewise depends on two factors: (1) the number of electrons (the quantity Q) flowing through the resistor and (2) the difference in potential (voltage) across it. Expressed in an equation (using W for energy),

$$W = E \times Q$$

or

$$\text{Joules} = \text{volts} \times \text{coulombs}$$

But since 1 coulomb is the quantity of electricity transported by 1 amp in 1 sec,

$$Q = I \times t$$

or

$$\text{Coulombs} = \text{amperes} \times \text{seconds}$$

Using this relation, we may rewrite our first equation

$$W = E \times I \times t$$

or

$$\text{Joules} = \text{volts} \times \text{amperes} \times \text{seconds}$$

We usually express heat in calories rather than joules. You will recall that 1 cal = 4.186 joules. So

$$\text{Heat} = \frac{W}{4.186} = \frac{E \times I \times t}{4.186}$$

$$= 0.24 \, E \times I \times t$$

or

$$\text{Calories} = 0.24 \, \text{volts} \times \text{amperes} \times \text{seconds}$$

The number of calories generated in a resistor in a given time can be measured with a suitable calorimeter, so the above relation can be checked experimentally.

EXAMPLE: How many calories are generated in 1 min in an electric laundry iron which draws 5 amp from a 110-volt line?

SOLUTION: Heat = $0.24 \, E \times I \times t$. In this problem $E = 110$ volts, $I = 5$ amp, and $t = 60$ sec. Hence

Heat = 0.24×110 volts $\times 5$ amp $\times$ 60 sec

= 7920 cal

How Is Electric Power Computed?

For many purposes it is important to know the *rate* at which electrical energy is used. This is the *electric power* (P) spent or dissipated in a resistor. Expressed in an equation,

$$P = W/t = (E \times I \times t)/t = E \times I$$

or

$$\text{Watts} = \frac{\text{joules}}{\text{seconds}} = \text{volts} \times \text{amperes}$$

The power spent in any resistor is equal to the voltage across it multiplied by the current through it.

This is the basic equation for computing electric power. Two other useful forms of this equation can be obtained by applying Ohm's law to the resistor. Since $E = I \times R$,

$$P = E \times I = (I \times R) I = R \times I^2$$

or

$$\text{Watts} = \text{ohms} \times (\text{amperes})^2$$

The power spent in any resistor is directly proportional to the square of the number of amperes through it.

Futhermore, since $I = E/R$,

$$P = E \times I = \text{E} \, (E/R) = E^2/R$$

or

$$\text{Watts} = \frac{(\text{volts})^2}{\text{ohms}}$$

The power spent in any resistor is directly proportional to the square of the voltage across it.

EXAMPLE 1: How much power is used in an electric iron which draws 5 amp from a 110-volt line?

SOLUTION: $P = E \times I$. In this problem, $E = 110$ volts and $I = 5$ amp. Hence

$$P = 110 \text{ volts} \times 5 \text{ amp} = 550 \text{ watts}$$

EXAMPLE 2: How much power is dissipated in a 500-ohm resistor in which the current is 0.5 amp?

SOLUTION: $P = R \times I^2$. In this problem, $R = 500$ ohms and $I = 0.5$ amp. Hence

$$P = 500 \text{ ohms} \times 0.5 \text{ amp} \times 0.5 \text{ amp}$$
$$= 125 \text{ watts}$$

EXAMPLE 3: How much power is dissipated in a 500-ohm resistor when the voltage across it is 100 volts?

SOLUTION: $P = E^2/R$. In this problem $E = 100$ volts and $R = 500$ ohms. Hence

$$P = \frac{100 \text{ volts} \times 100 \text{ volts}}{500 \text{ ohms}} = 20 \text{ watts}$$

Other Energy Conversions

So far we have considered electric power and energy converted into heat in a resistor. An electric lamp converts some of the electrical energy it receives into light. Electric motors convert electrical energy into work and mechanical energy. Radio transmitting antennas convert electrical energy into radio waves. Storage batteries on charge convert electrical energy into chemical energy. So electrical energy and power may be transformed into any one of several other forms.

There are two chief types of electric current, *direct* and *alternating*. Direct current (DC) is obtained from batteries and direct-current generators. Alternating current (AC) is obtained from alternating-current generators. Most communities use alternating current for light and power.

The equations that we have just derived for electric power and energy apply to resistors, motors, and all other devices which use *direct current*. They also apply to *resistors* which use *alternating current*. But when alternating current circuits contain electromagnets or capacitors, the basic power equation usually has to be modified by introducing another factor called the *power factor*. The power factor is a fraction whose value is between one and zero. The power used by an alternating-current motor may be only 0.8 EI. The factor 0.8 is the power factor.

What Is a Kilowatthour?

Although the joule is a satisfactory unit for measuring work and mechanical energy, other units are found more convenient for electrical energy. To illustrate, a 10-watt lamp uses 10 joules of electrical energy per second. In 10 sec, it will use 10×10 joules $= 100$ joules. So, in general we may write

$$\text{Watts} \times \text{seconds} = \text{joules}$$

For brevity we call the product of watts and seconds *wattseconds*. The watt-second is thus a new name for the joule. We can build up larger energy units, such as watthours and kilowatt-hours in this same way. Since there are 3,600 sec in 1 hr,

$$1 \text{ watthour} = 3,600 \text{ wattseconds}$$
$$= 3,600 \text{ joules}$$
$$1 \text{ kilowatthour} = 1,000 \text{ watthours}$$
$$= 3,600,000 \text{ joules}$$

The *kilowatthour* (kwh) is the unit commonly used in measuring electrical energy.

$$\text{Kilowatthours} = \frac{\text{power in watts}}{1,000}$$
$$\times \text{time in hours}$$

361

A 1,000-watt lamp uses 1 kwh in 1 hr. A 100-watt lamp will operate for 10 hr and a 10-watt lamp for 100 hr on 1 kwh of energy.

What the Power Company Sells

The bill we get from the electric power company is based on the number of kilowatthours we use in a given period; in some cases other items, such as service charges and taxes, may also enter into the bill. We do not buy *electricity*, since we only borrow electrons from the power company lines. As many electrons flow in the return wire as in the wire leading into a house. A change in potential does occur, however, as these electrons pass through the lamps, heaters, motors, and other devices that may be turned on. This is why an emf must be provided to force the electrons to flow through the house wiring. Mechanical work is required at the power plant to drive the electric generators which furnish this emf. The generators convert mechanical energy

into electrical energy. Free electrons in the power wires serve merely as a medium for transporting this energy from the power plant to the point where we wish to use it. *Power companies sell electrical energy* delivered to the outlet of the consumer.

Reading a Kilowatthour Meter

The power company usually installs a *kilowatthour meter* on the premises to measure how much electrical energy a consumer uses. Such a meter automatically multiplies the power used by each lamp, motor, and other device by the length of time each device is turned on and then adds all of these different products. The net result is indicated by pointers on the several dials of the meter. The difference between the meter reading one month and that a month later is the number of kilowatthours for which the consumer is billed.

It is not difficult to learn to read a meter and you may find such knowledge useful in checking a bill for electrical energy. Figure 15–1 shows four dials often used on meters. Each number of the right dial represents 1 kwh. The pointer on this dial goes around once while the pointer on the next dial toward the left moves one division. Therefore, each division on the second dial represents 10 kwh. In the same way each division on the third dial from the right represents 100 kwh and each division on the dial at the extreme left represents 1,000 kwh. To read the meter, we usually begin *at the right*. In Fig. 15–1, the pointer on the right-hand dial is at 7, so we write 7 as the right-hand digit. The pointer of the second dial toward the left is between 6 and 7, so we write 6 as the second digit. The third digit is clearly 9. It is difficult at first to decide whether the pointer on the left dial has

A kilowatthour meter is used to measure the electric energy consumed. (*General Electric Company*)

362

Fig. 15–1. The dials of a kilowatthour meter.

passed 4 or not. But when we notice that the reading of the preceding dial is 9, we know at once that the pointer has not yet reached 4. So we write 3 for the fourth digit. The reading is therefore *3 9 6 7* kwh.

Cost of Operating Appliances

Appliances use different amounts of electric power, or wattage. Cost of operation depends on wattage and length of time used. Table 15–1 shows the average or probable wattage of some common appliances. If you know the number of hours any appliance is operated in a month, you can compute from the table the probable number of kilowatthours it will consume in that period. The cost of electrical energy varies from as much as 8 or 10 cents per kilowatthour in some localities to 1 or 2 cents per kilowatthour in others. Furthermore, many power companies use a step schedule under which the consumer pays at a certain rate for the first block of kilowatthours and at a lower rate for additional quantities. If you can find the cost of electrical energy in your community, you can compute the probable cost per month of operating any device shown in Table 15–1.

EXAMPLE: What is the cost of operating a 75-watt radio 4 hr a day for a 30-day month, when the cost of energy is 3.5 cents per kilowatthour?

SOLUTION: The total operating time is $4 \times 30 = 120$ hr (per month). The total energy used is 75 watts $\times$ 120 hr = 9,000 watthours or 9 kwh. The cost is

9 kwh $\times$ 3.5 cents per kilowatthour =
31.5 cents

Table 15–1.   Estimated Power Consumption for Common Appliances

Appliance	Watts
Clock	2
Coffee percolator	350
Hotplate	1,650
Ironer	800
Lamp, fluorescent (household)	15 and 20
Incandescent (household)	15–300
Laundry iron	500–1,000
Phonograph	25
Radio	55–75
Range (all switches turned to full or high)	7,000–20,000
Razor	10
Refrigerator (household)	170
Roaster	1,000
Sewing machine	60–90
Television	250
Toaster, automatic	1,150
Nonautomatic	450
Vacuum cleaner	375–600
Waffle iron	660–800
Washing machine	175

363

How an electric iron is constructed. (*General Electric Company*)

Electric Heating Devices

Practically all the common household appliances which convert electrical energy into heat have the same fundamental type of construction. A coil of wire or ribbon, made of nichrome, chromel, or other alloy of high resistivity, is used for the *heater element*. The windings of this coil are supported by a sheet of mica, by a ceramic form, or by some other heat-resistant insulating material. The stream of electrons flowing through this coil produces heat. The photograph on this page shows the construction of an electric laundry iron. Figure 15–2 shows how the coil in an electric heater is supported.

Electric furnaces are used for obtaining high temperatures. One type of furnace employs resistance rods which carry large currents. In an arc furnace, the heat is produced by an *electric arc* which is formed between two electrodes. Temperatures as high as 6000°C can be reached with electric arcs under special conditions. The carbon electrode arc furnace operates at about 3000°C.

In arc welding, the arc is formed between the metal to be welded and the tip of a welding rod, both of which get very hot at the ends of the arc. The welding rod melts and fuses with the metal to form the weld. This type of welding has many important industrial uses. In spot welding, intense heat for making the weld is developed when a large electric current passes through the joint to be welded.

Infrared lamps used for quick drying of paint and for other purposes have filaments which heat to a red glow when electric current passes through them. They give off a large amount of infrared radiation, which is reconverted to heat when it is absorbed.

Why Wires Get Warm

Even a copper wire, no matter how large, has some resistance. So when electric current is set up in a wire, heat is generated. How hot a given wire becomes depends on the size of the current through it and how fast it can get rid of heat. For this reason, there is a practical limit to the amount of current a wire of a given size can carry with safety. If the safe limit is much exceeded, the wire may become so hot its insulation burns. So an overloaded wire is a fire hazard in a building. The allowable carrying capacity of copper wires of different size and insulation is given in tables prepared under the direction of the National Board of Fire Underwriters.

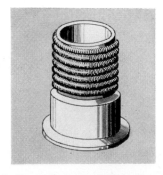

Fig. 15–2. The resistance coil of an electric heater is supported by a ceramic cylinder.

Fuses for Safety

To prevent damage to wiring from excessive currents such as may result from a short circuit, *fuses* are commonly placed in series with the power lines where they enter a building. Individual circuits within a building are usually fused independently. Fuses are made of a soft alloy which melts at a low temperature. Each fuse is marked with a number which indicates the *maximum* current in amperes the fuse is rated to carry. When the current much exceeds this value, the soft fuse link melts and opens the circuit before the wires get overheated.

When a fuse blows out, the cause should first be located and removed from the line. The power switch should be pulled or opened. Then the blown fuse should be removed from its socket and replaced by a new fuse of the same rating. The power switch should then be closed again. Many fuses have transparent mica windows so that you can easily see by the discoloration which fuse is blown. Fuses are protective devices and should not be replaced with coins or bridged over with copper wire.

Circuit breakers are often used in place of fuses in modern electric systems in houses and other buildings. A circuit breaker acts as an automatic switch that opens the circuit when the current exceeds a pre-set value. Circuit breakers can be re-set after they have been tripped by an overload and do not need to be replaced each time as fuses do.

Electrical Energy from Heat

Although electrical energy can be converted into heat on an unlimited scale, only relatively small amounts of electrical energy can be obtained directly from heat. A *thermocouple* or *thermal*

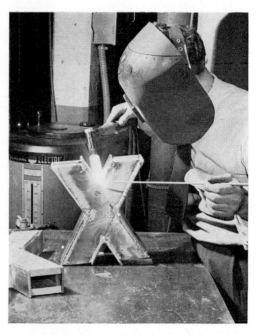

An electric arc welder being used to fabricate an aluminum stand. The transformer in the background supplies the electric current for the arc. (*General Electric Company*)

junction is a device which converts heat into electrical energy. A thermocouple consists of two wires of different metals, joined end to end to form a circuit. When the temperature of one junction is different than that of the other, an emf is set up in the circuit. A suitable ammeter or milliammeter, inserted into the circuit as shown in Fig. 15–6, will indicate that a current is produced. Iron and copper wires may be used to form the junctions, although iron and constantan are better. Almost any two metals will show this effect.

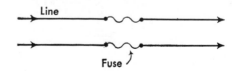

Fig. 15–3. Fuses are placed in series with the service line.

Fig. 15–4. A plug-type fuse often used in electric circuits in houses and shops.

The thermal emf developed in this way is only a few millivolts. Quite a large current may be produced, however, if the circuit resistance is kept very low. Thermocouples are used in one type of electric thermometer. Thermocouples are also used in one kind of ammeter designed to measure alternating current. A number of thermocouples in series form a thermopile which may be used to detect and measure heat radiation.

▶Do You Know?

1. What is the name of one device that converts electrical energy into sound?
2. What type of current is used for light and power in your home? in your school?
3. What is the voltage at the electric outlets in your home?

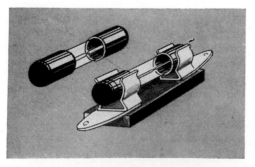

Fig. 15–5. A cartridge-type fuse.

4. Where is the kilowatthour meter for your home located?
5. What is the cost of 1 kwh of electrical energy in your community?
6. What happens inside an electric lamp when it burns out?
7. Where is the fuse box in your home located?
8. How do you replace a burned-out fuse?
9. Is there a fuse in the electric circuit of most automobiles? Where would such a fuse be located?
10. From where is electric power obtained to operate the lights of an automobile?
11. How does a thermocouple work?

ELECTROCHEMICAL ACTION

Interesting and important events involving electromotive forces, electric currents, and chemical reactions occur in the borderland world of atoms where physics and chemistry overlap.

Liquids Conduct Electricity

Can an electric current pass through a liquid such as water? Figure 15–7 shows a simple test that we can make to see whether water can act as a part of an electric circuit. Two clean carbon rods, mounted in a porcelain holder so that they do not touch, dip into the water in the beaker. The rods are connected in

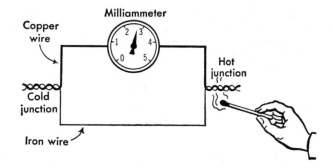

Fig. 15–6. An emf is set up in a thermocouple when the temperatures of the two junctions are different.

series with a lamp and a double cord, so that any stream of electrons that flows through the lamp when the cord is plugged into a power outlet will have to pass through the water. In Fig. 15–7a where the liquid is distilled water, the lamp remains dark when we plug in the power cord. Touching the two carbon rods together will close the circuit and will cause the lamp to glow brilliantly. In Fig. 15–7b the liquid is a weak salt water solution. Here the lamp will glow as soon as we plug in the cord. In this case the lamp will glow only a little brighter if we touch the two carbon rods together. These experiments show that salt water is a fairly good conductor of electric current while distilled water does not conduct current well enough for us to observe. More careful tests show

that distilled water is a fairly *good insulator*. CAUTION: This and other experiments involving electric power from a power socket should be undertaken only under the direct supervision of your teacher.

Water solutions of mineral acids, bases, and salts are fairly good conductors. These solutions, like the salt water in Fig. 15–7b, are called *electrolytes*. Oils, gasoline, kerosene, alcohol, carbon tetrachloride, and sugar solutions are poor conductors. In fact, oils that are free from water vapor are excellent insulators for high voltages. While distilled water is a nonconductor, ordinary tap water, which contains mineral salts in solution, is a fairly good conductor. Sea water is a very good conductor of electricity.

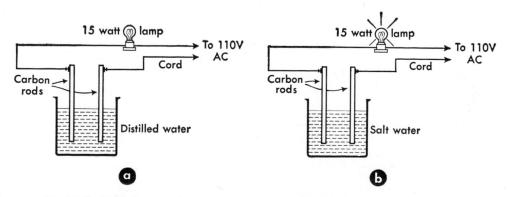

Fig. 15–7. Distilled water does not conduct electricity; salt water is a good conductor.

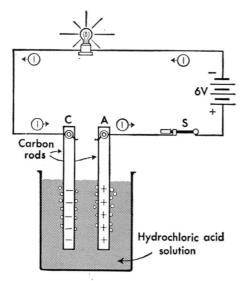

Fig. 15–8. An electric current causes a permanent chemical change in an electrolyte through which it flows.

Electrolytic Cells

Figure 15–8 shows an arrangement resembling that of Fig. 15–7 but with several modifications that simplify it. A 6-volt battery, which may be either a storage battery or dry battery, furnishes the emf for this circuit. A miniature 3.8-volt flashlight bulb serves as an indicator of electric current. Hydrochloric acid solution is here used as the electrolyte instead of salt water. When the switch is closed, the lamp will glow, indicating that there is electric current in the circuit. This current is set up by the battery and so is *direct current.*

Almost at once you will notice bubbles of gas forming and rising around both carbon rods. In a short time you may be able to detect the characteristic odor of chlorine above the container. The passage of electricity through this *electrolytic cell* causes the hydrochloric acid to *decompose* to form the gases liberated at the carbon rods. Electric

current causes a *permanent chemical change in the electrolyte.* This change is a fundamental difference between electrolytes and other kinds of electric conductors.

The electrolytic cell of Fig. 15–8 consists of the *electrolyte,* which is the hydrochloric acid solution, and the *electrodes,* which are the carbon rods. The battery forces electrons through the wires up to the electrode C, which is called the *cathode* (negatively charged). At the same time it moves electrons away from the electrode A, which is called the *anode* (positively charged). The chemical decomposition of an electrolyte by an electric current is called *electrolysis.*

Why an Electrolyte Conducts

The *dissociation theory* offers a reasonable explanation of why an electrolyte conducts electricity. A molecule of hydrochloric acid consists of one hydrogen atom bound to one chlorine atom. Its chemical formula is HCl. When this acid dissolves in water, some of its molecules ionize and dissociate. This means that the molecule breaks apart, the hydrogen and the chlorine going their separate ways. But this separation is not without a division of property, for the chlorine atom seizes from the hydrogen atom the only electron it possesses. The chlorine atom is left with an excess of one electron and the hydrogen atom without its electron. So the chlorine atom has a negative charge of one electron unit and the hydrogen atom a positive charge of one unit. Atoms in a charged condition, such as these, are called *ions.* The symbols for these ions are Cl^- and H^+. Ions carry electric charges through an electrolyte.

The electrolyte in Fig. 15–8 contains many Cl^- ions and an equal number of

H⁺ ions. The Cl⁻ ions are repelled by the negatively charged cathode C and attracted by the positively charged anode A. These electrostatic forces cause the Cl⁻ ions to migrate toward the anode. When a Cl⁻ ion reaches the anode, it surrenders its extra electron and becomes a neutral atom again. Two chlorine atoms combine to form a molecule of chlorine gas, which collects in bubbles on the anode. In a similar way, H⁺ ions migrate simultaneously toward the cathode. Each of these receives an electron from the cathode, which always has an excess because of the action of the battery. The H⁺ ion then becomes a neutral hydrogen atom again. Two of these atoms combine to form a molecule of hydrogen gas, which forms in bubbles on the cathode.

For every electron taken into the electrolyte at the cathode, a corresponding electron leaves the anode. The battery is constantly removing the surrendered electrons from the anode and replacing those lost by the cathode. This results in a steady flow of electrons

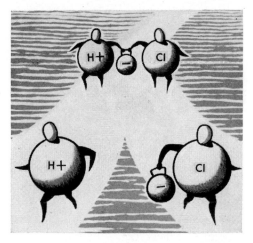

Fig. 15–9. When a molecule of hydrochloric acid dissociates, a hydrogen ion and a chlorine ion are produced.

through the wires and battery. *In the liquid electrolyte, negative ions move in the same direction as the electrons in the wires; at the same time positive ions move in the opposite direction.* So electric current in an electrolyte involves the motion of both positive and negative ions.

If a salt of a metal, such as copper sulfate, is dissolved in water to which a

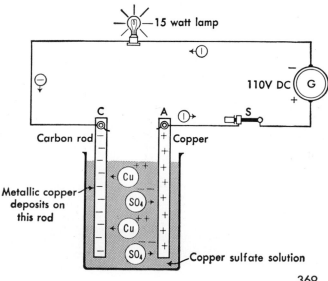

Fig. 15–10. An electrolytic cell for simple copper plating.

369

little sulfuric acid has been added, the positive ions in the electrolyte will be copper ions as well as hydrogen ions. Each copper ion will be an atom which has lost two electrons and so will have two units of positive charge. Such an ion is written Cu^{++}. If this solution is used as the electrolyte in an electrolytic cell, a smooth layer of metallic copper will be plated on the cathode by the electric current that passes through the cell. A clean metal object placed as the cathode will become covered with the copper plate.

Many objects made of iron or steel are plated with a thin layer of copper, nickel, cadmium, or chromium to prevent rusting and corrosion or to improve their appearance. Tableware is sometimes electroplated with silver and jewelry with gold. In all electroplating, the *object to be coated is the cathode* in an electroplating vat through which *direct current* is forced. A solution of some salt of the metal to be deposited is used for the electrolyte. A piece of the same metal is used for the anode, although a carbon anode can be used when it is not necessary to restore the metal ions in the electrolyte. Temperature, concentra-

tion of the electrolyte, the size of the current, position of anodes, and the time are all carefully regulated to plate the object with a smooth, uniform layer of the desired thickness.

How Aluminum Is Obtained

Aluminum has become one of our most useful metals. Because it is light in weight, does not tarnish easily, is a good conductor of heat, and is somewhat acid-resistant, it is used extensively in the manufacture of kitchenware. Because it can be combined with other light metals, such as magnesium, to form strong, tough alloys, aluminum is much used in the construction of aircraft of all kinds.

The chief ore of aluminum is *bauxite*, aluminum oxide. In extracting the metal, purified oxide is dissolved in melted cryolite, a mineral found in Greenland. The melted solution is used as the electrolyte in a large carbon-lined iron tank. The tank serves as the cathode of an electrolytic cell. Carbon rods extending into the molten electrolyte form the anode. Direct electric current passing through the cell deposits molten aluminum metal at the bottom of the tank (the cathode),

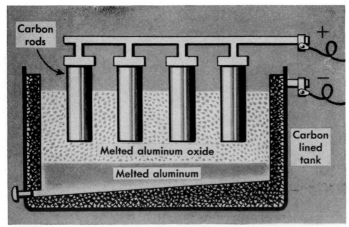

Fig. 15–11. The plan of an electrolytic cell for extracting aluminum from its ore.

370

This photograph shows the parts used in a process for obtaining a pure metal by electrolytic refining. (*Copper and Brass Research Association*)

where it can be drawn off as pure aluminum.

Large amounts of electrical energy are required for this process. For this reason, the aluminum industry has grown up in the Niagara Falls area, in the Tennessee Valley, and in other sections of the country where the sources of electrical energy are plentiful and inexpensive.

The electrolytic method of extracting aluminum from its oxide was invented by Charles M. Hall in 1886, when he was a graduate student at Oberlin College, Ohio. Previous methods of extracting the metal were slow and costly.

Magnesium, copper, and many other metals important in modern living also are obtained by electrolysis from their natural ores and compounds.

Water Decomposed by Electricity

Distilled water alone does not have enough ions to conduct electricity readily, but the addition of a little sulfuric acid makes the solution a good conductor. Figure 15–12 shows an apparatus designed to collect the gases formed at the electrodes when an electric current passes through such an electrolyte. The actions that occur in such a cell are quite involved. The end result is that water molecules are used up to form hydrogen and oxygen gases, while the sulfuric acid remains in solution. The volume of hydrogen gas that collects above the cathode is always twice the volume of oxygen gas that collects above the anode. These gases can easily be identified by simple

371

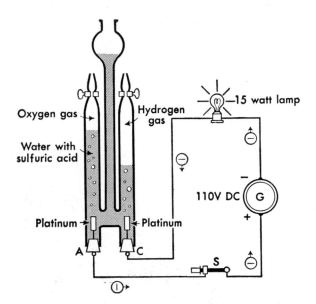

Oxygen gas

Hydrogen gas

Water with sulfuric acid

—15 watt lamp

110V DC (G)

Platinum

Platinum

A   C

S

Fig. 15–12. Water is decomposed into oxygen and hydrogen gases by an electric current.

chemical tests. Electrolysis is one of the industrial methods used to obtain oxygen and hydrogen gases.

▶Do You Know?

1. What is the difference between an atom and an ion?
2. What is used for an electrolyte in nickel plating? For an anode?
3. Why is the volume of hydrogen gas obtained by the electrolysis of water always twice that of oxygen gas obtained?
4. Why are platinum electrodes used for the electrolysis of water in the apparatus of Fig. 15–12?
5. Is sterling silverware 100 percent silver? How does silverplate differ from sterling?

TRANSFORMING CHEMICAL ENERGY

An electric current causes a chemical change or reaction in an electrolyte. It would be reasonable to expect that under suitable conditions a chemical reaction might in turn cause an electric current.

372

How a Simple Cell Works

Figure 15–13 shows a strip of copper and one of zinc inserted into a solution of hydrochloric acid. A voltmeter connected between these two metal electrodes indicates a voltage, with the zinc negative and the copper positive. A simple *voltaic cell* such as this is the source of an electromotive force. Any two dissimilar metals that are acted on by the electrolyte may be used for electrodes, but some combinations give more emf than others. Different electrolytes, also, may be used, but again some are better than others.

In the cell in Fig. 15–13 a molecule of hydrochloric acid (HCl) ionizes to form H^+ and Cl^- ions. Atoms from the zinc plate go into solution as Zn^{++} ions, each atom leaving two of its electrons on the zinc plate, charging it negatively. The presence of large concentrations of Zn^{++} ions in the electrolyte drives some of the H^+ ions to the copper electrode. Each of these hydrogen ions seizes an electron from the copper to make it a neutral hydrogen atom again. Two of these atoms combine to form a molecule of hydrogen, which is then liberated as a gas at the copper plate. This removal of electrons from the copper plate gives it a positive charge. These reactions continue until the zinc plate has a negative charge sufficient to pull back any more Zn++ ions that may try to leave it and the copper plate has a sufficient positive charge to repel any more H+ ions that may approach it. When an external electric circuit is provided, electrons flow through it steadily from the zinc to the copper plate, while the internal chemical reactions operate to replace electrons that flow away from the zinc and remove those that collect on the copper. *Zinc is used up in this cell as the stream of electrons continues to flow.* This simple cell is called a *primary cell.*

Polarization in a Cell

We have seen that hydrogen gas is liberated at the positive (copper) electrode of the simple cell. If we take a voltmeter reading and then short-circuit the cell in Fig. 15–13 by connecting the two electrodes with a short piece of copper wire, we soon notice small bubbles (hydrogen) covering the copper plate. When the short circuit is removed, the voltmeter reads less than it did originally. We may be able to restore the voltmeter reading, at least in part, by shaking the bubbles off the copper. A cell with an excess of hydrogen gas about its positive electrode is *polarized. Polarization reduces the emf of a cell and increases its internal resistance.* When a cell has to furnish a steady current, some means of depolarizing it must be provided.

How a Dry Cell Is Constructed

Primary cells with liquid electrolytes were once in common use. They were

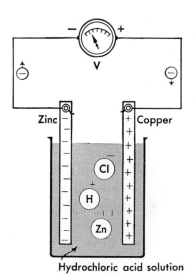

Fig. 15–13. A simple voltaic cell converts chemical energy into electrical energy.

inconvenient, because they were not rugged and were easily spilled. The *dry cell* has now replaced practically all other types of primary cells. Figure 15–14 shows the internal construction of a dry cell. The zinc can serves both as a container for the cell and as a negative electrode. The carbon rod through the center is the positive electrode. The electrolyte is a solution of ammonium chloride, NH_4Cl, and zinc chloride, $ZnCl_2$. The zinc can is lined with a layer of porous pulp, which has been saturated with the electrolyte. A pasty mixture of the electrolyte with powdered graphite and manganese dioxide, which acts as the depolarizer, is packed around the carbon rod to fill the can. The can is sealed at the top with sealing wax or asphalt to prevent evaporation. This is a *paste* cell, rather than a *dry* cell. When it becomes really dry it is useless. The *fuel* of this cell is the zinc, which is used up as the cell operates. The electrolyte also undergoes a chemical change as the cell is used.

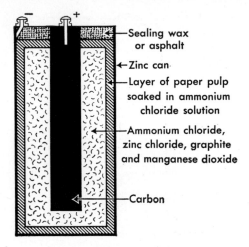

Fig. 15–14. Construction of a dry cell.

The emf of a new dry cell is about 1.5 volts, *regardless of the size of the cell*. The larger cells can furnish more current for longer periods of time, but their emf is no greater than that of the smallest cell of the same kind. On short circuit, a new No. 6 (6-in.) dry cell will give from 30 to 40 amp of current. The current from such a cell should be kept below 0.25 amp for regular service. At higher currents, the cell usually forms hydrogen faster than the manganese dioxide can

oxidize it, and the cell soon becomes polarized. The cell *recovers* after a period of rest, when the depolarizer has had time to remove the excess hydrogen. As a cell ages, its emf drops somewhat and its internal resistance increases. Smaller cells generally age faster than larger ones.

The Storage Battery

Dry cells are not suitable for use in starting an automobile because they cannot furnish the required power economically. The *storage*, or *secondary-cell*, type of battery is much better adapted to this type of service. The principle of the storage battery can be shown with the simple demonstration cell of Fig. 15–15. The cell consists of two clean lead plates, which act as electrodes, and a dilute solution of sulfuric acid for the electrolyte. To *charge* the cell, the switch S is thrown to the right. This connects the cell in series with the generator and the lamp resistor. The generator *forces* electric current through the cell, as indicated by the glowing lamp. You will notice gas liberated at *both* electrodes.

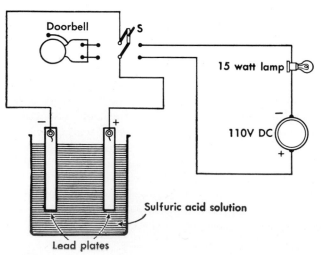

Fig. 15–15. A schematic circuit for charging and discharging a simple storage cell.

This is oxygen at the anode and hydrogen at the cathode, produced by the electrolysis of water in the electrolyte. But other chemical changes also occur in this cell. After 10 min or so you will notice that a chocolate-brown coating has formed on the positive plate. This is lead dioxide, the *active material* of the positive plate. At the same time, a layer of gray spongy lead forms on the other plate. Spongy lead is the *active material* of the negative plate.

After the cell has been charged for 10 min or more, it may be discharged by throwing the switch to the left. This disconnects the generator and lamp and connects the doorbell directly to the cell. If the doorbell is of a suitable type, it will ring for a minute or more as the cell discharges. A voltmeter connected across the electrodes just before the cell starts to discharge will indicate a little more than 2 volts, showing that an emf has been developed in the cell by the charging process. When the cell discharges, the active material on both plates changes to a white crystalline lead sulfate, $PbSO_4$. You may be unable to see this change. This cell may be charged and discharged repeatedly.

Storage-battery Construction

While the plates for some storage batteries are formed by a process somewhat similar to that used in the demonstration cell, most battery plates are made in a different way. In this process, each plate consists of an antimony-lead frame with grids that form meshes into which a paste of the active material is forced under pressure. The plates are then *formed* by charging. The active material on the positive plate becomes chocolate-brown lead dioxide, while that on the negative plate becomes gray, spongy lead. The plates are then

assembled into a unit in which negative plates alternate with positive plates, with wood, rubber, or glass insulating separators between adjacent plates. Each unit is placed in its own jar or container. Each cell has an emf of approximately 2 volts. In a 6-volt automobile battery, three cells are mounted in the same case and connected *in series*.

The Battery Hydrometer

In the charging process, water is used up from the electrolyte and sulfuric acid produced. The specific gravity of sulfuric acid is greater than that of water, so charging a storage battery raises the specific gravity of its electrolyte. On discharge, sulfuric acid is used up and water is produced. This causes the specific gravity of the electrolyte to fall. For these reasons, a *hydrometer*, which measures the specific gravity of the electrolyte, can be used to determine how fully a battery is charged.

An automobile battery is fully charged when its specific gravity is from 1250 to 1300 (1.250 to 1.300), and completely discharged at about 1175. Some storage batteries which do not have to furnish such large currents and withstand sub-zero weather are made with lower specific gravities.

Care of the Storage Battery

1. *Distilled* water (or rain water) should be added to the electrolyte from time to time to replace water lost by evaporation and electrolysis. The plates should be kept well covered. Ordinary tap water is often injurious to a battery because of the chemicals it contains.

2. Sulfuric acid *should not* be added to raise the specific gravity of the electrolyte in a battery that needs charging.

3. In charging a battery, the positive terminal of the battery must be connected to the positive side of the charging line.
4. The battery should be kept well charged. When a battery stands partially discharged for a while, some of the lead sulfate hardens and cannot be broken down again by charging.
5. The battery should not be discharged at an excessive rate, since this may cause the plates to buckle and short-circuit. This ruins the battery.
6. Do not charge so fast that the electrolyte gets hot. This tends to soften the active material so that it falls out of the grids which shortens the useful life of a battery.

Modern "fast chargers," used for emergency charging of automobile batteries, employ currents as high as 100 amp at the start of a charge. At this rate, they can charge a battery "while you wait."

PRECAUTIONS: (1) Sulfuric acid, even in dilute solutions, destroys clothing and fabrics with which it comes in contact. Its action can be neutralized by ammonia water, if applied at once. (2) Keep all lighted matches, cigarettes, and sparks away from the vent of a charging battery. The oxygen and hydrogen liberated by electrolysis when the battery "gases" form an explosive mixture which needs only a flame or spark to set it off.

▶**Do You Know?**

1. Why is the simple cell of Fig. 15–13 called a *voltaic* cell?
2. Sometimes bubbles of hydrogen gas collect on the zinc plate in a voltaic cell. What causes this action?
3. What is meant by the "shelf-life" of a dry cell?
4. Name several uses for dry batteries.
5. What is an Edison storage battery?
6. How many years of service should be expected from an automobile storage battery?
7. Why is a partially discharged storage battery more likely to freeze in cold weather than a fully charged one?
8. Name several uses for storage batteries.
9. Why does a storage battery "gas" when it is being charged?

HIGHLIGHTS

The *electrical energy dissipated in a resistor* is given by $W = E \times I \times t$, or joules = volts $\times$ amperes $\times$ seconds.

The *heat developed in a resistor* is given by $H = 0.24 E \times I \times t$, or calories = 0.24 $\times$ volts $\times$ amperes $\times$ seconds.

Electric power used in a resistor is given by $P = E \times I = R \times I^2 = E^2/R$, or watts = volts $\times$ amperes = ohms $\times$ (amperes)^2 = (volts)^2/ohms.

The *kilowatthour* is used to measure electrical energy.   1 kwh = 3,600,000 joules.

Fuses are links with a low melting point placed in a circuit for safety.

A *thermocouple* converts heat energy directly into electrical energy.

Some liquids are fairly good conductors of electricity, while others are very poor conductors.

376

An *electrolyte* differs from other conductors in that an electric current passing through it produces a permanent chemical change in the electrolyte.

Positive and negative *ions* are the carriers of electricity through an electrolyte.

An *electrolytic cell* has an *anode*, a *cathode*, and an *electrolyte*.

Electrolysis is the process of decomposing an electrolyte by passing an electric current through it.

Aluminum is extracted from its ore by an electrolytic process.

Water may be *decomposed* into oxygen gas and hydrogen gas by electrolysis.

A *voltaic cell* converts chemical energy directly into electrical energy.

A *dry cell* has a zinc negative electrode, a carbon positive electrode, ammonium chloride and zinc chloride for the electrolyte, and manganese dioxide for the depolarizer. Its emf is about 1.5 volts.

Polarization causes the emf of a cell to decrease and the internal resistance to increase.

A *dry* cell is a *primary* cell; a *storage* cell is a *secondary* cell.

Storage cells must first be charged before they develop an emf of their own.

The emf of a lead-plate–sulfuric acid storage cell is about 2 volts.

PROBLEMS: GROUP A

1. What is the cost of operating a 60-watt radio an average of 3 hr a day for a 30-day month when the price of electrical energy is 4 cents per kilowatthour?

2. What is the current in amperes in a 60-watt lamp operated at 115 volts?

3. What is the cost of operating a 500-watt electric toaster 20 min a day for a 30-day month when the price of electrical energy is 5 cents per kilowatthour?

4. What does it cost for electricity to do a 2-hr ironing, if the iron takes 500 watts continuously and the price of electrical energy is 5 cents per kilowatthour?

5. What is the cost of operating a 75-watt lamp 5 hr a day for a 30-day month when the price of electrical energy is 3 cents per kilowatthour?

6. How many watts are dissipated in a 50-ohm resistor which carries 0.25 amp of current?

7. How many watts are dissipated in a 50-ohm resistor when the voltage across it is 50 volts?

8. How many calories of heat are developed in 1 min by an electric heater which draws 0.75 amp at 110 volts?

9. What is the cost of operating a 2-watt electric clock for a 30-day month when the price of electrical energy is 5 cents per kilowatthour?

10. How many watts of electric power are used in sixteen 40-watt fluorescent lamps connected in parallel?

11. How many cells (2 volts each) are in a 120-volt storage battery? How are these cells connected?

12. How many calories of heat are produced in a minute in a water heater which takes 10 amp of current at 120 volts?

13. What is the cost of electrical energy for operating a television receiver an aver-

age of 3 hr a day for a 30-day month if the receiver requires 250 watts at 120 volts? Assume the price of electrical energy is 3 cents per kilowatthour.

14. If an electric ironer requires 800 watts of electric power at 120 volts, what is the cost of electricity for doing a 2-hr ironing? Assume the price of electrical energy is 3 cents per kilowatthour.

15. If a burner of an electric stove uses 10 amp of current at 240 volts, how many kilowatthours of energy will this burner use in operating a total time of 50 hr? In 75 hr of operation?

GROUP B

1. How many watts are dissipated in a resistor when the voltage across it is 50 volts and the current through it is 10 ma?

2. What is the maximum current which can be carried by a 50-watt 500-ohm resistor without exceeding its rating?

3. How many coulombs of electricity are required to deposit 1 lb of electrolytic copper if each coulomb deposits 0.000329 g?

4. How many coulombs of electricity are required to separate 1 kg of aluminum from its ore by the electrolytic process? Each coulomb deposits 0.000093 g.

5. What is the cost of charging a 6-volt battery, if it must be charged for 20 hr at 6 amp and 7.5 volts? Assume that the charger is 20 percent efficient and the price of electrical energy is 5 cents per kilowatthour.

6. What is the resistance of a 75-watt lamp which operates at 115 volts?

7. What is the maximum voltage that may be applied to a 50-watt 500-ohm resistor without exceeding its rating?

8. What is the maximum current that may be carried by a 150-watt 90-ohm laboratory rheostat without exceeding its rating? What is the maximum voltage that may safely be applied to this rheostat?

9. How many kilowatthours of electrical energy are required to produce 500 kilocalories of heat?

10. What is the cost of charging a storage battery for 24 hr if the charging generator must furnish 14 volts and the average charging current is 5 amp? Assume that the cost of electrical energy delivered by the generator is 5 cents per kilowatthour.

THINGS TO DO

1. Collect, mount, and label as many different kinds of electric fuses as you can. Find out how each is used.

2. Read the electric meter in your home (kilowatthour meter). Record your reading and compare it with the reading shown on the latest bill or statement from the power company. Why should you expect your reading to be somewhat higher than that shown on the statement?

3. Can you "taste" electricity? To find out, connect copper wires to the terminals of a *single dry cell*. (CAUTION: Do not use higher voltage than this.) Place the bare ends of these wires at points on your tongue about a half inch apart, *without touching the bare ends together*. Describe the taste and explain why it occurs.

4. To find which of two wires of a direct-current circuit is positive, connect two dry cells in series, connect *bare copper* wires to the terminals of this battery, and push the ends of these wires into a

freshly cut apple or potato. Within a short time the freshly cut part of the apple or potato around one of the wires will usually turn green. To which terminal is this wire connected? What happens around the other wire?

5. Collect and label different types of dry cells currently available. New types have been developed recently for use in miniature electronic apparatus, such as hearing aids, computers, guided missiles, and pocket radios.

16.

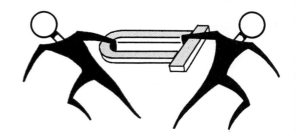

Electricity and Magnetism:
Force in Magnetic Fields

MAGNETS AND ELECTRIC CURRENTS

Lodestone, with its marvelous property of attracting and holding small pieces of iron and other lodestone, has been known since ancient times. Thales of Miletus (about 600 B.C.) mentioned this effect in his writings. There is some evidence that it may have been known as early as 1200 B.C. Many legends and fabulous tales concerning magnets and magnetism occur in early literature. Lodestone was found in large amounts in an ancient country of Asia Minor called *Magnesia*, and it became known in Greece as *magnes lapis*, or magnesian stone. From *magnes* the words magnet, magnetism, and magnetite were derived.

380

What Is a Magnet?

The lodestone known to the early Greeks is a black ore of iron (Fe_3O_4) that we now call *magnetite*. Pieces of this ore can attract and hold other pieces of the ore and also bits of iron that may be nearby, as shown in Fig. 16–1. In the course of time it was discovered that a piece of lodestone—a *natural magnet*—could give this property of attraction to pieces of hardened iron that came into contact with it without losing any of its own strength. In this way, *artificial magnets* were produced. Electric currents now provide a more effective method of making artificial magnets. Artificial magnets which lose their magnetism quickly after they are removed from the influence of the parent magnet or the electric current are called *temporary* magnets. Those which retain their magnetic properties are called *permanent* magnets. Magnets are made in many different shapes and forms, including straight rods and bars, disks, and U shapes or horseshoes.

Magnets have a wide variety of uses. They are a necessary part of the telephone receiver and the electric bell as well as of the electric motor and generator. Temporary magnets are used to lift and move large quantities of scrap metal. In surgery a small powerful magnet is used to remove magnetic metal particles that have become embedded in an eye or the skin of a person.

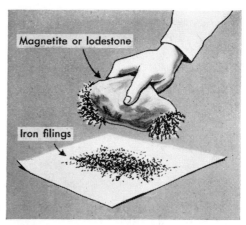

Fig. 16–1. Iron filings cling to a piece of lodestone or magnetite.

Magnetic-pole Action

When we mount a light magnetized bar or needle, as shown in Fig. 16–4, the

Fig. 16–2. Bar, disk, and horseshoe types of permanent magnets. Large permanent magnets may be cast in a wide variety of forms to fit particular industrial needs. A magnetic material called *Alnico* is used for this purpose.

The Poles of a Magnet

When we dip a piece of lodestone into iron filings, the filings cling to the stone in dense clusters in some places and not at all in others, as shown in Fig. 16–1. Filings cling to a bar magnet as shown in Fig. 16–3. The regions where the filing clusters form are called *magnetic poles*. The two poles of a bar magnet are normally each a short distance in from the end of the bar. Every bar or horseshoe magnet has at least two poles. Under unusual circumstances, a bar magnet may be made so that it has more than two poles.

Fig. 16–3. Iron filings cling in clusters at the poles of a bar magnet.

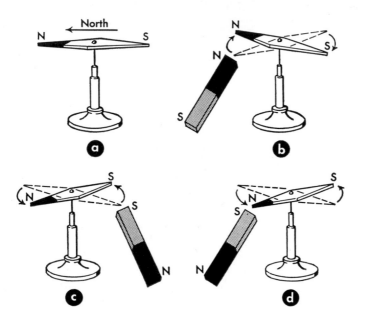

Fig. 16–4. Like magnetic poles repel; unlike poles attract.

magnet will turn so that when it stops, its long axis is always approximately north and south. A suitably shaped piece of magnetite also has this property of pointing in a definite direction. This may be why it is called *lodestone*, which means *way* or *leading* stone. An electrically charged rod mounted in the same way will come to rest wherever it happens to stop. It does not point in a definite direction. This ability to point in a definite direction is one of the distinguishing differences between a magnetized body and a body charged with static electricity.

The pole at the end of the compass needle that points approximately north is called a *north pole*, abbreviated N pole. The pole at the other end of the needle is called a *south pole*, abbreviated S pole. A north pole and a south pole are always associated; we cannot have one kind of pole on a magnet without the other.

When we bring the N pole of a bar magnet near the N pole of the compass, the needle is deflected as shown in Fig.

16–4b. The *two north poles repel each other*. The two S poles have a similar effect on one another. But when we bring the S pole of the bar magnet near the N pole of the needle, they attract. The N pole of the bar magnet will likewise attract the S pole of the compass needle. You may test these observations for yourself if you have a magnetic compass and a magnet.

Unlike magnetic poles attract and like poles repel.

Magnetism and Electric Current

In the early days of exploration in electricity scientists seemed to suspect some connection between electric currents and magnetism. No such effect was observed with the weak currents that could be obtained from the early batteries. One day in 1819 Professor Hans Christian Oersted, of the University of Copenhagen, Denmark, while lecturing to his class on electricity, accidentally discovered that when he laid a wire carrying an electric current *parallel* to a magnetic compass needle, the needle would deflect as if acted on by a magnet. This simple discovery has proved to be one of the most important scientific discoveries ever made, for every electric motor operates on the principle that Oersted explained in the report of this discovery published in 1820.

Figure 16–5a shows a compass needle placed close under a long, straight wire, which extends north and south *parallel to the needle*, as Oersted must have placed it. We know that when we close the switch, electrons begin to flow through the wire from *south* to *north*. We can observe that the N pole of the needle is deflected toward the *east* and the S pole toward the *west*. When the battery is reversed and the switch again closed as in Fig. 16–5b, electrons will flow through the wire from *north* to *south*. Then we can observe that the N pole of the needle is deflected toward the *west*. If the compass needle is placed above the wire, its deflection in each case is opposite in direction from what it was initially. If the wire is placed in an east-west position at right angles to the compass needle, *small currents* through the wire do not affect the compass needle at all, but some large currents may cause it to turn 180 degrees.

The following is a convenient rule for determining the direction the needle will be deflected when the direction of the current is known or the direction of the current when the direction of deflection is known.

Imagine you have placed your left hand with its palm toward the wire on the same side as the compass needle with the extended thumb pointing in the direction the electrons are flowing; the extended fingers will then point in the direction the north pole of the compass will be deflected.

Direction of Electric Current

You have no doubt seen diagrams in some books and magazines that show electric current directed through a circuit from the *positive* toward the *negative* terminal of the battery. This is just contrary to the direction we have shown for the current. You may wonder how this difference has arisen.

There is very good experimental evidence today that only electrons are free to move through a solid conductor, such as a copper wire. But this evidence is of recent origin and was not available to the early explorers in the world of electricity. Benjamin Franklin and others assumed that only *positive charges were free to move* through wires and conductors. From this point of view, an electric

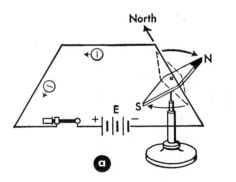
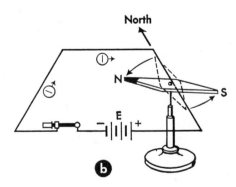

Fig. 16–5. An electric current affects a magnetic compass.

current would be a *stream of positive charges* moving through the wires of the external circuit away from the positive and toward the negative terminal of the battery or other source of emf. This view of an electric current was accepted and used for 150 years before it was found that positive charges are bound up with atoms and only electrons—negative charges—are free to move through conductors. But even though we are now quite certain that the older concept of electric current is an error, still many people continue to use it because it is familiar and serves almost every purpose just as well as the newer concept of moving electrons. The situation is much the same as with the concept of *suction;* although we know there is no such force, we continue to use the idea for everyday purposes because it is convenient and familiar. This is why you will still find in some books and articles on electricity circuit diagrams with arrows indicating an electric current opposite in direction from that we have shown in this book.

In many of the effects of an electric current, the direction of the current is not important. A stream of electrons moving in one direction is equivalent in effect to a stream of positive charges moving in the opposite direction. When we wish to find the direction of the magnetic forces set up by an electric current, the left-hand rule on p. 383 is used.

Effects of an Electric Current

We can detect the presence of an electric current only by the effects it produces. One of its most important effects is shown when electric currents flow through nearby parallel wires. In Fig. 16–6 two fine wires several feet long are supported about 1 in. apart

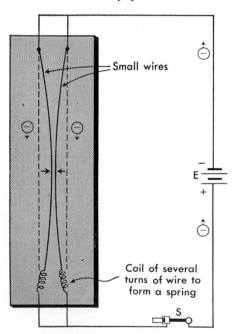

Fig. 16–6. Two parallel wires attract each other when electrons flow through them in the same direction.

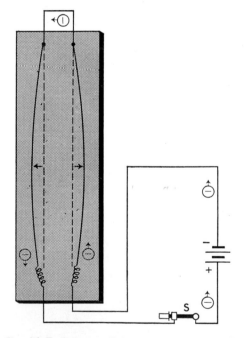

Fig. 16–7. Two parallel wires repel each other when electrons flow through them in opposite directions.

384

and are parallel. When switch S is closed, the wires spring together, as if strongly attracted to each other. Then electrons are flowing side by side in the same direction through the two wires. When the circuit is arranged as shown in Fig. 16–7 and the switch is closed, the wires move apart, as if strongly repelled by each other. In this case, electrons flow in opposite directions through the two parallel wires. There is no attraction or repulsion when the circuits are open and no flow of electrons. We must conclude, then, that the forces between the two wires are associated with the flow of electrons. These forces are entirely different from the forces acting between bodies charged with static electricity—electrons at rest—for these forces disappear as soon as the *flow of electrons* stops. We speak of these forces between wires carrying electric current as *magnetic forces*.

We have now found that magnetic forces of attraction and repulsion exist between (1) poles of magnets, (2) the pole of a magnet and an electric current, and (3) electric currents in parallel conductors lying alongside each other.

►**Do You Know?**

1. Where in the United States is magnetite found?
2. Where are the poles of a horseshoe magnet located?
3. How can a bar magnet with more than two poles be made?
4. Make a list of the differences you know of between the properties of magnetized bodies and those of charged bodies.
5. Does the magnetic compass in Fig. 16–5 also push on the wire? Explain.
6. What is the effect of electrons flowing in opposite directions through two parallel wires 1 in. apart?

MAGNETIC FIELDS

You have seen that one magnet can push or pull on another without actually touching it. How can this effect be explained?

Suppose we lay a sheet of paper or thin glass over a bar magnet and dust iron filings evenly over the sheet. When we tap the sheet gently, the filings line up in a pattern which suggests more or less definite lines, as shown in Fig. 16–8. The imagined lines along which the filings seem to arrange themselves are called *lines of force*. The needle of a compass placed at any point on the sheet will tend to align itself with the line of force through that point. If we could obtain a single small north pole alone, and place it at the north pole of the bar magnet, this free north pole would move along one of the lines of force on its way to the south pole of the bar magnet. In sketching a line of force, we often put an arrow on it to indicate the direction a free north pole would move if placed there. *Lines of force come*

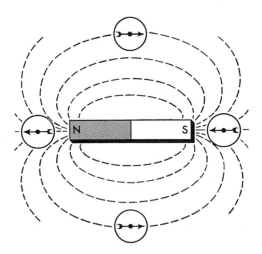

Fig. 16–8. The magnetic field around a bar magnet.

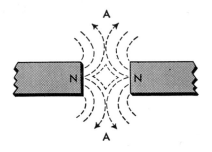

Fig. 16–9. The magnetic field around like poles of two bar magnets placed end to end.

out of a magnet at its N pole and enter at its S pole.

The region around a magnet in which attraction and repulsion can be detected is called a *magnetic field*. A magnetic field is, therefore, filled with these imaginary lines of force. The only convenient way we have of representing a magnetic field is by means of a diagram or drawing showing some of the typical lines of force. Arrows may be placed on these lines to show the *direction of the field,* that is, the direction that an N pole would take if placed there. The *relative strength* of the magnetic field is shown by the degree of crowding of the lines. The field is stronger, that is, the magnetic force acting on the pole of another magnet placed there is greater, where the lines are crowded more closely together. You can verify this statement by examining Fig. 16–8 again. We know from experience that a compass needle will be pulled

more strongly when it is placed nearer either pole of the bar magnet. In these regions also, the lines of force converge and become closer together.

Attraction and Repulsion

In Fig. 16–9, in the region marked A, lines of force from one north pole are for some distance parallel to those from the other north pole. If these lines were to push sidewise on one another, the two magnets would be pushed apart. We know from experience this is the case. *Parallel lines of force exert a sideward force on one another when their directions are the same.*

We have adopted the convention that lines of force leave a magnet at a north pole and enter at a south pole. Careful tests then show that as many lines leave the north pole as enter the south pole. Breaking a bar magnet results in new poles at the break, as shown in Fig. 16–11. These are some of the reasons why we believe that the lines continue right on through the metal so that each one is a *closed loop*.

In Fig. 16–10 the closed lines link the two magnets together. If these lines are under tension and tend to shorten as a stretched rubber band does, then the two magnets would be drawn together, as we know they are. *Lines of force act like closed loops that are stretched and tend to contract.*

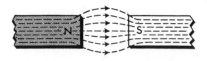

Fig. 16–10. The magnetic field around unlike poles of two bar magnets placed end to end.

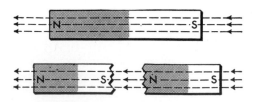

Fig. 16–11. When a bar magnet is broken, new poles appear at the break.

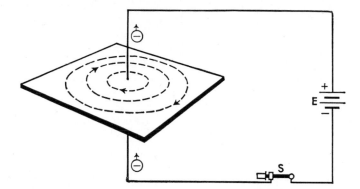

Fig. 16–12. The magnetic field surrounding an electric current.

Current and the Compass Needle

In Fig. 16–12 electrons flow upward in the wire through the plane of the sheet of cardboard. Iron filings dusted on the cardboard line up in a pattern of *concentric circles* about the wire when the card is tapped. The needle of a test compass set at different positions on the cardboard aligns itself with the lines of force and indicates their direction. When the direction of the electric current is reversed, the needle of the test compass reverses, indicating a reversal of the direction of the lines of force. There is no evidence of a magnetic field about the wire when the circuit is open and no electrons flow.

Grasp the conductor with your left hand (in imagination only) so that your extended thumb points in the direction the electrons are flowing; then your fingers encircle the conductor in the direction of the lines of force. If we know the direction either of the current or of the lines of force, we can find the direction of the other by this rule. This is another rule that becomes a right-hand rule when we think in terms of the older, conventional electric current.

Currents in Parallel Wires

When electric currents are in the same direction through two neighboring parallel wires, their magnetic fields overlap. In the region between the wires, the lines of force are parallel, but *in opposite directions*. Some of the lines in one field merge with those in the other and encircle both wires, as shown in Fig. 16–13.

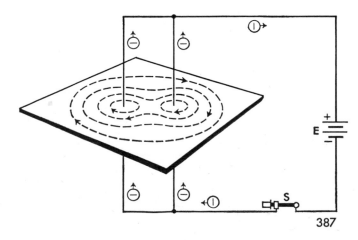

Fig. 16–13. The magnetic field around two parallel wires when electrons flow through them in the same direction.

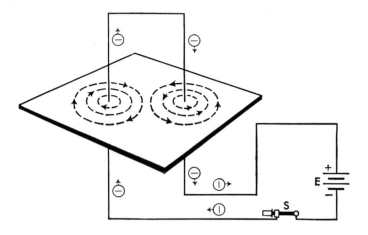

Fig. 16–14. The magnetic field around two parallel wires when electrons flow through them in opposite directions.

The wires could be observed to draw nearer each other if the current were large enough, just as in Fig. 16–6. This pulling together of the wires may be pictured as resulting from a tendency of the lines of force to shorten.

When currents are in opposite directions in neighboring parallel wires, their magnetic fields again overlap. In the region between the wires, the lines of force are parallel and *in the same direction*, as shown in Fig. 16–14. Sidewise repulsion of these lines pushes the wires apart as shown in Fig. 16–7.

The Magnetic Field of a Coil

An iron filing map of the magnetic field surrounding a coil through which there is an electric current shows lines of force similar to those in Fig. 16–15. The lines produced by the individual turns of the coil merge so that many of the lines actually encircle the entire coil. If the coil is made so that iron filings fall inside it, you can usually see that the lines continue through the coil and form closed loops. A test compass shows that one end of the coil acts like a magnetic north pole while the other end acts like a south pole. If the direction of the electric current is reversed, the magnetic poles of the coil are also reversed. A simple left-hand rule for expressing the relation of the direction of the magnetic field and that of the electric current is **Grasp the coil with your left hand (in imagination only) so that your fingers encircle the coil in the direction the electrons flow; then your extended thumb points toward the north pole of the coil.**

If we know either the direction of the electric current or that of the magnetic

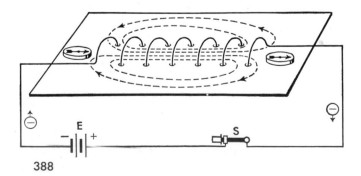

Fig. 16–15. The magnetic field about a coil through which electrons are flowing.

field, we can always find the other by this rule. This, too, is a rule that becomes a *right-hand rule* for the older, conventional concept of electric current.

By increasing the number of turns of wire on the coil or by increasing the number of amperes through the coil (or by both methods), we can increase the strength of the magnetic field produced. In fact, the strength of the field depends on the *product* of the amperes and the number of turns. This product is called the *ampere-turns* of the coil.

Some Metals Become Magnetized

If you will compare Fig. 16–8 with Fig. 16–15, you will be impressed with the striking similarities between the magnetic field of a bar magnet and that of a coil carrying an electric current. We have seen that the electric current is an orderly motion of electrons through the wires of the coil. Many scientists believe that the magnetic field of a bar magnet is also due to some orderly type of motion of electrons in the metal. Many electrons are associated with each atom of metal. Perhaps a spin or other type of motion of one or a group of these electrons may make a tiny magnet of each atom, with its own north and south poles. The atom itself is the most elementary type of magnet, but magnetic atoms may act in groups as miniature magnets.

The atoms of most substances act as if they have practically no external magnetic field at all, while those of a few substances are but slightly magnetic. Of all the chemical elements, *iron, nickel,* and *cobalt* are in a class by themselves. Their atoms seem to have quite strong north and south poles. Nickel and cobalt are less magnetic than iron. Several other chemical elements also are magnetic but very much less so than iron, nickel, or

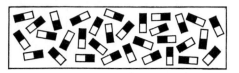
Fig. 16–16. Probable arrangement of miniature magnets in an unmagnetized bar of iron.

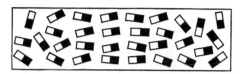
Fig. 16–17. Probable arrangement of miniature magnets in a partially magnetized bar of iron.

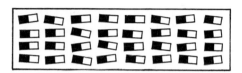
Fig. 16–18. Probable arrangement of miniature magnets in an iron bar magnetized to saturation.

cobalt. Some alloys, however, are much more magnetic than iron.

In an ordinary unmagnetized iron bar, the miniature magnets are believed to be arranged with the north pole of one adjacent to the south pole of another but without any orderly direction, as shown in Fig. 16–16. The external magnetic field of any considerable group of these miniature magnets would be zero. When these miniature magnets are arranged so that the north poles of a majority of them point in the same direction as in Fig. 16–17, their external fields add and produce a magnetic field outside the bar. From this point of view, magnetizing a bar is merely a matter of aligning these minute magnets and demagnetizing a matter of disarranging this alignment. If the miniature magnets stay lined up after the aligning force is removed, the bar becomes a permanent magnet. If

389

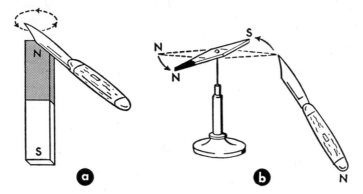

Fig. 16–19. Poles may be induced in a knife by stroking it on a strong permanent magnet.

they quickly fall out of line and become disarranged again, the bar is only a temporary magnet. When more of the miniature magnets are aligned, a stronger magnet is produced. When all are lined up as in Fig. 16–18, the magnet can become no stronger. The metal is then said to be *saturated*.

How Magnets Are Made

One way of making a permanent magnet is by stroking a piece of hard steel over one pole of another permanent magnet. Figure 16–19a shows how the blade of a pocketknife may be magnetized by this method. Notice the kind of pole produced at each end of the knife. Poles produced in this way are called *induced* poles.

A bar of soft iron often becomes magnetized when it is in a strong mag-

netic field, whether it comes into contact with the other magnet or not. The poles acquired by the bar under these circumstances are also said to be *induced*. Figure 16–20 shows the relation of the *inducing* and the *induced* poles. You will have no difficulty understanding this process if you will think of the bar of iron gathering in lines of force at one end and sending them out again at the other end. The area where the lines *enter* the iron is an *induced south pole* and the area where they *leave* is an *induced north pole*. The induced poles can be tested with a compass.

An effective way of magnetizing a piece of magnetic material is to place it within a coil which is carrying an electric current, as shown in Fig. 16–21. The magnetic field of the coil, if it is strong enough, will align the miniature magnets

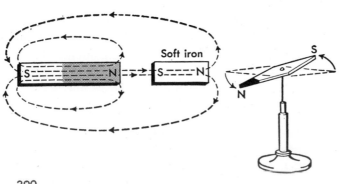

Fig. 16–20. Poles may be induced in soft iron without actual contact.

of the material so that their north poles point along the axis of the coil. The field produced by the miniature magnets of the steel and the electric current together is much stronger than that produced by the electric current alone.

If the rod in Fig. 16–21 is hard steel, most of the miniature magnets remain in alignment after the current is stopped or the rod is removed from the coil. In this way, a permanent magnet is produced. Permanent magnets are made of such materials as carbon steel, chromium steel, cobalt steel, tungsten steel, and patented alloys which have special trade names. Two such alloys which have many important uses are *nipermag* and *alnico*. Nipermag is an alloy of iron, nickel, aluminum, and titanium; alnico is an aluminum-nickel-cobalt alloy of iron. Permanent magnets made of these alloys are several times as strong as those made of ordinary hard steel. They also retain their magnetism without change for a longer time.

If a *soft-iron* rod is used in the coil of Fig. 16–21, most of the miniature magnets fall out of alignment as soon as the current is turned off. The iron is then only a temporary magnet. Special forms of soft iron such as Armco magnet iron and silicon steel are used for temporary magnets. Many different alloys have been developed which are very easily magnetized and extremely useful when temporary magnets are required. Among these are various forms of *permalloy*, *perminvar*, and *mumetal*.

How Magnetism May Be Removed

Any effect which tends to disturb the alignment of the miniature magnets will usually reduce the strength of a magnet. Pounding, jarring, and severe vibration tend to make a strong magnet weaker. This is one reason why telephone re-

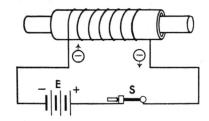

Fig. 16–21. A coil carrying an electric current is used to magnetize a steel rod inside the coil.

ceivers, which contain permanent magnets, should not be handled roughly. All magnetic materials lose their magnetic properties at some definite temperature. For many materials, this temperature is between 700 and 850°C, which is a cherry-red heat. For some materials this critical temperature is lower and for some it is higher than the range indicated. Most magnets become weaker with age, unless specially treated and protected.

If a permanent magnet is placed in a strong magnetic field which reverses its direction periodically and the strength of the field is gradually reduced to zero, practically all its magnetism can be removed. A field like this can be set up by sending an *alternating current* (AC) through a coil made of many turns of wire. The strength of the magnetic field depends on the number of amperes through the coil and the number of turns on it. The current can be reduced gradually to zero by means of a rheostat, or the sample may simply be withdrawn slowly from the coil while the current is still on full. A jeweler uses a device of this kind to remove magnetism from the parts of a watch.

Uses for Permanent Magnets

The development of strong permanent magnets such as alnico magnets has made it possible now to use permanent magnets for many purposes that formerly required electromagnets.

Several types of microphones used in radio broadcasting and in public-address systems make use of strong permanent magnets. Alnico is well suited for this purpose. A powerful permanent magnet is an essential part of one common type of loudspeaker used in radios and sound amplifiers. Magnetic chucks are used in machine shops for holding pieces of metal for grinding and other operations. These chucks are built around a system of strong permanent magnets. Ammeters, voltmeters, speedometers, magnetos, and electric clocks are among the many devices that employ permanent magnets.

A giant electromagnet crane is used to load steel rails on a railroad car in this plant. (*U.S. Steel*)

You will no doubt observe other uses for permanent magnets since they are employed in many home appliances.

The Electromagnet

The principle illustrated in Fig. 16–21 is utilized in making electromagnets. The core of such a magnet is made of soft iron, which is easy to magnetize strongly and which loses its magnetism quickly when the electric current is stopped. The strength of such a magnet depends upon the number of ampere-turns of the coil, as well as the design of the iron core.

A powerful electromagnet is used on a crane to handle scrap iron and to grasp heavy iron parts which have to be moved in shops and factories. Electromagnets are also used in track switches for trains, magnetic brakes, electric valves, electric clocks and timers, and in electric bells and buzzers.

How a Doorbell Works

A doorbell is an electromagnet with a special circuit-breaking device on it. Figure 16–22 shows how a doorbell is constructed and the circuit which operates it. When the button is pushed or the switch is closed, electric current is set up in the two coils which are wound and connected so that they produce opposite magnetic poles at the two ends of the U-shaped iron core. These magnetic poles pull the soft-iron armature against the pole pieces, which interrupts the circuit at the breaker points and stops the current through the coils. The pole pieces then quickly lose their magnetism and release the armature. A spring then pulls the armature back to its original position, which closes the circuit again at the breaker points. This completes one stroke of the bell and the following stroke is ready to begin.

1. How can the properties which are ascribed to magnetic lines of force account for the pattern of the lines in the field of a bar magnet?
2. In applying the left-hand rules, why is it advisable not actually to grasp the wire?
3. In Fig. 16–19 what kind of pole would be produced at the point if the knife blade were stroked on the south pole of the bar magnet?
4. In Fig. 16–19 why should the blade not be rubbed back and forth on the pole of the magnet?
5. Why is an electromagnet useless for removing brass or copper from a mixture of materials?
6. Would it be satisfactory to use a brass rod for the core of an electromagnet? Explain.
7. What is a nonmagnetic watch spring? What are its advantages?
8. Would alnico be satisfactory for the core of a doorbell magnet? Explain.
9. Are filings from soft iron any better than filings from hard steel for making iron filing maps of magnetic fields? Explain.
10. Physicians sometimes use magnets for removing foreign particles from a patient's eye. Would this method be successful in removing a bit of aluminum? Explain.
11. How can magnetism be removed from a permanent magnet?

THE EARTH AS A MAGNET

The mystery of why a compass needle points approximately north and south was dispelled when it was suggested that the earth itself acts like a huge magnet with two poles. This idea was advanced in 1600 by Sir William Gilbert, court

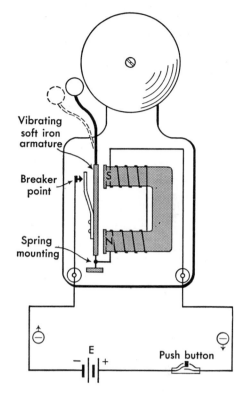

Fig. 16–22. How a doorbell works.

physician to Queen Elizabeth I of England. To account for the north pole of a compass pointing north, the magnetic pole in the northern hemisphere must be considered a *south* pole and that in the southern hemisphere a *north* pole.

The Earth's Magnetic Poles

The magnetic poles do not coincide with the geographic poles, which are at the ends of the earth's axis. The magnetic pole in the northern hemisphere has been visited and marked several different times. It has been located on a peninsula in northern Canada, just off Baffin Bay, some 1,200 miles from the geographic North Pole. Surveys made in recent years indicate that this pole does not remain fixed in one position but shifts with time. In fact, it appears that there may actually be several magnetic poles in the northern hemisphere, located as much as 200 or 300 miles apart. The opposite magnetic pole in the southern hemisphere lies on the Antarctic Continent south of Australia. The two poles do not lie at opposite ends of a diameter of the earth, since a line joining them would miss the center of the earth by about 750 miles.

Magnetic Declination

Figure 16–23 shows some lines of force in the earth's magnetic field. At any location on the earth, a compass needle tends to line up with the line of force through that point. An ordinary compass needle is usually loaded slightly at one end, so that it will remain horizontal even though the lines of force dip downward into the earth. The compass needle points approximately toward the north *magnetic* pole, but its direction is affected also by local factors, such as currents of electricity in the earth and nearby magnetic materials. So observations have to be made to determine the actual compass

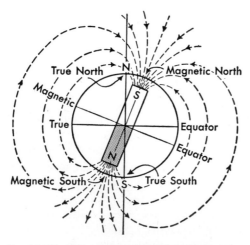

Fig. 16–23. The earth as a huge magnet with a magnetic field extending far out into space.

direction at any given place. At some locations the compass needle points true north, at others it points west of north and at still others it points east of north. The angle between the compass direction and true north at any location is called the *magnetic declination* of that place. Mariners often call this angle the magnetic *variation*. A knowledge of the exact value of the magnetic declination at different points on the earth is important to surveyors, navigators, and others who depend on the magnetic compass for direction.

Magnetic Inclination, or Dip

When a compass needle is mounted parallel to the earth's magnetic lines of force so that it is free to turn about a horizontal axis, one end will point downward. In the northern hemisphere the north pole of the needle is the lower, and in the southern hemisphere, the south pole is the lower. The angle between the horizontal plane and the direction the dip needle points is called the *magnetic inclination*, or *dip*. At the magnetic pole in the northern hemisphere the dip needle will stand vertical with its north end down, so the inclination here is 90 deg. At the magnetic pole in the southern hemisphere, the needle will again stand vertical, but with its south end down. The inclination at places between the earth's magnetic poles is less than 90 deg.

The Earth's Magnetic Field

The declination, inclination, and strength of the earth's magnetic field at any location are constantly changing. The changes are of three principal types: (1) a slow, gradual change from year to year, (2) a daily change which occurs with greater or less regularity every day, and (3) magnetic storms.

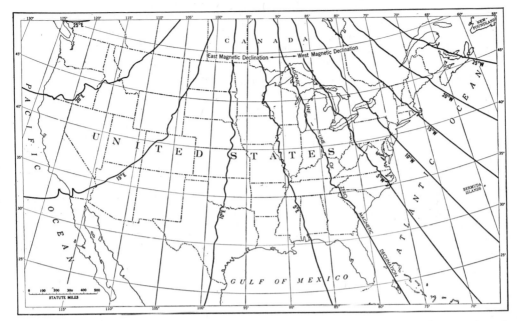

Isogonic (magnetic) map of the United States for the year 1945. The agonic line passes through Georgia, Michigan, and the intervening states. (*U.S. Coast and Geodetic Survey*)

The direction of the compass needle at any location does not remain fixed, but shows a gradual change. At London, England, for example, the compass pointed about 12 deg east of north in 1580. It then began moving westward until by 1810 it stood about 24 deg west of north. Since then it has been moving eastward again. This change seems to be caused by a gradual shift in the location of the earth's magnetic poles. The daily changes are small and can be detected only by delicate apparatus.

Magnetic storms cause erratic but temporary changes in the earth's magnetism. During a severe magnetic storm, the needle may shift direction several degrees. These magnetic disturbances occur at irregular times and may last for a few hours or a few days. They seem to be associated with sunspots and nearly always accompany unusual ac-

tivity of the *aurora* or "northern lights." They are not connected with thunderstorms or other weather disturbances. Magnetic storms often interfere with telegraph and radio communication.

▶You Will Be Interested to Know

The early Chinese are generally believed to have discovered that a piece of lodestone, suspended so that it is free to turn, will come to rest always in the same position. From this discovery they developed a crude kind of magnetic compass which they seem to have used only as a curiosity. Marco Polo may have brought one of these Chinese compasses back to Europe when he returned from his fabulous journey to Cathay (China). The magnetic compass became widely used in Europe as an aid to navigation during the twelfth or the thirteenth century.

1. What are the magnetic declination and inclination at your location?
2. The sailors with Columbus on the first transatlantic voyage are reported to have been greatly alarmed when they discovered that the compass needle no longer pointed north. Why did the needle shift its direction as they sailed westward?
3. A ship of special construction, the *Carnegie*, was used for 15 years in making magnetic measurements at sea. The ship was built entirely of wood, bronze, and other nonmagnetic materials. Why could iron and steel not have been used for the engines and fittings?
4. How is a magnetic compass on shipboard compensated for the effect of iron and steel on the ship?
5. A small magnetic compass with a needle floating in liquid is sometimes attached to the windshield or instrument panel of an automobile. How are these compasses compensated for the magnetic effect of the metal in the car?
6. Do you know of a type of compass that is not magnetic? Explain.
7. What evidence do you know to prove that the earth is a magnet? Locate the North and South magnetic poles.

HIGHLIGHTS

Parallel wires carrying currents in the *same* direction *attract* each other; parallel wires carrying currents in the *opposite* direction *repel* each other.

Lodestone is a form of iron ore called *magnetite*. It is a natural magnet.

Most magnets in actual use are artificial.

Magnets have at least *two* poles, a north and a south pole.

Like poles repel and unlike poles attract.

A wire carrying an electric current can deflect a nearby compass needle.

A *magnetic field* is a region in which a magnetic force can be detected.

Lines of force are used to represent a magnetic field. A line of force is the path along which a free north pole would tend to move.

Lines of force (1) leave a magnet at its N pole and enter at its S pole, (2) are closer together where the magnetic force is greater, (3) repel each other sidewise, and (4) act like closed loops that tend to shorten.

The lines of force about a wire carrying an electric current consist of a series of concentric circles whose direction is given by the following rule:
Grasp the conductor with your left hand (in imagination) so that your thumb points in the direction electrons flow; then your fingers will encircle the conductor in the direction of the lines of force.

The magnetic field of a coil carrying a current is similar to that of a bar magnet. Its direction is given by the following rule:

Grasp the coil with your left hand (in imagination) so that your fingers encircle it in the direction electrons are flowing in the wire; then your extended thumb will point toward the north pole of the coil.

Magnetizing an iron bar is a process of aligning its tiny elementary magnets.

Demagnetizing is a process of disarranging the alignment of elementary magnets.

Hard steel and alloys such as alnico are used for *permanent* magnets; soft iron is used for *temporary* magnets.

The earth acts as a huge magnet whose magnetic poles do not coincide with the geographic poles.

The angle between the compass direction and the true north is called magnetic *declination*.

The magnetic *inclination* is the angle the dip needle makes with a horizontal plane.

The earth's magnetic field is constantly changing. *Magnetic storms* occur, as well as secular (long-period) and daily changes.

THINGS TO DO

1. Obtain a strong magnet and test each kind of United States coin to see if it is magnetic. Try also a Canadian nickel if you can obtain one. Explain any difference you observe.
2. Magnetize a large needle by stroking it with a good bar or horseshoe magnet. Then float the needle on a thin flat cork in water in a glass dish. The needle should assume a magnetic north-south position. Use this needle to test the magnetism of a second needle. Hold one end of it near the point of the first.
3. Make an electromagnet. Obtain a steel bolt or large steel nail. Wind on the bolt or nail a few dozen turns of insulated magnet wire (No. 30, double-cotton or enamel-insulated copper wire is suggested). Connect the ends of this coil to a single dry cell and see if the iron core will pick up nails, tacks, or iron filings. Open the circuit and see if the clinging nails, tacks, or filings fall off. Explain what you observe.
4. Obtain a magnetic compass and test the base of your school flagpole (steel) for magnetism. If you find the pole magnetized, determine whether the base is an N or an S pole. Explain.
5. If you are near an airport, find out from the official in charge what types of compasses or other direction-finding equipment are used in the airplanes stationed at that airport.

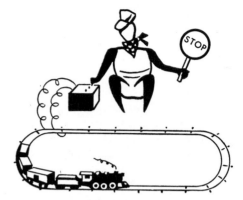

17.

Electricity and Mechanical Work:
Alternating and Direct Currents

INDUCED ELECTROMOTIVE FORCES

We have seen that a stream of electrons moving through a wire is accompanied by a magnetic field. We shall now see that it is possible for moving magnetic fields to set streams of electrons in motion and shall look into some situations where this occurs.

Figure 17–1 represents a coil of wire *AB* connected to a sensitive galvanometer *G*, an instrument for detecting small electric currents. A bar magnet NS can be moved about in the vicinity of the coil. When the N pole is approaching end *B* of the coil as shown in Fig. 17–1, the galvanometer will deflect in one direction, say to the right. This

deflection indicates that an electric current is set up in the coil circuit. When the N pole moves away from *B*, the galvanometer will deflect toward the left. This indicates that a current is now set up in the opposite direction from the first. The deflections obtained with the corresponding motions of the S pole of the magnet are just opposite those obtained with the N pole. Keeping the magnet stationary and moving the coil will produce the same effect as that caused by keeping the coil stationary and moving the magnet. *When both coil and magnet are stationary, there is no deflection of the galvanometer.* An electric current set up in a coil in this way is called an *induced* current.

Motion of a magnet with respect to a coil produces an *induced electromotive force,* which in turn sets up an induced current. A current can thus be induced only in a closed circuit, while an emf can be induced in any circuit, whether it is closed or open.

Emf Induced by Electric Current

An electric current also can induce an emf, as may be shown with the simple apparatus of Fig. 17–2. Two coils of wire, *AB* and *CD,* are placed end to end. A soft-iron rod, which passes through both coils, acts as a magnetic core and makes the effect we are to observe larger and easier to see. *Secondary coil AB* is connected to a galvanometer *G. Primary coil CD* is connected in series with a battery *E* and a switch *S.* With this apparatus, we can show that

1. Closing the switch may cause a momentary movement of the galvanometer pointer to the left.
2. With the switch closed, a steady electric current is set up in the primary coil, but there is no deflection of the galvanometer pointer.
3. Opening the switch may cause a momentary movement of the pointer to the right.
4. With the switch open, there is no deflection of the pointer.

From these observations, we may conclude that

An emf is induced in the secondary coil whenever the electric current through the primary coil is changing (starting or stopping).

What Is a Flux-turn?

The total number of magnetic lines of force through any given area is called the *magnetic flux* through that area. One line of force from the bar magnet in Fig. 17–3a is represented as *interlinking* once with the electric circuit. The electric

circuit and the magnetic field are then said to be *linked* with one *flux-turn.* In Fig. 17–3b, two lines of force interlink once with the circuit, so the *linkage* is two flux-turns. In Fig. 17–3c one line interlinks with two turns of the circuit, so the linkage is again two flux-turns. *Flux-turns equal the number of lines of force times the number of turns of circuit with which they interlink.*

Causes of Induced Emf

When we keep in mind the pattern of lines of force about a bar magnet, we can see that any motion of the magnet with respect to the coil in Fig. 17–1 must result in a *change* in the number of flux-turns that link the coil. We found that during this motion, an emf was induced in the coil. There is no *change* in flux-turns when both the coil and the magnet are stationary, and under this condition, there is no induced emf. The moment the switch in Fig. 17–2 is closed, electrons begin to flow through the primary coil. The accompanying magnetic lines of force begin to spread out from the primary coil, so that more and more of them link with the secondary coil. Thus the number of flux-turns of the secondary coil is *changing* as long as the primary current is growing. It is during

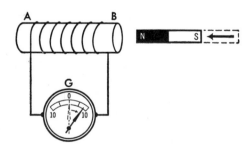

Fig. 17–1. Moving the magnet sets up a flow of electrons in the coil circuit, as indicated by the deflection of the galvanometer. This is called an *induced* electric current.

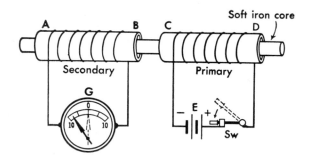

Soft iron core

this interval that an induced emf appears in the secondary circuit. When the primary current becomes *steady*, there is *no further change* in flux-turns in the secondary coil. With a steady primary current, there is also no induced emf. When the switch is opened, the primary current falls rapidly to zero, and the accompanying lines of force collapse and vanish. During this interval the number of flux-turns is *changing* and an emf is induced in the secondary circuit.

An emf is induced in a circuit whenever the number of flux-turns of that circuit is changing.

Size of Induced Emf

When we move the magnet in Fig. 17–1 slowly, the flux-turns change slowly and the induced emf indicated by the galvanometer is small. When we move the magnet more rapidly, the flux-turns change more rapidly and the induced emf is larger. It can be shown

that the size of any induced emf depends on *how fast* the flux-turns are changing. The relation is expressed in the equation

$$\text{Induced volts, } E' = \frac{\text{change in flux-turns}}{10^8 \times \text{seconds}}$$

The induced emf is one volt when the flux-turns are changing at the rate of 100,000,000 or (10^8) per second. This statement is sometimes taken as the definition of a volt.

Direction of Induced Current

If you will examine carefully the events shown in Figs. 17–1 and 17–2 you will find that the induced electric current has one direction when the flux-turns of its circuit are increasing and the opposite direction when the flux-turns are decreasing. Increasing the flux-turns by bringing the north pole of a magnet up to a coil produces an induced current opposite in direction from that produced by increasing flux-turns by bringing up

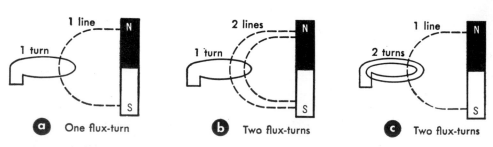

Fig. 17–3. Flux-turns, or flux-linkages, between the magnetic field and the electric circuit.

a south pole. The direction of the induced electric current must depend not only on whether the flux-turns are increasing or decreasing, but also on the *direction* of the magnetic lines of force that thread or encircle the electric circuit.

An electric current induced in a closed circuit has its own set of magnetic lines of force that accompany it in the same way that lines of force accompany any flow of electrons. We found in Chapter 16 that these lines of force encircle the conductors of the circuit in a definite direction that is related to the direction in which the electrons are flowing (left-hand rule). So the magnetic lines of force that accompany an induced electric current set up flux-turns of their own. These flux-turns may encircle the conductors or thread the circuit either in the same direction as the original flux-turns which induce the current, or in the opposite direction.

The direction of the induced current is such that its lines of force tend to oppose the change in flux-turns that induces the current. This statement is known as *Lenz's law.* The induced emf or voltage, which is the direct cause of the induced current, must likewise have such a direction that it will cause electrons to flow in the direction indicated by Lenz's law.

In Fig. 17–1 when the N pole of the bar magnet is approaching the coil, an *increasing* number of lines of force from the magnet pass through the coil from B to A. A check shows that at the same time electrons of the induced current flow upward in the turns at the front side of the coil. By the left-hand rule, this current sets up lines of force of its own which pass through the coil from A to B, producing an induced N pole at B. The direction of the lines of force due to the induced current is opposite that of

the lines due to the approaching N pole of the bar magnet; they thus tend to cancel or oppose *the increase* in the latter set of lines. Notice that the magnetic pole at B due to the induced current is an N pole when the N pole of the bar magnet is approaching and an S pole when the N pole of the bar magnet is moving away. Thus the effect of the induced current is always to oppose the action that causes it and in this respect it is like reaction studied in mechanics.

How an Electric Generator Works

An electric *generator* is a machine which *converts mechanical energy into electrical energy.* The essential parts of a simple generator are shown in Fig. 17–4. A strong magnetic field is set up between the two pole pieces, N and S. A rectangular coil, consisting in this case of a single turn of wire fastened rigidly to a shaft, is placed in this magnetic field, as shown in the figure. The shaft is perpendicular to the magnetic lines of force.

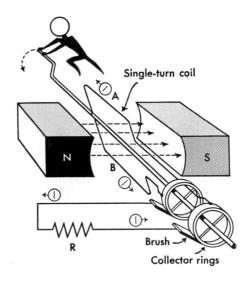

Fig. 17–4. An emf is induced in the single-turn armature when it is rotated in the magnetic field.

401

Each end of the coil is connected to a separate brass collector ring, on which a carbon *brush* fits. The *collector rings* are mounted rigidly on the shaft, but are insulated both from the shaft and from each other. When the shaft turns, the rings slip under the brushes so that the wires connecting the external load resistor R are not twisted by the rotation.

In operation, the shaft and coil of a generator must be turned by hand or by some driving machine such as a gasoline engine, a turbine, or a motor. The lines of force from the magnetic field link with the coil, so that the coil circuit has a certain number of flux-turns at any instant. As the coil rotates, its flux-turns change and an emf is induced in it. This causes a current through the load resistor R.

Emf Produced by a Generator

The rotating coil of the simple generator of Fig. 17–4 is called its *armature*. The armature of an electric generator is the part in which the emf or voltage is induced. Figure 17–5 shows an end view of the armature of Fig. 17–4 at several successive positions in its rotation. Let us follow the conductor A as the armature makes one complete turn in order to see what happens to the induced emf. The induced emf may cause electrons to flow in conductor A either toward you or away from you as you face the end of the armature coil. We shall use the symbol ⊙ to indicate that electrons are urged to flow toward you and ⊗ to indicate that electrons are urged to flow away from you. Electrons in conductor B will always be urged to flow opposite to those in conductor A. That is, when those in A are urged toward you, those in B are urged away from you.

Without considering all the details, we may summarize what happens during one rotation of the simple armature coil as follows: When A is in positions 1 and 5, the flux-turns of the armature coil are momentarily not changing at all, so the induced emf at these positions is zero. At 3 and 7 the flux-turns are changing most rapidly, so the largest values of induced emf occur at these points. As A moves from 1 through 3 to 5 the induced emf urges electrons to move away from you as you face the figure. As A moves from 5 through 7 back to 1 again, the induced emf urges electrons to move toward you, so that the emf in this half turn is just opposite to that in the first half turn.

When conductor A has made one complete rotation and is back at position 1 the emf has passed through one *complete cycle* and is back at zero again. You will notice that the induced emf or voltage reverses direction at positions 1 and 5.

Figure 17–6 shows the *waveform* of the

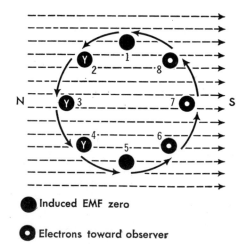

● Induced EMF zero

⊙ Electrons toward observer

⊗ Electrons away from observer

Fig. 17–5. Direction of the induced emf in one conductor as the armature coil makes one turn.

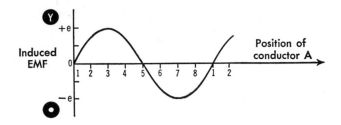

Fig. 17–6. The waveform of the emf induced in the conductor A of Fig. 17–4. This is an alternating emf or voltage.

emf or voltage induced in the single-turn armature as it makes one complete turn at uniform speed. The electric current through load resistor R in Fig. 17–4 varies in the same manner. This is an *alternating voltage* and the current is an *alternating current*. In contrast with this induced voltage, the emf or voltage developed in a battery is steadily in one direction, that is, it urges electrons to flow around the circuit in a *steady* current which always maintains the same direction. This is why we call the current from a battery *direct current*.

▶You Will Be Interested to Know

After Oersted announced his discovery (1820) of the magnetic fields that accompany electric currents, scientists set out to search for the complementary effect, electric currents that may be produced by magnetic fields. Michael Faraday in London tried many different experiments in his search that extended over a period of nine or ten years, and was forced to write in his notebook after every one, "No results." Finally on August 29, 1831, he tried a new experiment and succeeded in finding the long-sought effect. This was the discovery of the principle of electromagnetic induction, on which our present electric generators operate. We owe our present concept of imaginary magnetic lines of force to Michael Faraday.

The principle of electromagnetic induction was discovered in America in the same year by Joseph Henry, then a teacher at the Academy at Albany, New York. Henry did not know about Faraday's discovery when he made his discovery independently, for means of communication were very slow at that time. Joseph Henry became a professor at Princeton University and later became the first permanent Secretary of the Smithsonian Institution of Washington, D.C. He is one of two Americans honored in having a physical unit—the henry, a unit of inductance —named for him. The other was Alexander Graham Bell, for whom the bel (and decibel) were named.

A Generator for Direct Current

Suppose a reversing switch is installed between the brushes and the load resistor in Fig. 17–4. Such a switch is shown in Fig. 17–7. When this switch is thrown to the right, brush A is connected to terminal A of the resistor, and brush B to terminal B. When the switch is thrown to the left, brush A is connected to terminal B and brush B to terminal A. If this switch is thrown every time the induced emf in the armature coil is just ready to pass through zero, the electric current through resistor R will not reverse direction but will be a series of pulses, all in the same direction, as shown in Fig. 17–8. Two pulses will occur for each rotation of the coil. This is a direct current, since the electrons flow in one

403

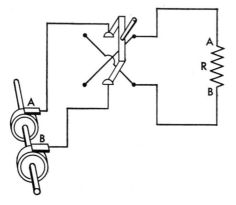

Fig. 17–7. A reversing switch could be used to interchange the connections from the brushes to the load resistor R.

collector rings, which are no longer needed. As the shaft and coil turn, each commutator bar slips from under one brush and makes contact with the other just when the induced emf in the coil is reversing direction. So, no matter how fast the shaft is turned, the switching operation, called *commutation*, will occur at just the right time.

Chief Parts of a Generator

Every generator must have a *magnetic field*, usually called merely a "field," and an *armature* in which the emf is induced. One of these must be rotated with respect to the other by some other source of power. The part that rotates is called the *rotor*, while the part that remains stationary is the *stator*. The same terms were applied to the corresponding parts of a turbine. The armature is the rotor and the field the stator in direct-current generators. In alternating-current generators, the field usually is the rotor and the armature the stator. However, in some smaller types of alternating-current generators, the armature rotates and the field is stationary, just as in the direct-current machines. Alternating-current generators are often called *alternators*.

direction only. It is, however, a *pulsating* rather than a *steady* direct current such as we get from a battery.

If the generator rotates rapidly, the reversing switch in Fig. 17–7 would have to be operated faster and more skillfully than human hands can move. In a practical direct-current generator, this reversing operation is performed automatically by a *commutator*. A commutator is made up of cylindrical segments of copper or brass, attached to the shaft as shown in Fig. 17–9. The segments are insulated from each other and from the shaft. Each end of the coil is attached to one commutator segment, or *bar*. Brushes are fitted on the commutator, as shown in the figure. The commutator takes the place of the

Exciting the Generator Field

Electromagnets with soft-iron cores, rather than permanent magnets, are used for the fields of practical generators. Direct current must be furnished to the coils of these electromagnets to excite the field of the generator. A direct-current generator can furnish current for exciting its own field. Three different connections for a *self-excited* direct-current generator are shown in Fig. 17–11. Each of these types of field windings makes a generator which has different characteristics from the others.

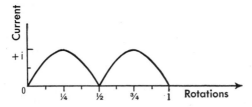

Fig. 17–8. The waveform of a pulsating direct current produced by a commutator attached to the generator.

404

The Armature

The armature of a practical direct-current generator is made up of a number of coils, similar to that of Fig. 17–4, spaced at equal angles around a cylindrical soft-iron frame or core. The two ends of each coil are attached to different commutator segments. By having more than one coil, commutation may be adjusted to occur before the current through the load resistor falls to zero. This results in a smoother form of direct current than that obtained from the single coil, as shown in Fig. 17–12. The soft-iron cylinder increases the magnetic flux through the armature coils and hence increases the size of the induced emf when the armature rotates at a given speed.

Power to Drive Generators

The rotor of a generator must be driven by some other machine that acts as a source of power. Some small generators are driven by hand. The crank ringer for older types of telephones is a generator of this type. The generator for charging the battery on an automobile is driven by the gasoline engine. Many generators are driven by electric motors. These motor-generator units are used chiefly when direct current is required and the power line furnishes alternating current. That is, they are used to convert one type of current into the other. Most large generators are driven directly by steam or water turbines. On shipboard and in some types of railroad locomotives, generators are driven directly by diesel engines. In every case, no matter how it is driven, the generator uses up mechanical energy and gives out electrical energy. *The generator converts one form of energy into another.*

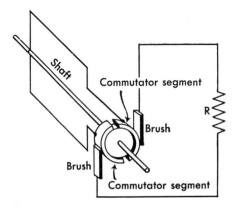

Fig. 17–9. The commutator automatically switches the leads of the external circuit from one conductor of the armature coil to the other.

Generators are built to deliver voltages from a few volts up to several thousand volts. Their electrical size is expressed in terms of the number of kilowatts of power they can develop under normal operating conditions. Large generators are capable of delivering more than 100,000 kw each. Not all of the mechanical power furnished to a generator appears as electrical output. Some is lost as heat in overcoming friction, and in wind resistance to the moving armature. Some is converted into heat by electrons flowing through the wires of the armature. Some of the electric power developed must be spent in exciting the field in self-excited generators. Because of these and other

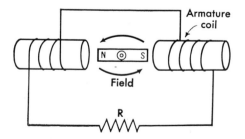

Fig. 17–10. The principle of an alternator with a rotating field.

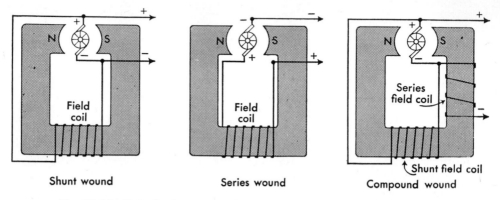

Fig. 17–11. Methods of connecting field windings of self-excited generators.

losses, the electrical output of a generator is less than the mechanical input. The efficiency of a generator alone may, however, exceed 80 percent. In modern steam power plants, 1 kwh of energy can be produced from less than 1 lb of coal.

▶Do You Know?

1. When the N pole of the bar magnet in Fig. 17–1 approaches the B end of the coil, the current induced in the coil produces a magnetic pole at B. What kind of pole is this?
2. When the N pole of the bar magnet in Fig. 17–1 is moving away from the B end of the coil, the induced current produces a magnetic pole at B. What kind of pole is this? How can you predict the kind of induced pole from Lenz's law?
3. If an alternating-current generator is speeded up, how will this affect the emf it produces?
4. Do you know of any type of electric generator that uses *permanent* magnets for its field? If so, what is it?
5. Why do generators used for electroplating have commutators?
6. What is a dynamo?
7. Approximately how many kilowatt-hours of electrical energy are used per month in your community? Your electric power company may be able to supply this information.
8. What changes can be made in the operation of a generator to reduce the voltage it produces?

ALTERNATING-CURRENT CIRCUITS

A large part of the electric power used in homes and factories consists of alternating voltage and current.

The cathode-ray oscilloscope, which we have already described in connection with the waveforms of sound waves, enables us to "see" an alternating voltage or an alternating current. When such a voltage is applied to the vertical deflecting plates of the oscilloscope, a

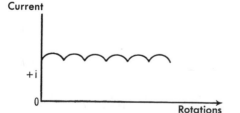

Fig. 17–12. More coils on the armature produce a smoother DC current.

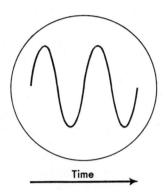

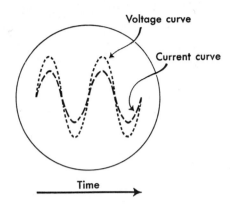

Fig. 17–13. An alternating voltage or current as it appears on the screen of an oscilloscope.

Fig. 17–14. An alternating voltage and the current it produces as they appear on the screen of an oscilloscope.

trace similar to that shown in Fig. 17–13 can be obtained by proper adjustment of the controls. With a suitable switching device preceding the oscilloscope, two voltages, a voltage and a current, or two currents may be observed at the same time. Figure 17–14 shows an alternating voltage and an alternating current *in phase*, viewed simultaneously on the screen of an oscilloscope. The voltage and the current are *in phase* (in step) because they both reach their zero values at the same time. It is possible for the current in an alternating current circuit to be ahead of or behind the voltage in phase.

Frequency of Alternating Current

When an alternating voltage or an alternating current has passed through all of its possible positive values and all of its possible negative values in succession and is all ready to start over again, it has then passed through *one cycle*. The number of cycles that are generated in a second is called the *frequency* of the *alternating* voltage or current. In the single-coil armature of Fig. 17–4, the frequency of the emf generated corresponds to the number of revolutions of

the shaft per second, but in more complicated generators several cycles may be generated during one revolution of the shaft.

Most commercial power plants in the United States generate electric power with a frequency of 60 cps. Other frequencies, such as 40 and 50 cps, are used for power and lighting in some localities. A frequency of 400 cps is quite commonly used in the electric circuits of airplanes. We have already seen that frequencies from 20 to 15,000 cps occur in sound and in electric circuits that transmit or amplify sounds. Frequencies from 10,000 to more than 1,000,000,000 cps are used in transmitting radio signals.

Higher frequencies are usually expressed in kilocycles per second and megacycles per second.

$$1 \text{ kilocycle (kc)} = 1{,}000 \text{ cycles}$$
$$1 \text{ megacycle (Mc)} = 1{,}000 \text{ kilocycles}$$
$$= 1{,}000{,}000 \text{ cycles}$$

The dials of radio sets are marked in kilocycles (per second) and megacycles (per second). When you tune in a station, you set the pointer to correspond to the

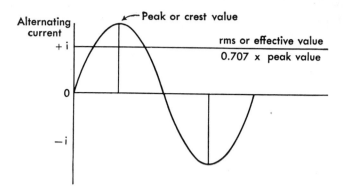

Alternating current
+ i

Peak or crest value

rms or effective value
0.707 x peak value

0

− i

frequency generated by the transmitter of the station you wish to receive.

Alternating-current Meters

An alternating current is constantly changing in value. Twice during each cycle its value becomes zero and twice it reaches a *maximum*, *crest*, or *peak* value, once in the positive direction and once in the negative. At all other times during the cycle the value of the alternating current lies between zero and the peak value. Ammeters for alternating currents are designed to indicate the *effective*, or *root-mean-square* (rms), value of the current that passes through them. This value is 0.707 times the peak value. Alternating-current voltmeters are likewise designed to indicate the rms value of the alternating potential between their terminals.

Amount of Alternating Current

You will recall that the amount of direct current set up in a circuit depends on the amount of voltage applied to the circuit and also on the resistance of the circuit itself. In alternating-current circuits, the amount of current set up also depends on the amount of voltage applied to the circuit. It likewise depends on the amount of resistance in the circuit, but in addition depends on another property of the circuit, called *reactance*.

Reactance

Reactance is caused by the presence of *capacitance* or *inductance* or both in the circuit. Capacitance is a property associated with electric capacitors, or condensers. Its value is expressed in *farads, microfarads,* or *micromicrofarads,* as you will recall from Chapter 13. *Inductance* is a property associated with coils of wire, especially with coils that have soft-iron cores. Its value is expressed in *henries, millihenries,* and *microhenries.* The reactance of a circuit depends also on the *frequency* of the voltage applied to the circuit. The value of reactance is expressed in *ohms.* The combined effect of resistance and reactance in a circuit is called *impedance.* The value of impedance is also expressed in ohms.

An alternating-current circuit which contains capacitors or coils or both usually has reactance as well as resistance, and so has impedance. Both the reactance and resistance play an important part in determining how much current will flow in the circuit and whether this current will be in phase (in step) with the voltage, or will be ahead of or behind the voltage.

1. Is the frequency of an alternating current the same as that of the emf which produces it? Explain.
2. What is the frequency of the electric current furnished by the power company in your community?
3. The nameplate on a radio sometimes bears this legend: 110 VOLTS, 60 CY. Is this radio designed to be used on alternating- or direct-current power circuits? How can you tell?
4. Why does frequency make no difference in the operation of electric irons, electric toasters, heaters, and other appliances that we have called resistors?
5. What is the frequency generated by each of the most prominent radio stations that you can pick up on your radio?
6. What is reactance? What is it caused by? In what unit is the value of reactance expressed?

When we were studying internal combustion engines, we passed lightly over the ignition system which furnishes the spark. We are now prepared to look into the principle on which such a system works.

A primary winding, with a separate secondary winding placed over it on the same iron core, makes up the spark coil, in which the high voltage for the spark is produced. The primary winding has a few turns of large wire, while the secondary has a great many turns of fine wire. The coils are connected as shown in Fig. 17–16. A six-sided (or eight-sided) disk is driven from the crankshaft. As it turns, this disk alternately opens and closes the primary circuit at the breaker points. Almost all the lines of force set up by current through the primary coil link with the secondary coil. Because of the great number of turns on the secondary coil, the number

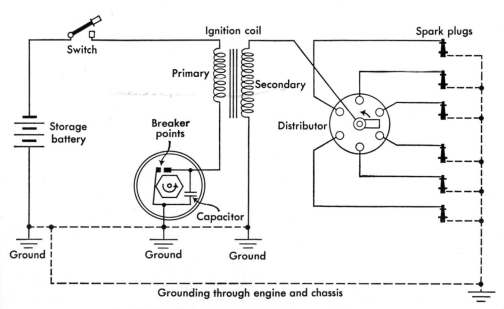

Fig. 17–16. The ignition system of an automobile engine.

of flux-turns linking with the secondary coil is very large. These all vanish when the primary circuit is broken and the current falls to zero. Thus the rate of change of flux-turns through the secondary coil is very high when the primary circuit is made and broken. This high rate of change in flux-turns induces a high voltage in the secondary circuit.

A rotary switch arm in the distributor head, also driven from the crankshaft, connects the secondary coil to each of the spark plugs in turn, just at the time the primary circuit is opened. The high voltage induced in the secondary coil causes a spark to jump between the points of the plug. The voltage induced at the break of the primary circuit is much higher than that produced at the make. The capacitor around the breaker points is designed to prevent sparks from jumping between the breaker points when they open and to intensify the spark at the spark plugs.

Another form of induction coil has a vibrator, much like that of a doorbell, to open and close its primary circuit. A coil and vibrator of this type is used in an automobile radio to obtain from the 6-volt battery the moderately high voltage (250 to 300 volts) needed to operate the tubes. The fundamental principle of every form of induction or spark coil is that the direct current through the primary coil must be interrupted in some way to induce high voltage in the secondary coil.

What Is a Transformer?

One big advantage of alternating current is the ease with which its voltage can be changed by means of a transformer. The transformer itself uses only a very small amount of power, so that changing voltage does not waste much electric power. Figure 17–17

410

shows how a transformer is arranged. The secondary coil is usually wound directly over the primary coil on a closed iron core. For clarity, the figure shows the two coils separated. We have already seen that voltage is induced in the secondary coil when current in the primary circuit is starting or stopping. When an alternating current is set up in the primary coil, the flux-turns that link the secondary coil vary with the primary current. An *alternating emf* is thus induced in the secondary coil. When the secondary coil is connected to a circuit, this induced voltage sets up a current in that circuit. The waveform of this voltage induced in the secondary coil of a well-designed transformer is the same as that of the voltage applied to the primary.

In a well-designed power transformer $\frac{E_1}{E_2} = \frac{N_1}{N_2}$, where E_1 is the voltage applied to the primary coil, E_2, the voltage induced in the secondary coil, N_1, the number of turns on the primary coil, and N_2, the number of turns on the secondary coil. When N_2 is greater than N_1, the secondary voltage is higher than the primary voltage. The transformer is then called a *step-up* transformer. In a *step-down* transformer, the number of secondary turns is less than the number in the primary coil. The secondary voltage is, therefore, less than the primary voltage. The power transformer (if there is one) in your radio set has both step-up and step-down secondary windings so that it gives a low voltage for the heaters in the tubes from the step-down winding and at the same time a high voltage for operating the tubes from the step-up winding. Transformers are used in a great many electrical devices which require voltages different from those available at the power outlet.

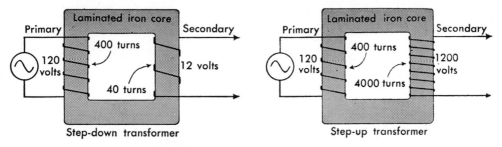

Fig. 17–17. Step-down and step-up transformers. Both the primary and the secondary voltages are alternating.

Distributing Electric Power

The alternators even at large power plants develop only a few thousand volts at the most. At voltages of this order, thousands of amperes would have to flow through the transmission lines to deliver the thousands of kilowatts that consumers require. Long cross-country lines have considerable resistance, even though wires as large as practical are used. Large currents flowing through these lines are accompanied by considerable loss in voltage and power in the lines themselves. If the voltage across the lines at the sending end is made higher, less current will be required to deliver a given amount of power. Less current, as you will recall from the rule $P = R \times I^2$, means less energy wasted as heat. So at the higher voltage, there is less voltage loss and less power loss in the lines for each kilowatt of power delivered. This is desirable, since the power lost in the transmission line can never be regained.

To illustrate: Suppose 100 kw is to be delivered over a 10-ohm transmission line to a resistance load. This might be done under one of the conditions shown in Table 17–1.

The transmission loss in this line is 50 percent when the sending voltage is 1,000 volts but only 0.01 percent when the sending voltage is 100,000 volts. Transmission of electric power over lines is, therefore, more efficient when higher voltages are used.

To obtain high voltages for transmission lines, the alternators are connected to the primary of a step-up transformer located near the power plant. The secondary of this transformer may be connected directly to the

Table 17–1. Power Loss in a 10-ohm Transmission Line

Voltage at receiving end, volts	Current, amp	Loss of voltage in line, volts	Voltage at sending end, volts	Power loss in line, kw	Power input at sending end, kw	Power loss, %
1,000	100	1,000	2,000	100	200	50.00
10,000	10	100	10,100	1	101	1.00
100,000	1	10	100,010	0.01	100.01	0.01

411

transmission line or to the primary of a second step-up transformer. The secondary of the final step-up transformer is then connected to the wires of the transmission line. In this way the voltage produced by the alternator is stepped up many fold. Voltages from 10,000 to 250,000 volts are commonly used on transmission lines in the United States. Losses and insulation difficulties make it impractical to go much above 250,000 volts.

At the receiving end of the transmission line, the voltage is again stepped down by means of a series of transformers. The voltage must be stepped down because the very high voltages used on the transmission line are too inconvenient and dangerous to handle for general purposes. In most localities, the voltages furnished for use in houses and public buildings is 110 to 120 volts or 220 to 240 volts.

Transformers and high-voltage transmission lines make it economically feasible to transmit electric power from the sites of great water power projects to cities several hundred miles away. Only alternating current can be used for this purpose at present, although engineers are searching for a plan for transmitting direct current more economically over similar or greater distances.

ELECTRIC MOTORS AND METERS

Electric generators require some form of mechanical energy to drive them and they, in turn, produce electrical energy. Electric motors, on the other hand, require electrical energy to drive them and they, in turn, produce mechanical energy.

We may demonstrate the fundamental principle on which direct-current motors work with the simple apparatus shown in Fig. 17–18. A thin wire AB is strung loosely between two supports so that it passes between the poles of a horseshoe magnet. The wire is part of a circuit

Huge transformers are used to change the voltage of electric power. (*Westinghouse Electric Corporation*)

which contains also a battery E and a switch Sw. When we close the switch, electrons flow through the wire from A to B. The wire springs downward at the instant Sw is closed and remains there as long as electrons continue to flow. This shows clearly that a *force pushes downward on the wire.* When the battery is reversed and we close the switch, the wire springs upward and remains there as long as electrons continue to flow from B to A. This shows clearly that a *force now acts upward* on the wire.

A force acts on any conductor which carries an electric current across a magnetic field. This force is perpendicular both to the magnetic lines of force and to the conductor. This action is just the reverse of that which occurs in a generator. There a conductor, which is pushed across magnetic lines of force by some outside mechanical force, has an emf induced in it. Here a conductor, which is carrying an electric current set up by an outside emf, has a magnetic force pushing on it.

Figure 17–19a represents the cross section of a wire carrying a current of electrons out of the plane of the page toward you. A few lines in the magnetic field around the wire set up by the elec-

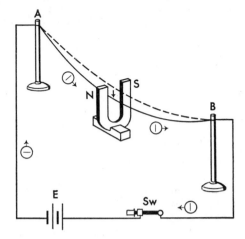

Fig. 17–18. A force acts on a wire that is carrying current across a magnetic field.

tric current in it are shown. Figure 17–19b shows some lines in the permanent magnetic field in the air space between a north and a south pole. Figure 17–19c shows how these two magnetic fields combine when the current-carrying conductor is placed in the space between the two poles. In the region above the wire, both sets of magnetic lines are parallel and have the same direction. The two magnetic fields add together in this region. One field tends to cancel the other in the region below the wire. The lines of force in the resulting field are, therefore, distorted as shown in Fig.

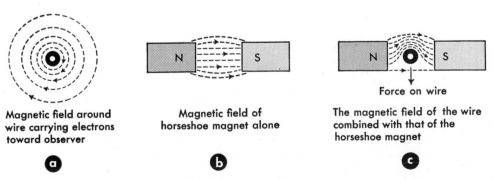

Magnetic field around wire carrying electrons toward observer

a

Magnetic field of horseshoe magnet alone

b

The magnetic field of the wire combined with that of the horseshoe magnet

Force on wire

c

Fig. 17–19. How the magnetic fields in Fig. 17–18 interact to produce a push on the wire.

413

17–19c. The tendency of lines of force to shorten results in a downward thrust on the wire. In a similar way we can make use of magnetic lines of force to explain why the wire is pushed upward when the electric current through it is reversed. Both theory and experiment show that the force on the wire (1) is greater when the wire is longer, (2) is greater when the electric current through the wire is greater, (3) is greater when the permanent magnetic field is stronger, and (4) is greater when the wire is perpendicular to the magnetic lines of force rather than at an oblique angle.

Why the Motor Turns

Figure 17–20a shows a single-turn coil of wire connected to a battery and placed in the space between the north and the south poles of a magnet. Figure 17–20b shows how the magnetic lines between these poles are distorted when electrons flow through the coil. *Because these lines tend to shorten,* wire A, which carries electrons toward you, is pushed downward and wire B, which carries electrons away from you, is pushed upward. This produces two equal torques, both of which tend to turn the coil in the same direction. If free to rotate, the coil will turn until its plane is perpendicular to the lines of force of the permanent field, with B above and A below. In this position, the coil will be linked with the greatest possible number of lines of force, counting both those of the permanent field and those of current through the coil.

A coil carrying a current in a magnetic field tends to turn so that it will have the greatest possible number of flux-turns.

How Direct-current Meters Work

The principle which we have just discussed is utilized in many direct-current ammeters and voltmeters. It is sometimes called the *d'Arsonval principle.* Figure 17–21 shows the essential parts of a d'Arsonval type of meter.

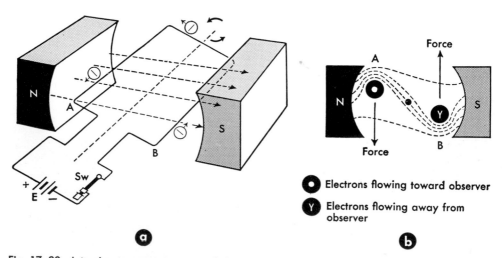

Electrons flowing toward observer

Electrons flowing away from observer

Fig. 17–20. A turning torque acts on a coil that carries a current over and back across a magnetic field. (a) Single-turn coil of wire connected to a battery E. (b) Note the distortion of the magnetic lines.

414

A horseshoe magnet NS furnishes a permanent magnetic field for the meter. A coil, consisting of a number of turns of fine wire wound on a light rectangular frame, is mounted in this magnetic field. A cylinder of soft iron, fixed inside the frame, serves to strengthen the magnetic field and to make the lines of force more nearly radial. The coil frame is mounted on a pivot and bearing, both front and back. It clears the soft-iron cylinder and the pole pieces of the magnet, so that it is free to rotate without bumping anywhere. In use, a small current passes through the coil, which then tends to turn so as to include the largest possible number of flux-turns. A light pointer, attached to the coil, moves across the dial as the coil rotates. A flat spiral spring with one end attached to the coil, winds up as the coil turns. The farther the coil turns, the tighter the spring winds and the greater is the restoring torque set up by this spring. The coil comes to rest when the restoring torque set up by the spring is equal to the torque tending to turn the coil. Thus more current, which produces greater torque, causes greater turning of the coil. When the circuit is broken and the current stops, the spring brings the coil and pointer back to their starting points.

The d'Arsonval movement is used in direct-current *galvanometers, ammeters,* and *voltmeters.* Of these, the galvanometer is the basic instrument. An ammeter is a galvanometer fitted with a suitable *shunt,* through which a large but definite portion of the current to be measured flows. A voltmeter is a galvanometer fitted with a suitable *multiplier,* or series resistor, which limits the amount of current flowing through the instrument. The dial across which the pointer swings may be marked off in amperes, volts, or other suitable units.

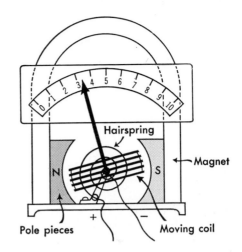

Fig. 17–21. A d'Arsonval type of ammeter or voltmeter.

Alternating-current Meters

When an alternating voltage is applied to a direct-current meter of the type we have just discussed, the coil is urged to turn in one direction during the first half-cycle and in the opposite direction during the second half-cycle. If the frequency is more than a few cycles, the coil will be unable to follow the rapid alternations, because of its inertia. In this case, the meter will read the *average value* of the current through it, which is usually zero. For this reason it is possible to burn out a direct-current meter without causing the pointer to move at all, if excessive alternating voltages are applied to it.

A common type of alternating-current meter, shown in Fig. 17–22, uses a moving soft-iron vane instead of a moving coil. The electrons flow through a fixed coil wound on a cylinder in which the movable vane and a fixed vane are mounted. Both vanes become magnetized by the current, so that like poles are produced at the same end of each vane. Repulsion of these like poles causes the

415

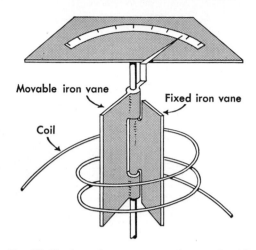

Movable iron vane

Fixed iron vane

Coil

Fig. 17–22. A moving-vane type of meter for AC voltages or currents.

movable vane to turn on its axis and swing the attached pointer across the dial. When the current through the coil reverses, the poles in both vanes reverse simultaneously, and thus the vanes continue to repel regardless of the current direction. This type of movement is used in both alternating-current voltmeters and alternating-current ammeters.

Meters with a d'Arsonval movement may be used to measure alternating current or voltage if a device called a *rectifier* is placed in series with the galvanometer

coil. This rectifier allows electrons to flow in one direction only. When an alternating voltage is applied to it, a pulsating direct voltage is produced. Consequently the current in the galvanometer coil consists of a series of direct-current pulses, which causes the coil to turn.

Direct-current Motors

The single-turn coil of wire shown in Fig. 17–20 will turn only until it has the greatest possible number of flux-turns, and then come to rest. The plane of the coil will then be perpendicular to the lines of force set up by the magnets. A commutator, mounted on the same shaft as the coil, as shown in Fig. 17–23, can be set so that it reverses the current through the coil every time the coil comes into this perpendicular position. The inertia of coil and shaft will then carry them right through the perpendicular position and the repeated reversals of the current will cause them to rotate continuously instead of stopping at the end of a half turn. The coil thus acts as the *armature* of a simple motor. The armatures of practical direct-current motors are constructed like those of direct-current generators. They have a number of coils placed systematically on

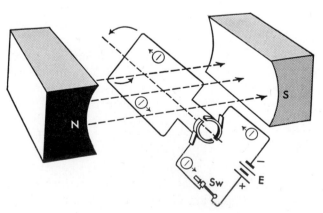

Fig. 17–23. Principle of an electric motor.

a soft-iron drum or cylinder. Their commutators have a number of bars or segments. This type of armature furnishes steadier power and smoother action than could be obtained from the single-turn coil shown in Fig. 17–23.

Electromagnets are used to provide the fields for direct-current motors, just as they are for direct-current generators. Current for exciting the field is obtained from the same source that provides current for the armature. Motors may be series-, shunt-, or compound-wound. Different types of field windings produce different speeds, torques, and other characteristics in motors.

A direct-current generator may be operated as a motor by sending current through its field and armature from an outside source. Only slight readjustment of the position of the brushes may be required for good operation as a motor.

Reversing the direction of the voltage applied to a direct-current motor will not reverse the direction in which its armature and shaft rotate, because this will reverse both the direction of the current through the armature and that of the current through the field coils. To reverse the motor, we must reverse the electric current through the field coils alone or through the armature alone, but not through both.

Alternating-current Motors

We have seen that when the direction of the field current and the direction of the armature current of a motor reverse simultaneously, the motor continues to run in the same direction. For this reason, *series-wound* motors with commutators can usually be operated either on direct or on alternating current. Such motors are called *universal motors*. The motors of vacuum cleaners and of some electric fans are usually of this type. Shunt-wound motors are not suitable for alternating-current operation.

Alternating current passes through the stationary field coils of an *induction motor* in such a way as to produce a rotating magnetic field. This rotating

This engineer is measuring the insulation resistance of a DC motor. The commutator and brushes of the motor are in the foreground. (*Westinghouse Electric Corporation*)

417

field induces currents in closed circuits in the armature. These induced currents set up strong magnetic fields which oppose the rotation of the magnetic field and in so doing push the armature around on its axis. The armature thus turns almost as fast as the rotating magnetic field. Induction motors, both large and small, are used very extensively and for a wide variety of purposes.

Some alternating-current motors are designed to run only when the armature speed is just right to keep in step with the alternations of the current which drives the motor. These are called *synchronous* motors. Synchronous motors are used to drive electric clocks and the turntables of some phonographs. Larger motors of this type are used whenever a constant speed is required.

Importance of Electric Power

There are a few outstanding inventions or applications of the principles of physical science that have had a profound effect on the social, economic, and even political life of our times. High on this list are the steam engine, the internal combustion engine, the electric generator and motor, and the electron tube, which we shall study in the next chapter. When Michael Faraday discovered the principle of electromagnetic induction in 1831, he could hardly have realized that huge generators operating on this principle would one day furnish power over wires to practically every city, village, and hamlet in his own country as well as in other countries of the world.

The first commercial electric power plant in the United States was put into operation in New York City in 1882. The generator was largely the invention of Thomas Edison, but many other people, some well known and some obscure, worked on the development of the principles that made this generator and the power plant possible. Generators at first were driven entirely by steam engines, and later by steam turbines. Steam-driven generators furnish about two-thirds of our electric power today. One-third or more of our electric power is generated at huge hydroelectric plants such as those at Niagara Falls, Hoover Dam, Grand Coulee, Bonneville, and the Tennessee Valley Authority (TVA).

Our modern cities could not exist without electric power. Can you imagine what would happen to a city like New York or Chicago if its electric power were cut off even for a day? There would be no lights to regulate traffic; no lights for the operating rooms of hospitals, except from emergency sources; no lights for streets, stores, factories, theatres, hotels, or homes; no power to run factories and shops; no power to operate elevators and escalators; no refrigeration; no power to pump water into the mains; no subway trains; no radio, television, or movies; no telephone calls or telegrams; and no newspapers. A city without these and other services connected with electric power would be dead indeed!

Confusion would result in almost every city or country home if electric service were cut off. You may find it interesting and instructive to list the services in your own home that would be impossible without electric power. Whether you live in a large city, a village, or in the country, you can readily see that we have become highly dependent on electricity to serve our needs. There is at present no other form of energy that promises to take the place of electrical energy. For this reason we must assure ourselves of an ample and uninterrupted supply in order to main-

418

tain and advance the high standard of our present way of life.

►Do You Know?

1. Why must the breaker points of the ignition system of a gasoline engine be kept clean and free from corrosion? Of what materials are these points made?
2. Is the transformer used with toy electric trains a step-up or a step-down type? Explain.
3. Do you know the location of the step-down transformer which furnishes power for your house? Where is it?
4. What is the value of the voltage furnished for domestic service by your power company?
5. How many different uses do you make of electric motors in your home?
6. Some radios are made to operate from direct or from alternating current. Why are power transformers not used in such radios?
7. Why will an electric clock designed for 60-cps power usually not keep time when operated from 50 cps?
8. Make a list of the operations in your home that would be affected by a failure in the electric power supply. How were these services performed in the days before electric power was available? What substitute for electric power would you have in performing these services today if the power supply were to fail completely?

HIGHLIGHTS

Flux-turns = number of lines of force X number of turns of circuit with which they link.

An electromotive force is *induced* in a circuit whenever its flux-turns change.

The size of the induced emf depends on the *rate of change* of flux-turns.

The *direction* of an *induced* emf is such that it would set up a current whose magnetic field opposes the change in flux-turns. This is Lenz's law.

Electric generators *convert* mechanical energy into electrical energy.

Generators have *fields* and *armatures*. The fields may be set up by electromagnets or in small generators by permanent magnets. The induced emf occurs in the armature.

In self-excited direct-current generators, the field windings may be in series, in shunt, or both with the load resistance. These are called *series-wound, shunt-wound,* and *compound-wound* generators, respectively.

Direct-current generators require *commutators* to produce a direct current from the alternating voltage induced in the armature.

Alternating-current generators are often called *alternators*. In large alternators, the magnetic field rotates and the armature is the stator.

The *effective,* or *root-mean-square,* value of an alternating current is 0.707 times its *peak* or *crest value.* Meters read rms values of alternating current and voltage.

The *frequency* of an alternating current is the number of cycles per second.

A *step-up transformer*, with more turns on the secondary than on the primary, is used to raise alternating voltage.

A *step-down transformer*, with more turns on the primary than on the secondary, is used to lower alternating voltage.

High voltages are used on power lines because the percent of power loss in the wires decreases as the voltage increases.

A coil carrying a current in a magnetic field tends to turn so that it has the greatest possible number of flux-turns. This principle accounts for the rotation of a motor and the turning of the coil in an electric meter.

A series-wound commutator-type motor can generally be used with either direct or alternating current.

A shunt-wound motor is not suited for alternating-current operation.

Induction motors and synchronous motors are used with alternating current.

PROBLEMS: GROUP A

1. What voltage is induced in a circuit in which the flux-turns are changing at the rate of 500,000,000 per second?
2. What voltage is induced in a circuit in which the flux-turns change 100,000,000 in 0.1 sec?
3. What is the peak value of the alternating current in a circuit in which the ammeter reads 10 amp?
4. What is the peak voltage across a capacitor when an alternating-current voltmeter connected across it reads 100 volts?
5. What is the voltage induced in a 1,000-turn coil when the magnetic flux linked with the coil is changing at the rate of 1,000 lines per second?
6. What is the voltage induced in a 5,000-turn coil when the magnetic flux linked with the coil is changing at the rate of 1,000,000 lines per second?
7. When the peak value of the alternating current in a circuit is 20 ma, how many milliamperes will an alternating-current milliammeter in this circuit read?
8. When the peak value of an alternating voltage across a resistor is 50 volts, how many volts will an alternating-current voltmeter connected across this resistor read?
9. When an alternating-current milliammeter in a circuit reads 100 ma, what is the peak value of alternating current in this circuit?
10. An FM radio station transmits on an assigned frequency of 91.1 Mc/sec. What is this frequency expressed in cycles per second?

GROUP B

1. What is the largest alternating voltage (measured by an alternating-current voltmeter) that can be applied safely to a 500-volt capacitor without exceeding its rating at the voltage peaks?
2. What is the largest alternating-current voltage (measured by an alternating-current voltmeter) that can be applied safely to a 2,000-volt capacitor without exceeding its rating at the voltage peaks?

3. The voltage (on an alternating-current voltmeter) across a resistor in an alternating-current circuit is 50 volts when the current (on an alternating-current milliammeter) is 20 ma. What is the resistance of this resistor?

4. The current (on an alternating-current ammeter) through a 500-ohm resistor is 0.1 amp. What is the voltage (on an alternating-current voltmeter) across this resistor?

5. The voltage (on an alternating-current voltmeter) across a 200-ohm resistor is 10 volts. What is the current (on an alternating-current milliammeter) flowing through this resistor?

THINGS TO DO

1. Examine the nameplates on any electric motors that are accessible to you. What information about the use of the motor can you get from these nameplates?

2. If there is an electric generating plant near you, find out the power rating of the generators in use, the voltage and frequency at which power is generated, and the voltage on the transmission lines leading from the plant. An official at the plant may be willing to give you this information.

3. Examine the internal design of a speedometer used on an automobile. A cutaway of a salvaged speedometer would be quite convenient for this purpose. Explain the principle on which the speedometer operates.

4. Examine the motor of a kitchen mixer, a vacuum cleaner, and an electric fan. Is direct- or alternating-current power required to operate each of these motors? Determine, if you can, whether the motors have brushes and commutators. At what speed does each motor normally run?

5. Collect and tabulate information on the number of kilowatthours of electric energy generated annually at each of the large Federal government power plants, such as Hoover Dam, Grand Coulee, and Muscle Shoals.

18.

Electricity for Communication:
Wires and Waves

COMMUNICATION OVER WIRES

Have you ever watched a telegraph operator tap off a message or listened to the sharp clicking of a busy telegraph sounder and wished you could understand the language they use? Have you ever sent a telegram and wondered how it could travel so quickly? Greetings, good news and bad, all can be brought to you speedily from far places by wire. The telegraph was the first practical invention to employ electrons for delivering messages.

Messages Are Sent by Telegraph

In its simplest form, a telegraph is only a long electric circuit with a battery

in series, as shown in Fig. 18–2. A *key* is used to open and close the circuit at the sending end. With this key, the sending operator taps out the message, letter by letter, in the dots and dashes of the telegraph code. At the receiving end, the circuit passes through the coil of the *sounder*, which is fitted with a movable tone arm and a sounding post. When the sending operator pushes down his key, he closes the circuit, setting electrons in motion throughout the long circuit. Thus a small electric current is set up through the coil of the distant sounder, making it an electromagnet. This magnet pulls the tone arm downward and produces a click. When the sending operator releases the key, it springs up and again opens the circuit. At the receiving station the tone arm, which is released when the circuit is broken, likewise springs up and the sounder makes a click with a slightly different sound. A trained receiving operator recognizes the interval of time between the two distinctive clicks as a dot or a dash. He translates the groups of dots and dashes back into letters and numbers and thus is able to write down the message he receives. Moving electrons are the messengers which carry your message over the wires from the sending station to the receiver.

The same pair of wires can carry messages both ways between stations. For a simple two-way system of this type, a key and a sounder are needed at each station as shown in Fig. 18–3. If stations are miles apart, *relays* are generally used in the circuit. Relays operate on much smaller currents than sounders and are used chiefly to key (open and close) other circuits in which sounders are placed (see Fig. 18–1). Some telegraph circuits use only one wire, but in this case the earth usually takes the place of the second wire and acts as the return part of the circuit.

Speeding Up the Telegraph

Experienced operators can send and receive messages with a key and sounder steadily at 30 to 40 words per minute. Higher speeds are sometimes reached but these can usually be kept up for only short periods of time. Automatic sending and receiving machines can operate continuously at speeds of 100 words or more per minute. These machines have replaced the hand-operated key and the sounder at most busy stations where many messages have to be handled. Keys and sounders are still used at temporary or remote stations.

In an automatic system, the message is first typed by hand on a machine with a keyboard that resembles that of a typewriter. This machine punches the message in a pattern of holes in a special paper tape. This punched tape is then fed automatically into a sending machine, which transmits the message in code over the wires to the receiving station. There an automatic receiving machine responds to the coded signals that come in on the wire and types out the message on a sheet of paper in ordinary letters and numbers. Some automatic receiving machines cut the message in perforated tape at the same time they print it on paper. The photograph

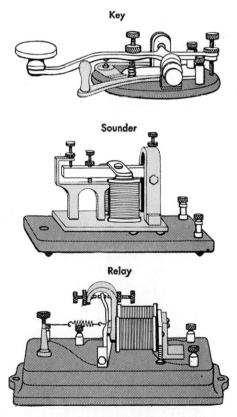

Key

Sounder

Relay

Fig. 18–1. Telegraph instruments.

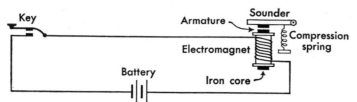

Fig. 18–2. A simple one-way telegraph circuit.

on this page shows automatic sending and receiving machines. A strip of punched tape containing a part of a message in code is shown on p. 425.

The Telephone and Your Voice

Useful as the telegraph is, it would hardly be a satisfactory device for carrying on a conversation with a friend, unless you both happened to be trained operators. The telephone, on the other hand, can speed your spoken words, or their counterparts, on dancing electrons through wires to a listener next door or

A teletypewriter room. The machine in the foreground receives messages and the other two act as transmitters to send messages. (*American Telephone and Telegraph Company*)

miles away and immediately bring his words back to you. You can now call almost anyone in the world from your home telephone. How does this convenient device work?

A simple telephone system consists of two essential parts, the *microphone* or *transmitter* and the *receiver*. These must be connected with suitable wires. Generally a battery also is needed. The microphone changes sound energy, such as that in your voice, into corresponding electrical energy, which is transmitted over the wires to the receiver. The receiver, in turn, changes the electrical energy back into the corresponding sound. For this reason, we can say that sound energy is not transmitted directly over a telephone.

How the Microphone Operates

A *diaphragm* and a *carbon button* are inside the case of an ordinary telephone microphone. The carbon button is a small chamber filled with polished granules of carbon. In a newer type of carbon-button microphone, a projection on the diaphragm extends into and closes the top of the chamber, as shown in Fig. 18–5. Sound waves striking the diaphragm cause it to move in and out through a short distance. This slight motion changes the pressure on the carbon granules in the chamber, causing corresponding changes in the electric resistance between granules. Similar changes then occur in the flow of elec-

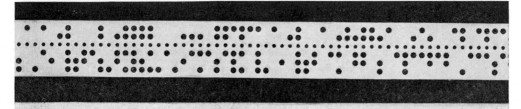

LONDON 3-15

EAST END OBSERVERS TODAY REPORTED AN INVASION OF SEVERAL

HUNDRED SIAMESE CATS.   FOR THE FIRST TIME IN 317 YEARS ONE

OF THE ANIMALS WAS SEEN CLIMBING THE TEMPLE BAR.   NO EXPLAN/

Teletype tape and the message it carries. The message shown is not necessarily the one on this sample of tape. (*American Telephone and Telegraph Company*)

trons through the microphone granules and the primary coil of the transformer shown in Fig. 18–4. An alternating emf of the same frequency and waveform as the original sound is thus set up in the secondary coil of the transformer, which is in the circuit leading to the distant receiver.

A microphone changes sound energy into electrical energy.

How the Receiver Operates

The telephone receiver contains a permanent U magnet, which pulls on a soft-iron diaphragm mounted close to its poles. Small electromagnets are attached

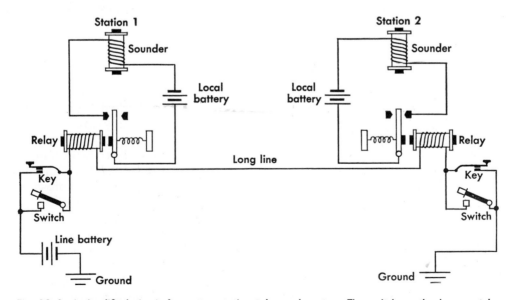

Fig. 18–3. A simplified circuit for a two-station telegraph system. The switch on the key must be closed to receive signals.

425

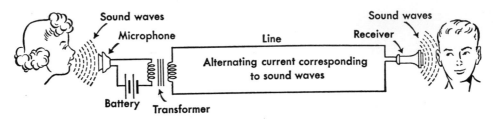

Fig. 18–4. The principle of the telephone.

to the poles of the U magnet so that they, too, can act on the diaphragm, as shown in Fig. 18–6. The coils of these electromagnets are connected in series with the telephone line. The alternating emf's set up by the sound waves at the transmitter cause electrons to flow back and forth through these coils and thus make the magnetic pull on the diaphragm alternately stronger and weaker. The diaphragm moves in and out in response to these changes in magnetic pull. This motion, in turn, produces sound waves

A stripped end of a regular telephone cable with several hundred wires for carrying messages is shown at the left. Each wire is insulated from the others, and the entire cable is wrapped with paper tape and then an aluminum sheath with a plastic jacket. A section of coaxial cable is shown at the right. Each of the eight larger tubes is a coaxial line. Each coaxial line is capable of carrying one television program or about 600 telephone conversations simultaneously. (*American Telephone and Telegraph Company*)

in the air, which are like those that acted on the distant transmitter. Thus sound waves go into the transmitter and similar sound waves come out of the receiver, but the energy transmitted over the wires is entirely electrical. Actual sounds are not transmitted over the wires.

A receiver changes electrical energy into sound energy.

More Service from the Telephone

You will see that the telephone circuit shown in Fig. 18–4 is so much simplified that it would be very limited in its usefulness. For two-way communication, we must have a transmitter and a receiver at each end of the line, with provisions for ringing. The same pair of wires can carry the voice signals both ways. One wire along with the earth connection usually makes a circuit for ringing. A central exchange is required for connecting the line of one subscriber with that of another when a call is put through. In a manual system, these connections are made by a "central" operator, the telephone girl, who plugs in the proper cords by hand. In an automatic dialing system, the connection from one line to another is made by electromagnetic relays, which are located at a central station and operated by the dial on the subscriber's telephone. The actual electric circuits of a modern telephone system are quite complicated. A recent extension of telephone service combines radio with the regular telephone network. A subscriber may now have a radiotelephone transmitter and receiver installed in his automobile or truck and place or receive telephone calls while he is traveling along the highway. Similar telephone service is available on some trains as they speed across the country. Ship-to-shore radio service also provides connection with the regular telephone lines from ships in a harbor or at sea.

Long-distance telephone circuits introduce still more problems. As the length of the telephone line increases, the electric signal becomes weaker and weaker so that finally it would fade to the point where the receiver could no longer reproduce the sound. For this reason, the electric signal has to be built up or *amplified* by electron tubes at *repeater stations* along the way. When you answer a long-distance call, the electric counterpart of your voice passes through one of these repeater stations every 20 to 50 miles.

Tracks for Your Messages

Some telegraph and telephone lines are strung on poles from place to place. Other lines are placed side by side in a cable enclosed in a metal tube. These cables are sometimes attached to poles, but are often buried underground. A single cable may contain several hundred individual wires, each insulated from the others. Two wires are required for one circuit, but the same pair of wires often carries twelve or more messages simultaneously, without mixing them up. Often telephone and telegraph signals are carried over the same wires at the same time.

Both telephone and telegraph messages are often transmitted over wires by a kind of "wired wireless" called *carrier current*. This is a type of radio

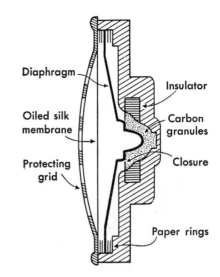

Fig. 18–5. Cross section of a carbon-granule microphone used in modern handsets.

signal that travels along the wires and enables the engineer to place many messages on the same pair of wires at one time. A special kind of cable called a *coaxial* cable and shown in the photograph on p. 426 is used for carrier current. Coaxial cable is used also to transmit television programs from one city to another.

►Do You Know?

1. What number would you call to send in a fire alarm by telephone?
2. What number would you call for police in an emergency?

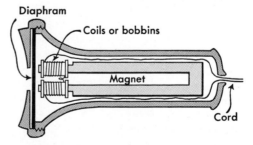

Fig. 18–6. How a telephone receiver is constructed.

3. When and by whom was the telegraph invented?
4. How are telegraph lines laid across the ocean?
5. Who invented the telephone and where was it first publicly demonstrated?
6. Why does the subscriber have to *crank* the telephone to signal the operator on some older types of rural telephones?
7. What types of microphones are used for broadcasting and public-address services?
8. What are some uses of "wired wireless" other than the use mentioned in the text?
9. How would interrupted or discontinued telephone service affect your city? How would it affect your home?

ELECTRON TUBES

If you have ever looked inside your radio, you have noticed a number of small tubes. In some radios these tubes are made of glass, while in others they are of metal. You know that your radio will not work if one of the tubes burns out. These tubes control the flow of electrons; they are called *electron tubes*.

Inside an Electron Tube

If you were to take one of these little tubes apart carefully, you would discover a number of facts about it. In the first place, if you break the glass bulb gently, you may notice a sharp sound, distinct from that of the breaking glass. Radio tubes have to be well pumped out and practically free from air or other gas in order to work. This is why they are often called *vacuum* tubes. When you break the glass, the sudden inrush of air to fill the vacuum inside the tube makes the sharp sound.

428

When you have removed the glass bulb, look for the metal plate supported by stiff wires. One of these wires goes to a prong in the base of the tube. This *element* or part of the tube is called *the plate*. If you cut the plate away, you will come next to one or more sets of fine wires stretched between stiff supports in a pattern that resembles the grid of a toaster or a broiler. Each of these sets is an element of the tube called a *grid*. Some tubes have no grids at all, some have one grid, and some have several separate grids. Each grid is connected to one of the prongs of the tube base or to a cap at the top of the tube.

If you cut and carefully remove the grid wires, you then come to the core of the electron tube. This is the element called the *cathode*, which must be heated for the tube to work. In some tubes the cathode is a little metal cylinder, which is heated by fine *heater wires* that thread through it. In other tubes, the cathode is a *filament*, much like the filament of an ordinary electric lamp, which is heated by electric current through it.

The Simplest Electron Tube

A diagram of the simplest type of electron tube is given in Fig. 18–7. This tube has only two elements, a cathode and a plate. If the plate is connected by external wires through the milliammeter and B battery back to the filament as shown in Fig. 18–7a, the meter will always read zero, indicating there is no flow of electrons through the circuit. The meter will continue to read zero, whether the B battery is connected as shown in Fig. 18–7a or whether it is reversed, as long as the filament remains cold. But if the cathode or filament is heated redhot by current from another battery as in Fig. 18–7b, or by alternating current,

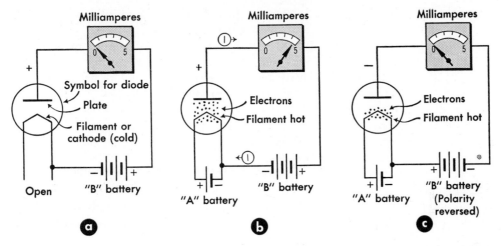

Fig. 18–7. Electrons flow in this diode tube circuit when the filament is hot and the potential of the plate is positive with respect to the filament.

the milliammeter will indicate a small current of electrons flowing from the plate, through the meter and B battery, back to the filament. If the B battery is now reversed as shown in Fig. 18–7c, the meter will again indicate that no electrons flow through the circuit, even though the filament is hot.

Current is set up in an electron-tube circuit only when the filament is hot and the potential of the plate is positive with respect to that of the cathode.

(Actually a few electrons may reach the plate from a hot cathode, even though the potential of the plate is zero or slightly negative.) This effect was discovered by Thomas A. Edison in 1883, when he was experimenting with the incandescent electric lamp. For this reason it is often called the *Edison effect.*

We have good evidence that the filament, when hot, emits electrons into the surrounding space, much as an evaporating liquid gives off molecules into the air above it. These emitted electrons are attracted to the plate when its potential is positive but are repelled and driven

back into the filament when the potential of the plate is negative with respect to that of the filament. The electrons that reach the plate from the filament must travel through the evacuated space within the tube. On their return trip to the filament, they pass through the external wires, the meter, and the B battery. Electrons cannot flow in the opposite direction through this circuit when the B battery is reversed.

An electron tube acts like a valve or a one-way street for electrons.

This and related effects have convinced scientists that an electric current in wires and metallic conductors consists of a flow of electrons rather than a flow of *positive* charges as was once assumed.

What a Grid Does

A tube which has only a filament (or cathode) and a plate has only a few uses. When a grid of fine parallel wires is placed near the filament so that electrons have to pass through it in going to the plate, the electron tube becomes much more useful. Most of the electrons

429

pass right through the spaces between the grid wires on their way from the filament to the plate. If the potential of the grid with respect to the filament is made positive, as shown in Fig. 18–8, the electrons are speeded up and the plate current increased. If the grid potential is zero, the plate current is less, and if the grid potential is made negative, the electrons have more difficulty passing through the grid and the plate current is still further reduced. If the grid potential is sufficiently negative, the electrons will not be able to get through the grid at all and the plate current will then be zero.

The size of the plate current of an electron tube can be controlled by changing the difference in potential or voltage between the grid and the cathode.

A tube with only a cathode and a plate is called a *diode*. One with a cathode, grid, and plate is called a *triode*.

Making Weak Signals Stronger

The electric signals set up by your voice have to go through repeater stations and be boosted up every 20 to 50

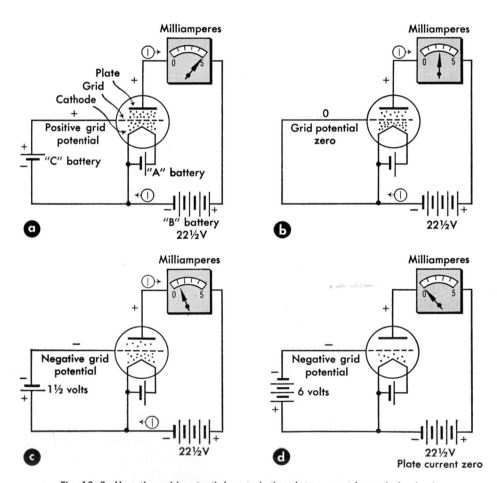

Fig. 18–8. How the grid potential controls the plate current in a triode circuit.

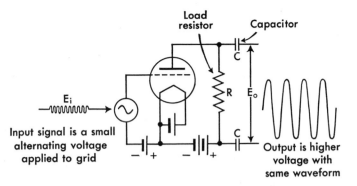

Fig. 18–9. How an electron tube amplifies a signal.

E_i

Input signal is a small alternating voltage applied to grid

Load resistor

Capacitor

C

R E_o

C

Output is higher voltage with same waveform

miles along a long-distance telephone line as has been mentioned. Electron tubes, with filaments, grids, and plates, are used to amplify these weak signals. If we apply a small alternating voltage E_i, such as that obtained from a microphone, to the grid of a triode, as shown in Fig. 18–9, then we can obtain a much larger voltage E_o of exactly the same waveform and frequency across the load resistor R. Not only is this output voltage larger, but it has more electric power associated with it than the original signal had. The electron tube takes electric energy from the battery or power supply and uses a part of this energy to increase the strength of the signal. This is the process we have in mind when we say that the tube *amplifies* the signal. The tubes in your radio amplify the very feeble radio-frequency voltages induced in the antenna by the passing radio waves. In the same way, electron tubes amplify the small voltages obtained from a phonograph pick-up and make them powerful enough to operate a loudspeaker.

A triode in a circuit can amplify a signal.

Electron-tube Oscillator

The output power that can be obtained from an electron tube connected as an amplifier is more than the power

in the original signal. Why can the tube not furnish power for its own input signal and still have some left over? This is actually what a tube does when it acts as an *oscillator* or a generator. Once such a tube is set into action it will keep on generating oscillations without any signal from the outside. The action is something like that of a wound-up pendulum clock which keeps on swinging without any further outside help until it is completely run down.

Figure 18–10 shows the principle of an electron-tube oscillator. Figure 18–11 shows one simple type of oscillator circuit for a triode tube. This circuit is used extensively for generating high radio frequencies. In Fig. 18–11 the frequency of the induced alternating current that flows through the load lamp is given (approximately) by the equation

$$f = \frac{1}{2\pi\sqrt{LC}}$$

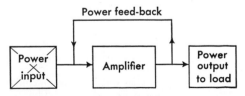

Fig. 18–10. Power from the output is fed back into the input circuit in an electron-tube oscillator.

431

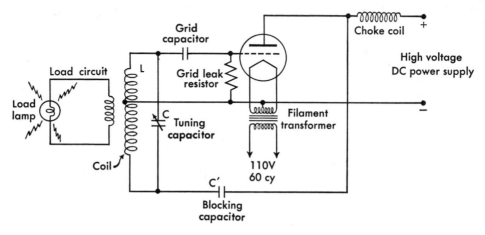

Fig. 18–11. Circuit diagram of a Hartley oscillator.

where L is the inductance of the coil expressed in henries and C is the capacitance of the capacitor expressed in farads. We can make the frequency *lower* by *increasing* the inductance of the coil or the capacitance of the capacitor. Likewise, we can increase the frequency by making the inductance or the capacitance smaller. Using this principle, we can design electron-tube oscillators that will generate alternating voltages at almost any frequency we may want, from a few cycles per second up to several thousand megacycles per second. *An electron-tube oscillator converts direct-current power from a battery or a power supply into alternating-current power whose frequency can easily be controlled.*

An oscillator is a fundamental part of every radio transmitter and of most radio receivers. An oscillator is used for many industrial purposes that require small amounts of power at frequencies other than that supplied by the power line.

An Electron-tube Rectifier

We have seen that electrons can flow through an electron tube in one direction only. Because of this valve action, an alternating voltage introduced into a tube circuit as shown in Fig. 18–12 will cause pulses of current when the plate potential is positive, but no current when the plate is negative. Although the current is in the form of pulses, it is always

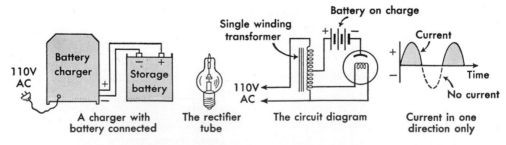

Fig. 18–12. Pulses of direct current are set up during one half of the voltage cycle.

in the same direction and is properly called a *pulsating direct current*. Any device which gives direct current when an alternating voltage is applied to it is called a *rectifier*. In radio sets, diodes are used for rectifiers in the power supplies and for detectors of the radio signal. Diodes are used as rectifiers in battery chargers, but these diodes usually have a small amount of some gas such as mercury vapor or argon in the bulbs to increase greatly the flow of electrons through the tube. Not all rectifiers use an electron tube. Some are made up of pairs of plates of different materials, arranged so that they make contact. Plates of copper and cuprous oxide, iron and selenium, and copper and magnesium sulfide are among the chief combinations used in dry-plate rectifiers.

What Is an "Electric Eye"?

There are other ways of causing a cathode to give off electrons besides heating it. *Ordinary light shining on a cathode* with a suitable surface will cause it to emit electrons. The number of electrons emitted from a given area per second in this way is usually much smaller than the number emitted from a hot cathode. The *photoelectric* cell used with the amplifier in a sound-motion-picture machine to reproduce the sound from the sound track operates on this principle. Photoelectric cells, often called *electric eyes*, are used in machines for sorting beans and for counting people who pass through a turnstile or automobiles that pass over a highway. Burglar alarms and devices for turning lights on and off automatically under the control of daylight use photoelectric cells. Cells of this kind are often used in instruments for measuring and matching colors. Some photoelectric cells consist of dry disks of two different metals and are not vacuum tubes at all.

The Transistor

The electron tube, whose operation we have described in this chapter, has recently been supplemented by an interesting new device called a *transistor*. Commercial transistors at present are made from the rare and expensive metal germanium. There seems to be some possibility that other less expensive materials can eventually be substituted for germanium in transistors.

A transistor acts much like a triode electron tube and will operate as an amplifier, an oscillator, or a detector.

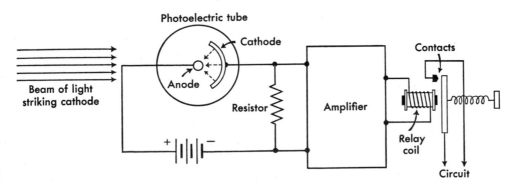

Fig. 18–13. Principle of the photoelectric tube. Interrupting the beam of light causes the relay to operate and close a circuit which may control a light or motor.

Since a transistor has no hot filament or cathode, it requires no A battery and no warm-up period; a battery of 10 to 15 volts is required to furnish a current of a few milliamperes at most for the transistor circuits. The battery may therefore be very small and its useful life quite long.

Some of the chief advantages of transistors in comparison with electron tubes are their smaller size and weight, their lower current and voltage requirements, and their rugged construction and long life. Some of their disadvantages are relatively higher cost, comparatively higher noise level, rather low frequency limit, low output power, and lack of uniformity. Some of these disadvantages will undoubtedly be overcome by further development of the transistor.

In applications such as computers, hearing aids, portable amplifiers, and in other low-current equipment where small size is an important consideration, the transistor seems to be well on the way to replacing the electron tube.

►You Will Be Interested to Know

It was many years after Edison's discovery before the emission of electrons by a hot cathode was clearly understood. The explanation of this effect had to wait for the discovery of the electron itself. This discovery was made in England by Sir John Joseph Thomson in 1897. Within a year or two he had made many measurements on the newly discovered "corpuscles," as he at first called electrons. Sir John Ambrose Fleming in 1904 built the first electron tube using the Edison effect, the emission of electrons from a hot cathode. This was a very simple tube with only a filament and a plate. Fleming used it as a detector for radio signals to replace the

434

crystal detector in common use at that time. He called his tube a *valve*, because of the way it controlled the flow of electrons. In 1906 Dr. Lee DeForest, an American scientist, placed a control grid in a Fleming valve and got an early form of our present triode. The screen-grid tube was invented about 1923 by Dr. A. W. Hull of the General Electric Research Laboratory and Professor Neil H. Williams of the University of Michigan when they were working together on a new method for measuring the electric charge of the electron.

►Do You Know?

1. A portable radio usually is ready to operate as soon as you turn on the power switch, while home radios require 10 to 20 sec before a signal can be heard. Why is this warm-up period necessary with home radios?
2. In some drinking fountains the water is automatically turned on when you bend down to drink. How is the flow of water controlled in these fountains?
3. Electric counters with photoelectric cells are sometimes used in traffic surveys to count the passing vehicles. How are such counters set up?
4. How does the sound track on a sound motion-picture film control the electron current through the photoelectric cell?
5. Explain the purpose of each of the three elements in a triode tube.

RADIO COMMUNICATION

Radio is one of the speediest ways of sending messages. Radio signals travel through space with the speed of light, 3×10^{10} cm or 186,000 miles/sec. This corresponds to about $7\frac{1}{2}$ times around the earth in 1 sec. No point on the earth is more than about 0.15 sec distant from any other point by radio. No wires are needed to connect the sending station with the receiver. Radio signals travel over jungles and mountains, oceans and polar ice caps, to places that cannot be reached by wires.

Radio is a form of electromagnetic energy, similar to light and the radiant energy we get from the sun. It travels through space in the form of waves, and travels better where there is no matter than it does through our atmosphere or through buildings. We have learned in recent years how to generate and shape these radio waves so that they will carry different kinds of messages from the sending station to the receiver. International Morse messages, all types of broadcast programs, facsimile telephoto pictures, and television scenes all ride from the transmitter to your receiver on the same kind of electromagnetic waves.

How Radio Waves Are Generated

Figure 18–14 shows a block diagram of the essential parts of a radio transmitter. An electron tube connected as an oscillator generates a small voltage at a very high frequency. A carefully ground plate cut from a quartz crystal is often used to keep the frequency of this oscillator from changing. Voltage from the oscillator is then applied to an electron-tube amplifier. Usually the output power from this amplifier has the same frequency as that of the oscillator, but sometimes the output frequency is two, three, or more times that of the oscillator.

The high-frequency power from the amplifier is fed into an antenna system, which may consist of wires, metal rods, or metal towers, properly arranged. Electrons surge back and forth in the antenna circuit, just as they do in the amplifier. Part of the power fed into the antenna is converted into heat in the wires or towers, but a considerable part of it passes into the surrounding space in the form of *radio waves*.

To send a dot-and-dash message, it is necessary to interrupt the amplifier in some way so that the waves will be broken into groups, shorter groups corresponding to dots and longer groups to dashes. To send the sounds of voice and music, it is first necessary to transform the sounds into electrical impulses, just as is done in the telephone. These electrical impulses are then used to *modulate* or shape the high-frequency power delivered to the antenna. The

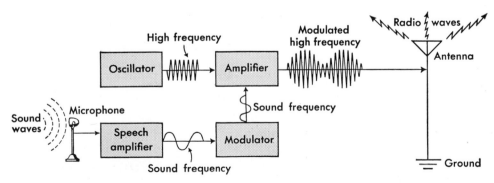

Fig. 18–14. How radio signals originate at a transmitting station.

435

Table 18–1.   Classification of Radio Frequencies

Frequency	Wavelength, m	Designation	Uses
10–30 kc	30,000–10,000	Very long waves or very low frequencies	Long distance; point-to-point; trans-oceanic circuits
30–300 kc	10,000–1,000	Long waves or low frequencies	Point-to-point; beacons; aviation beams
300–3,000 kc	1,000–100	Medium waves or medium frequencies	Ship-to-shore; distress signals; standard broadcast; aviation; police
3,000–30,000 kc	100–10	Short waves or high frequencies	Aviation; short-wave broadcast; police; amateurs; ship-to-shore; trans-oceanic telephone
30–300 Mc	10–1	Very high frequencies	FM broadcast; television; police; commercial telephone taxi; bus and truck service; aviation; amateurs
300–3,000 Mc	1–0.1	Ultrahigh frequencies	Television relay; commercial telephone; radar
3,000–... Mc	0.1–...	Superhigh frequencies or microwaves	Experimental; radar; television relay

waves radiated from the antenna are modulated or shaped in the same pattern, as shown in Fig. 18–14.

Wavelengths and Frequencies

Sometimes radio waves are described by their wavelengths and sometimes by their frequencies. From your study of sound, you will remember that these quantities are related in this way:

$$v = f \times L$$

For radio waves, v is the velocity with which the wave travels (300,000,000 m/sec); f is the frequency in cycles per second; and L is the corresponding wavelength expressed in meters.

EXAMPLE 1: What is the wavelength sent out by a radio station transmitting on a frequency of 1,000 kc/sec?

SOLUTION: Here

$$f = 1,000 \text{ kc/sec} = 1,000,000 \text{ cps}$$
$$v = 300,000,000 \text{ m/sec}$$
$$L = \frac{v}{f} = \frac{300,000,000 \text{ m/sec}}{1,000,000 \text{ cps}}$$
$$= 300 \text{ m}$$

EXAMPLE 2: What is the frequency of a ratio transmitter which sends out a wave 10 cm long?

SOLUTION: Here

$$L = 10 \text{ cm} = 0.1 \text{ m}$$
$$v = 300,000,000 \text{ m/sec}$$
$$f = \frac{v}{L} = \frac{300,000,000 \text{ m/sec}}{0.1 \text{ m}}$$
$$= 3,000,000,000 \text{ cps}$$
$$= 3,000 \text{ Mc/sec}$$

How Signals Are Received

An antenna connected to a receiver is usually necessary to pick up a radio signal. This antenna may be a simple wire stretched out horizontally or vertically, or it may be a loop or coil of wire consisting of a number of turns. A loop antenna is often mounted in the case of the radio receiver. For some purposes, much more elaborate receiving antennas are used.

An incoming radio wave cutting across a receiving antenna induces in it a small voltage, whose frequency and waveform correspond to those of the radio wave. This tiny voltage is amplified by means of electron tubes in the receiver. The voltage corresponding to the sound conveyed by the radio wave is then separated and amplified to operate the loudspeaker. The process of recovering the sound signal from the radio wave which carries it is called *detection* or *demodulation*. A sound signal recovered in this way will have the same frequency and waveform as those of the original sound which went into the microphone at the transmitter, provided that no *distortion* occurs in the transformations that have taken place.

Most modern radio receivers operate on the *superheterodyne principle* (Fig. 18–15). A receiver of this type contains an electron tube oscillator which generates a small voltage, different in frequency from that set up by the passing radio wave. These two high-frequency voltages "beat" together in the *converter* circuit of the receiver and produce a new voltage, whose frequency corresponds to the *difference* in their respective frequencies. The process is somewhat like the production of beats in sound by two tuning forks which have nearly the same frequency. This new frequency, called the *intermediate frequency* of the receiver, commonly lies between 450 and 500 kc/sec. The intermediate-frequency tuning of your receiver is set at the factory or service shop and you do not change it when you tune from one station to another. The intermediate-frequency voltage has exactly the same waveform and modulation as the original radio wave. The sound signal that it carries is recovered and amplified in the way that we have already described.

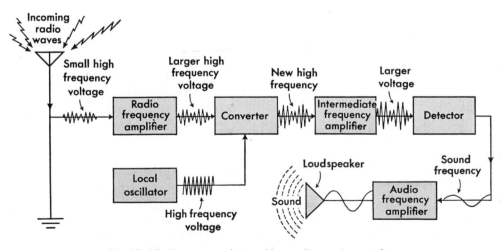

Fig. 18–15. How a superheterodyne radio receiver works.

Your Receiver Selects Stations

Two or more radio transmitting stations that cover the same area are usually assigned different frequencies by the Federal Communications Commission to avoid interference as much as possible. From all the radio waves that cut across a receiving antenna, the receiver should select the one to which it is tuned and reject the others. Receivers that are well-designed and well-adjusted are better able to reject unwanted stations than are those of poorer design.

The ability of a receiver to respond to one transmitting station at a time depends upon the fact that *resonance* occurs in electric circuits in much the same way as it does between two tuning forks. If an emf of a given voltage is applied to a circuit made up of a coil (inductance) and a capacitor (capacitance), as shown in Fig. 18–16, the amount of current in the circuit depends upon the *frequency* of the emf. At some particular frequency, the current will reach its largest possible value. At this frequency the circuit is *resonant*. A circuit of this kind can be made to resonate at a different frequency by adjusting the size of the coil, that is, changing its inductance, or by changing the capacitance of the capacitor. When you tune your radio, you adjust the ca-

pacitance of the capacitor in one or more circuits so that they resonate at the frequency of the station to which you want to listen. This enables you to bring in the station you want and keep out the others.

How Radio Waves Travel

Radio waves may travel by any one of several routes coming from a transmitting station to your receiver. The long and very long waves seem to follow the surface of the earth. Such waves are called *ground waves*. Short-wave stations have ground waves, too, but these ground waves usually travel only a few miles. Some waves start upward into the sky. These are called *sky waves*. Sky waves soon encounter a region of our atmosphere called the *ionosphere*. The ionosphere extends from about 40 to 250 miles above the earth and consists of several different layers in which the thin air is very highly ionized, as indicated in the photograph on p. 60. If the frequency is not too high, one or another of these layers may act like a mirror and reflect the radio wave back to earth again. Short-wave broadcasts, which reach out long distances, usually travel over the "sky route." The layer of the ionosphere that returns standard broadcast waves back to earth is more effective and probably higher at night than during daylight

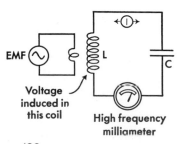

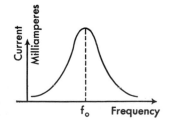

Fig. 18–16. An electric circuit that resonates.

hours, so the night range of standard broadcast stations is generally much greater than the daylight range.

For short waves, the nearest returning sky waves may reach the earth at a point that is many miles from the transmitter, while the ground wave dies out within a few miles. There is, then, a region just beyond the range of the ground wave into which no waves from the transmitter penetrate. The distance from the transmitter out to the nearest point of return of a sky wave in this case is called the *skip distance*. The skip distance for short waves may be as much as several thousand miles at times. It is thus possible to be actually *too close* to a short-wave transmitter to receive signals from it.

If the frequency of a transmitting station is high enough, its sky waves may all pass right through the layers of the ionosphere and not be reflected back to earth at all. The highest frequency that can be reflected back by the ionosphere is generally between 20 and 50 Mc/sec, but differs from day to day and from year to year. Radio waves whose frequencies are above this range, such as those used for FM, television, and radar, travel entirely through the lower layers of the atmosphere close to the earth. They are usually not reflected back from the ionosphere. For these reasons, their range is much shorter than that of waves of lower frequency.

►You Will Be Interested to Know

When we tune in a broadcast from a radio station or focus a moving image on a television screen, we rarely pause to remember how much we are indebted for these experiences to the pioneers in the field of electricity. Many years of patient careful work on the part of thousands of workers preceded the voice we hear from the loudspeaker and the image we see on the screen. We can mention here only a few of the most outstanding contributions.

Michael Faraday, as we know, invented the idea of imaginary lines of force to explain the effects observed in magnetic and electric fields. Faraday himself was not well trained in mathematics, so he needed some graphic way such as lines of force to express his ideas. A young friend of Faraday's the Scotch mathematical physicist, James Clerk Maxwell, reduced Faraday's discoveries to precise mathematical equations and showed that light must be a kind of combined electric and magnetic wave. Maxwell then predicted that a similar kind of wave with much longer wavelength than light would be produced by rapidly alternating electric currents. More than 20 years later, in 1888, a young German scientist, Heinrich Hertz of Karlsruhe, discovered these electromagnetic waves predicted by Maxwell. Hertz's apparatus was quite crude by present-day standards. He set up very short radio waves by means of an electric spark. You will recall that there were no electron tubes in those days. His detector was also a small spark that jumped across an air gap in a wire circle. Guglielmo Marconi, an Italian, became intensely interested in how these electric waves of Hertz could be used to carry on communication. By 1901 Marconi had developed his apparatus so well that he was successful in sending the first radio signal across the Atlantic, from Poldhu in Cornwall, England, to St. Johns, Newfoundland. This historic signal was the single letter *S*, which is three dots in the telegraph code, repeated a number of times. Our present form of television was still in the laboratory stage when Marconi died in 1937, but he did live to see his infant invention, the "wireless," grow up into our present system of radio communication, one of the world's greatest industries.

On the Beam

Radio waves can be reflected and bent or refracted, just as sound and light waves can. A mirror reflects light; the corresponding device which reflects radio waves is called simply a *reflector*. A lens bends or refracts light bringing it to a focus; the corresponding device in radio is called a *director*. With reflectors and directors properly arranged about a transmitting antenna, it is possible to focus the radio waves into a beam, much like the beam of light sent out by a searchlight or the headlights of an automobile. Highways in the sky for airplane routes are marked out by narrow radio beams. Planes are equipped with devices that indicate when the plane is on the beam and enable the pilot to follow the beam from one point to another. Beams are often used for communication between two fixed stations in order to avoid unnecessary interference and expenditure of power. Broadcast stations sometimes use reflectors so that their signals will be stronger in one direction than another.

Reflectors and directors are often used with receiving antennas, too, especially when receiving FM and television signals. When properly adjusted, they give a stronger signal from a station in the direction for which they are set and reduce the strength

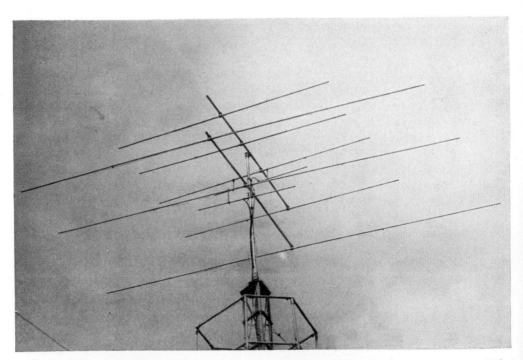

A directional antenna with radiators, reflectors, and directors used to transmit and receive very high frequency signals. The four horizontal rods above constitute an antenna for 50 Mc signals; the three rods below are an antenna for 28 Mc signals. (Photo by Grover C. Baker)

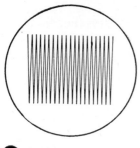 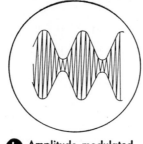 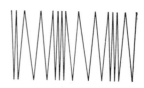

Fig. 18–17. (a) and (b) Unmodulated and AM radio signal, as they would appear on the screen of an oscilloscope. (c) How FM would appear if the effect were greatly exaggerated.

of unwanted signals and interference from other directions. Some types of antennas have a decided directional effect even without the use of reflectors and directors.

What Is FM?

An ordinary radio wave that is carrying no signal or sound looks like Fig. 18–17a when viewed on an oscilloscope. Such a wave is called a *carrier*. We must modulate this carrier wave to have it transmit sound. Figure 18–17b shows how a modulated wave appears on an oscilloscope. This modulated wave is carrying a sound signal which will come out of a receiver as a single steady tone. You will note that the height or *amplitude* of the radio wave changes in accordance with the waveform of this tone. This is called *amplitude modulation* (AM). All standard broadcast stations use amplitude modulation. Another way to modulate a carrier is by changing its *frequency* in accordance with the waveform of the sound, keeping its amplitude always the same. This method is called *frequency modulation* (FM). Figure 18–17c shows a frequency-modulated carrier as it might appear on an oscilloscope if it were modulated much more than is

usual. Frequency modulation is used chiefly by stations operating on very high frequencies, and for this reason the consistent range of these stations is limited to a few hundred miles or less, even under the most favorable conditions.

Radio Echoes

A beam of radio waves sent out by a transmitter will be reflected by any object that it strikes. Different materials reflect radio waves in different degrees. Metals are good reflectors, while the earth, water, trees, and buildings are somewhat poorer reflectors. If the beam is sent out in short pulses with a fraction of a second between pulses, a suitable radio receiver nearby may pick up both the original pulse and the reflected wave. The difference in time between these two signals will be the time required for the radio wave to travel out to the reflecting object and back to the receiver. Generally this time is too short to be noticed by ear, but if the signals are put on an oscilloscope, the original and reflected signal can be separated and seen. The time between the arrival of the original and reflected signals can be measured by determining the speed of the spot of light across the screen of the oscilloscope. The distance out to the reflecting object can then be computed from this time and the known velocity of radio waves, just as the distance to a large cliff can be determined by timing the echo of a sound it reflects.

This principle of radio "echoes" is used in a number of different devices. The distance up to the different layers of the ionosphere is found by timing the return of radio echoes from them. Radar systems, used to detect the presence of planes, ships, and many other objects operate on this principle. Narrow beams of radio waves are shot out to sweep across the sky or surface of the earth. These waves, bouncing off any object they happen to hit, are received on an oscilloscope on their return. This process reveals both the direction and the distance of any object within range. Radar devices are used for automatically aiming anti-aircraft and naval guns on distant targets, even when these targets are invisible to the eye. In one type of radar, the entire landscape below a plane in flight may be seen on the screen of the oscilloscope, much as one would see it directly with the eye in daylight. Photographs may be taken with this type of radar at night and through fog and overcast, as well as in daylight. Radar serves as an invaluable aid both to aviation and to ships at sea. It is also used by meteorologists to follow the course of storms.

Finding Direction by Radio

A radio compass consists of a sensitive radio receiver connected to a highly directional type of antenna that can be rotated. If the receiver is tuned to a distant station and the antenna rotated, the signal will be strongest in certain positions and practically vanish in

others. From this effect, the operator can determine the direction from which the radio wave seems to come. Perhaps you have noticed this effect with a portable radio that has a loop antenna mounted in its case. Radio beacon stations have been constructed at different points along the seacoasts and the shores of the Great Lakes. These beacons send out characteristic signals continuously. A navigator can take a bearing on each of two such stations with his radio compass and from these bearings determine his position, if he knows the exact location of the stations. A more elaborate system of beacon stations enables a navigator in the air or at sea to determine his exact position quickly from the difference in time between the arrival of the two signals from the pair of stations. This system is called *loran* (long-range navigation) in the United States.

Amateur Radio

Radio communication is a fascinating hobby for many persons, both young and old. Certain radio frequencies are set aside by Federal regulations for the use of amateur radio operators. On these frequencies, amateurs carry on private conversations by voice or code with fellow amateurs nearby or at great distances. Amateurs do a great deal of experimenting with radio apparatus which they design and build for their own use. In times of local disaster amateur operators have often provided emergency communication systems from the stricken area to the outside world.

Each amateur radio operator must pass a government examination and secure a license from the Federal Communications Commission, both for himself and for his station, before he is permitted to send out any signals. The Commission

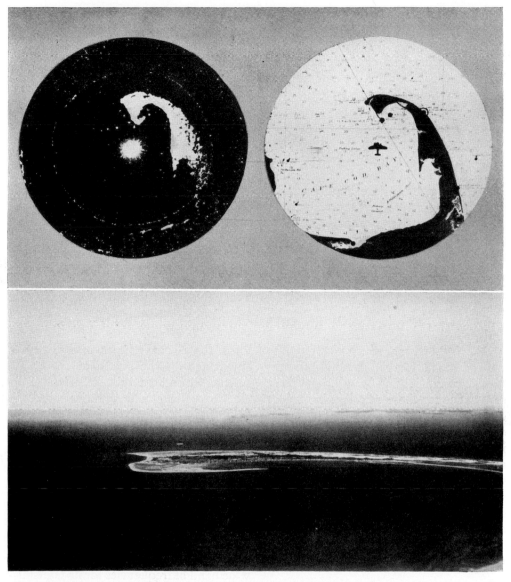

Upper left, view on the radar screen of a plane over Nantucket Island. The plane is at the central bright spot. *Upper right,* chart on the same area. *Lower,* aerial view of the same area. (*Ordnance magazine*)

assigns call letters to identify his station. Amateur calls in the continental United States begin with W or K, followed by a number from 0 to 9 which identifies the section of the country in which the station is located. W or K and the number are then followed by two or three letters which identify a particular station. For example, W9USA would refer to a station in the continental United States, in the ninth call area (in the vicinity of Chicago).

Amateur stations in other countries are assigned different distinctive prefix letters.

An amateur radio operator must use his station only for private communication with other licensed amateur stations. He is not permitted to send out entertainment programs or use his station for pay. There are more than 115,000 amateur radio stations in the United States today, and the number is increasing. There are amateur radio stations in practically every country of the world, but the number in the United States exceeds that in all other countries.

Television

Have you ever been televised or seen one of your friends on a television screen and heard his voice from the loudspeaker? Television, which enables us to see and hear a football game in progress miles away, is now a commonplace experience for those who live in or near cities. Television service is rapidly being extended to other areas and it seems probable that soon almost every community in our country may have television sets which will bring entertainment and report the events of the world. This system of "seeing at a distance" seems destined to have a very profound influence on what we do, how we spend our leisure time, and how we live.

Transmitting Television Scenes

The system by which distant scenes are transmitted so that they can be tuned in on a television receiver and focused on its screen is complicated. While we cannot enter into the details, we can examine some of the principal features of this system. Whether the scene to be transmitted is a "live" one or is recorded on motion-picture

444

film, the first step is to obtain a good, clear image of it on the screen of the television transmitting tube. The scene must be focused by a system of optical lenses, much like the lenses used in a camera.

This image is then *scanned* with a very narrow beam of electrons, something like the beam of electrons in an oscilloscope tube. Scanning consists of sweeping the electron beam across the field of the image from left to right, blanking it out while it is returning to the left side and dropping down two lines, and sweeping it across again. This is repeated until the whole field is covered. The beam is then returned to the upper left corner and the whole field is scanned again along the alternate lines that were skipped the first time over. This method is called *interlaced scanning*.

As the electron beam sweeps across the image on the screen of the transmitting or camera tube, it produces an electric voltage which varies with the brightness of the points of the image struck by the beam. This voltage is used to *modulate* the radio-frequency carrier wave emitted by the transmitting station, much as voltages from voice and sound signals modulate the carrier of a conventional broadcasting station.

How Television Is Received

A television signal requires a very wide band of frequencies for its transmission. Such wide bands are available only in the very high frequency, the ultrahigh, and the superhigh frequency or microwave regions. Because television signals are transmitted on these upper radio frequencies, which travel chiefly through the lower layers of the atmosphere, they can be received only at short distances from the sending point. It is, therefore, important that the antenna of a transmitting station and that of a receiving station be as high as possible to cover the greatest distance satisfactorily. It is often desirable that the receiving antenna be designed to pick up the maximum amount of signal from one given station and reject interfering signals from other directions. This is why different forms of *beam-antenna arrays* are generally used for receiving television signals, especially at some distance from the transmitter. When we wish to receive a station in a different direction, it is generally necessary to turn the beam antenna so that it faces the desired station. In some receiving installations, a small electric motor is provided to rotate the beam antenna. Television signals from 50 miles or more away usually vary considerably in strength and reliability with weather. They are generally stronger and steadier in summer than in winter. Occasionally television signals are reflected from one of the layers of the ionosphere and then travel long distances from the transmitter. Such long-distance signals are subject to fading.

The picture tube in the receiver, called a *kinescope*, is also much like the tube in an oscilloscope. When a sufficiently strong signal is tuned in, the electron beam in the kinescope tube scans across the field *in step with* the scanning in the camera tube at the transmitter and builds up the picture line by line. In sweeping across a line, the electron beam becomes *weaker* at points corresponding to *bright* points of the image on the screen of the camera tube at the transmitter, and is full bright where there is no image. The picture on the screen of the receiver is thus built up of lighter and darker spots. The actual circuits used to tune in, focus, and control the receiver picture are quite complicated.

►**Do You Know?**

1. Where are the transmitters of your local broadcasting stations located? What is the rated power of each station?

2. Are there any FM stations in your vicinity? On what frequencies do they transmit?

3. Are there any television stations in your vicinity? On what channels do they transmit?

4. Do you know any local amateur radio operators? What are the call letters of their stations? On what frequencies do they usually operate?

5. Does your local police department use radio for communication to squad cars? What frequencies are used?

6. Why is the range of an FM station or a television station only 100 miles or less while that of a standard broadcasting station of the same power may be up to 500 or 1,000 miles?

7. What does it mean to a pilot of an airplane to be "on the beam"?

8. Make a list of the uses for radio with which you are acquainted in addition to the broadcasting of entertainment. Which do you consider the most important use of radio?

9. What three essential parts are found in all triode tubes? Describe what each part does.

10. Describe how a rectifier tube changes incoming alternating current into outgoing direct current.

11. How is radio used to operate and control model airplanes? What frequencies and how much power are used for this purpose? If you know a model-airplane enthusiast, perhaps you can arrange for him to demonstrate for your class.

445

HIGHLIGHTS

The essential parts of a simple telegraph are a *key* and a *sounder*. Most telegraph messages are sent and received by automatic machines.

The essential parts of a telephone are the *microphone* or *transmitter* and the *receiver*.

Repeater or *amplifier* stations every 20 to 50 miles amplify the voice and sound signals on long-distance telephone lines to keep them from becoming too weak to be heard.

A number of telephone conversations and telegraph messages may be sent over the same pair of wires without getting mixed up.

Electrons are emitted by *hot cathodes* or *filaments* in electron tubes.

These emitted electrons flow through the vacuum in the tube to the *anode* or *plate*, if the potential of the plate is kept positive with respect to the cathode.

A *diode* is a tube which has only a cathode and a plate. Diodes are used to *rectify* alternating voltage and to *detect* or *demodulate* radio signals.

A *rectifier* produces a *direct* current in a circuit to which an *alternating* voltage is applied.

A *triode* has a *cathode*, a *plate*, and a *control grid*. The control grid regulates the plate current in the tube circuit. Triodes may act as *detectors*, as *amplifiers*, and as *oscillators*.

Radio ground waves travel along the earth. *Sky waves* start upward. If its frequency is right, a sky wave is reflected back to earth by one of the layers of the *ionosphere*.

Sky waves of very high frequencies go right through the layers of the ionosphere. Radio waves at these frequencies travel from the transmitter to the receiver entirely through the layers of the atmosphere close to the earth. These waves are used for FM, television, and radar.

Radio waves can be *focused* into narrow beams, much as light can.

In *amplitude modulation*, AM, the height or amplitude of the radio wave varies so that it corresponds to the waveform of the sound it "carries."

In *frequency modulation*, FM, the amplitude of the radio wave does not change, but the frequency varies with the sound.

Radio echoes are used in exploring the ionosphere and in radar.

Radio compasses are used to find the direction from which a signal is coming.

446

PROBLEMS: GROUP A

1. What is the length of the radio wave from a broadcast station which is transmitting on a frequency of 700 kc/sec?
2. What is the frequency of the radio wave from a station which is transmitting on a wavelength of 15 m?
3. Early in 1947 radio engineers of the United States Army sent out radar signals which are believed to have echoed back from the moon. The distance to the moon is about 240,000 miles. How many seconds must have elapsed between the reception of the original signal and the echo?
4. How many *microseconds* would elapse between the reception of the original radar signal from a nearby transmitter and the echo from an airplane 100 miles away?
5. What is the wavelength of the signal from an amateur radio station which transmits at 3,930 kc/sec?

GROUP B

1. How many seconds are required for a radio signal to travel completely around the earth? Assume that the distance the signal travels is 26,000 miles.
2. How many seconds would be required for a radio wave originating on the sun to reach the earth? The average distance to the sun is about 93,000,000 miles.
3. If the capacitance of the capacitor in Fig. 18–11 is 150 micromicrofarads and the inductance of the coil is 150 microhenries, what is the approximate frequency at which the oscillator will operate?
4. What must be the size (in microhenries) of the coil used with a 250-micromicrofarad capacitor in the oscillator of Fig. 18–11 to produce a frequency of 1,500 kc/sec?
5. What must be the size (in micromicrofarads) of the capacitor used with a 200-microhenry coil in the oscillator of Fig. 18–11 to produce a frequency of 1,000 kc/sec?

THINGS TO DO

1. Look up the symbols used in the international Morse code and write your name in the dots, dashes, and spaces of this code.
2. If you are acquainted with an amateur radio operator in your vicinity, make arrangements for him to demonstrate to all or part of your class how radio amateurs carry on communication with other amateurs.
3. Make a list of the television stations that can be received regularly in your community; indicate the number of the channel in which each operates and find out, if you can, what frequencies are covered by these channels.
4. If you can get a burnt-out or replaced glass radio tube, remove the glass bulb carefully and see if you can identify the plate, the control grid, and the cathode or filament of the tube. If the tube has more than one grid, try to find out what the grids are. For safety, you should place a paper bag over the glass tube before breaking the bulb.
5. If you have a table-model radio with a built-in loop to serve as an antenna, try turning the whole radio case while the radio is tuned to a station. Often you can demonstrate very clearly in this way the direction from which a radio signal is being received. Explain.

447

Unit **5.**

Light in Our World

PREVIEW

Light is the form of energy which enables us to see. Men through the ages have been interested in light and have sought explanations of many different effects of light. The science of astronomy is founded on light because the astronomer obtains information about the universe chiefly from light reaching us from the sun, stars, and other heavenly bodies.

One of the most puzzling questions in the long history of science has been, "What is light?" Early scientists thought that light must be made up of tiny particles that enter the eye and cause us to see. Later scientists were sure that light is a form of waves. There is now evidence that light acts sometimes like waves and sometimes like very small packets of energy called *quanta*.

We use many different optical instruments which are designed to aid the eye in seeing. Mirrors and eyeglasses are simple optical instruments which you know about. Microscopes enable us to see small objects with more detail than could be seen with the eye alone. Telescopes help us to see distant objects clearly and extend the distance to which our eyes can see. Cameras enable us to photograph a scene and preserve a picture record for later use. The eye, too, is an optical instrument with several unusual features that have not yet been duplicated by scientists.

This unit will introduce you to these and many more of the scientific facts about light.

19.

Illumination and Reflection:
Measuring Light Intensity

ILLUMINATION

Our chief source of light is the sun. When we strike a match, build a fire, or switch on the headlights, however, we set a source of light into operation. Every primary source of light converts some other form of energy into light. Any body that acts as a source and gives off light of its own is called a *luminous* body. The sun and distant stars are luminous bodies; hot furnaces, burning gas flames, and glowing filaments of electric lamps are likewise luminous bodies. Luminous bodies *radiate* light energy, just as vibrating bodies give off sound energy and transmitting antennas radiate radio energy.

450

The football that we see sailing neatly over the bar between the goal posts gives off no light energy of its own; neither do our desks and chairs nor this book from which we read. We can see such bodies only when light from luminous bodies falls on them and is reflected from their surfaces. Bodies that we see only by reflected light are called *illuminated* bodies. The moon and the planets (Mercury, Venus, Earth, Mars, Jupiter, Saturn, Uranus, Neptune, and Pluto) are illuminated bodies. We see them only by the sunlight reflected from their surfaces. Light-colored smooth surfaces such as white walls of a room reflect much of the light which strikes them. Dark surfaces reflect less light.

Intensity of Illumination

Direct light from the sun at midday is too bright to view directly. Light from a distant star at night may be almost too faint to be seen. Our eyes react differently in these two cases because sunlight and starlight as they enter our eyes differ in *intensity*.

Suppose we had a concentrated source of light well away from other objects and arranged to give off light equally in all directions. Then imagine that we place a perfectly transparent spherical shell so that the source of light is at its center, as shown in Fig. 19–1. If there is no absorption, all of the light energy given off by the source in a second must pass outward through the spherical shell. *The energy that passes through one unit area of the shell in a second determines the intensity of light at a point on the shell.*

When light falls on any surface and is reflected from it, that surface is *illuminated* by the light, as has been explained. The intensity of light at the illuminated surface is often called the *intensity of illumination*, or simply the *illumination*. We expressed intensity in sound as so many watts per square centimeter. It would be reasonable to expect that we could use the same units to express the intensity of illumination. However, this is not the set of units generally used for illumination, as we shall now see.

What Is Candlepower?

It is difficult to measure light directly from watts. A more convenient way is to compare the light given off by a lamp with that given off by some standard source. Originally a candle, made and burned in specified ways, was used as a standard source, although the *standard*

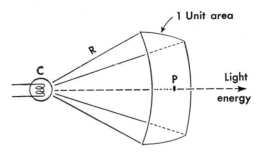

Fig. 19–1. The intensity of illumination is the light energy per second through a unit area.

candle of today is determined from certain standard electric lamps. An ordinary 60-watt electric lamp may radiate light equal to 50 standard candles. A large searchlight may be equivalent to millions of standard candles. The standard candle is thus a unit of light. When we wish to refer to the total light radiated by a source of light, we speak of its *candlepower*. The candlepower of a large electric lamp, for example, may be 500 candles.

The Foot-candle

If you replace a 40-watt bulb in your desk lamp with a 60-watt one, you will increase the candlepower of the lamp. You will readily notice that the illumination on the page of a book lying on the desk is likewise increased. If you move the book farther away from the lamp, the illumination on the page will decrease. So the candlepower of the source of light and the distance of the page from it are factors that determine illumination.

Suppose we wish to find the illumination at a point P on the spherical shell of Fig. 19–1. Let C represent the total candlepower of the source of light. All of this light must flow outward through the transparent shell, if none of it is absorbed along the way. The total surface area of the shell is $4\pi R^2$ square feet, if

451

1 candle   50 candles

Fig. 19–2. The light power of a lamp is expressed in *candles*.

the radius R is given in feet. Light power per unit area at any point P on the shell is therefore given by the equation

$$I = \frac{C}{4\pi R^2}$$

This is one way to express the illumination I at a point P which is R feet from a source of light whose candlepower is C candles.

If the distance of the point P from the source is twice as great, R is doubled and the illumination becomes *one-fourth* as great: if the distance is multiplied by three, the illumination becomes *one-ninth* as great, and so on.

Illumination is inversely proportional to the square of the distance from a given source of light.

This is another *inverse-square* law, similar to those for gravitational force and the intensity of sound.

The *foot-candle* is a standard unit used for measuring illumination. This is the illumination at a point *one foot from a one candlepower source*. At a distance R feet from any source whose candlepower is C candles, the illumination in foot-candles is expressed by the equation

$$I = \frac{C}{R^2}$$

Notice that this equation for illumination in foot-candles differs from the previous one for light power per unit area.

EXAMPLE: What is the illumination given by a 250-candlepower lamp at a point 10 ft from the lamp?

SOLUTION: Here $C = 250$ candles and $R = 10$ ft.

$$I = \frac{C}{R^2} = \frac{250}{10 \times 10}$$

$$= 2.5 \text{ foot-candles}$$

The Lumen

We used lines of force to represent magnetic fields. The stronger a magnetic pole, the more lines were assumed to come out of it. In a somewhat similar way, we use lines to represent *lumens* of light flowing outward from a source as shown in Fig. 19–3. The more powerful the source of light, the more lumens originate on it; 4π or 12.56 lumens are assumed to originate on each candle of the source. *The total number of lumens is 12.56 times the number of candles in a source of light.* A lamp whose candlepower is 100 candles has a power of $100 \times 12.56 = 1,256$ lumens.

It can be shown that 1 lumen/ft² represents an illumination that is exactly the same as 1 *foot-candle*. Hence the illumination at some point in a room may be expressed as 10 foot-candles or as 10 lumens/ft². Figure 19–3 shows why these two units of illumination are equivalent.

What Is a Photometer?

We use an instrument called a *photometer* to measure illumination. This type of instrument can be used to measure the total light power given off by a source. Many kinds of photom-

452

eters have been used in the past; those used now are nearly all photoelectric instruments similar in principle to the one shown in the photograph on this page. Light falling on sensitive photoelectric disks sets up a small electric voltage which registers on a meter. The amount of voltage depends on the intensity of illumination on the surface of the disk. The meter can be marked to read directly either in foot-candles or in lumens per square foot. Some photometers are called *foot-candle meters*. A form of photometer called an *exposure meter* is used by photographers to measure illumination and from this to determine exposure time and other camera adjustments for taking good pictures.

The illumination in full noontime sunlight on a summer day is about 10,000 foot-candles. On a very cloudy day the noontime illumination may fall to 500 foot-candles or less. In places with little natural illumination we rely on artificial light. We can see objects more easily and more distinctly when the illumination is high than when it is low. Reading and other close work in dim light causes excessive strain on our eyes. In offices, shops, and factories, dim light may result in mistakes and accidents. Table 19–1 gives numbers of foot-candles needed for best results on different kinds of work. It is of interest to note that according to this table major league baseball and sewing require the highest levels of illumination.

Many schoolrooms and homes are not adequately lighted for the type of work performed. It is neither necessary nor desirable in many cases to bring the illumination in the whole room up to the levels shown in Table 19–1, but the illumination on the material on which we work should approximate these values.

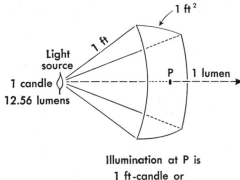

Illumination at P is
1 ft-candle or
1 lumen/ ft²

Fig. 19–3. One lumen per square foot is equivalent to 1 foot-candle.

How We Get Light

Artificial light may be obtained by burning such fuels as gas, gasoline, kerosene, paraffin, tallow, or wood. Our chief source of artificial light, however, is electricity. Several different effects of electric currents are utilized, resulting in different types of lamps.

Carbon-arc lamps. If two carbon rods connected into an electric circuit

Weston Photronic foot-candle meter for measuring the intensity of illumination. (*Weston Electrical Instrument Corporation*)

Table 19-1. Levels of Illumination*—Good Present-day Practice

Area	Foot-candles
Baseball, seats, during game	2
Before and after game	5
Infield, major league	200
Semiprofessional	20
Outfield, major league	100
Semiprofessional	20
Basketball, college and professional	50
High school	30
Churches and auditoriums	10
Sunday school rooms	20
Football field	10–50
Homes, general	5
Reading (supplementary)	20
Music (supplementary)	10–50
Sewing	20–200
Kitchen, general	20
Laundry	50
Library	30–50
Schools, auditorium, assembly only	10
Study halls	30
Class rooms	30
Drawing room	50
Gymnasium	20–50
Laboratories	30–50
Lecture rooms	30–50
Sewing room	100

* From "Levels of Illumination," Lamp Division, General Electric Company.

as shown in Fig. 19–4 are touched together for a moment, their tips become hot and some of the carbon vaporizes. If the tips are then separated about ½ in, the hot carbon vapor will continue to conduct electric current from one rod to the other. The vapor and the ends of the rods become white-hot and emit intense light. This is the principle of the arc lamp. Arc lamps are not convenient for home lighting, but are used in many places where a power-

454

ful light is needed, such as in giant searchlights, in motion picture projectors and in the klieg lights used for motion picture and television studios.

Incandescent-filament lamps. Incandescent-filament lamps are hot-filament type electric lamps. A coiled filament of resistance wire is sealed in a glass bulb from which the air has been pumped and a small amount of inert gas such as nitrogen or argon admitted before sealing. Electric current through the wire filament heats it to incandescence. Some of the electric energy supplied to the filament is converted into light. Some filament lamps are made as small as a grain of wheat; others are large enough to handle several kilowatts of electric power.

Gas-glow lamps. Many of the electric lamps used for outdoor-sign lighting are made of long glass tubes bent into the desired shapes. Electrodes are sealed into the ends of the tubes. After the air has been thoroughly pumped out, a small amount of some gas such as neon is admitted into the tube, which is then sealed off. Electric current through the ionized gas in the tube is accompanied by the emission of considerable light and relatively little heat. The color of the light depends on the kind of gas used and the color of the glass in the tube. Neon produces a brilliant orange-red light that is easy to see even through a fog. Argon produces a blue glow and helium gives almost white light. Mercury vapor gives a bluish-green light. Other colors are obtained by using glass of different colors. Gas-glow lamps in general are not very satisfactory for reading or other close work.

Sodium vapor lamps. A very efficient type of electric lamp used for street and highway lighting contains sodium which vaporizes and acts as a conductor of

This modern bank furnishes an illustration of good lighting practice. Fluorescent lamps, used in a ceiling lighting system, give an average illumination of 50 foot-candles in the circulation area, 40 foot-candles on the counters, and 60 foot-candles on the check desk. (*General Electric Company*)

electric current. This lamp produces a yellow light. While sodium lamps give off a great amount of light, they are not suited for general illumination purposes because of their color.

Fluorescent lamps. Fluorescent lamps are used for the same general purposes as hot-filament lamps. One form of fluorescent lamp has a filament sealed in one end of a glass tube and another electrode at the other end. The tube contains a little mercury which vaporizes when the filament gets hot. An electric current is then set up through the mercury vapor from one end of the tube to the other, just as in a gas-glow lamp. The mercury vapor gives off both visible and ultraviolet light. The ultraviolet light strikes the fluorescent coating on the inside surface of the glass tube and causes it to glow brilliantly. The color of the light given off by the lamp depends upon the material used for the fluorescent coating. Fluorescent lamps produce a great deal of light with little heat. This is why

their efficiency in lumens per watt of electric power used is relatively high.

►You Will Be Interested to Know

The earliest form of electric light was the carbon arc, invented by Sir Humphry Davy in 1810. This lamp was clumsy and not suited for home and indoor lighting. The incandescent-filament lamp was invented by Thomas Edison

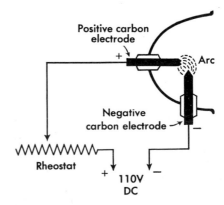

Fig. 19–4. How carbon electrodes are connected in an electric circuit to make an arc lamp.

"Grain of wheat" lamp side by side with the largest type of filament lamp made. Look carefully near the end of the pointing finger for the tiny lamp. (*General Electric Company*)

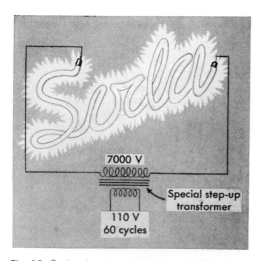

7000 V

Special step-up transformer

110 V
60 cycles

Fig. 19–5. An electric circuit for a neon glow lamp.

in 1878. The first lamp of this type had a carbonized thread for a filament and burned out after glowing a few minutes. Better filaments made of carbonized bamboo fibers increased the amount of light the lamp gave off and extended its life. All incandescent lamps prior to 1906 had carbon filaments. In that year, the first lamps with tungsten and tantalum filaments were made. Filaments of these metals could be operated at temperatures much higher than was possible with a carbon filament, and so gave off more light that was whiter and more nearly like daylight than the reddish light from a carbon filament. However, the early metallic filaments were brittle and easily broken so that the life of a lamp was short. Dr. W. D. Coolidge of the General Electric Research Laboratory developed a method of heat-treating tungsten so that it can be drawn into fine wires. This invention at once made better filaments possible. But tungsten at high temperature sublimes readily, especially in the high vacuum inside the light bulb. The metal vapor then deposited on the cooler glass bulb and blackened it. This deposit reduced the light that the bulb gave off. To reduce blackening, an inert gas such as nitrogen or argon was admitted into the bulb and sealed off after the air had been thoroughly pumped out.

The bulb of our modern electric lamp is frosted on the inside to diffuse the light and avoid glare. The filament is a coil of tungsten wire that is operated at a higher temperature than was possible in the early lamps. Present-day lamps give off more than 1 candle of light for every watt of electric power used, whereas the early lamps gave only about 0.65 candle per watt. The modern electric lamp costs less and lasts much longer than the early ones.

1. Is a lighted flashlight a luminous body or an illuminated body? Explain.
2. Would you expect the inverse-square law to hold if light has to pass through fog or smoke from its source to you? Explain.
3. If your school has a foot-candle meter available, measure the illumination in your laboratory. Is it up to the recommended values?
4. For what purposes is a "grain of wheat" lamp used?
5. If your school has a football field lighted for night games, what is the total wattage rating of the lamps used in one cluster?
6. Move a comb rapidly back and forth as you hold it close to your eye and look at a neon sign through the teeth of the comb. Why do the teeth seem to stand still when you move the comb at the right speed?
7. What were the sources of artificial light in Colonial times? What were the sources of artificial light at the time the first incandescent electric lamp was made (1878)?
8. Make a list of the ways in which the electric lamp has contributed to our present civilization.
9. Who invented the incandescent lamp?

THE NATURE OF LIGHT

What kind of energy is light? This question has perplexed philosophers and scientists for centuries. It will be no wonder if you, too, find it a little perplexing. We do not yet have an entirely satisfactory answer to the question but there are three theories concerning the nature of light with which every science student should become acquainted.

What Is Light?

It was once believed that light consisted of tiny weightless particles called *corpuscles*. It was supposed that these minute corpuscles were shot off from luminous bodies, traveled in straight lines, and bounced off or passed into objects that they struck. Corpuscles entering our eyes were supposed to enable us to see the objects from which they came. Sir Isaac Newton was a strong advocate of this corpuscular, or emission, theory. The corpuscular theory served to explain quite satisfactorily all the effects and phenomena of light that were known in Newton's time. This theory held until the early part of the nineteenth century.

Many new discoveries concerning the behavior of light were made during the nineteenth century. Some of these did not fit well with the corpuscular theory, but they could be explained much better by the wave theory that gained in favor. The seventeenth-century Dutch physicist, Christian Huygens, had worked out the basis for this theory more than a century before, but it met such opposition at the time that it was not generally accepted. *The essence of this theory is that light is a wave form of energy.* James Clerk Maxwell (1831–1879) later reduced this theory to a sound mathematical basis and showed that visible light, ultraviolet, and infrared are all forms of electromagnetic waves that originate from electrical changes. At the same time he predicted the existence of radio waves, which were later discovered in the laboratory by Heinrich Hertz, as has already been mentioned. Almost all the more common effects associated with light can still be explained more satisfactorily by means of this wave theory.

Further discoveries concerning light

have been made in the present century. Some of these discoveries seem to indicate that light occasionally acts not as continuous waves, but rather as little bundles or packets of energy called *quanta*. The amount of energy in a quantum is not always the same, but depends on the wavelength or frequency of the light. Thus this newer *quantum theory* of light has some of the features of the corpuscular theory and some of the wave theory.

The wave theory will serve to explain adequately practically all the effects of light that we shall consider in this and the chapters that follow.

The Speed of Light

Whatever the true nature of light, we know that it travels with great speed. Galileo once tried to measure its speed in much the same way that he measured the speed of sound. His apparatus consisted of a pair of lanterns, one for himself and one for his assistant. Each of the lanterns was equipped with some sort of shield so that the light could be exposed to view or concealed. Galileo went to the top of one hill and sent his assistant to another a known distance away. The plan was that Galileo should show his light first; then the assistant should expose his light as soon as he saw Galileo's lantern. Galileo planned to measure the lapse of time between the moment he uncovered his light and the moment he first saw his assistant's light on the opposite hill. This was a good experiment but it did not work, because the time was much too short for Galileo to observe with the methods he had to use. It seemed that light went from one hill to the other and back in no time! Galileo had to conclude that as far as he could observe, the travel of light was instantaneous.

458

One of the first persons to cast serious doubt on the belief that light travels instantaneously from one place to another was a Danish contemporary of Newton named Roemer. Roemer was observing the eclipses of one of the moons of Jupiter, of which there are eleven or more, and noticed that the actual duration of eclipse varied from the time astronomers had calculated. The sign (+ or −) of this discrepancy seemed to depend on whether the earth in its orbit is moving away from Jupiter or toward it. Roemer suggested that the accumulated difference in time is the number of seconds required for light to travel from one side of the earth's orbit to the other. According to Roemer's calculations, the speed of light turned out about 186,000 miles/sec.

Fizeau, a French physicist, made a laboratory measurement of the speed of light in 1849. He used the same general principle as Galileo had used, but had much more refined and accurate apparatus for measuring short intervals of time. One of the best measurements of the speed of light was made by Albert A. Michelson in California in 1926. He set up stations on two mountains about 22 miles apart. The distance was carefully measured. By an ingenious arrangement of mirrors, a flash of light was shot from one station to the other and back again. The time it took for the two-way journey was accurately measured. From a number of observations, Michelson obtained an average speed of 299,796 km/sec after he had made corrections for the effect of air. Light does not travel quite so fast through our atmosphere as it does in a vacuum and it travels even more slowly through water. In round numbers

The speed of light in free space is 300,000 km/sec or 186,000 miles/sec.

While these two values are not exact or equivalent, they are close enough to the exact values for most practical purposes. We often find it convenient to express the speed of light as

$$v = 3 \times 10^5 \text{ km/sec}$$
$$= 3 \times 10^8 \text{ m/sec}$$
$$= 3 \times 10^{10} \text{ cm/sec}$$

You will recall that this is also the speed of radio waves, and the speed of the radiation that comes to us from the sun. When you consider the 345 m or so that sound travels in a second, you will see that even the supersonic speeds that men occasionally attain in jet planes are but a snail's pace compared with the speed of light.

The Light Year

EXAMPLE: If light travels 186,000 miles/sec, how far will it travel in a year?

SOLUTION:

Number of seconds
  in a year   = 86,400 × 365
             = 31,536,000
Miles light will travel
  in a year   = 186,000 × 31,536,000
             = 5,865,696,000,000

In round numbers this is 6 million million or 6×10^{12} miles. This distance is the astronomer's measuring stick called a *light year*. The distance to the nearest star, Alpha Centauri, is 4.3 light years. The light from Arcturus requires 40 light years to reach us. The faint light from this star was focused on a photoelectric cell and used to turn on the lights at The Century of Progress exhibition in Chicago in 1933. This light must have left the star in 1893, the year of the first (Columbian) World's Fair in Chicago. We never see a star as it is at present, but always as it was when the light we receive was emitted. Some stars have been located with the Mount Wilson telescope, which has a mirror 100 in. in diameter, that are estimated to be hundreds of millions of light years from us. Even more distant celestial objects can be located with the 200-in. giant telescope on Mount Palomar.

▶Do You Know?

1. About how many stars can one see in the sky without the aid of a telescope?
2. What are the differences between sound energy and light energy? Make a list of as many as you can.
3. In what respects is the method Fizeau and Michelson used to measure the speed of light similar to the echo method of measuring the speed of sound?
4. Explain the meaning of the term *light year*.
5. What important contribution did James Clerk Maxwell make to the theory of light?
6. What is the quantum theory of light?

REFLECTION OF LIGHT

With sound waves, reflection results in echoes or in reverberation. With light waves, reflection may result in images such as those seen in a mirror or in a quiet pool of water.

If you drop a pebble into a pool of still water you will see a succession of *wavefronts* spreading out from the spot as expanding circles. A small source of light, out of range of all objects that might act as reflectors, would send out light waves in all directions, rather than in a single plane. Wavefronts from the light would then be expanding spheres rather than circles.

To explain why the waves fill up all the space between the expanding wave-

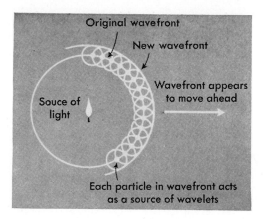

Fig. 19–6. Huygen's wavelets and the new wave-front.

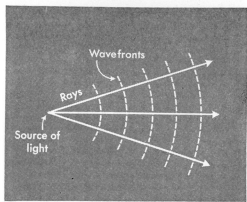

Fig. 19–7. Convex wavefronts and diverging rays.

fronts, it may be assumed that each particle on a wavefront acts as a new center of wavelets which in turn spread out. If there are no obstacles in the way, these wavelets cancel each other in all directions except forward and thus form a new wavefront ahead of the old one.

Rays of Light

People speak of *rays* of light and *beams* of light but rarely mention waves and wavefronts. What are rays and beams and how are they related to wavefronts? Any line drawn perpendicular to a wavefront is a *ray*. A ray shows the direction in which a wavefront is moving.

Figure 19–7 shows *convex* wavefronts expanding outward from a point source of light. The rays in this case are spreading apart or *diverging*. Figure 19–8 shows a portion of a wavefront that has expanded so far that this limited portion is practically a plane. The rays in this case are *parallel*. Figure 19–9 shows *concave* wavefronts that occur when light is coming to a focus. Here the rays are running together or *convergent* and will cross at the focal point. You will see that rays can be used to show the general shape of wavefronts, and rays are much

easier to diagram than wavefronts. This is why we use rays extensively rather than actual waves in the articles that follow.

The portion of successive wavefronts included between two neighboring rays is called a *beam of light*. It is often convenient to think of a beam as a *bundle of rays*. A beam may be divergent, convergent, or parallel, depending on how its rays are directed.

The Law of Reflection

The apparatus in Fig. 19–10 shows how light waves are reflected. A projector or an illuminator is used as a source of light. S is a slit through which a narrow beam enters. This beam strikes a plane mirror at M and is reflected along the path MR. The mirror is set so that the line MN is perpendicular or *normal* to its surface. When the apparatus is properly adjusted, the path of the beam of light can easily be seen. We find that the angle SMN is always equal to the angle NMR, no matter how much the mirror is turned. If the beam were made so narrow that we could consider it a single ray, still these angles would remain equal. The angle SMN formed by

460

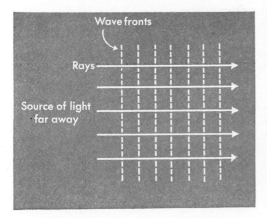

Fig. 19-8. Parallel wavefronts and parallel rays.

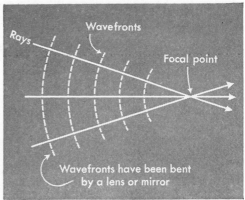

Fig. 19-9. Concave wavefronts and converging rays.

the *incident ray SM* and the normal MN is the *angle of incidence*. The angle NMR formed by the normal and the reflected ray MR is the *angle of reflection*. We may, therefore, conclude that when a ray of light is reflected from any surface

The angle of reflection is equal to the angle of incidence.

We may also observe that these angles lie in the same plane. This is the basic law of all types of reflection.

An Image in a Plane Mirror

Figure 19-11 shows how rays from a source of light are reflected and form an image in a plane mirror. S represents a very small source of light. SO and SO' represent any two nearby rays from the source to the plane mirror MM'. The ray SO is reflected along OR with the angle of reflection NOR equal to the angle of incidence SON. The ray SO' is reflected in the same way along $O'R'$. Other incident rays lying between SO and SO' are reflected so that they lie in order between OR and $O'R'$. The rays we have chosen are only two representative rays. In reality a wide beam of divergent rays is reflected from the mirror.

If some of these reflected rays shown in Fig. 19-11 enter your eyes, you think you see the light source S not in front of the mirror where it actually is, but at a point *behind the mirror*. This is the point S' from which the diverging reflected rays appear to come. The *image* you see at S' is an optical illusion, because the rays of light do not actually pass through S'. Such an image is called a *virtual* image.

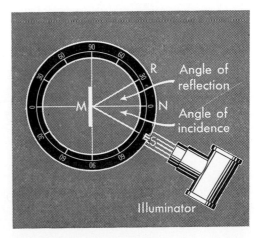

Fig. 19-10. The angle of reflection is equal to the angle of incidence.

461

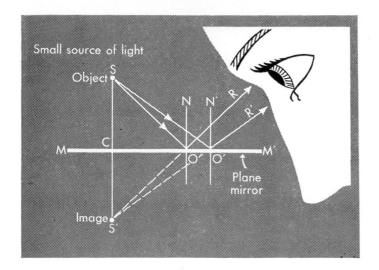

Fig. 19–11. How a virtual image of a point is formed in a plane mirror.

We can use the law of reflection and certain theorems in geometry to prove that the line SS' in Fig. 19–11 is perpendicular to the plane of the mirror MM' and that the distance $SC = CS'$. We often call the small source of light in Fig. 19–11 the *object* whose *image* is formed by the mirror. Then we may state in general that

The virtual image in a plane mirror appears as far behind the mirror as the object is in front of it.

Locating the Virtual Image

Ordinarily we use a mirror to see the image of an entire object, not just a point. Now that we know how to locate the image of a point, however, we can easily use the same principle to locate the image of the whole object. The object may be any body, luminous or illuminated; it does not need to be a lamp or other direct source of light. In Fig. 19–12, let the arrow AB represent

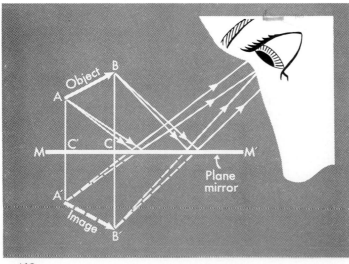

Fig. 19–12. Locating the virtual image of an object in a plane mirror.

an object. To locate the image of this object, we shall first locate the image of each end point. Then we will assume that the *images of all other points on the object lie in order between the images of the end points.* Draw AC perpendicular to the mirror MM'. Extend AC to A', making $CA' = AC$. This locates A', the image of the end point A. In the same way, locate B' the image of the end point B. Then connect A' and B' and assume that the images of all other points of the object will lie in order along $A'B'$. To locate the image of an object in this way, we have only to locate the images of *two* points on the object.

The size of the virtual image formed by a plane mirror is the same as that of the object.

"It's Done with Mirrors"

Plane mirrors are used for many purposes. They are convenient and useful equipment for washrooms, dressing tables, and vanity cases. A rear-view mirror enables us to keep an eye on the road and still see cars approaching from the rear. Several plane mirrors set at the proper angles in a tube allow us to see around a corner or over a wall. This is the principle of a simple periscope. We can see *three* images in two plane mirrors set together like the covers of a book so that they form a right angle. Besides the usual image in each of the mirrors, there is an *image of these two images* formed by light rays that undergo two reflections.

Concave Mirrors

If you could examine the mirror surface in an automobile headlight you would find it curved like the inside of a saucer. This curved mirror helps send light energy out in a narrow beam. The curved mirrors that we shall consider are called *spherical mirrors* because their reflecting surfaces are parts of spheres. Fig-

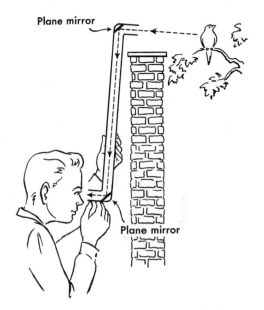

Fig. 19–13. How a simple periscope works. Better-grade periscopes use glass prisms rather than plane mirrors for reflectors.

One of nature's giant mirrors. (Lowell Whiteman, Steamboat Springs, Colo.)

463

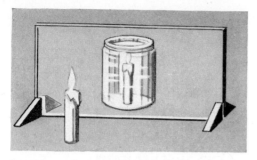

Fig. 19–14. The candle in front of the plate glass appears to burn in the jar of water back of the glass.

ure 19–15 shows some of the terms used in discussing spherical mirrors. We shall consider in this book only spherical mirrors in which the angle formed by the two radii drawn from the center of curvature to the opposite edges of the mirror is small. These are described as *small-angle* or *narrow-aperture mirrors*.

If we attach a concave spherical mirror to an optical disk as shown in Fig. 19–16, we can easily see how the mirror reflects light rays that are parallel and close to the principal axis. In the figure these parallel rays strike the mirror on the concave or dished side. After reflection all of the rays pass through the same

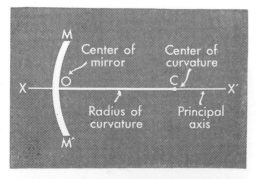

Fig. 19–15. Terms used in connection with spherical mirrors. MM' represents a spherical mirror whose center of curvature is at C. CO is the radius of curvature. XX' is the principal axis, which passes through both C and O, the center of the mirror.

point on the principal axis. This point is called the *principal focus* of the mirror. The distance from the mirror to the principal focus is called the *focal length* of the mirror.

The focal length of a spherical mirror is half its radius of curvature.

A mirror with a shorter radius of curvature will have a shorter focal length and will bring rays parallel to the principal axis to a focus closer to the mirror.

Images in a Concave Mirror

A concave mirror can produce a *real* image as shown in Fig. 19–17. This image can be caught on a screen, if the screen is placed in just the right position. We can see the image without a screen, if we place our eyes in position to receive the rays reflected from the mirror. Then the image seems to stand out in space in front of the mirror. We cannot see the real image from the back or side, however, unless it is first caught on a screen. The image is upside down (*inverted*) and is larger than the object, but if the positions of the candle and screen were interchanged, the real inverted image on the screen would be smaller than the actual candle.

If you hold a concave mirror close to your face, you may find that it can also produce a virtual image, which you can see as you look in the mirror. This image is right-side up (*erect*). You will probably not like the virtual image you see in the mirror, however, because it is enlarged and reveals unsuspected irregularities in the skin.

Dentists and physicians use concave mirrors to concentrate light into the mouth, nose, or ears of the patient. The reflectors back of the lamps in projectors and searchlights are concave mirrors. Often these mirrors are parabolic rather than spherical. Some large telescopes use concave mirrors to form real images of distant stars.

Locating Concave-mirror Images

There is an easy way to trace some rays of light reflected by a spherical mirror and to locate the position of the image formed. We have only to follow a few simple rules:

1. To locate the image of a point, find where the rays from that point cross (real image) or appear to cross (virtual image) after reflection.

2. The real or apparent intersection of any *two* rays from a point *after reflection* locates the image of that point, since all of the other rays from the point must pass through this intersection also to form a clear image.

3. The direction of each of three special rays after reflection is known and easily drawn: (*a*) a ray parallel to the principal axis passes through or appears to pass through the principal

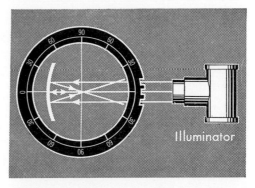

Fig. 19–16. A concave mirror brings parallel rays to a focus.

focus after reflection, (*b*) a ray through the principal focus is parallel to the principal axis after reflection, and (*c*) a ray perpendicular to the mirror is reflected back on itself.

Diagraming the Mirror Image

Figure 19–18 shows how to use these rules to locate the real image formed by the concave mirror in the setup of Fig. 19–17.

Fig. 19–17. Real and virtual images produced by a concave mirror.

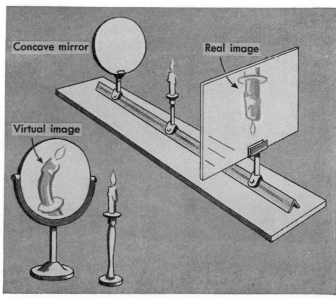

Concave mirror

Real image

Virtual image

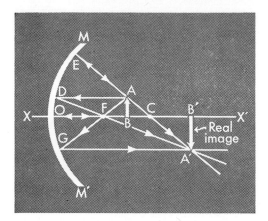

Fig. 19–18. Locating a real image formed by a concave mirror. F is the principal focus of the mirror.

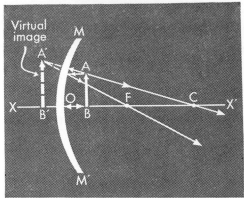

Fig. 19–19. Locating the virtual image formed by a concave mirror. F is the principal focus of the mirror.

AB represents the object (candle). This line is placed perpendicular to the principal axis and with one end on it to simplify our problem.

1. Draw the ray *AD* from *A* parallel to *XX'*. Draw this reflected ray from *D* through *F*, the principal focus.
2. Draw the ray *AE* perpendicular to the mirror, that is, along a radius. After reflection, this ray will pass right back on itself. A third ray *AFGA'* through *F* may be drawn, but this is not necessary.
3. The point *A'* where these rays reflected from *A* intersect is the image of the point *A* of the object.
4. Since *B* is on the principal axis, its image is also on the principal axis.
5. Since *AB* was taken perpendicular to the principal axis, its image must likewise be perpendicular to this axis.
6. Let us then draw *A'B'* through *A'* perpendicular to *XX'*. The image of every point of *AB* will lie in order on *A'B'*. *A'B'* is the *image* of the object *AB*.

The construction shows why the image is inverted and enlarged. It is a *real* image because rays from points on the

object actually pass through corresponding points on it after reflection. If the object were placed where the image now is, a real image would be formed where the object now is. This image would then be smaller than the object.

Figure 19–19 shows how to use the ray method to locate a virtual image formed by a concave mirror. In this case, the object must be placed between the mirror and the principal focus. The image is erect and appears to be behind the mirror. You will easily see why the image looks larger than the object.

Convex Mirrors

If we attach a convex mirror to the optical disk as shown in Fig. 19–20, we can readily see what this mirror does to rays parallel to the principal axis. Notice that the reflected rays spread out or diverge as if they came from a common point behind the mirror. This point is the principal focus. The focal length is again half the radius of curvature of the mirror.

Convex mirrors can form only virtual images that are erect and smaller than the object and that lie back of the mirror.

Some rear-view mirrors are convex. Images seen in them are reduced in size, but objects farther to either side of the mirror can be seen than with a plane mirror. A ray diagram for locating an image formed in a convex mirror is shown in Fig. 19–21.

Reflection from Rough Surfaces

We have considered so far only regular reflection from smooth surfaces, accompanied by the formation of images. When light rays reflect from rough surfaces, we see no images. Each ray is reflected with the angle of reflection equal to the angle of incidence, but the rays are scattered or *diffused* after reflection. No image is formed because the surface slopes differently at different points. Figure 19–22 shows how this occurs. We see the reflected rays as if they originated at points on the reflecting body, so we see the surface of that body rather than an image of the source of light.

Many reflecting surfaces diffuse a part of the light energy that falls on them but reflect some light directly. The part that is reflected directly produces on bright days an effect we call *glare*. Glare

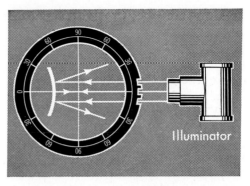

Fig. 19–20. A convex mirror causes parallel rays to diverge after reflection.

may come from the smooth surface of a lake or highway. Print on a smooth glossy paper is often difficult to read because of glare. Paper that diffuses much of the reflected light is generally used for magazines or books to avoid glare.

►Do You Know?

1. As you look at your image in a plane mirror, your *right* hand corresponds to the *left* hand of your image. Explain.
2. Sometimes in a piece of clean plate glass you can see *two* images of a light.

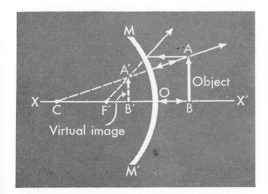

Fig. 19–21. Locating an image formed by a convex mirror.

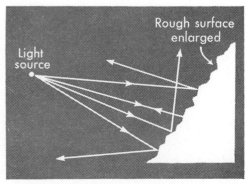

Fig. 19–22. Light reflected from a rough surface is diffused.

How are the two virtual images formed?

3. Have you ever seen a "laughing gallery" at an amusement park? How are the grotesque images seen in the mirrors formed?
4. What is the purpose of the frosted surface on the inside of a light bulb?
5. What is indirect lighting, and what special advantages does this system have?
6. What is a ray of light?
7. What is a beam of light?
8. What is a wavefront?
9. What relationship exists between an angle of reflection and an angle of incidence?

SHADOWS

You cast a shadow on a sunny day or a moonlit night only because light travels in straight lines, that is the rays are straight rather than curved. The shadow of a metal disk held in front of an electric lamp is produced as shown in Fig. 19–23. There is a region just back of the disk that receives no light at all directly from the lamp. This region would be perfectly dark if it did not receive light by reflection from nearby objects or from another source. This region is sometimes called the *umbra* of the shadow. Outside the umbra is a region that receives light from only a part of the lamp. This

The length and direction of the shadows have much to do with the way we interpret what we see. Look at this picture first in the usual way and then upside down. (C. H. Stoelting Company, Chicago)

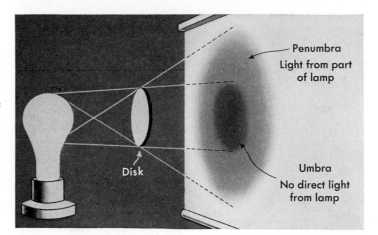

Fig. 19–23. The shadow of a disk showing umbra and penumbra regions.

Penumbra
Light from part of lamp

Disk

Umbra
No direct light from lamp

region is called the *penumbra*. The penumbra is entirely dark where it touches the umbra and gradually becomes brighter as it approaches its outer edge.

The length of shadows is used to calculate the height of mountains on the surface of the moon as well as the height of minute projections on objects which are magnified in a powerful microscope.

Have you ever seen an eclipse of the sun or the moon? These events occur so exactly on schedule that astronomers can predict eclipses almost to a second. Since the moon and the earth are both *illuminated* rather than *self-luminous* bodies, each one casts a shadow in sunlight. Eclipses on the moon occur when the moon is in the earth's shadow and eclipses of the sun occur when the earth is in the moon's shadow.

Figure 19–24 shows how an eclipse of the moon is caused. An eclipse of the moon can occur only when the moon is on the opposite side of the earth from the sun. Eclipses of this sort occur only at the phase of the moon called *full moon*.

Figure 19 25 shows how an eclipse of the sun is caused. An eclipse of the sun can occur only when the moon is on the same side of the earth as the sun. Such an eclipse occurs when the moon's phase is called *new moon*.

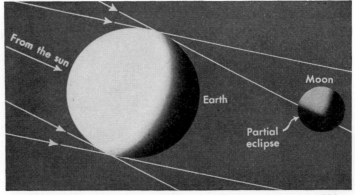

Fig. 19–24. How an eclipse of the moon occurs.

From the sun

Earth

Moon

Partial eclipse

469

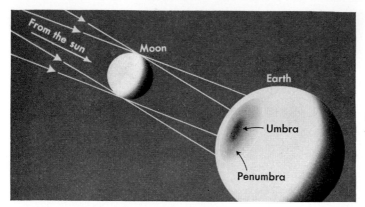

Fig. 19–25. How an eclipse of the sun occurs.

►**Do You Know?**

1. When we aim a gun or an arrow we are assuming that light travels in a certain way. What is this characteristic on which we rely?
2. Why should we use smoked or colored glass before our eyes when we want to look directly at the sun?
3. Can we see the beginning of an eclipse of the sun at the *instant* it actually occurs? Why?
4. Define the terms *umbra* and *penumbra*.
5. Explain the difference between a virtual image and a real image.
6. What is meant by the term *focal length?*

HIGHLIGHTS

Light is the form of energy that enables us to see.

Intensity of illumination is the light power per unit area at any point.

The *standard candle* or the *candle* is a unit of light power.

Illumination is directly proportional to the candlepower of the source of light and inversely proportional to the square of the distance from the source.

4π *lumens* are given off by each standard candle in a source of light.

A *photometer* is used to measure illumination.

Our chief source of light, aside from the sun, is the electric lamp.

Some types of electric lamps are: carbon-arc, metal-filament, gas-glow, sodium-vapor, and fluorescent.

In the *corpuscular* theory, light is considered as very small particles shot off by luminous bodies.

In the *wave theory*, light is treated as electromagnetic waves.

In the *quantum* theory, light is regarded as packets of energy called *quanta*.

The speed of light is about 3×10^{10} cm/sec or 186,000 miles/sec.

A *light year* is about 6 million million miles.

Regular reflection of light produces images; *diffuse reflection* scatters light and enables us to see illuminated objects.

In reflection, the angle of reflection is equal to the angle of incidence, and these angles lie in the same plane.

Plane mirrors form *virtual images* that appear to lie behind the mirrors.

Spherical *concave* mirrors may form either *real* or *virtual* images.

Spherical *convex* mirrors can form only *virtual* images that appear to lie behind the mirrors and are smaller than their objects.

The *focal length* of a spherical mirror is half its *radius of curvature.*

Umbra and *penumbra* are parts of a shadow.

Eclipses of the sun and moon are caused by shadows.

PROBLEMS: GROUP A

1. A lamp has a power of 25 candles. How many lumens does it give off?
2. If it requires about 54.5 years for light from the North Star to reach us, about how many miles away is this star?
3. The distance to the sun is about 93 million miles. How long does it take light from the sun to reach us?
4. What is the illumination in foot-candles at a point 20 ft from a 500-candlepower lamp? Assume there is no reflection from other surfaces.
5. What is the illumination expressed in lumens per square foot at a point 10 ft from a 50-candlepower lamp? Assume there is no reflection.
6. What is the illumination, expressed in foot-candles, at a point 50 ft from a 10,000-candle arc lamp, assuming there are no reflections?

7. Show by means of a ray diagram how a real image larger than the object can be formed by a concave spherical mirror. Is this image erect or inverted?
8. Show by means of a ray diagram how a real image smaller than the object can be formed by a concave spherical mirror. Is this image erect or inverted?
9. Show by means of a ray diagram how a virtual image can be formed by a concave spherical mirror. Is this image erect or inverted, larger or smaller than the object?
10. Show by means of a ray diagram how a convex spherical mirror forms an image of an object. Is this image real or virtual, erect or inverted, smaller or larger than the object? How does this image differ from the image formed in a concave spherical mirror.

GROUP B

1. The distance to the moon is about 240,000 miles. How many seconds does it take for light reflected from the moon to reach the earth?
2. In Michelson's 1926 experiment to measure the speed of light, what part of a second was required for the light to travel the 22 miles and return?

3. Two lamps, one 10 candlepower and the other 40 candlepower, are placed 6 ft apart. At what point between them should a screen be placed so that it will receive equal illumination from both lamps?

4. Show by means of a ray diagram where an object should be placed in front of a concave mirror to produce an image half as large as the object. Is this image real or virtual? Erect or inverted?

5. Show by means of a ray diagram where an object should be placed in front of a concave spherical mirror to produce an image the same size as the object. Is this image real or virtual? Erect or inverted?

6. A 50-candle lamp placed 50 cm from a screen produces the same intensity of illumination on the screen as a test lamp placed 35 cm from the same screen. What is the candlepower of the test lamp?

7. How far from a screen must a 25-candle lamp be placed to produce the same illumination on the screen as a 50-candle lamp 60 cm from the screen?

8. A test lamp placed 30 cm from a screen produces the same illumination on the screen as a 50-watt lamp which is 100 cm from the screen. If these lamps have an efficiency of 1.2 candles per watt, what is the watt rating of the test lamp?

9. How far from the page of a book must a 60-watt lamp be placed to produce an illumination on the page of 10 foot-candles? Assume the efficiency of the lamp is 1.0 candle per watt.

10. A 100-watt lamp and a 75-watt lamp are 5 ft apart. At what point between them should a screen be placed to receive equal illumination from these two lamps? Assume that the efficiency of both lamps is the same.

THINGS TO DO

1. Make a list of six or eight well-known stars that can be seen in the heavens in your location and find out the distance of each of these stars from the earth (in light years). What determines the brightness of stars we see?

2. Try setting two rectangular mirrors with their faces vertical and their edges together to form a right angle. Look into this combination mirror directly toward the line joining the two mirrors and examine closely your image seen there. Watch in the mirror while you comb your hair. What is unusual about this image? Explain.

3. Set up the experiment shown in Fig. 19–14 and see if you can make the candle appear to burn in the beaker of water.

4. Set up two plane mirrors with their faces vertical and parallel and 3 or 4 in. apart. Place a lighted candle or a lighted electric lamp between the mirrors near one end. Look at this candle and its reflection from the opposite end of the mirrors. How many images of the candle can you see? Are these images all equally bright? How are these images arranged? Explain this effect.

5. Try to obtain a shadow without a penumbra region. To do this, make a light-tight box for an electric lamp, using black paper. Then make a small hole in this shield so that light can come through this hole only. Hold an opaque object, such as a penny, 8 or 10 in. in front of the hole and set up a screen to catch the shadow of the penny. Examine the edge of this shadow to see if it is sharp and distinct. A darkened room is best for this experiment. Explain the effect.

20.

Refraction and Lenses:
Control of Light Rays

THE PROCESS OF REFRACTION

Have you ever observed that a stick or rod pushed endwise into clear water appears to bend sharply at the water line? Have you noticed that a pool or tub of clear water always looks more shallow than it actually is? These and other effects come about because light rays do not always travel in straight lines. Bending occurs when light *passes from one medium to another*. The bending of rays of light in passing from one medium to another is called *refraction*.

Figure 20–1 shows how a narrow beam of light is bent or *refracted* when it passes from air into water. You will notice that the beam seems to travel along one straight line in air and along another straight line in water. A narrow beam of light passing from air into clear glass is refracted in the same manner.

How an Entering Ray Bends

Figure 20–2 shows a single ray of light AO striking the surface of a glass plate at the point O. The line $N'ON$ is normal (perpendicular) to the surface of the plate at O. When a light ray strikes any surface, some portion of the light is always reflected. So, some of the energy in the ray AO is reflected along the ray OC. Notice that the angle of reflection, NOC, is always equal to the angle of incidence, AON. The remaining portion of the energy of the incident ray

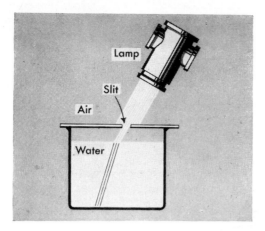

Fig. 20–1. A narrow beam of light is refracted as it passes from air into water.

passes into the glass along the refracted ray OB. The angle $N'OB$ formed by the normal and the refracted ray is called the *angle of refraction*. When a light ray passes obliquely (not perpendicularly) from air into glass, the angle of refraction is *always less than* the angle of incidence. A ray that is normal or perpendicular to the surface of the glass is not bent at all as it passes into the glass.

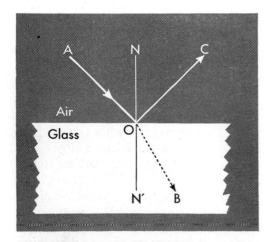

Fig. 20–2. How a ray of light is reflected and refracted at the surface of a glass plate.

A ray of light passing obliquely from air into glass, water, or other more dense medium is bent toward the normal.

How an Emerging Ray Bends

Rays of light from objects under water have to pass up through the water and out into the surrounding air to enable us to see the objects. Light rays often pass right through a plate of glass, and emerge on the opposite side. Can you guess how these rays bend as they pass out of the water or the glass into the air beyond?

Figure 20–3 shows the path of a narrow beam passing through a glass plate. If the faces of the plate are parallel, the emerging beam is parallel to the beam that strikes the plate. Figure 20–4 shows how a single ray is refracted as it leaves the glass plate and passes into air. $N'O'N''$ is normal to the surface of the plate at the point O' where the ray AO' strikes. The angle of refraction, $N'O'B$, is now larger than the angle of incidence, $AO'N''$. When a light ray passes obliquely from glass into air, the angle of refraction is *always greater than* the angle of incidence.

A ray of light passing obliquely from glass, water, or other more dense medium into air is bent away from the normal.

Why Light Rays Bend

A simple analogy will suggest why light rays bend as they pass from one medium to another. Figure 20–5 represents a column of troops marching across a cleared pavement and about to enter a patch of snow. When snow is several inches deep, a man's step in it will usually be a little shorter than on bare pavement. If this is the case, then even though the men all keep step, the speed of those in the snow will be somewhat less than the speed of those still

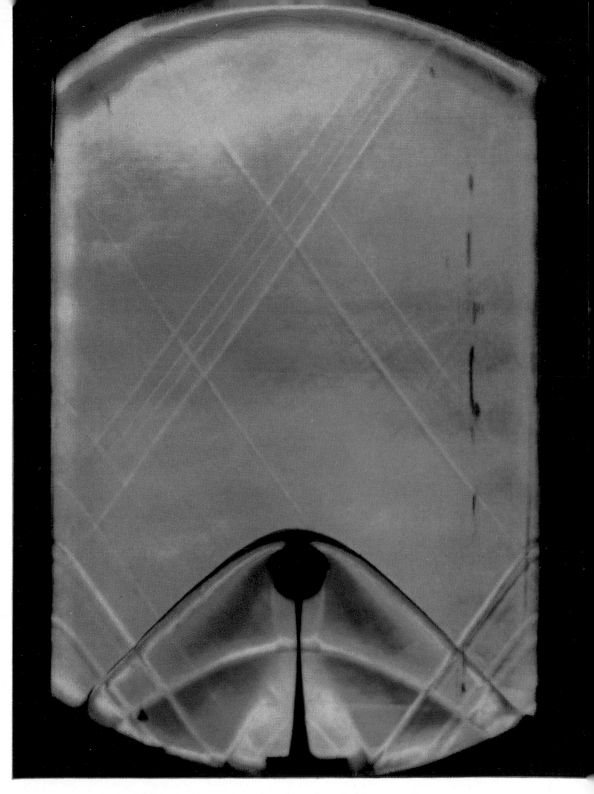

PLATE I The guided missile has become an important factor in national security. The color pattern in this picture, created through an ingenious use of light, a prism, and mirrors, helped scientists at the Aberdeen Proving Ground learn what happens in the air stream in front of a missile going 3,000 mph. (American Iron and Steel Institute)

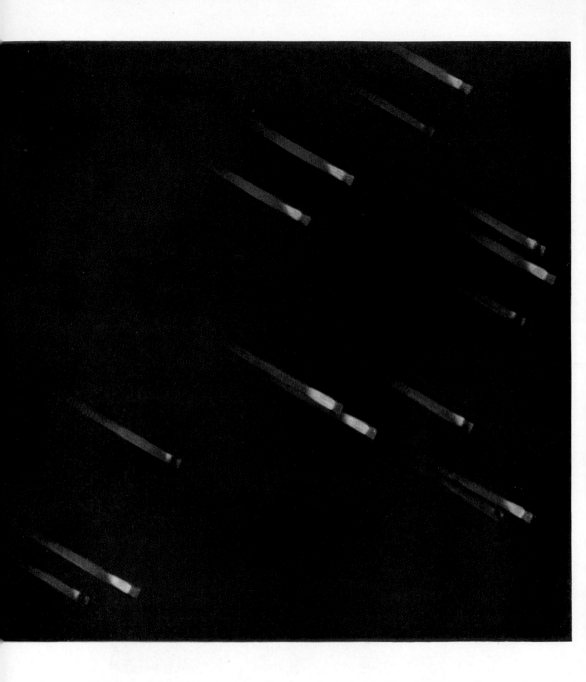

PLATE II Information concerning the elements present in the atmosphere of a star, its surface temperature, its color, and its candlepower is obtained largely from the spectrum of the star. This photograph shows the spectra of a cluster of stars in their natural colors. It was made with a special 26-in. objective prism, an astronomical telescope, and Kodachrome film, exposed for 1 hr. As many as 26 spectral lines have been detected in a stellar spectrum of this type, which is less than ¼ in. long. (Bausch & Lomb Optical Company)

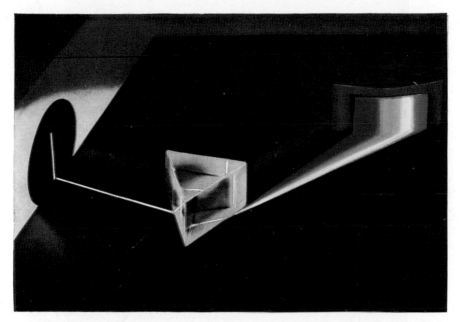

PLATE III   *Above:* A beam of white light passing through the slit at the left and into the glass prism is separated into continuous bands of color as it emerges. The array of color bands shown on the screen is called a *continuous spectrum*. The colors of shorter wavelengths such as blue and violet are bent more in passing through the prism than are the colors of longer wavelengths such as yellow and red. (From A. W. Smith, *The Elements of Physics,* McGraw-Hill Book Company, Inc., New York, 1948) *Below:* The relationship between color and wavelength. (From R. L. Weber, M. W. White, K. V. Manning, *College Physics,* McGraw-Hill Book Company, Inc., New York, 1952)

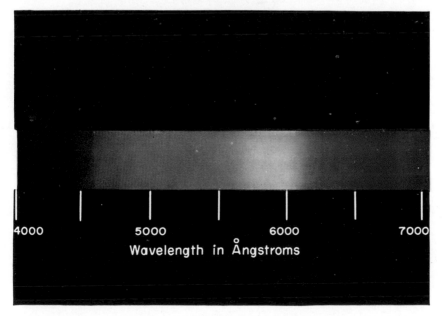

4000   5000   6000   7000
Wavelength in Ångstroms

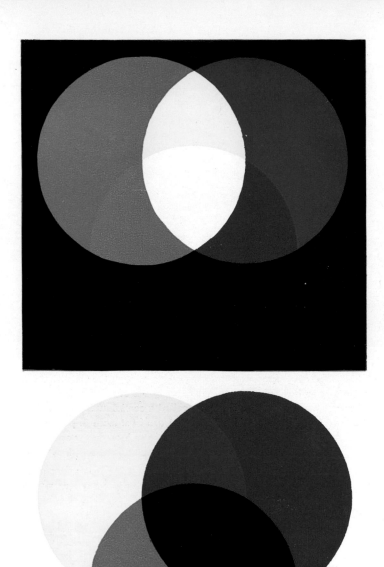

PLATE IV The top picture demonstrates the *additive method* of color mixing. Note the color produced when one primary color of light overlaps another. If all three primaries of the right proportion are superposed, white light is produced. The lower picture demonstrates the *subtractive method* of color mixing. The overlapping color disks show colors produced when primary colors of pigments, or paints, are mixed. If all three primaries are mixed in the right proportion, black is produced.

PLATE V The colored images on the background screen are produced by beams of white light from three different spotlights, each reflected from the surface of each of the four color-filter disks on the table. The beam from each spotlight strikes the surface of a given filter disk at a different angle. Each filter disk thus produces three images on the screen, each one of a different color. The surfaces of these special color-filter disks consist of two very thin transparent layers of deposited metal separated by about one wavelength. The colors are produced by *interference* between the light waves reflected from these two layers. (Bausch & Lomb Optical Company)

PLATE VI Ruling machine with diamond stylus engraving a metal plate with fine parallel lines called a *grating*. Gratings used in spectroscopes and spectrometers may have 30,000 or more lines per inch. The prismlike action of gratings is demonstrated here by the spectral colors produced by white light reflected from the grating. (Bausch & Lomb Optical Company)

PLATE VII   The colored mass in the tip of the capillary tube is 20 micrograms of pure plutonium hydroxide. Plutonium is one of the new chemical elements made in an atomic reactor. It has a half-life of about 50 years and is one of the few elements known to be fissionable. (Life Magazine, copyright, Time, Inc.)

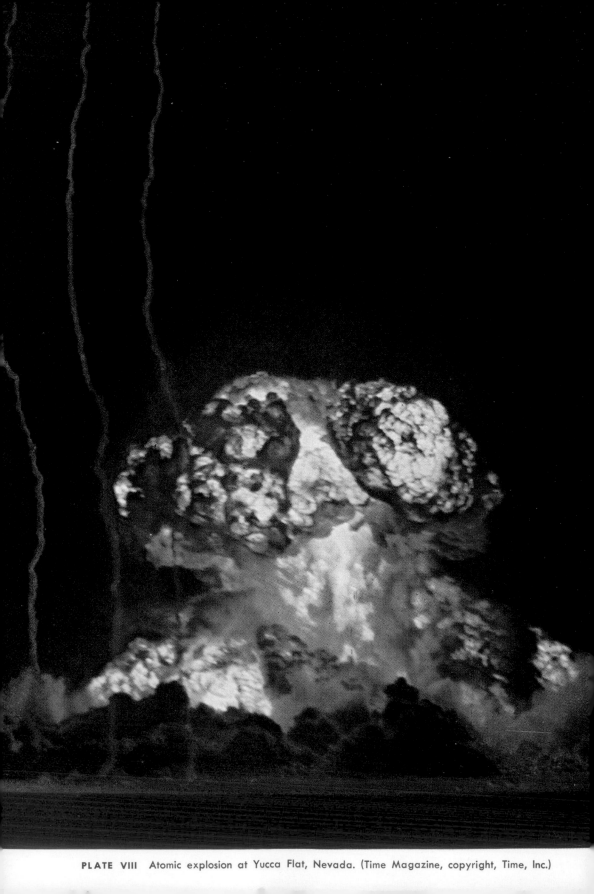

PLATE VIII Atomic explosion at Yucca Flat, Nevada. (Time Magazine, copyright, Time, Inc.)

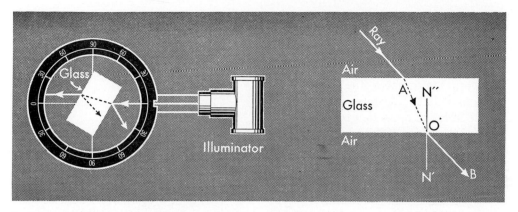

Fig. 20–3. A beam of light passing through a glass plate is refracted at both surfaces of the plate.

Fig. 20–4. How the ray of light is refracted as it emerges from the glass plate.

on hard pavement. The men in the left file reach the snow first while those in the right file are still on bare pavement. So while the right file moves ahead a distance AB on the pavement, the left file will move only a distance $A'B'$ in the snow. Unless special precautions are taken to maintain the original direction of march, the column will make a partial turn to the left and move across the snow in a new direction. This change in direction is due to the fact that the speed in snow is different from the speed on pavement. Light rays behave similarly. **Light rays bend in passing from one medium to another because the speed of light is different in the two media.**

The Index of Refraction

Does the angle through which a light ray bends depend in any way on the size of the angle of incidence? Suppose we adjust the apparatus of Fig. 20–3 so that the angle of incidence of the beam that enters the glass plate is *zero*. The incident beam is then normal to the surface of the plate. The part that is reflected reverses and goes back along the incident beam. We can easily see

that a portion of the incident beam passes into the glass plate without bending. If we increase the angle of incidence, however, both the angle of refraction and the *angle through which the beam is bent* become larger. The

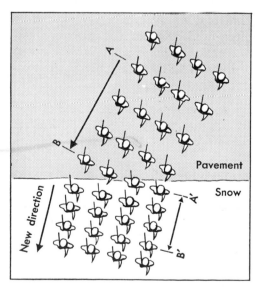

Fig. 20–5. A marching column changes direction on entering the snow, if precautions are not taken to maintain the original direction of march. The ranks are supposed to guide left in this picture.

475

amount of bending for any given material may be expressed as a number, which is known as the *index of refraction* of that material. The higher the index number, the greater the bending or refraction that takes place.

The index of refraction is actually the ratio of the speed of light in one medium to its speed in another medium.

Index of refraction =

$$\frac{\text{speed of light in first medium}}{\text{speed of light in second medium}}$$

The index of refraction of water with respect to air is approximately 4/3 or 1.33. This means that the speed of light in water is only three-fourths its speed in air.

Speed in water = 3/4 × 300,000 km/sec

= 225,000 km/sec

The index of refraction of glass with respect to air differs widely with the kind of glass. For crown glass, a kind often used in lenses, the index is about 3/2 or 1.5. This means that the speed of light in this glass is only about two-thirds that in air.

Speed in crown glass = 2/3 × 300,000 km/sec

= 200,000 km/sec

Table 20–1. Indexes of Refraction with Respect to Air

Material	Index
Water, pure, at 20°C	1.333
Quartz, fused	1.46
Glass, crown	1.51
Glass, heavy flint	1.65
Carbon disulfide at 20°C	1.625
Diamond	2.417

476

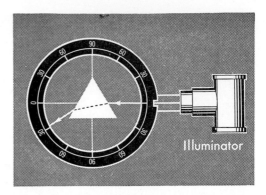

Fig. 20–6. A ray of light is bent toward the thicker part of a prism as it passes through.

The larger the index of refraction, the more sharply the medium bends a ray that strikes it at a given angle. The index of refraction is a pure number without any unit or denomination since it is the ratio of two like quantities. It is customary to consider the medium of greater speed as the *first medium* and that of slower speed as the *second medium*, so that the index of refraction given in tables is always greater than unity.

How a Glass Prism Bends a Ray

Prisms made of glass or other transparent material are often used to refract light. Figure 20–6 shows how a ray is bent in passing through a glass prism. If we try different angles for the incident ray, we shall always find that

A ray of light passing through a prism is bent toward the thicker part of the prism.

The Critical Angle

If we set the prism as shown in Fig. 20–7, the ray emerging from the prism just skims along parallel to the surface of the glass. If we set the prism so that the ray in the glass strikes the rear surface at still a greater angle, *no ray at all passes through* as shown in Fig. 20–8.

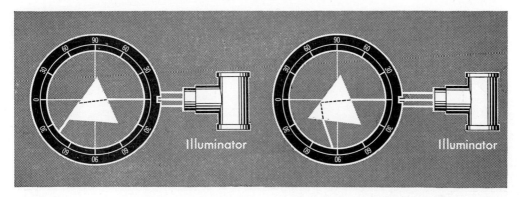

Fig. 20–7. At the critical angle, light rays just emerge and become parallel to the refracting surface.

Fig. 20–8. Total reflection occurs when the angle of incidence exceeds the critical angle.

All the energy in the ray is then reflected back into the glass, with the angle of reflection equal to the angle of incidence. We have *total reflection* at the glass surface. Total reflection occurs when light rays are passing from a slower to a faster medium and the angle of incidence exceeds a certain value known as the critical angle.

Size of the Critical Angle

For a ray of light passing from water to air, the critical angle is found to be about 48.6 deg. If a light ray in water strikes the surface at an angle greater than this, it cannot pass out at all, but is totally reflected into the water. For glass whose index of refraction is 1.5, the critical angle is about 41.8 deg.

Reversing a Ray

Total reflection may be used to reverse a light ray and send it back parallel to its original direction. Figure 20–10 shows how a right-angle glass prism can do this. Notice that the ray in the glass strikes the first rear surface at an angle greater than the critical angle for glass in air. The ray is totally reflected and passes to the second rear surface, where it is again totally re-

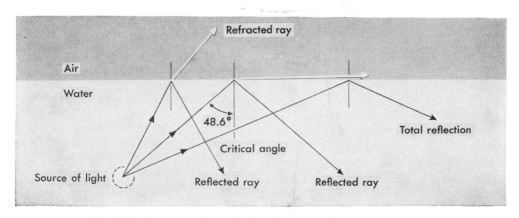

Fig. 20–9. Refraction, the critical angle, and total reflection in water.

477

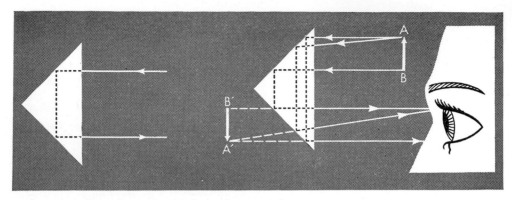

Fig. 20–10. Two total reflections reverse a ray in a right-angle prism.

flected. Both reflecting surfaces must be well polished. The original ray and the return ray are both perpendicular to the front surface of the prism.

Figure 20–10 also shows how a right-angle prism can produce an image. Notice that the image is virtual, is inverted, and lies behind the prism. Right-angle totally reflecting prisms are used in binoculars to reflect the light beam back and forth several times through the tube to achieve as much magnification as can be obtained with a longer tube.

A right-angle glass prism and total reflection may be used to turn a beam of light through 90 deg as shown in Fig. 20–11. Total reflection occurs at the rear surface of the prism because the angle of incidence there (45 deg) exceeds the critical angle for glass (usually less than 42 deg). Two right-angle prisms arranged as shown in this figure may be mounted in a suitable tube to form a periscope. When carefully constructed, such a periscope can produce brighter and clearer images than one made of plane mirrors can produce. The scene before the top prism is reflected in the horizontal light rays which travel downward and reappear as horizontal rays from the lower prism.

478

The periscope (see p. 463) is often called the eye of a submarine. While the periscope indicates what is going on above the water, a submarine may move unseen below the surface. Periscope tubes on submarines are usually made of bronze or some other material which resists the action of salt water. The submarine periscope tube may be 40 to 50 ft in length and 6 in. in diameter. The top of the tube which sticks out of the water is tapered to about 2 in. in diameter to help reduce the trail which locates a submarine traveling below the surface. Periscopes are mounted in submarines so that the operator inside the submarine can turn the tube in any direction and thus scan the entire horizon. Periscopes are most useful on clear days. However, modern knowledge of infrared rays has made it possible to use periscopes successfully on foggy days and at night.

Refraction Deceives the Eye

We often see an underwater object in a position different from where it actually is. Figure 20–12 shows how we can see a fish ahead of its actual position.

The speed of light in air is slightly

less than its speed in a vacuum; the denser the air, the slower light travels through it. For this reason, a beam of light from the sun passing obliquely through our atmosphere travels slightly faster in the upper layers than in those close to the earth and consequently is bent a little toward the earth. This enables us to see the sun when it is actually below the horizon.

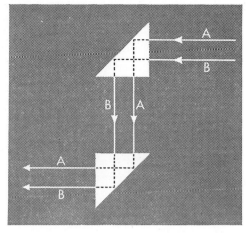

Fig. 20–11. Total reflection in prisms is used to turn a beam of light through 90 deg.

►Do you Know?

1. Is the speed of light in diamond greater or less than its speed in air? Explain.
2. Is the speed of light in water greater or less than its speed in glass?
3. Is the critical angle for diamond (in air) greater or less than that for glass? Explain.
4. Why is there no critical angle for a ray of light *entering* water from air?
5. What causes the wavy appearance in a beam of light that passes through the air just above a hot stove?
6. Why do objects seen through an ordinary window glass often appear distorted?

LENSES FOR LIGHT

Nearly all optical systems, including the eye, depend on lenses for their operation. Lenses serve useful purposes only because they can bend or refract light rays.

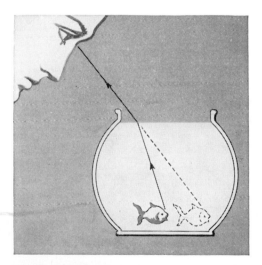

Fig. 20–12. Refraction causes us to see an underwater object at other than its true position.

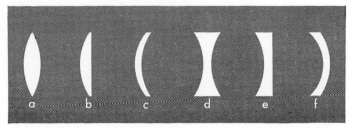

Fig. 20–13. Some types of spherical lenses in common use: (a) double convex; (b) plano-convex; (c) convex meniscus; (d) double concave; (e) plano-concave; (f) concave meniscus.

479

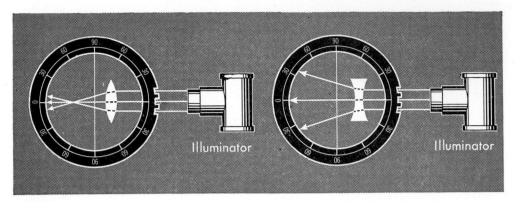

Fig. 20-14. A *converging* lens causes parallel rays to come to a focus.

Fig. 20-15. A *diverging* lens causes parallel rays to spread as if they were coming from a point.

Have you ever tried to start a fire with a "burning glass" held in bright sunlight? Such a glass is an example of a lens. Lenses focus light rays and form images in somewhat the same way that curved mirrors do. The lenses in which we shall be interested are spherical, that is, their surfaces are portions of spheres.

In Fig. 20-13, lenses *a*, *b*, and *c* are thicker in the middle than at the edge. These lenses cause parallel rays of light to converge and come to a focus, after passing through the lens, as shown for a double convex lens in Fig. 20-14. Such lenses are called *converging* lenses.

Lenses *d*, *e*, and *f* in Fig. 20-13 are thicker at the edge than at the middle. These lenses cause parallel rays to diverge or spread after passing through the lens as shown for a double concave lens in Fig. 20-15. Such lenses are called *diverging* lenses.

Light rays in passing through a lens are bent toward the thicker part of the lens.

Focal Length of a Lens

Figure 20-16 shows rays of light parallel to the *principal axis*, passing through the converging lens *LL'*. These rays, after passing through the lens, cross at the *principal focus F*.

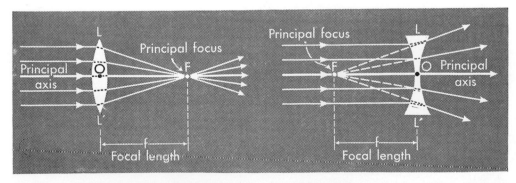

Fig. 20-16. Parallel rays through a converging lens.

Fig. 20-17. Parallel rays through a diverging lens.

The distance from the center of a lens to the principal focus is the focal length of the lens. In our discussion of lenses, we shall deal only with very thin lenses, so thin in fact that it will make no real difference whether we measure the focal length from the *center* of the lens or from its *nearer face*. This will simplify matters for us since the action of thick lenses is more difficult to explain.

In the diverging lens of Fig. 20–17, the principal focus is at F, the point back of the lens from which the emerging rays seem to come. The distance OF is the focal length of this lens.

It is not true that the focal length of a lens is half of the radius of curvature of one of its surfaces, as was the case with a spherical mirror. The focal length depends upon the index of refraction of the material of the lens, as well as on the radius of curvature of each surface. If the lens is made of glass whose index of refraction is 1.50, and the radii of the two surfaces are equal, then the focal length turns out to be just equal to one of the radii. *In this case,* the principal focus of a double convex lens *lies at the center of curvature* of one of the lens surfaces. If the index of refraction of the glass is other than 1.50, the principal focus is not at the center of curvature.

Real Images

Figures 20–18 and 20–19 show real images formed by a converging lens. We have to place the screen in just the right position with respect to the object and the lens to catch the image and have it sharply focused. You will notice that the image is real, inverted, and lies on the opposite side of the lens from the object. You can see this image without using a screen if your eye receives the rays that pass through the lens. This image, too, seems to stand out in space just as does the real image formed by a concave mirror. The image and the object distance of Fig. 20–18 are interchanged in the arrangement of Fig. 20–19. When the image is farther from the lens than the object is, the image is larger than the object; when the image is closer to the lens than the object is, the image is smaller than the object.

Virtual Images

Have you ever looked at a page of fine print through a "reading glass"? A reading glass is a simple magnifying glass or converging lens used to make the print on the page appear larger, as shown in Fig. 20–20. The lens produces a *virtual* enlarged image of the printed

Fig. 20–18. A real image formed by a converging lens can be caught on a screen.

Fig. 20–19. The image and object distances in Fig. 20–18 may be interchanged.

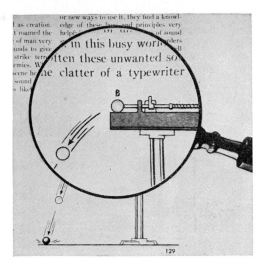

Fig. 20–20. A reading glass is a converging lens that forms a virtual image.

characters. You will observe that this virtual image is on the same side of the lens as the object. If you try a reading glass, you will find that it will enlarge the print only when the glass is within a certain distance from the page; if the glass is farther from the page, you get no virtual image.

To produce a virtual image, the object must be at a distance less than the focal length from a converging lens.

Thus a converging lens can produce either a real or a virtual image, depending on the position of the object with respect to the principal focus of the lens. As image-forming devices, converging lenses are similar to concave mirrors.

►You Will Be Interested to Know

The first lens appeared centuries ago; no one knows the exact time or place. Its discovery was probably accidental. The Roman naturalist and author, Pliny the Elder, writing in the first century of the Christian era, mentions the lens action of glass spheres filled with water. There is some evidence that this action may have been known as much as 500 years before Pliny's time. The first actual use of lenses seems to have been for eyeglasses, which were invented in the thirteenth century. By the year 1600, lens grinding had become an established art.

Galileo ground his own lenses and with them built one of the first telescopes. He improved his lenses and built other telescopes until he finally had one that made objects seen through it seem thirty-two times as large as normal. When Galileo focused his telescope on the heavenly bodies, both he and his associates were astonished at the things it revealed. He discovered that the planet Venus passes through phases just as our moon does. He saw *four* moons (satellites) circling around the planet Jupiter. The new telescope showed mountains and craters on the surface of our moon. Dark spots were visible on the surface of our sun. From the motion of these *sunspots* Galileo deduced that the sun must be rotating on its own axis. Through this remarkable telescope, Galileo saw the Milky Way no longer as a haze in the sky, but as myriads of faint stars.

These astronomical discoveries of Galileo had a profound effect on the scientific thinking of his era. Claudius Ptolemy, a Greek astronomer who lived in Egypt during the second century of the Christian era, was the founder of the Ptolemaic theory of the universe which had held sway for 14 centuries. According to this theory, the earth was the center of the universe. The fixed stars were studded in a vast dome which surrounded the earth and rotated once a day. The moon, sun, and planets were supposed to move around the earth in independent orbits that lie between the earth and this dome. Nikolaus Copernicus, an early sixteenth-century Polish astronomer, abandoned the Ptolemaic theory and evolved a new one in which the sun is regarded as the center of our planetary system and the earth is merely one of the planets that revolve around the sun. The discoveries of Galileo and others with this new telescope did much to establish the sun-centered theory of Copernicus and overthrow the earth-centered theory of Ptolemy.

Images in Converging Lenses

In the previous chapter we learned how to use the ray method to locate an image formed by a mirror. We need to make only a few changes in the rules to use the same method to locate an image formed by a lens.

1. To locate the image of a point, find where rays from that point cross (real image) or appear to cross (virtual image) after passing through the lens.
2. The real or apparent intersection of any *two* rays from a point *after passing through the lens* locates the image of that point, since all of the other rays from the point must also pass through the same intersection to form a clear image.
3. The direction of each of three special

rays after passing through the lens is known and easily drawn without special construction:

a. A ray parallel to the principal axis passes through or appears to pass through the principal focus after passing through the lens.
b. A ray that passes through one principal focus of a *converging* lens on its way to the lens emerges parallel to the principal axis. A ray starting toward the principal focus on the opposite side of a *diverging* lens emerges parallel to the principal axis.
c. A ray that passes through the *center of the lens* emerges parallel to its original direction. In a very thin lens, we may consider that this ray passes through without appreciable sidewise displacement.

Diagraming the Lens Image

Figure 20–21 illustrates how to use these rules to locate a real image formed by a double convex lens.

LL' represents a thin double convex lens, with *O* the center of the lens. *XX'* is the principal axis. *F* is the principal focus for rays passing from left to right and *F'* the principal focus for rays passing from right to left. In a double convex lens, the focal length *OF* is equal to the focal length *OF'*. *AB* represents

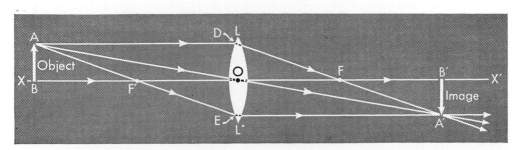

Fig. 20–21. Locating a real image formed by a converging (double convex) lens.

the object. This is placed perpendicular to the principal axis and with the end B on the axis, to simplify our problem.

1. Draw the ray AD parallel to the principal axis striking the lens at D. This ray will be refracted toward the thick part of the lens at D and again when it leaves the lens. However, if the lens is very thin, we will make no serious error in showing *all of the refraction at one surface of the lens*. So we draw the emerging ray from D through the principal focus, F.
2. Draw the ray AO through the center of the lens and continue it beyond the lens.
3. If you wish, draw a third ray from A through the principal focus F', striking the lens at E. After passing through the lens, this ray will emerge parallel to the principal axis. This ray is not necessary but can be used as an alternate for either of the other two rays from A.
4. Extend the rays that pass through the lens until they intersect at A'. A' locates the position of the image of A.
5. Then draw $A'B'$ through A' and perpendicular to the axis XX'. $A'B'$ is the image of the object AB.

It is easy to see from the construction why the image is real and inverted.

Figure 20–22 shows how to locate the image of an object AB whose distance from the lens is less than the focal length.

1. Draw the ray AD parallel to the principal axis. Continue the ray through the principal focus F after it passes through the lens.
2. Draw the ray AOE through the center of the lens without any bending.

These two rays from A are *diverging* after they pass through the lens. They appear to come from a common point A' back of the object. A' locates the image of A, and $A'B'$ is the image of the object AB. It is easy to see from the construction why this image is virtual and erect. The image appears larger than the object because it is farther away from the lens than the object is.

Images in Diverging Lenses

Figure 20–23 shows how to locate the image of an object AB formed by a diverging lens.

1. Draw ray AD from A parallel to the principal axis XX'. After passing through the lens this ray will proceed along DG as if it came directly from the principal focus F, back of the lens.
2. Draw the ray AOE from A through the center of the lens and beyond without bending.

These two rays are diverging after they pass through the lens. They appear to come from the common point A' back of the lens, which locates the image of A. Then $A'B'$ is the image of the object

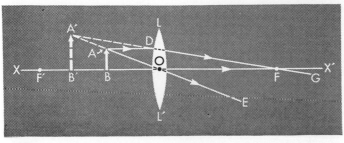

Fig. 20–22. Locating a virtual image formed by a converging (double convex) lens.

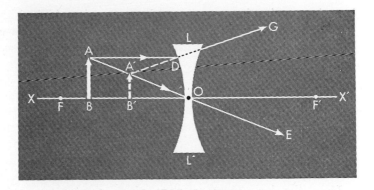

Fig. 20–23. Locating a virtual image formed by a diverging (double concave) lens.

AB. You can see from the construction that only one ray from A actually passes through A'; all the others appear to pass through this point. For this reason, the image at A' is a virtual image. The image formed by this type of lens is always closer to the lens than the object, and is always smaller than the object. This is the only kind of image that a diverging lens can form.

Where Is the Image?

We have seen that the kind of image formed by a thin spherical lens and its position depend on the type of lens and on its focal length, as well as on the position of the object. We can now collect what we have found out about images in a table that should be convenient for reference. *Concave mirrors*

Table 20–2.   Images Formed by Spherical Lenses

Kind of lens	Position of object	Position of image	Description of image
Convex (converging)	Between the lens and the principal focus	Farther from the lens than the object and on the same side	Virtual, erect, and enlarged
Convex	At the principal focus	At infinity	No image formed
Convex	More than the focal length and less than twice the focal length from the lens	More than twice the focal length from the lens and on the opposite side from the object	Real, inverted, and enlarged
Convex	Twice the focal length from the lens	Twice the focal length and on the opposite side of the lens from the object	Real, inverted, same size as the object
Convex	More than twice the focal length from the lens	More than the focal length and less than twice the focal length from the lens on the opposite side from the object	Real, inverted, and reduced
Concave (diverging)	Any position	Closer to the lens than the object and on the same side	Virtual, erect, and reduced

form images in the same general way that *convex lenses* do, and *convex mirrors* in the same way as *concave lenses*.

A Quick Test for Lenses

Often you can tell a diverging from a converging lens simply by noticing whether it is thicker at the middle or at the edge. The following simple optical test will also show whether a lens is diverging or converging:

1. Hold the lens above a page of a book so that you can see the virtual image of the print formed by the lens.
2. Move the lens parallel to the page.
3. (*a*) In a *diverging lens*, the image of the print appears to move in the *same direction* as that in which you move the lens; (*b*) in a *converging lens*, the image appears to move in the *opposite* direction from the lens; and (*c*) in plane glass, the image does not appear to move at all.

If possible, try this test on your own or on a friend's eyeglasses.

Rays That Wander

In locating images formed by lenses, we have assumed that all rays from a point that emerge from a lens pass (or appear to pass) through the same focal point. This is an ideal situation. Unfortunately not *all* the rays from a point on an object come to a focus at precisely the same place after emerging from a spherical lens. The rays that pass through the outer edge of the lens are bent a little more and come to a focus slightly nearer to the lens than do those which pass through the center of the lens. Figure 20–24 shows how rays parallel to the principal axis "wander away" from the principal focus. This effect is called *spherical aberration*. Images formed by large spherical lenses may be somewhat blurred and indistinct because of spherical aberration.

One way to reduce spherical aberration is to place a stop or diaphragm close to the front side of the lens. The diaphragm cuts out the rays that would pass through the edge of the lens and permits only those close to the center to pass through. The disadvantage of this method is that it cuts down the amount of light that gets through the lens and so reduces the brightness of the image. The diaphragm on a camera lens serves this purpose and at the same time increases the depth of focus, bringing objects at different distances into focus simultaneously. Lenses can be ground to correct for spherical aberration, but

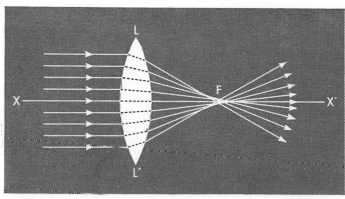

Fig. 20–24. Rays near the edge of a spherical convex lens come to a focus slightly nearer to the lens. This effect is called *spherical aberration*.

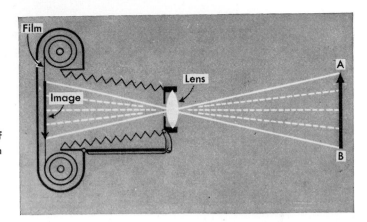

Fig. 20–25. A real image of an object is focused on the film by the lens in a camera.

their surfaces then are no longer spherical. Sometimes a combination of several spherical lenses is used to reduce spherical aberration. Spherical aberration occurs also in images formed by spherical mirrors. Diaphragms and surfaces with special (parabolic) curvatures are used to reduce spherical aberration in mirrors.

►Do You Know?

1. If you wear eyeglasses, are the lenses diverging or converging?
2. Is the lens used in a flashlight diverging or converging?
3. Are lenses ever made of clear plastic material? Do you know any uses for such lenses?
4. Why do goldfish look larger than they actually are when viewed through the side of a bowl?
5. Lenses are sometimes placed in front of the screen of a television tube to enlarge the picture. What type of lens is suitable for this purpose?

LENSES AT WORK

Have you ever taken a picture with a camera? Did you realize that what you caught and preserved on the photographic film was actually a *real image* of the scene on which you aimed the camera? Figure 20–26 shows the essential parts of a simple camera. You will notice that the camera has a converging lens. The *objects* for this lens are the things at which you point the camera. The focal length of the lens is short, so that the objects are all much farther than the principal focus from the lens. For this reason, the lens produces a *real* image of an object. This image is inverted, reduced in size, and a little more than one focal length behind the lens. To get a good picture, the image must be focused sharply on the photographic film. Some cameras are provided with a bellows to allow the photographer to adjust the distance from the lens to the film for best focus. In some types of cameras an auxiliary *finder* is used to determine when the camera is in focus. When the photographer is ready to take the picture, he snaps the shutter open and shut again quickly so that the image falls on the photographic film for only a fraction of a second. Light produces a chemical change when it falls on the film. The brighter parts of the image affect the film more than the darker parts do. When the *exposed* film is *developed*, a *negative* is obtained from which positive prints of the picture can be made.

Different types of cameras. *Top*, box camera; *middle*, compact miniature folding camera; *bottom*, reflex camera.

How to Use Your Camera

There are three general types of cameras used by amateur photographers; the box camera, the compact folding or miniature camera, and the reflex camera. Other kinds of cameras are usually modifications or combinations of these types.

Each type of camera has certain desirable features and also certain limitations. The manufacturer is interested in helping you take good pictures and usually supplies a booklet of instructions with each camera. This instruction booklet is an important aid in learning how to use your camera most effectively. It will help you learn the possibilities and limitations of your camera. You should get a copy of this booklet and read it carefully.

When a picture is taken, a certain amount of light is permitted to pass through the lens to strike the sensitized film. This film requires a definite amount of light per unit area for a good picture, that is, the film has a fixed sensitivity to light. For this reason, the lens must be opened wider to admit more light on a dull day and closed partly to reduce the amount of light on a bright day.

A *diaphragm* is used to open and stop down (close) the lens. The hole in the diaphragm for admitting light is called the *aperture*. Reducing the aperture of your camera reduces the amount of light passing through the lens but also reduces the spherical aberration. Reduced spherical aberration makes the image *sharper* and also gives it *depth*. The *iris diaphragm* used quite generally today has an ingenious arrangement of moving parts for changing the size of the aperture. Modern lens barrels are calibrated and the aperture adjustments are marked for your guidance.

f/stop System

The f/stop numbers marked around the edge of the camera lens have been obtained by dividing the focal length of the lens by the diameter of the iris diaphragm, at any given setting. The f numbers, such as $f/2.8$, $f/4$, $f/5.6$, $f/8$, and others, indicate successive *decreases* of one-half in the intensity of the light falling on the film. You should be careful to determine the proper f/stop to use for each picture you take.

Shutter Speeds

All cameras have certain shutter speeds and these are just as important to know as the f/stop markings. Shutter speed markings also are often found around the lens housing and are usually designated as 1/25, 1/50, 1/100, which indicate fractions of a second that the lens is open to admit light to the film. The amount of light from a given source that strikes the film depends on *both the shutter speed and the stop opening used.* Inexpensive cameras rarely have shutter speeds faster than 1/50 sec while the more expensive models usually offer a wider choice up to 1/500 sec.

Selecting the Film

Selecting the proper film to use is just as important as selecting the camera. First find the correct film size for your camera. This is usually marked on the camera or given in the instruction booklet that comes with the camera. If you do not know the correct film size, take your camera to a reputable photo-supply store and have the attendant tell you the proper film number to buy and how many exposures you can make on a roll. To take pictures in color, ask for indoor or outdoor color film, depending on the type of color picture you wish to take.

Camera with a flash attachment. (*Eastman Kodak Company*)

Setting the Exposure

The film is coated with a special chemical emulsion that is directly affected by light in such a way as to record the image from the lens. This image is often called a *latent* or hidden image, since it is apparent only after the film has been acted upon by the developer. Since the sensitivity of the film to light is constant,

A test exposure strip showing underexposure, normal exposure, and overexposure.

the amount of light for each exposure must be the same or the picture will be either underexposed or overexposed. Examples of such exposures are shown in the photograph on p. 489. It is, therefore, very important to have the exposure correct for the film and to know the proper shutter speed and f/stop to use.

The manufacturer of the film, like the manufacturer of the camera, is interested in your getting good pictures. A booklet or instruction sheet is supplied with each film. The information on this instruction sheet includes a range of exposure values to be used under various conditions of lighting and picture taking. These exposure values were obtained from many tests with the film. The exposure settings for every picture you take should follow that recommended on this instruction sheet if you expect to get good pictures. An exposure meter may not be needed if these values are followed closely. If you own an exposure meter or have one available, you can determine more exactly the proper exposure to use.

Developing the Negative

After you have snapped the picture, the exposed film is ready to be processed. You may do this yourself or have it done commercially, as many amateurs do. If you prefer to develop your own negatives and then to make your own prints from them, you will find the necessary chemi-

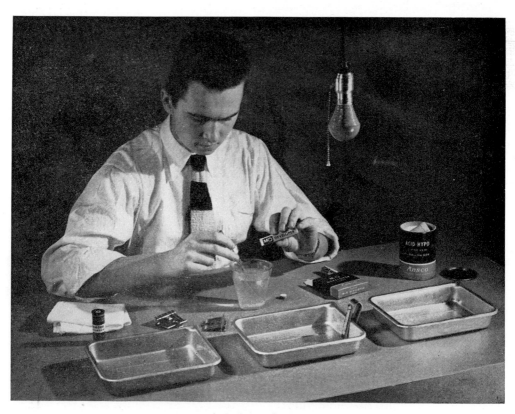

A darkroom layout.

cals and instructions available at camera shops and other places where photographic supplies are available.

►Do You Know?

1. What materials are used in flash bulbs?
2. How is a flash bulb flashed?
3. How can "close-up" pictures be taken with a camera?
4. Why is a sunshade often used on a camera when outdoor pictures are being taken?
5. Does your camera have a "fast" or a "slow" lens?
6. Why should you wipe your camera lens with soft cleansing tissue before taking outdoor pictures in sunlight?

The Eye as a Camera

Each one of our eyes contains a very remarkable optical system, resembling that of the simple camera. Figure 20–26 shows the arrangement of the principal optical parts of the eye.

The eyelid corresponds to the shutter of a camera. The *pupil* corresponds to the diaphragm of a camera. The pupil is the black circular hole that can be seen at the center of the *iris*. The iris is the circular membrane that surrounds the pupil and contains the pigments that give the eye its distinctive color. The *cornea* and the *crystalline lens* correspond to the lens system of a camera. The cornea is the slightly bulging part easily seen at the front of the eyeball. It is filled with a clear liquid called the *aqueous humor*. Because of its shape, the cornea acts as a converging lens. The crystalline lens is located within the eyeball just back of the pupil. It is made of clear transparent tissue and is shaped somewhat like a double convex lens. It also acts as a converging lens. The cornea and the crystalline lens acting together

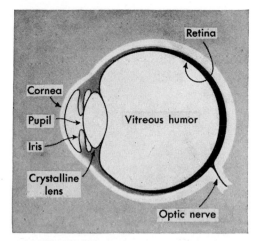

Fig. 20–26. The eye as an optical instrument.

produce a *real, inverted,* and *reduced* image of an object at which we look. We interpret what we see as right side up, even though the image is inverted.

The *retina* on the back wall of the eyeball corresponds to the photographic film. The image of an object must fall exactly on this retina if we are to see it clearly, just as the image in a camera must be focused on the film to obtain a clear picture. The retina contains sensitive ends of the optic nerve. When light falls on these nerve ends, they are stimulated and send impulses over the optic nerve to the brain. The strength of one of these impulses depends on the intensity of the light striking the nerve ends in the retina. The brain translates these impulses into the object we see. In this way, a "picture" is developed automatically and practically instantaneously by the retina. When we shift our eyes from one object to another, the old image vanishes quickly and the retina is ready at once to receive the new image.

How the Eye Is Focused

In a camera, the distance between the lens and the film has to be a little longer for an object close to the camera than for

491

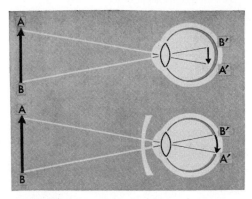

Fig. 20–27. Image and correcting lens in near-sightedness.

one farther away. A photographer focuses the camera on the object by adjusting this distance so that a clear image is formed on the film. The eye accomplishes the same result in a much more ingenious way. The distance from the crystalline lens to the retina in a given eye always remains the same, while the *crystalline lens automatically changes its focal length* to bring the images into sharp focus on the retina. To see objects close to the eye, the lens becomes thicker at the middle, thus shortening its focal length. To see objects farther away, the lens becomes flatter, thus increasing its focal length. Small muscles within the eyeball make these changes in focal length automatically, without any attention from us. This process is called *accommodation*. The eyes can change focus very rapidly, especially in young people. We can look at the print on a page 12 in. from our eyes at one moment and shift our glance instantly to objects on the distant horizon, with no appreciable wait for our eyes to refocus themselves.

Seeing and Light Intensity

Light rays from an object must enter the eye in order that we may see at all. In dim light, these rays carry but little

492

energy and consequently the image formed on the retina is faint. The *pupil* then expands automatically to admit more rays and more energy, thus making the image brighter. Certain changes also occur in the retina to make it more sensitive to the faint image. In strong light the image may become so bright that it overstimulates the nerve ends in the retina, which results in seeing poorly. The pupil then automatically closes so that it admits less light energy into the eye. This protects the retina and forms a better image. Looking directly at a very strong light may cause serious damage to the retina.

Lenses as Aids to Vision

Normal vision. For normal vision we should be able to see clearly objects that are nearby as well as those at a distance. We should be able to see small objects most distinctly and in greatest detail when they are properly illuminated and held about 10 in. or 25 cm from the eye. People whose eyes do not focus the images of nearby or distant objects clearly on the retinas are said to have *defective vision*, although defective vision may be due to other causes as well. Three common types of defective vision that can usually be improved or "corrected" by lenses used as eyeglasses are the following:

Nearsightedness. The lens system of a nearsighted eye forms an image *in front of* the retina for objects more than a given distance away. This condition is shown in Fig. 20–27. The lens of the eye is too thick; even with the best adjustment the eye can make, the focal length of the lens is still too short to push the image back to the retina. A nearsighted person must hold things close to the eye to see them clearly and distinctly. He will habitually hold a book closer than

10 in. from his eye when he reads. A *diverging* lens of the proper focal length placed in front of the eye will push the image back to the retina and help this person see objects clearly at a normal distance.

Farsightedness. The lens system of a farsighted eye forms an image of nearby objects *behind* the retina as shown in Fig. 20–28. A person with this defect of vision may habitually hold a book or newspaper at arm's length in order to see the print more clearly. A *converging* lens of proper focal length placed in front of the eye will bring the image up to the retina and help this person see more clearly at a normal distance.

Astigmatism. In astigmatism the lens system of the eye is not spherical, but is curved more in one plane than in another. As a result, a person with astigmatic eyes may be able to focus clearly on one set of lines in Fig. 20–29, while the other lines are poorly focused. Some lines in the figure will seem brighter than the others. In this type of defect, eyeglasses with lenses ground with different curvatures in different planes may help the individual to focus on all lines simultaneously. These lenses are commonly called *cylindrical lenses.*

Sometimes persons cannot focus their eyes either for nearby or for distant objects. This condition is common in older people. To see well under all circumstances, these persons need either separate pairs of glasses, one for near work and one for distant vision, or *bifocal* lenses. Bifocal lenses are really two lenses in the same mounting. The lower lens is designed for seeing nearby objects and the upper lens for distance. *Trifocal* lenses for near, intermediate, and distant vision are coming into use. *Contact lenses* are sometimes used to correct faulty vision in cases where it is impossible or

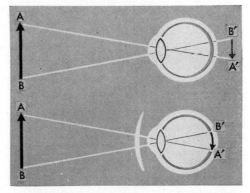

Fig. 20–28. Image and correcting lens in farsightedness.

impractical to use the conventional type of eyeglasses. These contact lenses fit close against the eyeball and extend under the eyelid.

►You Will Be Interested to Know

Bifocal glasses were invented by Benjamin Franklin for his own use. The following account is quoted from *Benjamin Franklin* by Carl Van Doren:[1]

By August, 1784, he [Benjamin Franklin] could not without them "distinguish a letter

[1] From *Benjamin Franklin* by Carl Van Doren, The Viking Press, 1938.

Fig. 20–29. These lines will not appear equally bright to a person with astigmatism.

even of large print." Before that year, he had used "two pairs of spectacles which I shifted occasionally as in travelling. I sometimes read and often wanted to regard the prospects. Finding the change troublesome and not always sufficiently ready, I had the glasses cut, and half of each kind associated in the same circle."

Depth in Vision

Have you ever looked at pictures through a stereoscope? With this device, each eye looks at a separate view but we see a single picture. This picture seems to stand out in space; that is, it seems to have a third dimension, depth, which is lacking in an ordinary photograph. The two views may at first look like duplicates, but they are in reality the same scene taken from slightly different positions. Each eye, looking at its own view of the scene, sees the same objects, but from slightly different angles, just as they would see the objects in the actual scene. Double cameras are available for taking a picture on two separate films from slightly different angles simultaneously. Often color film is used with this type of camera. When the two colored transparent prints of the scene are viewed through a stereoscopic viewer, objects seem to stand out almost as in the original scene. It is possible to project two such pictures so that the images overlap on the screen and give an impression of depth. Motion pictures that seem to have a third dimension (depth) are made by utilizing this principle.

How Pictures Are Projected

The principle of a projector for throwing enlarged images of pictures on slides on a screen is shown in Fig. 20–30.

A strong source of light, such as a high-power electric lamp, is placed in a housing just in front of a curved mirror. *Condenser lenses* in front of the lamp collect and converge the rays of light from it. The picture to be projected is on the *slide*. Parts of the slide are transparent, so that light rays pass through; other parts are dark or opaque so that little or no light gets through them. The light and dark pattern forms the picture which becomes the *object* for the *objective lens*. The objective-lens system may be moved back and forth with respect to the slide in order to focus the image exactly on the distant screen. The objective-lens system inverts the image, and at the same time reverses it sidewise. Thus to have it *appear right side up* on the screen, the slide must be placed in its holder *upside down* and reversed side

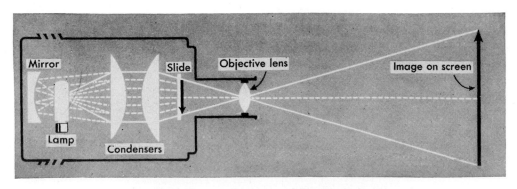

Fig. 20–30. Parts and principle of the slide projector.

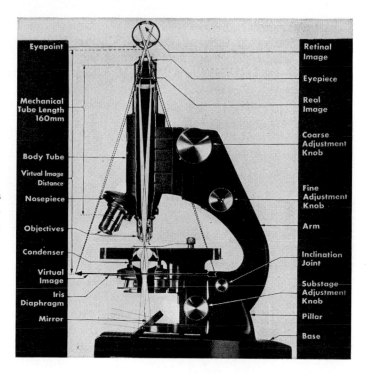

Eyepoint	Retinal Image
Mechanical Tube Length 160mm	Eyepiece
	Real Image
Body Tube	Coarse Adjustment Knob
Virtual Image Distance	
Nosepiece	Fine Adjustment Knob
Objectives	Arm
Condenser	Inclination Joint
Virtual Image	
Iris Diaphragm	Substage Adjustment Knob
Mirror	Pillar
	Base

The parts and the images formed by a compound microscope. (*American Optical Company, Instrument Division, Buffalo, New York*)

to side. With a given lens, the image on the screen is smaller when the screen is close to the projector and larger when the screen is farther back from it. With a suitable arrangement of the illumination system in the projector, the image of an opaque object, such as the page of a book, may be thrown on a screen in a similar way.

Pictures That Seem to Move

A projector for motion pictures operates on the same basic principle as the slide projector just described. Motion-picture film consists of a series of separate "still" pictures, or *frames*. The object is in a slightly different position in each succeeding frame. The film is placed in a projector so that each frame in turn becomes the object for the objective lens. The images are thrown on the screen in rapid succession, 24 or more frames per second. A suitable automatic shutter in the projector blanks off the light on the screen while the film is being shifted from one frame to the next. What we see when we look at the screen is really a sequence of rapidly changing still pictures, which gives an effect of moving objects.

The Microscope

The human eye is in some ways an excellent optical instrument, but there are many objects so small we cannot ever hope to see them with our unaided eyes. A *microscope* is often used to aid us in seeing objects so small they are invisible to the unaided eye. The simple reading glass of Fig. 20–20 is a crude form of microscope. Any converging lens of short focal length may be used as a simple microscope.

The magnification produced by a microscope is the ratio of the length of any line on the image to the length of the corresponding line of the object.

495

Thus a microscope which gives a magnification of 25 times, 25 ×, or 25 *diameters* would make a line 0.01 cm long on a given object appear to be 0.25 cm long on the image. The amount of magnification without distortion that can be produced with a simple magnifying glass is quite limited, perhaps not more than about 25 times. When higher magnification is needed, a *compound microscope* as shown in the photograph on p. 495 is generally used.

The *objective* is a small converging lens of *very short* focal length. The object that we wish to examine is placed almost at the principal focus of this objective lens. The lens produces a *real* enlarged image within the tube of the microscope. We must illuminate the object quite strongly if we wish to obtain a bright image, because the light that comes from the small object becomes much dimmer when it is spread over the larger area of the enlarged image.

The *eyepiece* contains one or more lenses arranged to act as a converging lens with short focal length. When properly focused, the real image produced by the objective falls just inside the principal focus of the eyepiece lens. This lens system produces an enlarged *virtual* image of this real image. It is this enlarged virtual image that we see when we look into the eyepiece of a properly focused microscope. Magnifications up to 2,000 × or more can be obtained with the best compound microscopes.

The Telescope

Have you ever looked at the moon through a telescope? Mountains and craters on the surface of the moon can easily be seen through even a low-power instrument. Telescopes are designed to help us see things that are far away.

One type of astronomical telescope (called a *refractor*) has an objective lens and an eyepiece for examining the real image, just as the compound microscope has. The objective, however, is a converging lens with a *very long* focal length, rather than a very short one. It

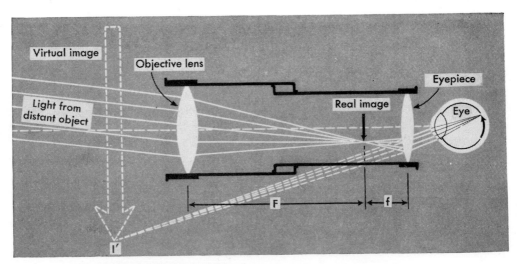

Fig. 20–31. How a refracting telescope forms an image of a distant object.

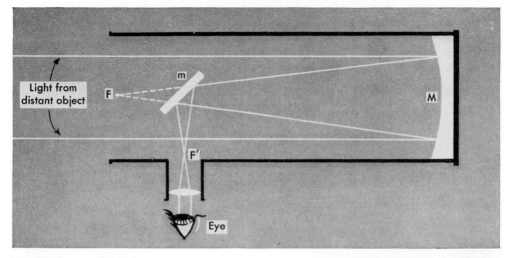

Fig. 20–32. A real image of a distant object is formed at F' by the concave mirror M of a reflecting telescope.

forms a real image of a distant object practically at its principal focus. This image lies inside the tube of the telescope, just inside the principal focus of a converging eyepiece as shown in Fig. 20–31. The lens of the eyepiece then forms a virtual image of this real image. The astronomer usually focuses the eyepiece so that the virtual image is far away and easy to look at. An astronomer looking into his telescope always sees objects upside down and reversed sidewise as compared with the way they would appear if he could see them directly with his unaided eye. The tube of the telescope does not need to be large enough to contain the virtual image. Why?

The refracting telescope of Fig. 20–31 requires an objective lens that has a large *diameter* (distance across from edge to edge) in order to gather enough light from very faint stars to make them visible or to photograph them. One of the largest refracting telescope now in use is located at Yerkes Observatory at Lake Geneva, Wisconsin. Its 40-in. lens

will gather about 26,000 times as much light from a distant star as the unaided eye, so a great many faint stars that we can never see with the eye alone are revealed by this telescope.

Reflecting Telescope

The 40-in. lens in the Yerkes telescope is about the largest that it is practical to make. Very large lenses are very heavy. For this reason they are difficult or impossible to mount as rigidly and as accurately as is required. Furthermore, small temperature differences may cause unequal expansion in a large lens and lead to troublesome distortions in the images formed.

The most powerful telescopes for investigating the farthest regions of the heavens use *concave mirrors* rather than lenses to focus the light from distant objects. These telescopes are called *reflectors*. Figure 20–32 shows how a reflector telescope forms a real image of a distant object.

A small plane mirror placed on the principal axis of the mirror at a 45-deg

497

The Hale 200-inch reflecting telescope in the Mt. Palomar Observatory pointing toward the zenith. (*Mt. Wilson and Palomar Observatories*)

angle reflects the converging rays so that the real image of a distant object is formed in a side tube in which the eyepiece is mounted. An eyepiece that produces an enlarged virtual image of this real image is used to examine it. Some reflecting telescopes have other arrangements for viewing or photographing the real image.

The largest reflecting telescope in regular use prior to 1949 was the 100-in. reflector at the Mount Wilson Observatory (California). The concave mirror of this instrument is 100 in. across and is capable of collecting about 160,000 times as much light energy from a faint star as the human eye alone can collect.

It is estimated that stars several hundred million light years from the earth are made visible by this telescope. A distance of 100 million light years is about 600,000,000,000,000,000,000 miles, a distance so great that we cannot imagine it. A 200-in. reflector set up in the observatory on Mount Palomar (California) was tried out late in 1949 and is now in regular use. The mirror of this giant telescope is capable of collecting about 640,000 times as much light as the human eye from a faint star. It is estimated that it can reveal stars that are about twice as far from the earth as the farthest one that can be seen or photographed with the 100-in. reflector.

►You Will Be Interested to Know

The giant 200-in. telescope enables astronomers to explore farther than ever before into the outer fringes of the universe. This instrument is a monument to the imagination of an American astronomer, George Ellery Hale, who persuaded the General Education Board to make a gift of 6 million dollars for its construction. The 200-in. mirror was cast of special Pyrex glass on December 2, 1934, at the Corning Glass Works, Corning, New York. It was held in an oven at constant temperature for 2 months and then was cooled slowly (annealed) for 8 months more to be sure it was free from internal strains. A trial mirror of the same design had been cast earlier, but this one proved to have imperfections that made it unsatisfactory. The huge mirror was crated and moved to California on specially constructed freight cars. The mirror was carefully ground to a focal length of about 55 ft and accurately polished in the shops of the California Institute of Technology. When completed the huge mirror was moved by truck to the observatory on Mount Palomar, a solid granite block 30 miles long and 10 miles wide about 85 miles southeast of Pasadena. The circular steel dome which houses the telescope is 135 ft high and 135 ft in diameter. The complete assembly of the mirror and its mounting weighs more than 500 tons. This heavy mechanism is mounted precisely on an axis parallel to that of the earth. Its motion is controlled by clockwork to hold it on a distant star as the earth rotates on its axis.

The telescope is controlled jointly by the California Institute of Technology and the Carnegie Institution of Washington, D.C.

►Do You Know?

1. Can an object move too rapidly for our eyes to see it? Explain.
2. What is the shape of the pupil in a cat's eye? How far does it open in the dark?
3. In bifocal glasses does the lower (reading) lens or the upper (distance) lens usually have the shorter focal length?
4. How are 3-D movies made?
5. What types of lenses are used in a slide projector and how are they used?
6. Why is it necessary to insert a slide upside down in a slide projector?
7. What adjustments are made to focus the picture which is on a slide in a projector on a screen?
8. How are "slow-motion" movies produced?
9. About how much magnification can be obtained with an *electron microscope?*
10. The images seen in a terrestrial telescope (used for looking at faraway objects on the earth) are "right side up" rather than inverted. How is the image made right side up?
11. Why can the images of very faint stars formed by a telescope be photographed more easily than seen with the eye?
12. In what way is knowledge gained by use of a microscope important to you and to society as a whole?
13. In what way is knowledge gained from the use of powerful telescopes important to you and to society?
14. How many times is the image of a distant object inverted in passing through the optical systems of the refracting telescope (Fig. 20–32) and the astronomer's eye?

HIGHLIGHTS

Light rays are *refracted* when they pass obliquely from one medium into another.

A ray of light passing obliquely from air into glass, water, or another denser medium is *bent toward the normal*.

A ray of light passing obliquely from glass, water, or another denser medium into air is *bent away from the normal*.

Light rays bend in passing from one medium to another because the speed of light is different in the two media.

The index of refraction is $\dfrac{\text{the speed of light in a given medium}}{\text{the speed of light in a second medium}}$.

A ray of light passing through a glass prism is bent *toward the thicker part of the prism*.

Total reflection occurs when rays of light are passing from a slower to a faster medium and the angle of incidence is greater than a certain *critical angle*.

Light rays passing through a lens are bent *toward the thicker part of the lens*.

The distance from the center of a lens to its principal focus is its *focal length*.

Converging lenses form either real or virtual images; *diverging lenses* form only virtual images.

Spherical aberration is one defect of wide lenses that causes blurred images.

Two factors in camera exposure control are the *f/stop* used and the *shutter-speed* setting.

The *f*/stop number indicates the relative amount of light striking the film.

The *human eye* has parts that correspond to those of a camera.

The *crystalline lens* of the eye *changes its focal length* automatically to focus the image of an object on the retina.

Nearsightedness may often be corrected by means of eyeglasses with diverging lenses; *farsightedness* requires converging lenses, and *astigmatism* cylindrical lenses.

Bifocal lenses are aids for persons who need glasses for distant as well as close vision.

Microscopes enable us to see objects too small for the unaided eye.

Telescopes enable us to see or photograph objects too faint and far away for the unaided eye.

Refractors are astronomical telescopes that use *large lenses* to collect light from distant heavenly bodies.

Reflectors are astronomical telescopes that use concave mirrors for collecting light rays from distant bodies.

The largest refracting telescope uses a 40-in. objective lens; the largest reflecting telescope uses a 200-in. mirror.

500

PROBLEMS: GROUP A

1. The index of refraction of diamond is 2.417. What is the speed of light in diamond?

2. The speed of light in a sample of glass is 2.14×10^{10} cm/sec. What is the index of refraction of this glass with respect to air?

3. The focal length of a converging lens is 25 cm. A pin is placed on the principal axis 50 cm from the lens. Draw a ray diagram to show how and where this image is formed. What kind of image is it?

4. The focal length of a converging lens is 20 cm. An object is placed on the principal axis 100 cm from the lens. Where is the image of this object? What kind of image is it? Draw a ray diagram to show how and where this image is formed.

5. The focal length of a diverging lens is 50 cm. An object is set on the principal axis 25 cm from the lens. Draw a ray diagram to show how and where this image is formed. What kind of image is it?

6. Show by means of a ray diagram where an object should be placed so that a converging lens will produce a virtual image of it. Is the image erect or inverted, larger or smaller than the object?

7. Show by means of a ray diagram where an object should be placed so that a converging lens will form a real image of it, smaller than the object. Is this image erect or inverted?

8. Show by means of a ray diagram where an object should be placed so that a diverging lens will form a virtual image of it. Is the image erect or inverted, larger or smaller than the object?

GROUP B

1. The refractive index of flint glass is 1.65. What is the speed of light in this glass?

2. The focal length of a converging lens is 20 cm. A pencil is set on the principal axis 10 cm from the lens. Draw a ray diagram to show how and where the image is formed. What kind of image is it? Is the image erect or inverted?

3. The focal length of a diverging lens is 20 cm. An object is placed on the principal axis 30 cm from the lens. Draw a ray diagram to show how and where the image is formed. What kind of image is it? Is the image erect or inverted?

4. The formula for a lens is $\dfrac{1}{D_o} + \dfrac{1}{D_i} = \dfrac{1}{F}$, where D_o is the distance of the object from the lens, D_i the distance of the image from the lens, and F the focal length of the lens. If the focal length of a converging lens is 10 cm and the object is 15 cm from the lens, how far is the image from the lens?

5. If the focal length of a converging lens is 15 cm, how far from the lens must the object be placed to produce an image 25 cm from the lens? See the lens formula in Problem 4.

6. If the focal length of a converging lens is 25 cm, where must an object be placed to produce a real image at the same distance from the lens as the object? See the lens formula in Problem 4.

7. A telescope with objective-lens focal length of 1,600 cm and magnifying power of 400 has what focal length of the eyepiece lens?

$$\text{Magnification} = \frac{F \text{ of objective}}{f \text{ of eyepiece}}$$

THINGS TO DO

1. To demonstrate how we can see the sun after it has actually sunk below the horizon, obtain a deep coffee cup. Place a penny on the bottom of the cup and stand so that as you sight over the edge of the cup you can see only a little of the rim of the penny lying on the bottom. Then have someone pour clear water gently into the cup without disturbing your position or that of the penny. Account for what seems to happen to the penny.

2. Have you found your blind spot? Hold a pencil vertically about 6 in. in front of your eyes. Focus your eyes on a distant building or landscape while you move the pencil back and forth across your line of vision. At some position the pencil should practically disappear. Explain.

3. Close the fingers of your left hand so that there is a small tube or channel between the fingers and palm through which you can see. Hold this closed hand to your left eye and look through the tube at some well-lighted object. Then hold the palm of your right hand with the fingers extended in front of your right eye and look with both eyes at the well-lighted object. You should then get the optical illusion of seeing through a nonexistent hole in your right hand.

4. Obtain a large converging lens, such as might be used as a reading glass or the condenser lens in a slide projector. On a bright day aim this lens at the sun and hold a sheet of paper at the principal focus of the lens. After a short time you may be able to set the paper afire. Explain why this is possible.

5. Select a spot to set up your camera well away from automobile and city lights. Load with fast film, open the stop on the camera lens as far as possible, and set for a time exposure. Mount the camera securely, and after nightfall on a clear moonless night aim it directly at Polaris, the North Star. Open the shutter and expose the film for at least two hours. Account for the arcs that appear on the photograph you obtain.

21.

Color and Spectra:
Color around Us

DISPERSION OF LIGHT

Have you ever observed a rainbow and wondered what causes its beautiful band of colors? Sir Isaac Newton showed many years ago that these colors come from sunlight. He produced rainbow colors by passing a narrow beam of sunlight from his window through a glass prism. We can easily repeat Newton's experiment and obtain our own band of rainbow colors as shown in Plate III. A converging lens placed ahead of the prism so that it can focus parallel rays on the screen helps to sharpen the color bands, but you can obtain reasonably good colors without the lens.

Separating White Light

Light from which the full band of colors can be obtained is called *white* light. Sunlight or daylight is practically white light, although we shall find later that some of its colors are much reduced or missing entirely. The beam of white light that enters the prism in Plate III is split and emerges as many rays of different colors. If you will look closely, you will see that the violet rays are bent more than the red as they pass through the prism. This means that the index of refraction for the violet rays is greater than that for the red rays. In other words, the speed of violet light in glass is less than that of red light. The separa-

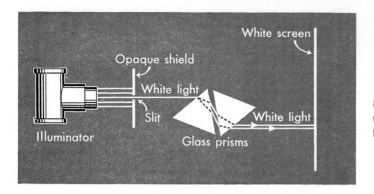

Fig. 21–1. Colored rays from the first prism may be recombined by a second prism.

tion of white light into colors by the glass prism is called *dispersion*.

To prove even more conclusively that these colored rays come from white light, Newton passed the colored rays emerging from the first prism through a second, similar prism. The beam from the second prism appeared white again when it fell on the screen, as shown in Fig. 21–1. A converging lens following the second prism to focus the emerging rays on the screen improves this experiment, but is not necessary for observing the effect. The colored rays that are separated from white light by the first prism are recombined by the second prism (and the lens).

How Red Differs from Blue

We have already seen that light may act as waves, similar in many respects to infrared and radio waves. Scientists have developed methods of measuring the wavelength of light waves with a high degree of accuracy. The results of such measurements show that

The wavelength of red light is longer than that of violet light.

The wavelengths of orange, yellow, green, and blue fall in this order between those of red and those of violet light, as shown in Plate III.

It is important for us to realize that

504

the difference between violet light and red is primarily one of wavelength (or frequency). We have found this same kind of difference useful in other situations. The difference in frequency of radio broadcasting stations enables us to separate stations on the dials of our radios. We might with some justification say that one radio broadcasting station has a different *color* from another. In sound, we found that we could distinguish one sound from another when the sounds have different pitch, that is, their waves have different frequencies. So *color* in light is like *pitch* in sound. With this analogy in mind, we might then say that violet is about one octave higher than red.

Now that we know how color is related to wavelength, we may state our conclusions from the experiment in Plate III in another way.

The shorter the wavelength of the incident light, the less is its speed in glass and the greater is the index of refraction of the glass.

Any refracting medium, like glass, in which the speed of light depends on its wavelength is capable of separating white light into bands of color. Water, carbon tetrachloride, and especially carbon disulfide all produce considerable dispersion of white light into several different colors.

What Is an Angstrom?

You will notice in Plate III that the wavelength of light is only a small fraction of a centimeter, about 0.000059 cm for yellow light. People who work with light waves usually prefer to use a much smaller unit than the centimeter for expressing the wavelengths of light. The *angstrom* (A), named for a Swedish scientist, is one of several different units used for this purpose. There are 100,-000,000 A in 1 cm. The wavelength of yellow light may be expressed as 5900 A. Use of angstrom units eliminates the small decimal fractions required when we express wavelengths in centimeters. Plate III shows the wavelengths in air of different colors obtained from white light.

Wavelength and Frequency

Wavelength, frequency, and speed of light are related in exactly the same way that these quantities are related in radio and in sound waves.

$$\text{Speed} = \text{frequency} \times \text{wavelength}$$

We already know that the speed of light in air is about 3×10^{10} cm/sec. The wavelength of yellow light is about 0.000059 cm. So the frequency corresponding to yellow light is approximately

$$f = \frac{3 \times 10^{10} \text{ cm/sec}}{0.000059 \text{ cm}} = 5.1 \times 10^{14} \text{ cps}$$

This frequency is about 510,000,000 Mc/sec. You can begin to realize how high this frequency is when you compare it with the 0.5 to 1.7 Mc/sec used for standard radio broadcasting and 300,000 Mc/sec, the frequency of very short radio microwaves.

The frequency of a light wave does not change as it passes from air into glass. But we have already seen that its speed in glass is less than that in air. So it must follow that its wavelength is shortened as it passes from air into glass, just as the pace of troops marching from a pavement into snow may be shortened. In discussing light waves, we usually speak of their wavelengths, rather than their frequencies. The wavelengths to which we then refer are their *wavelengths in air* or, more exactly, in a vacuum.

What Wavelengths Can We See?

Our eyes can respond only to a limited range of wavelengths, just as our ears can respond to a limited range of sound frequencies. The deepest red that we can see has a wavelength of a little more than 7000 A and the deepest violet a wavelength of about 4000 A. Thus the eye has a range of just less than 1 octave! The ear has a range of nearly 10 octaves.

Radiations with wavelengths that we can see constitute *visible light*. Radiations with wavelengths just longer than the visible red are called *infrared;* radiations with wavelengths just shorter than the visible violet are called *ultraviolet*. We learned something about infrared radiation when we studied how heat is transferred from place to place. Ultraviolet radiations are present in sunlight and the light from arc lamps. They can best be detected by photography or by the fluorescent light they produce when they fall on certain materials.

What Causes a Rainbow?

The rainbow, with its beautiful arcs of color, is associated with sunlight that breaks through the clouds immediately after the passing of a summer storm. Sometimes we who live in the middle latitudes can see a bow in the

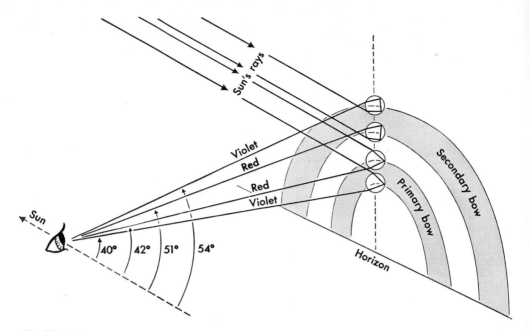

Fig. 21–2. How a rainbow is formed. Note the angle at which each different color is observed. Does a tall person see the same rainbow as a short one?

western sky in the early morning hours, but more often we observe it in the eastern sky in the late afternoon. Occasionally we can see a rainbow in the spray of a waterfall or lawn sprinkler. In every case, when we face the rainbow, the sun is at our back. We have good evidence that a rainbow is caused by the action of millions of little water droplets falling from the passing cloud or present in the spray. The bands of color in a bow are caused by dispersion of white sunlight by these droplets.

Figure 21–2 shows how individual raindrops can refract entering rays of sunlight, reflect these rays at the back surface of the drop, and refract the rays again as they emerge from the drop.

Scientists have found that we receive much more light from those drops which the sun's rays strike at an angle of about 59 deg than from any other drops. Because the index of refraction of water

506

is different for different wavelengths, we receive strong *red light* from drops that are in such positions that the angle between the sun's rays and the returning rays is about 42 deg as shown in Fig. 21–2. We receive strong *violet* light from drops in position to make this angle about 40 deg. The other colors lie between these boundaries in order of their wavelengths.

If you were above the raindrops looking down on them, you might see the rainbow as a complete circle as aviators sometimes do. When you are on the ground, the earth cuts off a portion of the circle and you can see only an arc of colors.

The drops which send you red light are never the same ones from instant to instant. Furthermore, the drops that send red light to a companion a few feet from you are not the same raindrops that send red light to you. If you walk toward a rainbow a constantly changing set of drops sends you red light and the rainbow seems to retreat before your eyes in a very tantalizing fashion. You never overtake it. The proverbial pot of gold at the end of the rainbow is indeed safe from discovery!

Sometimes a second rainbow appears with its colors reversed outside the *primary bow*. This *secondary* bow is caused by light rays that are reflected *twice* inside the drops. Other bows or portions of bows can sometimes be seen.

Lenses and Color

It was pointed out in the preceding chapter that the focal length of a lens depends on the index of refraction of the glass of which the lens is made. In fact, the focal length is greater when the index of refraction is smaller. We have now observed that the index of refraction of glass is less for the longer waves of red light than for the shorter waves of violet. These facts must mean that the focal length of a simple lens is longer for red light than for violet. We may say that a simple lens has a different focal length for each different wavelength of light! If we adjust the lens so that the image is properly focused for red light, it will then be slightly out of focus for violet and the other colors. This defect in a simple lens is called *chromatic aberration*. The effect of chromatic aberration is an indistinct image fringed with bands of color. If you have ever examined the image formed by a simple inexpensive lens, you may have noticed these color fringes.

Lenses are often made in two parts to correct for chromatic aberration. For a converging lens, one part may be a converging lens made of crown glass and the other part a diverging lens made of flint glass. After the two parts are ground so that they fit perfectly and are polished, they are cemented together with a clear cement that becomes invisible. Figure 21–3b shows a converging lens built up in this way. The converging crown-glass lens refracts and disperses light rays; the diverging flint-glass lens brings the dispersed rays together again but does not entirely correct the refraction produced by the first lens. The result is a composite lens that converges parallel rays of light without separating them into colors. The composite lens is called an *achromatic lens*. Its focal length is longer than that of the converging crown-glass lens alone.

An achromatic lens is expensive to make because the parts of it must be ground to fit perfectly together. Achromatic lenses are used in microscopes, binoculars, field glasses, and some cameras.

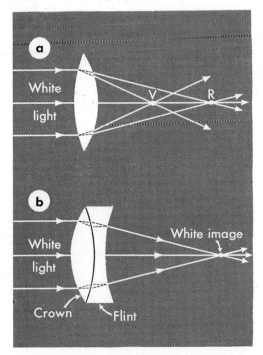

Fig. 21–3. Construction of an achromatic lens.

1. Sometimes wavelengths of light are expressed in *microns*. How long is a micron? How many angstroms are there in a micron?
2. What color is on the upper side of a primary rainbow?
3. Do we ever see a natural rainbow at noon (in the temperate zone)? Explain. Would it be possible to see a rainbow at noon if we were far enough north? Explain.
4. Explain how wavelength, frequency, and speed of light are related.
5. Define the term *index of refraction*.
6. What is meant by dispersion of light?

SPECTRA AND WAVELENGTHS

If you will examine the bands of color in Plate III carefully, you will notice that there is no gap or boundary line between the orange and the yellow. Each hue seems to merge imperceptibly into the next because white light contains *all* the wavelengths that we can see. The prism sorts them out and arranges them neatly side by side in order of wavelength, from the longest red at one end to the shortest violet at the other. Light of a definite wavelength is capable of stimulating the sensation of a particular hue. So we should expect a gradual merging of one characteristic hue into another as the light which our eyes receive changes from the longest visible wavelength toward the shortest visible wavelength.

We call this orderly arrangement of wavelengths a *spectrum*. Plate III shows a *continuous spectrum;* none of the visible wavelengths is missing. White light, such as that from a very hot solid or liquid, produces a continuous spectrum. The

508

spectrum of the light emitted by the hot filament of an electric lamp is a continuous one.

What Is a Spectroscope?

A *spectroscope* is a special instrument used to observe and study spectra. If it is properly equipped, we can use it also to *measure* the wavelengths of different kinds of light. Then it is called a *spectrometer*. A simple spectroscope is shown in Fig. 21–4. The essential parts of this instrument are a collimator, a refracting (and dispersing) prism, a telescope on a movable arm, and a suitable mounting. The telescope shown has provisions for reflecting a wavelength scale so that it can be seen on the spectrum when you look into the telescope.

The principle of the spectroscope shown in Fig. 21–4 is almost the same as that used by Newton when he first performed his experiments with the colors from sunlight. The *collimator* is a tube with a narrow slit at one end and a converging lens at the other. The slit admits a narrow beam of light from whatever source is placed in front of it, and the lens forms the emerging light into a narrow parallel beam. The prism refracts and disperses the beam that comes from the collimator. The prism is usually made of glass, although it may be made of other materials, such as quartz. The telescope provides an easy way to focus the spectrum produced by the prism so that overlappimg of adjacent wavelengths is much reduced. This arrangement results in a much more distinct spectrum than we can get from a prism alone. The telescope has to be in one particular position to catch the rays of violet light and in another position to catch those of red. This is why the arm on which the telescope is mounted is movable. If you have a simple spectroscope available in your school laboratory and place an electric lamp in front of the slit of the collimator, you should be able to adjust the telescope so that you can see a continuous spectrum in all colors.

What Is a Bright-line Spectrum?

If we soak the end of a strip of asbestos in salt water (NaCl solution) and then hold the wet strip in the blue part of a bunsen flame, we shall notice that the flame becomes a brilliant yellow. This is called a *sodium flame.* Suppose we place the flame in front of the slit of a spectroscope so that the yellow light passes into the collimator tube. If we then look into the telescope and adjust it properly we shall see only a single bright yellow line rather than a continuous spectrum of all colors. *This line is the image of the collimator slit formed by the lenses in the collimator and telescope.* It is yellow because the light with which it is formed consists of a single wavelength that is just right to stimulate the sensation of yellow. In reality the light consists of two slightly different wavelengths that are so nearly alike, however, that they generally appear as a single one. A spectrum that consists of one or more bright lines like this one is called a *bright-line spectrum.*

Monochromatic Light

Light, such as that from a sodium flame, all of which has the same wavelength, is called *monochromatic* (one color) light. Even if light consists of a number of different wavelengths, it may still be called monochromatic, provided the wavelengths are all very nearly the same. A sound which consists of a single frequency is called a *pure* sound or tone. Monochromatic light, which has only one wavelength, produces a *pure* color.

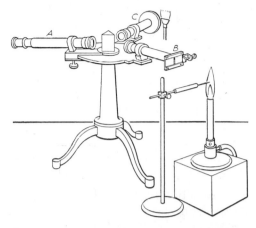

Fig. 21–4. A spectroscope. A is a telescope for viewing and examining the spectrum produced by the glass prism on the center table. B is the collimator with an adjustable slit at the end next to the bunsen flame. The material whose spectrum is being examined is placed on the rod held in the flame. C is an arm containing an illuminated scale which can be reflected from the face of the prism into the telescope, when desired. The arm C and the scale are useful only when the spectroscope is used as a spectrometer for measuring wavelengths.

Causes of Bright-line Spectra

Scientists have proved that when we put ordinary salt in the bunsen flame the characteristic yellow light *comes from sodium atoms* in a gas or vapor state. These atoms receive energy from the hot flame and thus become *excited.* When they calm down and return to their normal unexcited state, they give off this energy in the form of radiation, some of which may be visible light. A sodium atom excited in this way can radiate strong visible light only at wavelengths of 5890 and 5896 A. These wavelengths are so close together that they generally appear in the bright-line spectrum as a single line.

Suppose we add a little lithium chloride to the salt solution and again soak the tip of the asbestos strip in it.

509

When we hold the wet strip in the bunsen flame, we shall now observe a new red line in the spectrum along with the yellow one of sodium. This new line is caused by a wavelength sent out by lithium atoms that have been excited by the flame. A little thallium chloride added to the solution in which the asbestos strip is dipped will give a new green line in the spectrum. Thus each kind of atom when excited in this way acts something like a minature radio transmitting station and sends out signals on its own assigned wavelength or wavelengths.

Light from Atoms

Only a few kinds of atoms can be excited strongly enough in a bunsen flame to cause them to emit visible light. In most cases other means must be taken to excite atoms so that they radiate light waves that we can see. Sometimes substances whose spectra we want to observe or photograph are placed in a very hot electric arc to excite their atoms; sometimes an electric spark or an electric current is passed through the gas or vapor that contains the atoms. In all these cases, the atoms receive much more energy and so become much more strongly excited than in a bunsen flame. When thus strongly excited, atoms generally give off light at more than one wavelength at the same time. In most cases they radiate simultaneously not only on wavelengths in the visible region, but on too-short-to-see wavelengths in the ultraviolet and on too-long-to-see wavelengths in the infra-red. Atoms of a given kind no longer act like a single minature radio station broadcasting on a single wavelength, but rather like a group of radio stations broadcasting on several different wave-lengths.

510

Fingerprinting Atoms

Scientists have found that each of the wavelengths that cause the bright lines in the spectra of the photograph on Plate III can come from one and only one kind of atom. Thus when we receive light from the bunsen flame on the definite wavelengths of 5890 and 5896 A, we are certain that the flame contains radiating *sodium* atoms. Light on a wavelength of 6708 A indicates lithium atoms and a wavelength of 5350 A indicates thallium atoms. Thus we can identify the atoms by the wavelength or wavelengths they send out.

The situation becomes somewhat more complicated when atoms are strongly excited and radiate on several wave-lengths simultaneously. But even here scientists have found that each kind of atom radiates a pattern of wavelengths that is different from that radiated by any other kind. Even if many different kinds of atoms are present in a substance and all are radiating, still each kind sends out its own pattern of wave-lengths just as if the others were not there. To a trained eye, the photograph of a bright-line spectrum identifies the atoms that send out the light just as surely as fingerprints identify a person. This is the basis of *spectrum analysis*, a very important method used in industry to analyze samples of materials and to keep a running check on factory products. Impurities can be detected even in very small samples. Many centuries ago Archimedes discovered the famous prin-ciple that bears his name when he was faced with a problem of determining whether there was silver in Hiero's new crown. Modern scientists might like to solve a similar problem by chipping off a small sample from the crown and photographing its spectrum.

Fraunhofer Lines

If you were to look at the spectrum of sunlight in a spectroscope, you would at first notice a continuous array of colors. But if your spectroscope were good enough and you looked more closely you would see distinct *dark lines* crossing the spectrum from top to bottom. A prominent line in the yellow is usually easy to see. These lines are called *Fraunhofer lines* in honor of a German scientist, Joseph Fraunhofer, who discovered them in 1814. The lines had been observed earlier than this, however, by another scientist. Fraunhofer mapped about 600 of these dark lines in the otherwise continuous spectrum of the sun.

Forty-five years after Fraunhofer discovered these dark lines in the solar spectrum, Kirchhoff showed how they could be produced in the laboratory and advanced a theory to explain them. He found that when a strong beam of white light on its way into a spectroscope passes through hot sodium vapor the spectrum produced is continuous with a dark line across the yellow. Careful measurement showed that this line is double and at just the wavelength on which sodium atoms emit light when they are excited in the bunsen flame. According to his theory, atoms act like resonant tuning forks. When we set them "into vibration" they emit light at certain wavelengths. On the other hand, when light containing these wavelengths strikes the same atoms, it sets them into vibration by resonance. Thus the sodium atoms absorb energy from the beam of white light at one or two particular wavelengths and in turn are set into vibration. They radiate this energy again, scattering it in all directions. In this way, the *beam* of white light is

weakened at these particular wavelengths and a dark line occurs here in the spectrum we see. This (double) dark line is the *dark-line spectrum* of sodium.

Each chemical element has its own characteristic dark-line spectrum that is related to its bright-line spectrum in much the same way that a photographic negative is related to a positive print. There may, however, be lines in the bright-line spectrum of a given element that do not occur in the dark-line spectrum. Chemical elements can be identified by the wavelengths they absorb as well as by those they emit.

The sun is believed to have a very hot interior surrounded by a cooler gaseous envelope. White light originating in the interior has to pass through this envelope on its way to the earth. Atoms in this cooler envelope would absorb their characteristic wavelengths from the white light. This is believed to cause the Fraunhofer lines that we observe in the spectrum of the sun. From measurements of the wavelengths of Fraunhofer lines, scores of elements such as hydrogen, oxygen, sodium, calcium, and iron have been identified on the sun.

►You Will Be Interested to Know

Spectroscopes were used during the total eclipse of the sun in 1868 to analyze for the first time the light coming from the brilliant outer edges of the sun's envelope, or *chromosphere*. Janssen, a French astronomer, found in his photographs of the spectrum many lines for which he could not account. Sir Norman Lockyer, an English astrophysicist, noticed especially a new brilliant *yellow* line in the photographs he took. After careful measurement and study, Lockyer concluded this line was due to some new element not then known on earth. Because the element was identified with the spectrum of the *sun*, he called it helium, from *hēlios*, the Greek word for sun. Some authorities credit Janssen with the discovery of helium, while others give the credit to Lockyer.

In 1895 Sir William Ramsay found the yellow line of helium in the spectrum of a particular kind of mineral. This was the first positive indication of the presence of helium on the earth. In 1900 Ramsay isolated some quantity of this new inert gas. This is one illustration of how the spectroscope has been a useful instrument for unlocking some of the hidden secrets of the physical universe.

The Doppler Effect in Light

Do you recall the Doppler effect in sound? While a source of sound is approaching a listener (or the listener approaching the source) the apparent pitch of the sound is raised, and while the source is moving away, the apparent pitch is lowered. We should expect the same principle to apply to light and every other form of wave motion. Translated into terms of light, this principle becomes:

The color corresponding to a particular wavelength radiated by a source of light is shifted toward the violet end of the spectrum when the source is approaching us and toward the red when the source is moving away.

The lines in the spectrum of a star, for example, make excellent markers by which to measure any such shift that may occur. When an astronomer finds the spectral lines of some element such as calcium shifted toward the violet end of the spectrum, he infers that the star is moving toward us; when he finds the lines shifted toward the red end he concludes that the star is moving away. By observing the amount of shift, he may even determine approximately how fast the star and the earth are moving apart.

Astronomers have observed that the lines in the spectra of nearly all distant nebulae or giant stars are shifted toward the red. This fact has led to a theory that the nebulae are moving away from each other; that is, that the celestial universe itself is constantly expanding.

Kinds of Spectra

The bright-line and dark-line spectra that we have discussed originate in individual atoms. Molecules, or chemically connected groups of atoms, can also be excited so that they radiate and absorb light energy. Their spectra usually contain groups of many fine lines so close together that they often appear as a band of color. Such spectra are called *band spectra*. Table 21–1 shows different kinds of spectra and their origins.

►**Do You Know?**

1. Why does the light from a neon sign appear red?
2. Why do scientists usually *photograph* spectra when they want to bring out all the faint lines possible?
3. In what respects are light waves similar to radio waves?
4. Do you know a method, other than the methods mentioned in the text, that a scientist might use to analyze a sample of gold for suspected silver?

Table 21–1. Classification of Spectra

Emission	Absorption
Continuous: hot solids and liquids	Continuous: solids and liquids
Bright line: hot gases, free atoms	Dark line: gases, free atoms
Bright band: hot gases, molecules	Dark band: gases, molecules

5. Explain how the Doppler effect in light is used to determine which way a star or nebula in distant space is moving.
6. Explain the meaning of the expression *bright-line spectra*.
7. What is monochromatic light?
8. What is the difference between a spectroscope and a spectrometer? What is a collimator?

MIXING COLORS

Color has a profound influence on us and on our way of living. It makes a difference, for example, whether the traffic light is red, amber, or green. The color of our clothes may affect the way we feel as well as the impression we make on others. The combination of colors in the furnishing of a room can make it a drab or a pleasant place in which to live.

Complementary Colors

We have seen how Newton used a glass prism to separate the wavelengths of white light into a continuous spectrum of colors and how he used a second prism to recombine these wavelengths to produce white light again. Interesting things happen if the rays of one or more colors are removed before they pass into the second prism. Scientists have developed ingenious combinations of collimator, prisms, lenses, and mirrors to remove any desired group or groups of wavelengths before the rays are recombined. Suppose the *red* wavelengths are removed. It is found that when the remaining wavelengths are recombined, they produce a bluish-green spot on the screen on which they fall.

Red and bluish-green are called *complementary colors*. When combined in the right proportions they produce the same visual effect as white light.

Every color in the spectrum has a complementary color. Complementary colors produced in this way are not pure colors (monochromatic) but consist of a mixture of wavelengths. In fact, any color and its complementary color (of this type) together contain all the wavelengths of visible light. A few spectral colors with their corresponding complementary colors are shown in Table 21–2.

It has been found that our eyes do not require *all* the wavelengths of visible light to enable us to "see white light." Two single wavelengths will suffice, provided they are just the right ones. For example, a certain monochromatic red (wavelength 6540 A) and a particular monochromatic bluish-green (wavelength 4920 A) look nearly white when their mixture falls on a screen. These two pure colors are also called complementary because together they can produce the same visual effect as white light. Monochromatic yellow (wavelength 5850 A) is in the same way complementary to a monochromatic blue (wavelength 4850 A). Many other specific pairs of monochromatic colors also are complementary in this way.

New Colors by Addition

You may be a bit confused about a mixture of yellow light and blue giving white. If you have had any experience in mixing paints or water colors you have

Table 21–2

Spectral color	Complementary color
Red	Bluish-green
Orange	Greenish-blue
Yellow	Blue
Green	Magenta
Violet	Greenish-yellow

513

learned that this combination is used there to obtain *green*. The situation when we mix color *pigments* is different from the one we have been discussing. We will consider the matter of pigment mixing later in this chapter.

When two colored *lights* are combined or mixed, the color that results is a sensation due to all the wavelengths present in both lights. The wavelengths of one light are simply added to those of the other light to produce the new color. This is called the *additive method* of color mixing.

The Color Triangle

Red, green, and *bluish-violet* are often called *primary* colors, because all other hues can be obtained by mixing lights of these colors in different proportions. The complementary colors corresponding to these primaries are often called *secondary* colors. A triangle with primary and secondary colors arranged along its sides is a convenient device for representing colored light relations. The three primary colors are placed at the corners of the triangle. Red and bluish-violet combined in about equal proportions produce magenta, so magenta is placed as a secondary color at the mid-point of the side between red and bluish-violet. For similar reasons, blue-green is placed between bluish-violet and green, and yellow between green and red. Each secondary is thus placed on the side opposite its corresponding primary. Any secondary, such as yellow, combined with its primary, blue, can produce near-white. All three primaries or all three secondaries mixed in proper proportions can also produce near-white.

Familiarity with the colors of the spectrum and their complementary colors will help you to enjoy and appreciate color phenomena in everyday life.

514

How Colored Lights May Be Mixed

Sometimes colored slides are used with a special three-channel projector to throw disks of colored light on a white screen. The projector is arranged so that the three colored disks may be overlapped and their colors mixed on the screen. Plate IV shows overlapping disks of the primary colors just discussed. You will notice that the region where red and green overlap is yellow in color, just as you would expect from the color triangle. A bluish-green is produced where green and bluish-violet overlap. The overlapping of red and bluish-violet produces magenta, a *color not in the spectrum*. If red and bluish-violet are mixed in different proportions, other colors not in the spectrum, such as purple and crimson, are produced. Where the three primary colors overlap, the resulting light is near-white. In practice it is difficult to get slides whose colors are exactly those of the primaries, so their combination usually gives at best only a grayish white.

Colors Made to Order

A simple and convenient device for mixing colors additively is shown in Fig. 21–5. It consists of a rotator, which may be either motor or hand driven, and a set of colored cardboard disks. Each disk has a hole at its center for mounting on the shaft of the rotator and is split along a radius from the rim to the center hole. Several disks of different color can thus be fitted together and adjusted so that a sector of each of the colors is exposed on the face of the disk. The adjusted disks may be mounted on the shaft of the rotator, illuminated with daylight, and whirled rapidly. The wavelengths our eye receives from them are thus thoroughly mixed and the color we see is their composite effect. We can change the proportions of the component colors by changing the angle of the sectors exposed. Different combinations of colored disks along with black and white can be used to obtain a great variety of new and interesting hues, many of which do not appear in the spectrum. A color produced in this way could be described as so many *degrees* of yellow, so many of red, and so on. From such a description *and the same equipment* a color could be reproduced exactly at a later time or a different place. With a few trials, you should be able to produce a grayish-white by using the three primary colors shown in Plate IV if the colors on your disks are correct. If commercial disks are not available to you, you can make disks from white cardboard and paint colors on them.

Color in Nonluminous Objects

Have you ever wondered why one sweater looks green while another looks red? Where do objects that give off no light of their own get their colors?

When we look at a page of this book, we see it by "borrowed" light, the light it receives from different sources and sends back to our eye. If *white* light falls on the page and the paper reflects and diffuses a large percentage of this light equally well at all wavelengths, the page will appear *white*. If a smaller percentage of the incident light is reflected diffusely by the paper, the page will appear some shade of gray. Black ink absorbs nearly all the light at all wavelengths, and so reflects very little back to our eye. This is why the printed characters appear black and by contrast with the white stand out on the page.

If we illuminate the page with red light the only wavelengths available for the paper to reflect are those of red,

Fig. 21–5. A great variety of different colors can be produced with a color wheel.

so the page appears red. Since black ink absorbs all wavelengths, it will absorb the red. The printed characters will appear black on a background of red. You can easily try this for yourself if you have a red light available. Remember to darken the room to shut out daylight when you make the trial.

This does not explain why a sweater looks green, but it is a step in the explanation. Colored objects reflect more or less light from their surfaces by *regular* mirrorlike reflection but their color generally comes from *diffuse* reflection in a very thin layer next to the surface. Very fine particles of colored material called *color pigments* in this layer *absorb* some wavelengths much more completely than others. The pigments of dye in the wool of a green sweater absorb the wavelengths of red, orange, and violet almost completely. They absorb some of the yellow and the blue but relatively little of the green. So out of all the wavelengths of white light, those of green predominate in the light reflected from a green sweater. Thus the green sweater gets its color by *subtracting* or removing some of the wavelengths from white light that falls on it. In the same way, the dye pigments in a red sweater absorb more or less

515

completely the wavelengths of yellow, green, blue, and violet and reflect chiefly those of red. This process is called *selective absorption*. Colors produced by selective absorption are never pure colors like those in a spectrum.

Colors in Artificial Light

Have you ever noticed that a *blue* suit sometimes looks *black* under artificial light? Almost everyone knows from experience that cloth and fabrics seem to have somewhat different colors in daylight than they have in artificial light. Many types of artificial light are deficient or entirely lacking in some of the wavelengths of white light. A colored fabric under artificial light may not receive all the wavelengths that it can reflect. It cannot return the wavelengths that are lacking, and so its color must be different than in daylight. This is why fabrics are very difficult to match correctly for color under artificial light. Both red and blue fabrics appear black under sodium light which contains only the two wavelengths in the yellow.

New Colors by Subtraction

We are now ready to consider why *yellow pigment* mixed with blue pigment gives a *green* paint, ink, or dye. As we have seen, the yellow pigment absorbs from white light all colors except yellow and some red, orange, and *green*. The blue pigment absorbs from white light all colors except blue and some violet and *green*. When the two are mixed, the only color not *completely absorbed* by one or the other of the two kinds of pigment is *green*, so green is reflected back to our eye. Since this green results from the *subtraction* of wavelengths from white light, this method of color mixing is called the *subtractive method*. Many of the colors seen in nature are so produced.

Primary Pigment Colors

Artists and mixers of paints and inks have found that they can produce the greatest variety of hues by using three different colors (along with white and black). These colors, *crimson red, yellow,* and *light blue*, are called *primary pigment colors*. A primary pigment color cannot be produced by mixing of other pigments. Mixed in approximately equal proportions, the three primaries together produce a dark gray, which is as near to true black as can usually be obtained. *You will notice that these are not the same primary colors as those used for colored lights.*

These pigment primary colors can be arranged on a color triangle. Crimson red, yellow, and light blue are placed at the corners of this triangle. Yellow mixed with crimson red gives a *secondary* color, orange. This orange is the complementary color of light blue, since when mixed together they can produce near-black. White can never be produced by mixing colored pigments because of the subtractive process involved. Yellow and light blue produce the secondary color green, which in turn gives near-black when mixed with its corresponding primary crimson red. In the same way, crimson red mixed with light blue gives the secondary color, violet, which produces a near-black when mixed with yellow.

Filters for Light

Cobalt glass has a very deep blue color. It absorbs practically all the wavelengths of white light except those of blue and violet. This glass is often used as a *light filter* in laboratories and industrial plants to enable an operator to look directly at a brilliant flame or into a very hot furnace without injuring his eyes. The same kind of glass makes an excellent filter when we wish to look directly at the sun, as during an eclipse. Colored-glass or colored-film filters are used in photography to remove some of the strong light in particular portions of the spectrum so that the camera can photograph such things as bright lights, landscapes, and clouds. Colored sunglasses are used as light filters to protect the eyes on bright days in summer and in winter when the ground is covered with snow. All these filters operate on the same principle; they subtract certain wavelengths or bands of wavelengths from white light and transmit the remainder. They thus produce *absorption* spectra that generally are continuous over a wide band of wavelengths. Filters are available to screen out ultraviolet and infrared radiations. Ordinary glass is an excellent filter for ultraviolet. A special glass filter is sometimes used in powerful slide projectors to filter out infrared and thus keep the slides from becoming too hot.

Colors by Fluorescence

The coating inside a fluorescent lamp produces colored light in a very different way. It absorbs radiant energy at the invisible ultraviolet wavelengths produced by the excited mercury vapor in the tube and then emits this energy at once on wavelengths we can see. The effect is somewhat similar to that of a radio station that receives a signal on a very short wavelength and sends it out again at once on a longer wavelength. The material of the coating effectively changes the wavelength of radiant energy from the invisible to the visible region. This effect is called *fluorescence*. Fluorescent materials have been developed that appear white or faintly colored in white light, but give off brilliant live colors when illuminated with ultraviolet. Fluorescent paints, inks, and dyes are coming into common use.

Some materials will continue to glow and give off visible light for a time after ultraviolet or even visible light that fell on them is removed. These materials seem to store up some of the radiant energy and give it off gradually. This effect is called *phosphorescence*.

▶Do You Know?

1. What is color blindness? Is this defect of vision more common among men or among women?
2. What tests for color blindness must be passed by an applicant for a driver's license in your state?
3. What causes gloss or sheen on some colored objects?
4. How is the color *pink* produced?
5. For what range of wavelengths is the eye most sensitive?
6. If you placed a plate of red glass on one of blue and held the combination toward the light from a window, what color would you be likely to see through the two glasses?
7. When specific wavelengths of light are absorbed, as in a filter, what happens to the energy which they originally possessed?

POLARIZATION AND INTERFERENCE

Have you ever noticed colors in a soap bubble or in a thin film of oil on water? These colors are caused by *subtraction* of light waves from white light, but the subtraction occurs in a way entirely different from those we have considered. Film colors are due to the *interference* of light waves, an effect similar to that of nodes and antinodes in the interference of sound

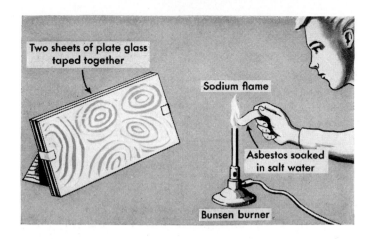

Fig. 21–6. Interference of light waves causes a pattern of dark lines to appear in the plate glass.

waves. The following experiment will help us understand this process.

Suppose we tape two sheets of clean plate glass together and set them near a sodium flame in a darkened room, as shown in Fig. 21–6. When we stand near the flame and look at the glass, we can usually see a pattern of dark lines that often looks like a giant fingerprint on the surface of the glass. These lines seem to move when we move our head. When we squeeze the pieces of glass together at one corner, the lines appear to race across the face of the glass. This pattern of lines is called an *interference pattern*.

A complete explanation of how these lines are formed is quite complicated. We can easily examine the principle, however, without considering all the details. The two sheets of glass do not fit together perfectly, because their surfaces are never absolutely plane and also perhaps because of small pieces of dirt we may fail to remove. As a result thin wedge-shaped air spaces occur between sheets of glass. We already have evidence that the dark lines are closely associated with these air spaces, because the lines move when we press on the glass and change the thickness of the wedge. To simplify the explanation, let us suppose

518

that the rays from the sodium flame strike the glass plates perpendicularly. Rays are reflected both at the *front* and at the *rear* boundaries of an air wedge. A ray reflected from the rear boundary must travel a little greater distance to reach the eye than one reflected from the front. Where the thickness of the air wedge is just right, the two reflected waves on their way to our eye will unite crest-on-trough, so that they tend to annul each other. We see a dark line connecting these positions. One of these lines is much like a contour line on a map. At nearby points where the thickness of the wedge is *one half-wavelength greater* or *one half-wavelength less*, the two reflected waves will also unite crest-on-trough and tend to annul. We see another dark line connecting these positions. *The thickness of the air wedge changes exactly one half-wavelength from one dark line to the next.* Remember that the wave reflected from the rear surface of the air wedge must cross the wedge *twice* and you should then have no trouble understanding why the difference in wedge thickness is only one *half*-wavelength from one line to the next. Between the dark lines are regions where the two reflected waves unite crest-on-crest and so reinforce each other. This results in bright lines that are generally less definite and less visible than the dark ones. The dark lines are similar to nodes and the bright lines to antinodes in standing waves.

Color by Interference

If an air wedge is but a few wavelengths in thickness, we can get interference effects with white light. Then at certain positions, the thickness of the wedge will be just right to annul one particular wavelength and partially annul adjacent wavelengths. Wavelengths in other parts of the spectrum may actually be reinforced. Bands of color will appear on the face of the glass, instead of the light and dark lines we obtained with monochromatic sodium light. The color at any given position is that which results when those wavelengths that are annulled are subtracted from white light. The colors seen in *very thin* soap films, *very thin* blown glass, and in oil films are produced in this way. These colors are never very strong because they are always diluted with much white light.

Polarized Light

Have you ever heard of polarized light? Do you know how this kind of light differs from the ordinary kind? A simple demonstration may help acquaint you with some of its properties.

The manufactured materials, Polaroid light-control materials, consist of molecules of a chemical compound embedded in a plastic sheet. Disks of sheet polarizer are often mounted between cover glasses in ring frames for convenience in handling. Disks of Polaroid light-control material can be used to demonstrate some striking effects of polarized light.

Figure 21–7a shows a projector set up

to throw a beam of ordinary white light on a screen. A disk of Polaroid light-control material P is inserted in the beam before the objective lens. This disk is called a *polarizer* because it makes *polarized light* of the beam. When we look at the screen with the polarizer in place, we see that the spot is a little dimmer than without the polarizer and has taken on a neutral gray color. This color is characteristic of the Polaroid

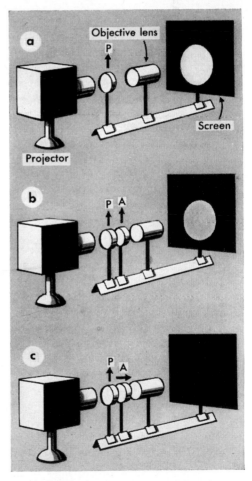

Fig. 21–7. An arrangement for producing and examining polarized light. P is a polarizer; A is an analyzer. The arrows indicate the directions of their polarizing axes.

519

Crossed disks made of Polaroid light-control materials do not allow light to pass through. (*Polaroid Corporation*)

light-control material and not of *polarized light*. The light on the screen looks like any ordinary light. If we examine an object held in this polarized beam, the object will look quite natural. When we rotate the polarizer P we can notice no change in the light.

Now let us place a second disk of Polaroid light-control material A just in front of the polarizer P as shown in Fig. 21–7b. This disk, which is just like the first one, is called an *analyzer*. Let us first set the polarizing axis of the analyzer A so that it is parallel with that of the polarizer P. The only change in the light we shall be able to observe is that it becomes a little dimmer because it has to pass through two disks of Polaroid light-control material instead of one. Let us now rotate the analyzer about an axis parallel to the beam of light and watch the spot on the screen. You may be surprised to observe that when the polarizing axis of the analyzer A is *perpendicular* to that of the polarizer P, the spot on the screen almost

or entirely disappears. *Light is transmitted when the axes of a polarizer and analyzer are parallel; little or no light is transmitted when their axes are perpendicular or crossed.*

Vibrations in Polarized Light

An analogy may help you understand what we mean by polarized light. Suppose we pass a rope through two sections of close picket fence, as shown in Fig. 21–8. If we move the rope up and down, the waves formed will pass through the vertical pickets to which they are parallel. The second section of horizontal pickets will block the waves.

Light waves are believed to consist of vibrating electric and magnetic fields. In ordinary light the electric vibrations are perpendicular to a ray; the waves are in all possible planes about the ray, like the pages of an open book around its binding edge. The polarizer P in Fig. 21–7 acts like the picket fence; the light that gets through it must be vibrating in one particular plane. Such light is called *polarized light*. The analyzer A acts like a second picket fence. Polarized light can get through it only when its polarizing axis is parallel to the plane in which the polarized light is vibrating. Thus the analyzer enables us to determine whether light is polarized or not and, if polarized, in what plane.

Sunlight reflected from water or the surface of a highway is partially polarized in a plane parallel to the earth. This is why Polaroid sunglasses are effective in filtering out much of the glare from reflected light on a bright day. Certain crystals, such as feldspar, polarize the light that passes through them. These crystals generally produce *two* images of any small object viewed through them. This effect is called *double refraction*.

Color in Polarized Light

Materials such as crushed cellophane and glass or clear plastic with strains in them produce a striking pattern of colored figures when placed between the polarizer and the analyzer in the apparatus of Fig. 21–7. As the analyzer is rotated the colors seen on the screen change constantly. When the analyzer is rotated 90 deg, the color at a given place on the image changes to the complementary color of the original color.

Scattering Light

Do you know why the sky appears blue to us while photographs taken from balloons indicate that it appears black from far above the earth? There is good evidence that the blue of the sky comes from sunlight scattered in all directions by dust particles, water particles, and even molecules in the atmosphere. It has been found that the short wavelengths of blue are scattered in this way much more completely than the longer wavelengths of red. The light we get from the sky is scattered or reflected light except when we look directly at the sun. This is why the sky is blue on a clear day. This also explains why the sun appears red at sunrise and sunset, when its rays have to pass through a thicker blanket of atmosphere than at midday. When more of the blue wavelengths are lost from the direct beam by scattering, the remaining light appears more or less red. The red appearance of the sun when the atmosphere is full of smoke or dust can be accounted for in the same way.

Scattered sunlight is partially polarized. If you examine the clear blue sky at right angles to the sun's rays with a disk of light-control material or a pair of Polaroid sunglasses, you will easily find that the light from the sky is much brighter when the polarizing axis of the disk is perpendicular to the sun's rays.

Using Polarized Light

Polarized light is often used to examine equipment made of glass to see whether it is free from strain. Polarizers are sometimes used with a television screen to improve the clarity of the picture. Polaroid light filters for windshields and Polaroid lenses for automobile lights have been proposed as a means of reducing or eliminating headlight glare in night driving.

Fig. 21–8. Waves in the rope pass through a picket fence only when their vibration is parallel to the pickets.

Polarized light is used also in chemical analysis and in examining crystals. Sugar solutions cause the plane of polarization to rotate when polarized light is passed through the solution. One kind of sugar rotates the plane clockwise, that is to the right. This is called *dextrose* (that is, right-handed sugar). Another kind of sugar rotates the plane counterclockwise, that is to the left. This sugar is called *levulose* (left-handed sugar). There are likewise right-handed and left-handed quartz crystals, which rotate the plane of polarized light to the right and to the left.

►Do You Know?

1. If the faces of two pieces of glass were perfect planes and if the air wedge between the pieces were exactly V-shaped, what would be the pattern of the dark lines seen in this glass in sodium light?

2. How do skilled mechanics use interference patterns to determine when a sample has exactly the same length as a standard measuring block?

3. How could you test whether sunlight reflected from the surface of a lake is polarized or not?

4. Do you know of any practical uses being made of polarized light? Name them.

5. Why does ice made in a refrigerator unit sometimes turn out white and sometimes clear?

6. If Polaroid lenses were used in headlights and a Polaroid screen on the windshield, how would the transmission planes of these polarizers have to be set?

HIGHLIGHTS

Refracting prisms *disperse* white light into a *continuous spectrum* of colors.

The *index of refraction* of glass depends on the wavelength of light.

The speed of shorter wavelengths in glass is less than that of longer ones.

The *angstrom*, one hundred-millionth of a centimeter, is used to express wavelengths of light.

The *visible spectrum* extends from about 4000 to more than 7000 A, a range of less than one octave.

Red has the longest wavelength in the visible spectrum, violet the shortest.

A *rainbow* is a continuous spectrum caused by the *reflection* and *dispersion* of sunlight by raindrops.

Achromatic lenses are designed to correct for *chromatic aberration*.

A *spectroscope* is used for observing spectra.

Continuous-emission spectra are obtained from very hot solids and liquids.

Bright-line emission spectra come from excited atoms of a gas or vapor.

Bright-band emission spectra come from excited molecules.

Absorption spectra may be *continuous, dark-line,* or *dark-band.*

Fraunhofer lines are dark lines in the solar spectrum.

Helium was first discovered in the sun's spectrum.

The *Doppler effect* enables astronomers to determine whether a star is approaching the earth or moving away.

The color of opaque objects is due to their absorption of certain wavelengths from white light and their reflection of those that remain.

When colored lights are mixed, the resulting color is produced by the combination of all their wavelengths; this is the *additive* method of color mixing.

Lights of complementary colors mix additively to produce white light.

The color of mixed pigments is determined by the wavelengths that escape absorption.

Pigment colors mix by the *subtractive* method.

Complementary pigment colors mix to produce black.

Colors can be produced by *interference, polarization,* and *scattering* of white light.

THINGS TO DO

1. Draw a diagram of a continuous spectrum of white light and color the different portions to show as nearly as possible the true spectral colors.
2. Try to form a rainbow from a garden or lawn spray on a sunny day. What is the largest arc you can obtain? What conditions would be necessary to obtain a complete circle?
3. Examine the light from the northern sky through a pair of Polaroid sun glasses on a clear day. Look toward the north through one lens at a time. What difference in brightness do you observe as you rotate the lens while looking through it?
4. Pour some clean water into a flat pan or dish. Then put a very small drop of olive oil on the surface of this water. Examine the surface under light that strikes at an angle. Describe any colors that may be visible and account for them.
5. Try to color sectors of a color disk (see Fig. 21–5) so that when the disk is spun it will appear white or near white. Try different proportions of the three primary colors shown in Plate IV.
6. Describe the colors of the United States flag when a red light shines on it. Describe the colors when the flag is viewed in daylight through a cobalt-blue glass.

Unit **6.**

Our World of Atoms

PREVIEW

The discovery of X-rays in 1895 marked the beginning of a new era in physics. The discovery of radium and radioactivity followed within a few years. These discoveries soon led to a better understanding of the nature of atoms.

The world of atoms is strictly a twentieth-century world, for before the present century little or nothing was known about the structure of an atom or what changes can take place within it. Many of the early explorers in this strange new world are still alive and continuing with their research work. What scientists know about this new world today may be only a beginning, for certainly it is far from complete. Each generation of young scientists for years to come will find plenty of unexplored effects within the atom to investigate and ample areas in which to make new discoveries.

It has been recognized for years that a tremendous amount of energy is locked within the core or nucleus of an atom. How to release this energy and put it to useful work has been an urgent problem on which many scientists have collaborated.

One of the most remarkable results of controlled bombardment of atomic nuclei has been the production of new atoms, some of which do not exist in nature. Another result has been the production of radioactive isotopes which can be used as tracers to study processes in plants and animals.

In this final unit of this book you will have an opportunity to see how scientists probe and explore within the atom and how energy within the atom is released.

22.

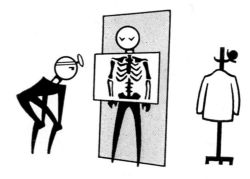

X-rays and Radioactivity:
Effects from within Atoms

THE ENERGY OF X-RAYS

X-rays were unknown before the year 1895. On November 8 of that year, Wilhelm Konrad Roentgen, Professor of Physics at the Royal University in Würzburg, Germany, first observed the effect of these strange new rays.

Roentgen was studying the glow (fluorescence) in glass and other materials produced by an electric discharge passing through a Crookes tube, a glass tube from which most of the air has been pumped. On this particular November day he happened to have near the tube a piece of paper coated with a special material that would glow when ultraviolet radiation falls on it. Roentgen

noticed that this paper would also glow whenever the Crookes tube was operated. He covered the tube with heavy black paper so that no ultraviolet or visible light could get out and still the coated paper glowed whenever the Crookes tube was operated. After many tests he concluded that an unknown kind of ray must be coming from the tube to cause the coated paper to glow.

Roentgen did not make a public report of his discovery for more than a month. During this time he made many careful tests with these new rays. He found that they pass through many substances that are opaque to ordinary visible light, but are stopped by pieces of metal. Lead proved to be an especially good absorber of these new rays. Roentgen also found that these rays can fog (or darken) a photographic plate, even when the plate is covered with light-proof paper and enclosed in a tight box. He made shadow pictures of the bones of his hand using these new rays. Since these rays were strange and of an unknown kind, Roentgen, letting X stand for the unknown, called them *X-rays*. They are still best known by this name although some people call them *Roentgen rays*.

The news of Roentgen's discovery spread quickly and aroused great interest in every civilized country of the world. Almost at once physicians and surgeons recognized that these new rays could provide an extraordinarily useful tool in their work. Within a short time X-rays were actually used in a difficult operation in a hospital in Vienna. Scientists consider the discovery of X-rays as the beginning of a new era in science called the era of *modern physics*. For his discovery of X-rays, Professor Roentgen was awarded (in 1901) the first Nobel prize in physics.

Have You Been X-rayed?

Have you ever had a tooth, a broken bone, or your chest X-rayed? If so, you were exposed to X-rays in order to make the picture. If you saw the developed X-ray film or plate, you will recall that it was a shadow picture in which the bones and denser parts of the body appeared a little brighter than the less dense tissues. Rays from the X-ray tube served somewhat the same purpose in making this picture as does visible light in making an ordinary photograph. Figure 22–1 shows the arrangement of parts for making an X-ray picture, and the photograph on p. 528 shows the bones of a hand on a developed film exposed in this way.

What Are X-rays?

At first scientists could not be sure whether X-rays were streams of fast-moving particles or waves similar to light waves. Effects were eventually discovered which indicated that X-rays act like light waves, and methods were developed for measuring their wavelengths. For most practical purposes we

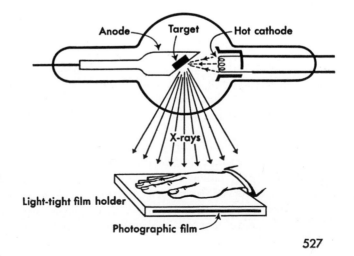

Fig. 22–1. How an X-ray photograph of a hand may be made.

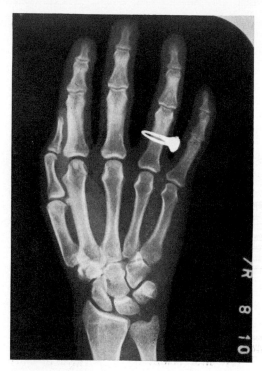

The usual X-ray picture is a negative. The separate bones of a woman's hand show clearly in this photograph. (Dr. I. J. Hershon)

now consider X-rays as electromagnetic waves similar in nature to light and radio waves but shorter in wavelength than ultraviolet waves, as indicated in Fig. 22–2. X-rays have wavelengths in the range from approximately 100 angstroms to 0.01 angstrom. It is because of their short wavelengths that X-rays are able to pass through wood, paper, fabrics, living tissue, and many other materials that are opaque to ordinary visible light.

You have seen that visible light and other forms of radiant energy sometimes act as if they consisted of little individual packets of energy called *quanta*. X-rays have been observed to behave in this same strange way. One of the little packets of radiant energy is also some-

times called a *photon*. The amount of energy in a photon is not the same for all photons, but is greater for one of shorter wavelength. This is why the X-ray photon may have thousands of times as much energy as a photon of visible light. It is also the reason why X-rays have such great penetrating power.

X-rays are not reflected from mirrors and refracted by lenses and prisms in the same way as visible light. They do, however, blacken photographic plates, as has been mentioned. They also cause fluorescent materials to glow. This effect makes possible the *fluoroscope* used by doctors in making X-ray examinations. Beams of X-rays ionize the air through which they pass and thus can cause the leaves of a charged electroscope to collapse.

How X-rays Are Produced

Figure 22–3 shows the principle of a modern tube for generating X-rays. Two electrodes, a filament or cathode, and a target or anode are sealed in a glass tube, from which as much of the air is pumped as is possible with the best vacuum pump. In operation the cathode is heated to incandescence by the passage of electric current through it. This filament then emits electrons in the same way that the filament in a tube in your radio does. A high direct-current voltage from a spark coil or a rectifier is applied in an external circuit between the filament and the target, with the potential of the target positive with respect to the filament. The electrons emitted by the filament are thus strongly attracted to the target, and they acquire high speeds and high kinetic energies as they travel through the tube. When these high-speed electrons strike the metal target, they are stopped suddenly. Ap-

528

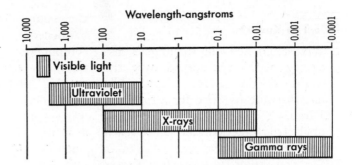

Wavelength-angstroms

Fig. 22–2. Wavelengths of visible light, ultraviolet X-rays, and gamma rays.

Visible light

Ultraviolet

X-rays

Gamma rays

proximately 98 percent of their energy is converted into heat, which must be carried away by a cooling system in order to prevent the target from melting. The remaining approximately 2 percent of their energy is changed into X-ray radiation. The X-rays thus come from the target of the tube. Those of longer wavelength are absorbed by the glass of the tube while the shorter ones pass right through the glass walls into the space outside the tube.

Short-wavelength X-rays (called hard rays) for deep penetration are produced by high target voltages; longer wavelength X-rays (called soft rays) for surface effects or shallow penetration are produced by lower target voltages. X-rays machines for ordinary examination and photographic work use target voltages from about 50,000 to 100,000 volts. Machines designed to produce very hard penetrating rays use several hundred thousand to 2,000,000 volts or more.

Precautions with X-rays

Any form of energy that can produce ionization can injure or kill living tissue, if the exposure is great enough. This is why overexposure to X-rays is dangerous to human beings and other animals. X-rays can cause surface burns that develop hours or even days after exposure and are very slow in healing. Lead sheets in sufficient thickness make one of the best shields or screens for protecting the operator of an X-ray machine from the dangerous effect of the rays.

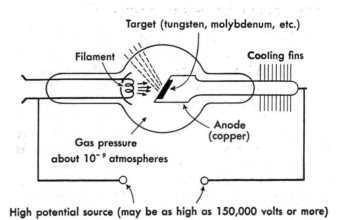

Target (tungsten, molybdenum, etc.)

Filament

Cooling fins

Anode (copper)

Gas pressure about 10^{-9} atmospheres

Fig. 22–3. An X-ray tube.

High potential source (may be as high as 150,000 volts or more)

529

1. Why could news of Roentgen's discovery of X-rays spread over the world within a few days while months were required for a report of Faraday's discovery of the principle of electromagnetic induction to reach the United States?
2. Do you know of uses for X-rays other than those mentioned in the text? Make a list of them.
3. If you look at the X-ray picture of the bones of your hand on a fluoroscope, would you see a picture corresponding to a photographic negative or positive?
4. Persons who take many X-ray pictures often wear gloves and aprons made of rubber or plastic impregnated with compounds of lead. What is the purpose of the lead?
5. Why is it seldom advantageous to make a positive print of an X-ray photograph?
6. A patient is usually required to drink a glass of barium sulfate just before an X-ray examination of the stomach and alimentary canal. What is the purpose of drinking the barium sulfate?

ATOMS BREAK UP IN RADIOACTIVITY

While the attention of most of the scientific world was occupied with the first exploration of X-rays, a related series of experiments of far-reaching importance was under way.

After learning of Roentgen's discovery of X-rays, Professor Henri Becquerel of Paris set out on a series of experiments to see if he could find any relation between X-rays and the properties of fluorescence and phosphorescence that occur in some natural substances. In the course of these experiments he happened to allow a piece of uranium compound to remain for some time on the black cover paper in which a photographic plate was tightly wrapped. When he later developed this plate, he was surprised to find it darkened, much as if it had been exposed to X-rays. This suggested that the uranium compound may have given off rays that darkened the photographic plate. Becquerel soon found that all materials containing uranium atoms do spontaneously give off rays which can ionize air, blacken photographic plates, and cause fluorescent materials to glow, just as X-rays do. These new rays were at first called *Becquerel rays*. The materials which give off these rays were described as *radioactive* and the process was called *radioactivity* (radiation-activity). You should not be deceived by the similarity in names: radioactivity and radio waves are entirely different effects that are only remotely related.

The Discovery of Radium

Marie Curie, a young research student in chemistry at the University of Paris (the Sorbonne), became intensely interested in these rays which Becquerel had discovered. She persuaded her husband, Pierre Curie, an able young physicist, to postpone his own research work and join her in a search for the source of Becquerel rays. One of the chief sources of uranium is an ore called *pitchblende*, so named because of its black pitchlike luster. The Curies together worked over a ton or more of this ore and by 1898 had obtained a few crystals of a substance many hundred times as active in giving off rays as uranium itself. This powerful radioactive material turned out to be a compound of a new chemical element which was later identified and called *radium*. In the course of their investigations, the Curies found that compounds of the chemical elements *thorium* and *actinium* are also radioactive. They discovered several other new elements, among them *radon*, a gas given off by radium, and *polonium*, named for Marie Curie's native country, Poland.

Uses of Radium

The intense rays emitted by radium and its compounds have been used extensively by physicians in the treatment of diseases such as cancer. For this use, the radium compound is usually sealed in a small metal needle or glass capsule. The needle or capsule is planted in the tissue to which the rays are to be applied. Radium is rarely prepared as a pure metal, but usually as a compound such as radium chloride. The radium compound remains in the needle, which can be removed from the tissue and used over and over again without appreciable loss of power. The price of radium is about $25,000 per gram. There are now much less expensive artificial sources of radioactivity that are replacing radium in medicine.

Alpha, Beta, and Gamma Rays

Tests eventually showed that the Becquerel rays given off when radioactive materials disintegrate must come from within the atoms themselves. The nature and origin of these rays, and the effect on the atoms that give off the rays were baffling questions. The answers to these questions were found only after a vast amount of experimenting and study had revealed much more about atoms than was known when the rays were discovered. It will be interesting, however, to examine some of the more important conclusions and see how they fit into the present atomic picture.

Investigators soon found that the rays from radioactive materials are of *three* different kinds. Experiments to show the different kinds of rays are outlined in Fig. 22–4. If a bit of radioactive material is placed at the bottom of a small hole drilled in a heavy block of lead the rays will come out of the hole much as bullets from a gun. Most of the rays that strike the sidewall of the hole will be absorbed by the lead. A narrow beam of the rays is formed in this way. If this beam is passed through a strong

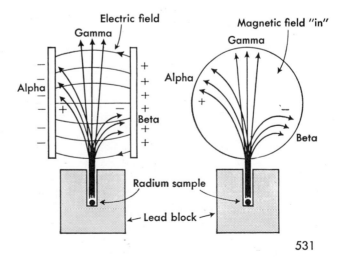

Fig. 22–4. A beam of rays from radium is split into three parts, (a) by an electric field, and (b) by a magnetic field.

electric field between two charged plates as shown at the left in Fig. 22–4 or through a strong magnetic field between the poles of a magnet as shown at the right in Fig. 22–4, the original beam will be split into *three* parts. A plate coated with zinc sulfide will glow in the dark at spots where strong rays strike it. Such a plate can be used to observe that the original beam is split into three parts. It would be better to have all this apparatus, including the coated plate, in a vacuum so that molecules of air would not interfere with the emitted rays.

The portion of the beam which bends to the left in Fig. 22–4 is attracted toward the negatively charged plate, so must have a *positive* electric charge. The rays in this portion of the beam are called *alpha rays* or *alpha particles*, named from the first letter of the Greek alphabet. The portion of the beam which bends toward the right is attracted toward the positively charged plate, so must have a *negative* electric charge. The rays in this portion of the beam are called *beta rays* (pronounced as in *bait*) or *beta particles*, named from the second letter of the Greek alphabet. The portion of the original beam that is not bent at all in passing through the electric field has no electric charge. The rays in this portion are called *gamma rays*, named after *gamma*, the third letter of the Greek alphabet. The same conclusions about the kind of electric charge of these rays can be reached by examining how they are bent in passing through the magnetic field at the right in Fig. 22–4.

Beta rays are high-speed electrons, the kind of particles encountered when you studied about electric charges and electric currents. They have negative electric charges, travel at very high speeds, can ionize air, and penetrate or

pass through bodies of matter. Gamma rays are X-rays of very short wavelength, and hence very penetrating. They travel with the speed of light, ionize air, and can pass through considerable thickness of metal plates or other material.

Alpha particles have been identified as nuclei of helium atoms, atoms without electrons in shells surrounding the nucleus. As soon as one of these alpha particles finds two electrons that it can attach to itself to fill out its electron shell, it becomes a full-fledged helium atom. Alpha particles are ejected with less speed than beta particles. They can ionize air and are easily absorbed by matter. It is remarkable that the complete nucleus of one kind of atom should be ejected spontaneously from the nucleus of another entirely different kind of atom, but that is what happens in this radioactive process. It is quite natural to ask what is left of the nucleus of the parent atom after the alpha, beta and gamma rays are given off. We shall consider this matter later in the present chapter.

Mev, a New Unit of Energy

A beta particle (electron) ejected with high speed from the nucleus of an atom has kinetic energy. The kinetic energy of this speeding electron could be expressed in ergs, but small as it is, the erg is still too large for convenient use for this purpose. So scientists have adopted a new unit of energy called the *electron-volt* to express the energy of atomic particles. One electron-volt (ev) is the amount of energy acquired by an electron when it moves from one point in an electric field to another point whose electric potential is 1 volt higher than that of the first point. In brief, this is the kinetic energy an electron acquires in moving through a difference of potential of one volt. Atomic particles under some conditions have thousands and millions of electron-volts of kinetic energy. Kev is used to denote 1,000 electron-volts, Mev to denote 1,000,000 electron-volts, and Bev to denote 1,000,000,000 electron-volts.

$$1 \text{ ev} = 1.6 \times 10^{-12} \text{ erg}$$
$$1 \text{ Kev} = 1.6 \times 10^{-9} \text{ erg}$$
$$1 \text{ Mev} = 1.6 \times 10^{-6} \text{ erg}$$
$$1 \text{ Bev} = 1.6 \times 10^{-3} \text{ erg}$$

These same new units of energy are used to express the kinetic energies of other atomic particles as well as electrons. For example, a 7-Mev alpha particle is one moving with such speed that its kinetic energy is 7,000,000 electron-volts.

How Rays Are Detected

You will recall that Becquerel used a photographic plate to detect the rays from uranium. This is still a convenient way to record rays and particles when conditions permit. The Curies used a charged electroscope to measure the intensity of rays from radium. This method is still used extensively. The electroscope is similar in principle to the gold-leaf electroscope used in studying static electricity. The electroscope has first to be charged so that the leaves diverge. The normal rate at which the leaves collapse can be timed with a stop watch. When a piece of radioactive material is brought near the charged electroscope, the rays and particles given off by the material ionize the surrounding air and cause the electroscope leaves to collapse at a faster-than-normal rate. The greater the number of particles given off by the radioactive material in a given time, the faster the leaves collapse.

Two other instruments used exten-

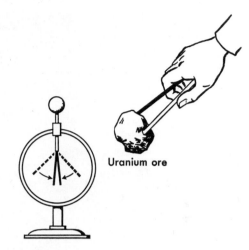

Fig. 22–5. The leaves of a charged electroscope collapse when a piece of uranium is brought near.

sively for detecting and measuring rays and particles are the Geiger tube (and counter) and the Wilson cloud chamber. Both of these depend for their operation on the ionization produced by rays and high-speed particles as they pass through a gas.

Geiger Tube

A Geiger tube consists essentially of two electrodes sealed into a glass or metal tube which contains a suitable gas at low pressure. An electric voltage is applied between the two electrodes. When energetic rays or particles come into the tube from the outside they ionize some of the gas molecules present. Ionization allows a pulse of electric current to pass through the tube from one electrode to the other. The effect of this pulse is usually amplified by electron tubes and made to operate a telephone receiver, a loudspeaker, or a counting device which registers the pulses on a dial. With an amplifier, particles can be made to produce sharp irregular pulses of sound in a loudspeaker. These sounds resemble the sounds of popping kernels

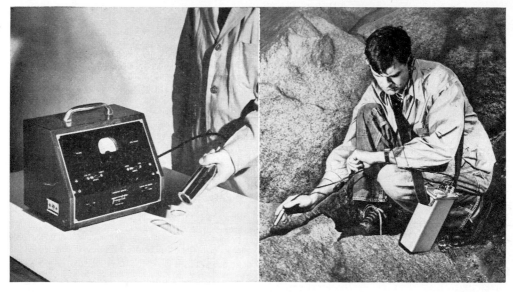

The picture at the left shows a technician using a Geiger counter to examine a beaker for radioactive contamination; the picture at the right shows a geologist with a Geiger counter exploring rocks that may be radioactive. (*Tracerlab, Inc.*)

of corn. If only a few particles enter the Geiger tube per second, the popping noises are separate and distinct. If a great many particles come into the tube per second, the noises will be more frequent and may blend into a steady roar. Geiger tubes and counters in use are shown in the photograph on this page.

Wilson Cloud Chamber

The cloud chamber invented by C. T. R. Wilson in 1911 is an instrument designed to make visible the tracks of rays and particles. While its chief use is for alpha particles, it can be used also for beta particles and gamma rays, if properly designed. The tracks of beta particles and gamma rays are usually not so clear and distinct as those of alpha particles. Figure 22–6 shows a Wilson cloud chamber.

The principle of the cloud chamber is

534

a simple one. Suppose a flat-bottom flask, such as that used in a chemistry laboratory, is partly filled with water which has been darkened with a little ink. Then a rubber bulb, such as might be used on a battery-testing hydrometer, is fitted over the neck of the flask and the flask is inverted. The air space above the water constitutes the *chamber*. The air in the chamber becomes saturated with water vapor. If the bulb is squeezed, the air is compressed and its temperature rises. It then takes on more water vapor. If the bulb is then released suddenly, the air in the chamber expands and cools to its dew-point, or below. Water droplets will condense around dust particles if any are present in the chamber. In the absence of dust particles the cooled air will become supersaturated. Under suitable conditions, droplets of water may condense around any gas ions that happen to be present. An alpha particle will collide with gas molecules in passing through this supersaturated air in the chamber. Molecules of gas are thus ionized along the path of the particle and water droplets condense at once around these new ions. These droplets appear as fog (or cloud) and serve to mark the track of the alpha particle. These tracks can easily be seen and even photographed if the chamber is properly illuminated.

The Periodic Table of Elements

If you have studied chemistry you already have some acquaintance with the periodic arrangement of the chemical elements shown in part in Table 22–1. A brief explanation may be helpful, in any event. Each rectangle contains the *name* of one of the chemical elements. Above the name is the *chemical symbol* for the element, a kind of shorthand symbol for the name itself. Thus above *hydrogen* is the symbol H and above *sodium* the symbol Na. In the upper left-hand corner of each rectangle is the *atomic number* of the element. The atomic number of hydrogen is 1, for example, and that of sodium is 11. Under the name of each element are one or more numbers called the *mass numbers* of the different *isotopes* of the element. Thus the mass number of one isotope of hydrogen is 1 and that of another isotope of hydrogen is 2. The number in bold type is the mass number of the most common (most abundant) isotope, where two or more are given. *Many elements have additional radioactive isotopes, produced artificially and not shown in Table 22–1.* Atomic number, mass number, and isotopes will be explained more fully later in this chapter.

All elements in one vertical column have similar chemical properties. The elements H, Na, K, and so on, in vertical column I, for example, form similar compounds and, in general, have a *valence* of +1. This means that *one* atom of the element will unite with *one* atom of chlorine to form the corresponding chloride. Likewise, the elements F, Cl, and so on in the vertical column VII all form similar compounds and, in general, have a valence of −1. This means that *one* atom of the element will unite with *one* atom of hydrogen to form a compound. The elements in vertical column VIII are all chemically inactive and form no known compounds.

The Number of Elements

For many years scientists were convinced that there could not be more than 92 chemical elements, several of which had not been discovered. Now it is known that the number of elements exceeds 92. Several new elements have been produced artificially or synthetically, as will be explained in the next

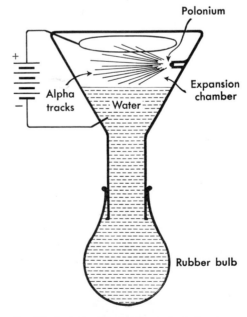

Fig. 22–6. A simplified Wilson cloud chamber.

535

Table 22–1. Portion of the Periodic Table of Chemical Elements

	I	II	III	IV	V	VI	VII	VIII
1	1 H hydrogen *1, 2*							2 He helium *3, 4*
2	3 Li lithium *6, 7*	4 Be beryllium 9	5 B boron 10, *11*	6 C carbon *12*, 13, 14	7 N nitrogen *14*, 15	8 O oxygen *16*, 17, 18	9 F fluorine 19	10 Ne neon *20*, 21, 22
3	11 Na sodium 23	12 Mg magnesium *24*, 25, 26	13 Al aluminum 27	14 Si silicon *28*, 29, 30	15 P phosphorus 31	16 S sulfur *32*, 33, 34, 36	17 Cl chlorine *35*, 37	18 A argon 36, 38, *40*
4	19 K potassium *39*, 40, 41	20 Ca calcium *40*, 42, 43, 44, 46, 48						

	I	II	III	IV	V	VI	VII	VIII
6–2	79 Au gold 197	80 Hg mercury 196, 198, 199, 200, 201, *202*, 204	81 Tl thallium 203, *205*	82 Pb lead 204, 206, 207, *208*	83 Bi bismuth 209	84 Po polonium 210	85 At astatine 210	86 Rn radon 222
7	87 Fr francium 223	88 Ra radium 226	89 Ac actinium 227 [90–98]					

90	91	92	93	94	95	96	97	98
Th thorium 232	Pa proactinium 231	U uranium 233, 234, 235, *238*	Np neptunium 237	Pu plutonium 239, 242	Am americium 243	Cm curium 245	Bk berkelium 245	Cf californium 246

chapter. The list of synthetic elements includes several new elements beyond uranium: No. 93, neptunium; No. 94, plutonium; No. 95, americium; No. 96, curium; No. 97, berkelium; No. 98, californium; and others not yet named. These elements beyond uranium do not occur in nature or occur only in such small quantities that they escaped detection until after they were produced artificially.

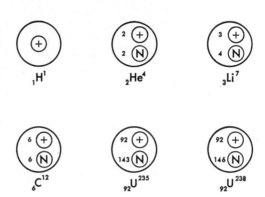

Fig. 22–7. Models of atomic nuclei.

Electron Shells

Each atom has a central core or nucleus. Electrons revolve around this nucleus in more or less definite orbits, much as the earth and other planets revolve around the sun. The normal number of electrons for each atom corresponds to the *atomic number* of the atom. Electron orbits whose average diameters are approximately the same make up an atomic shell. The orbits in any shell are probably inclined to one another so that no 2 electrons are in the same orbit. An atom may have 1 or several electron shells. Atoms of different chemical elements have different numbers of electrons in their shells. No more than 2 electrons can be in the innermost shell of an atom, no more than 8 in the second shell, and no more than 18 in the third shell. The number of electrons in the outermost shell of an atom determines its valence and some of its chemical properties. The electrons in this shell are called *valence* electrons. Hydrogen with a valence +1 has a single electron, as indicated in Fig. 22–7. Sodium with a valence +1 also has a single electron in its *outer* shell, but has 10 electrons in two inner shells (2 + 8). Helium, with 2 electrons in its first and only shell, seems to have its electron needs "satisfied." Neon, with 2 electrons in its inner shell and 8 in its outer shell, is also "satis-

fied." These atoms do not readily enter into chemical reactions. Even more complicated atoms with 8 electrons in their outermost shell are also chemically inactive and do not readily form compounds.

The Nucleus of an Atom

Alpha and beta particles and gamma rays emitted by radioactive atoms like uranium and radium come not from the electron shells of the atom but from the nucleus itself. An enormous amount of information gained from experiments and mathematical calculations indicates that the nuclei of atoms are apparently built up of two major kinds of minute particles called *protons* and *neutrons*. A *proton* is a particle whose mass is about 1,836 times that of an electron. It has a *positive electric charge* equal in amount to that of an electron. A *neutron* is a particle whose mass is very slightly greater than that of a proton. It has *no electric charge*. Protons and neutrons are sometimes called *nucleons*. The mass number of an atom is the number of nucleons (the number of protons + the number of neutrons) in its nucleus.

An atom as a whole is normally electrically neutral, that is, it acts as if it has as many units of positive charge as units of negative charge. This means that the number of electrons in its shells is just equal to the number of protons in its nucleus. Thus the number of protons in the nucleus is also the *atomic number* of the atom. *The number of neutrons in the nucleus of an atom is the mass number minus the atomic number of the atom.*

To illustrate, consider the nucleus of the most common isotope of helium, whose atomic number is 2 and mass number 4, as shown in Table 22–1. Mass number 4 shows that the nucleus has 4 nucleons (protons and neutrons) and atomic number 2 shows that 2 of these are protons. The remaining 2 nucleons must be neutrons. Figure 22–7

shows how this plan of construction works out for the nuclei of several different atoms.

Symbols for Nuclei

The symbols under the sketches in Fig. 22–7 are a shorthand method for representing these atomic nuclei. The *subscript* before the chemical symbol is the *atomic number*, the number of protons in the nucleus of the atom. The *superscript* following the chemical symbol is the *mass number*, the total number of protons and neutrons in the nucleus. Notice how different isotopes of uranium are written.

The chemical identity of an atom is fixed by the atomic number, that is

This cyclotron is one of several which are used for experiments with atomic particles. Note the huge size of this apparatus. (*Nevis Cyclotron Laboratories, Columbia University*)

538

the number of protons in the nucleus. For example, any atom with 1 proton in its nucleus (atomic number 1) is *hydrogen* regardless of the total number of nucleons it may have. Any atom with 2 protons (atomic number 2) is *helium*, any atom with 6 protons is carbon, and any one with 92 protons is *uranium*. Since the atomic number and the chemical symbol really tell the same thing, the atomic number is often omitted and you will often find uranium written as U^{235} and U^{238}.

What Are Isotopes?

Isotopes have already been mentioned in several chapters of this book. As early as 1910 scientists began to find evidences that the atoms of a given chemical element may not all be exactly alike. It seemed that the atoms might have different masses or weights, even though they act exactly alike in chemical reactions. An instrument called a *mass spectrograph* was developed to separate atoms whose masses are different. It was soon found that the element neon, for example, is not a single kind of atom but rather is a mixture of *three* different kinds, $_{10}Ne^{20}$, $_{10}Ne^{21}$, and $_{10}Ne^{22}$. About 90 percent of the atoms in neon gas have mass number 20, about 0.27 percent have mass number 21, and about 9.73 percent have mass number 22. An atom of $_{10}Ne^{21}$ has one more neutron in its nucleus than $_{10}Ne^{20}$ and $_{10}Ne^{22}$ has two more neutrons. Gas made up exclusively of $_{10}Ne^{22}$ atoms would have a density about 10 percent greater than that of $_{10}Ne^{20}$, but otherwise they would be chemically alike and could not be separated by chemical methods. These three atoms, differing only in mass, are called *isotopes* of neon.

Almost all the chemical elements have two or more natural isotopes.

Some elements have many more than two; tin, for example, has at least ten. Isotopes of many elements can be produced artificially. These artificial isotopes are generally radioactive and are relatively short-lived. The isotopes of uranium, U^{235} and U^{238}, have become quite famous and well known to everyone who has read about atomic energy.

Heavy Water

Have you ever heard of *heavy water*, water that is just a little denser than ordinary water? In the liquid left after most of the liquid hydrogen in a container had evaporated, Professor Harold Urey (then of Columbia University) found a type of hydrogen atom that is twice as heavy as an ordinary hydrogen atom. Ordinary hydrogen has a single proton in its nucleus but this heavy isotope has both a proton and a neutron, making its mass number 2 instead of 1. A special name, *deuterium*, is given to this heavy isotope of hydrogen and the symbol D is often used to represent it, instead of the expected symbol $_1H^2$. The nucleus of a deuterium atom, consisting of one proton and one neutron bound together, is often called a *deuteron*, just as the nucleus of an atom of ordinary hydrogen is called a *proton*.

A water molecule consists of two hydrogen atoms united with one oxygen atom. Its chemical formula is written H_2O. If a water molecule is formed by uniting an oxygen atom with two deuterium atoms (the heavy isotope of hydrogen), its chemical formula can be written D_2O. Such water is about 11 percent denser than water formed from ordinary hydrogen atoms and oxygen atoms and so is called *heavy water*. Heavy water looks like ordinary water and in most respects acts just like ordinary water. About 1 part in every 5,000 or so

HYDROGEN ATOMS CAN HAVE SEVERAL FORMS; THESE ARE ISOTOPES
(All hydrogen atoms have one proton)

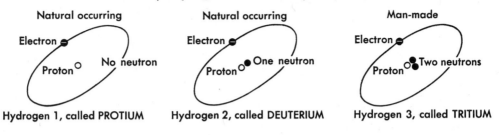

Natural occurring

Electron

Proton ○ No neutron

Hydrogen 1, called PROTIUM

Natural occurring

Electron

Proton ○● One neutron

Hydrogen 2, called DEUTERIUM

Man-made

Electron

Proton ○● Two neutrons

Hydrogen 3, called TRITIUM

ANOTHER FAMILY OF ATOMS WHICH ARE ISOTOPES

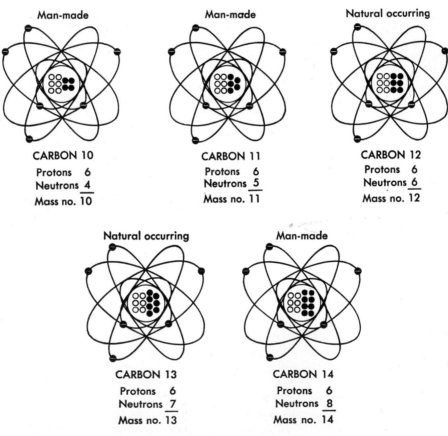

Man-made

CARBON 10

Protons   6
Neutrons 4
Mass no. 10

Man-made

CARBON 11

Protons   6
Neutrons 5
Mass no. 11

Natural occurring

CARBON 12

Protons   6
Neutrons 6
Mass no. 12

Natural occurring

CARBON 13

Protons   6
Neutrons 7
Mass no. 13

Man-made

CARBON 14

Protons   6
Neutrons 8
Mass no. 14

Fig. 22–8. Isotopes.

of ordinary water is of the heavy type. Other forms of heavy water, such as HDO, are possible. Heavy water is important in atomic research because it is an excellent material for slowing down fast-moving neutrons. Professor Urey received the Nobel prize in chemistry in 1935 for his discovery of deuterium.

Transmutation of Elements

Look up the element *radium* in Table 22–1. You will notice that its atomic number is 88 and its mass number is 226. The nucleus of an atom of this radium consists of 88 protons and $226 - 88$ or 138 neutrons. The nucleus of this atom is unstable, as the Curies found. At some unpredictable time it will undergo a sudden spontaneous change or *disintegration*, in the process of which it will eject an alpha particle. You will recall that an alpha particle is the nucleus of a helium atom, two protons and two neutrons tightly bound together. This change leaves the original atom with two less protons and four less nucleons, so it can no longer be a radium atom. It is, in fact, an atom of a new element called *radon* (a gas) whose symbol is $_{86}Rn^{222}$. The alpha particle is ejected from the radium nucleus with a speed of more than 9,000 miles/sec and an energy of nearly 5 Mev (million electron-volts). In the process of disintegrating, the original radium atom also emits a gamma ray, which is energy in the form of X-rays. The story of this disintegration can be written in shorthand.

$$_{88}Ra^{226} \rightarrow {}_{86}Rn^{222} + {}_2He^4 + energy$$

| radium nucleus | radon nucleus | alpha particle | gamma rays and heat |

The resulting radon nucleus in turn is quite unstable and soon disintegrates by giving off another alpha particle and becoming an isotope of another element *polonium* (also known as *radium A*).

$$_{86}Rn^{222} \rightarrow {}_{84}Po^{218} + {}_2He^4 + energy$$

| radon nucleus | polonium nucleus | alpha particle | heat |

The polonium nucleus very quickly disintegrates further by giving off another alpha particle, changing into an isotope of lead (also called *radium B*).

$$_{84}Po^{218} \rightarrow {}_{82}Pb^{214} + {}_2He^4 + energy$$

| polonium nucleus | lead nucleus | alpha particle | heat |

This isotope of lead is itself radioactive and soon disintegrates by emitting a beta particle (an electron) and a gamma ray, changing into an isotope of bismuth (also called *radium C*).

$$_{82}Pb^{214} \rightarrow {}_{83}Bi^{214} + {}_{-1}e^0 + energy$$

| lead nucleus | bismuth nucleus | beta particle | gamma rays and heat |

This bismuth isotope is also radioactive, disintegrating by giving off more alpha and beta particles and losing more energy by gamma rays and heat until it finally ends up as a stable isotope of lead, $_{82}Pb^{206}$.

How a beta particle, which is an electron, can come from a nucleus which has only protons and neutrons is not yet clearly understood. Some scientists suggest that the electron may be born there from a change of energy into mass. Some suggest that a neutron may be only a proton and an electron so closely bound together that the unit (neutron) appears to have no electric charge at all. The beta particle may then come from a neutron which throws it off and becomes a proton. In any event this change leaves the nucleus with the same mass number but adds another proton to increase its atomic number by 1.

Natural Alchemy

Do you realize what has happened in the series of disintegrations which has just been briefly sketched? Radium, one of the chemical elements which scientists originally thought were indivisible and unchangeable, has created from its own constituents other elements, helium (alpha particles), polonium, bismuth, and so on, finally ending up as lead. During all these changes the atom was giving up energy in the form of gamma rays and kinetic energy of alpha and beta rays, which ultimately became heat. This action is important, for if some chemical elements in nature can spontaneously change into others and release energy in doing so, scientists reasoned that there might be a chance of discovering the secret of this process and producing the same effects artificially. This secret has been discovered, at least in part. The alchemy of changing one chemical element into another (transmutation) is no longer a mystery.

What Is a Half-life?

If you could get a single radium-226 atom all by itself, how long would you have to wait before you could observe its disintegration? This is a very good question to which no one can know the exact answer. The change may happen at once or it may not happen for thousands of years. Statisticians can predict with considerable certainty how many traffic accidents will occur over a holiday weekend. They cannot possibly know beforehand which particular cars will be involved in these accidents. The same kind of thing is true with radio-active atoms. It can be predicted with certainty that half of the atoms in a gram of radium will change to radon and alpha particles within about 1,600 years, but which of the atoms will change or how soon a given atom will change cannot be known. Half of the atoms remaining unchanged at the end of the first 1,600-year period will disintegrate within the next 1,600 years, half of the

atoms then remaining will disintegrate within the next 1,600 years, and so on. This period, 1,600 years, is called the *half-life* of radium.

Each radioactive isotope has its own characteristic half-life. Radon-222, for example, has a half-life of about 3.82 days. Some radioactive isotopes have a half-life of only a few seconds, and others have a half-life of a few thousandths of a second. Some isotopes, on the other hand, have very long half-life. That of uranium-238, for example, is 4,600,000,-000 years. This is why some of this radioactive element is left in the ores of the earth after many millions of years.

Control of Radioactivity

You may wonder whether some way can be found to hasten, retard, or even stop entirely this radioactive disintegration. Could a piece of uranium be heated, subjected to pressure, exposed to strong light, or treated with X-rays to make the disintegrations occur in less time? Scientists have tried all these and many other things, too, but have found no effective way of changing the rate at which these changes occur. There is no known way, for example, to "turn off" the rays and particles emitted by the radium in the needle used for cancer treatment when they are not needed. The process goes on day and night whether the rays are used or not.

►Do You Know?

1. Why is it frequently necessary to put the radioactive material *inside* a Wilson cloud chamber to observe alpha-ray tracks while beta-ray tracks can be observed with the active material outside the chamber?
2. Oxygen has several isotopes. Would it be possible to have more than one kind of heavy water? Explain.

3. Give the name of any laboratory or industry in which a Geiger counter is used.
4. Why are radioactive materials usually shipped and stored in heavy lead containers?
5. What is meant by the *transmutation* of a chemical element?
6. From what parts of the world are ores of uranium obtained? How do prospectors search for uranium deposits?

HIGHLIGHTS

X-rays are electromagnetic radiations shorter in wavelength than ultraviolet waves.

Becquerel rays are emitted by uranium compounds and other radioactive substances. They consist of alpha particles, beta particles, and gamma rays.

Alpha particles are nuclei of helium atoms. They have a positive charge.

Beta particles are electrons. They have a negative charge.

Gamma rays are X-rays of very short wavelength and great penetrating power.

Radium is a strongly radioactive element discovered by the Curies.

Electron-volts and multiples of this unit are generally used to express the kinetic energy of atomic particles and rays.

Geiger counters and *Wilson cloud chambers* are instruments used to detect radioactivity.

Isotopes are atoms of the same chemical element which have the same chemical behavior and atomic number but which have different mass numbers.

Deuterium is an atom of *heavy* hydrogen, with a mass number 2 instead of 1 as for ordinary hydrogen.

A *deuteron* is the nucleus of a deuterium atom.

Heavy water, D_2O, is formed from deuterium and oxygen.

In *natural radioactivity* atoms of one chemical element change spontaneously into atoms of other elements and liberate energy.

The *half-life* of a radioactive isotope is the time required for one-half of the original atoms to disintegrate.

THINGS TO DO

1. Make a simple radiograph of a small key, a paper clip, or other metal object. To do so, obtain a piece of photographic film about 2 in. square and wrap it light tight in black paper, with the emulsion side up. This should be done in a dark room to avoid fogging the film. Fold a piece of cardboard, place the metal object inside the fold, and lay the cardboard on top of the wrapped film. Place a watch with a radium dial on top of the cardboard, with the radium face downward toward the film. Leave the watch in place for 24 hr. Then develop the film. You should have a reversed shadow outline of the metal object, if all has gone well.

543

2. Arrange for a demonstration of a Geiger counter, if one is available in your community. Geiger counters are usually on display at science museums in different cities.

3. Investigate and make a list of the various purposes for which X-rays are used. Your local or school library will probably furnish considerable information on this subject.

4. Make a table showing the half-life of some of the better-known radioactive isotopes, such as radium-226, polonium-210, sodium-24, carbon-14, iodine-130, cobalt-60, uranium-235, and uranium-238. Consult your local or school library.

23.

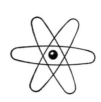

Nuclear Energy:
A New Source of Energy

ENERGY FROM ATOMS

You have now learned how atoms of uranium, radium, and a few other elements break up or disintegrate spontaneously, changing successively to other elements, and releasing energy which eventually becomes heat. Vast stores of energy seem to be locked up within the nuclei of atoms. We will now investigate some methods that have been developed to smash atoms and control the release of this energy.

Atomic Missiles

Much information about atoms has been obtained by bombarding them with suitable missiles. A fast-moving missile upon hitting an atom may jolt it and perhaps knock off some of its parts. The missile has to penetrate to the core or nucleus of the atom to cause it to split apart and release much energy. A missile suitable for this purpose has to be smaller than the atom and must have at least enough energy to break through the outer shells of electrons that surround the nucleus. Even after a missile gets inside the electron shells it has a much better chance of missing the nucleus than of hitting it, because most of the space "inside an atom" is actually empty. The estimated radius of an atom is 0.00000001 cm (order of magnitude) while the radius of a nucleus is only about 1/100,000 of this amount. Relatively little of the space within an atom is occupied by the electrons in the different shells.

You are already acquainted with some particles that can be used as missiles to hurl at atoms. Electrons could be used for this purpose. To be effective missiles, electrons must have very high speeds and high energies. It is very difficult for an electron to break through the electron shells of an atom, however, because it is strongly repelled as it nears the atom. The electron missile has the same kind of electric charge as the electrons in the shells of the atom and, as you will recall, like charges repel. Electrons are better missiles for producing X-rays than for splitting atoms.

Alpha particles, deuterons, and protons are other particles small enough for use as atomic missiles. Each of these has a positive electric charge and so can easily be speeded up by means of a suitable electric or magnetic field. Because its charge is *positive*, each of these particles is attracted and speeded up as it approaches the outer electron shells of an atom. But those particles which are able to pass through these shells encounter difficulty when they near the nucleus because both the nucleus and the missile have a positive charge and hence repel one another. One of the most effective missiles is the neutron, which has no electric charge and hence is not repelled or attracted by the electron shells or by the nucleus of the atom.

The Cyclotron

Huge machines have been built in research laboratories to deliver beams of high-speed electrons, protons, deuterons, and alpha particles for bombarding atoms. Among these are the Van de Graaff generator, mentioned in an earlier chapter, the cyclotron, the betatron, and the synchrotron. Of these the cyclotron is probably the most widely known.

A cyclotron consists of a powerful electromagnet with large north and south poles separated by a small gap. A flat metal box shaped like a pill box fits into the space between the two poles. This box is hollow and arranged so that the air can be pumped out of it. In this box or *chamber* are placed two hollow D-shaped metal electrodes called *dees*. The dees are electrically insulated from the box and from each other. They are

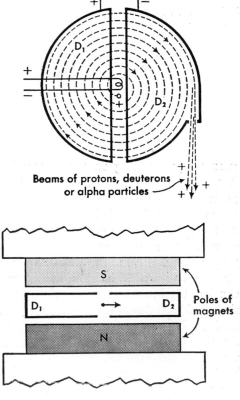

Fig. 23-1. The D's or dees, of a cyclotron and how the particles are speeded up as they move around the D's.

arranged back to back with a narrow gap between them. When a proton, deuteron, or alpha particle is released at the center of the chamber, it spirals around this center in a plane parallel to the faces of the dees because of the strong magnetic field across which it moves. An alternating voltage is applied to the two dees in such a way that each time the particle passes across from one dee to the other it is given a push, which speeds it up. After a particle has spiraled around perhaps fifty times and received two energetic pushes every round, it will be moving at very high speed. Its spiral path will then be near the outside perimeter of the dees. A negatively charged plate mounted on the wall inside the chamber may be used to deflect the high-speed particles from their spiral paths so that they fly out of the cyclotron through a window in the chamber wall. The atoms to be bombarded are placed in this beam of high-speed particles. Cyclotrons cannot be used successfully to speed up electrons to serve as missiles.

The first cyclotron was designed and built by Dr. Ernest O. Lawrence at the University of California in 1930. Since then other larger and more effective cyclotrons have been built and installed in leading atomic research laboratories of the world. Lawrence was awarded the Nobel prize in physics in 1939 for his development of the cyclotron and for the production of artificial radioactive isotopes.

Splitting an Atom

In 1931 two English physicists, Cockcroft and Walton, were bombarding *lithium atoms* with protons and found that *alpha particles* came flying out of the lithium, each with kinetic energy more than twenty times that of one of

The Westinghouse atom smasher, a special Van de Graaff generator, is being modernized for a research program. In this machine, electrons and other atomic missiles will be speeded up and shot into the nuclei of atoms. Scientists hope in this way to learn more about the mysterious forces that keep particles in the nuclei of atoms from flying apart. (*Westinghouse Electric Corporation*)

the proton missiles. The reaction may be expressed as follows:

$$_3\text{Li}^7 + {}_1\text{H}^1 \rightarrow {}_2\text{He}^4 + {}_2\text{He}^4 + 17.3 \text{ Mev}$$

lithium nucleus   proton   alpha particle   alpha particle   energy

This is a remarkable experiment, for the proton missile causes the lithium nucleus to split into two equal parts, each an *alpha particle*, the nucleus of a helium atom. In biology, when a cell divides to form two new cells, the process is called *fission*. When a nucleus of an atom divides into two equal or nearly equal parts, the process is likewise called *fission*. We may then say that the lithium nucleus in this experiment *undergoes fission*. Some scientists use the term *fission* only for the splitting

547

of *heavy* atoms such as uranium into two nearly equal parts.

Mass to Energy

The experiment in which a lithium nucleus is split to form two alpha particles (helium nuclei) is remarkable for another reason. Very careful measurements show clearly that *mass* seems to disappear in this fission process. Consider the following data:

Mass before fission:

Lithium nucleus	11.6492×10^{-24} g
Proton	1.6723×10^{-24} g
Total mass	13.3215×10^{-24} g

Mass after fission:

Alpha particle	6.6446×10^{-24} g
Alpha particle	6.6446×10^{-24} g
Total mass	13.2892×10^{-24} g

Loss in mass:

$$13.3215 \times 10^{-24} \text{ g}$$
$$-13.2892 \times 10^{-24} \text{ g}$$
$$\overline{0.0323 \times 10^{-24} \text{ g}}$$

While this is an extremely small amount of mass difference, nevertheless it is more than 0.2 percent of the total mass involved. A difference as large as this cannot be disregarded. What becomes of the mass that vanishes?

The new alpha particles formed by fission of the lithium nucleus fly apart with great speeds. In fact, the kinetic energy of the two together is about 17.3 Mev. The energy of the proton shot into the lithium nucleus has to be about 0.4 Mev. So there is a large increase in total energy during the process. Can it be that the mass that disappears is converted into energy? Albert Einstein had reached the conclusion that mass and energy are interchangeable and some years before this experiment had ex-

pressed his conclusion in the form of a now-famous equation:

$$E = m \times c^2$$

in which E is the amount of energy that appears when m units of mass disappear and c is the velocity of light (3×10^{10} cm/sec). If m is expressed in grams, E will be in ergs. The mass that is lost and the energy that appears in splitting the lithium nucleus, when measured experimentally has been found to fit Einstein's equation quite well. This equation may prove to be the most important single equation in all our physical universe. On this equation may hinge the fate of entire nations and even of civilization itself, *for this is the equation that describes the release of the vast reservoirs of energy stored in the nuclei of atoms.*

Atomic Fusion

It may also be possible for some light atoms or atomic particles to join together to produce new atoms and release energy. For example, suppose that two protons and two neutrons under suitable temperature and pressure could fuse together to form an alpha particle. Mass would disappear in this reaction, as shown in the following:

Mass before fusion:

Two protons	3.3446×10^{-24} g
Two neutrons	3.3497×10^{-24} g
Total mass	6.6943×10^{-24} g

Mass after fusion:

One alpha particle	6.6446×10^{-24} g

Loss in mass:

$$6.6943 \times 10^{-24} \text{ g}$$
$$-6.6446 \times 10^{-24} \text{ g}$$
$$\overline{0.0497 \times 10^{-24} \text{ g}}$$

This loss in mass would represent

nearly 0.75 percent of the total mass involved. A corresponding amount of energy in the form of gamma rays and heat should be released in this *fusion process*, as it is commonly called. It is believed that some process such as this takes place at temperatures of millions of degrees and pressures of perhaps billions of atmospheres within the bodies of the sun and stars. Radiant energy given off by these heavenly bodies may come from the loss of mass in the fusion of protons and neutrons to form helium nuclei (alpha particles). If this is the case, the sun must be losing mass, a possibility discussed in an earlier chapter.

The fusion of protons and neutrons may not occur all in a single step. A *triton*, $_1H^3$, is the nucleus of a *tritium* atom, a heavy radioactive isotope of hydrogen usually produced artificially, but occurring also in small amounts in air and water. A triton may possibly fuse with a proton or a deuteron under suitable conditions to form a helium nucleus and release very large amounts of energy. Very high temperature and pressure would be needed for this reaction. Such processes are often called *thermonuclear reactions*. The so-called hydrogen bomb is based on a reaction such as this.

Artificial Radioactivity

In 1932 Dr. Carl D. Anderson of the California Institute of Technology discovered a new atomic particle which has about the same mass as an electron and a positive electric charge equal in amount to that of the electron. This particle is called a *positron* or sometimes a *positive electron*. A positron has a very short life for it soon meets an electron and both disappear rapidly, forming gamma rays.

In 1934 a team of French scientists carried Dr. Anderson's experiment further by bombarding a thin sheet of aluminum with high-speed alpha particles. They were particularly interested in observing the positrons knocked out of the aluminum by these missiles. When they turned off the beam of alpha particles, they were astonished to observe that the positrons continued to come out of the aluminum. They found in the aluminum a material chemically like phosphorus, in fact a radioactive isotope of phosphorus. The half-life of this phosphorus isotope is only 2.55 min.

The reactions that occurred can best be written in two steps.

$$\underset{\substack{\text{aluminum}\\\text{nucleus}}}{_{13}Al^{27}} + \underset{\substack{\text{alpha}\\\text{particle}}}{_2He^4} \rightarrow \underset{\substack{\text{radioactive}\\\text{phosphorus}\\\text{nucleus}}}{_{15}P^{30}} + \underset{\text{neutron}}{_0n^1} + \underset{\text{heat}}{\text{energy}}$$

Notice that a neutron is represented by $_0n^1$, with atomic number 0 because it contains no protons and mass number 1 because it is 1 nucleon.

The radioactive phosphorus atom disintegrates very quickly giving off a positron and becoming an isotope of silicon.

$$\underset{\substack{\text{phosphorus}\\\text{nucleus}}}{_{15}P^{30}} \rightarrow \underset{\substack{\text{silicon}\\\text{nucleus}}}{_{14}Si^{30}} + \underset{\text{positron}}{_{+1}e^0} + \underset{\text{heat}}{\text{energy}}$$

Radioactive phosphorus was the first of a long list of artificial radioactive isotopes that have since been discovered. Artificial radioactive isotopes of a great many chemical elements can now be prepared in quantities by other means and are used extensively in biology, medicine, agriculture, and other branches of applied science, as well as in industry.

The positron is an interesting particle —how it happens to be present in the nucleus of an atom is still a matter of conjecture. Some scientists believe that

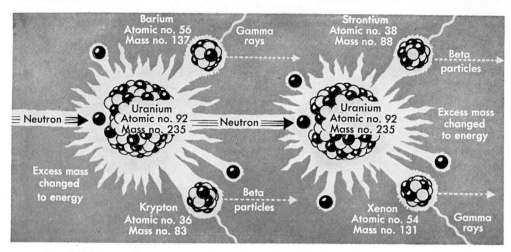

Fig. 23–2. The fission of a U-235 nucleus. A neutron enters the nucleus and causes the nucleus to split into two parts of unequal mass. At the same time the nucleus gives off beta and gamma rays as well as neutrons, which may cause fission of other U-235 nuclei. The nucleus at the left has split into barium-137 and krypton-83; the one at the right has split into strontium-88 and xenon-131.

it is thrown off by a proton, which then turns into a neutron.

Fission of Uranium-235

In 1938 two chemists in Berlin, Hahn and Strassmann, were bombarding uranium with neutrons and discovered traces of a material later identified as *barium* in the material with which they were working. This at first seems incredible, for there was up to that time no known way of getting barium from uranium. It was soon shown that some of the uranium atoms behave in a very unusual and unexpected manner when they are struck by neutrons. The evidence indicated that an atom of the uranium isotope U^{235} (about 0.75 percent of the atoms of natural uranium are U^{235}) can capture a neutron missile and then split into two nearly equal parts. These two parts are new *heavy* atoms, such as barium and krypton. This process is called *nuclear fission*, as was mentioned

earlier in this chapter. When fission occurs there is a loss in mass, and energy is released in the form of gamma rays, kinetic energy of the newly formed atoms and particles as they fly apart, and finally as heat. The fission of a single U^{235} nucleus in this way results in the release of about 200 Mev of energy, nearly ten times that released from a lithium atom which captures a proton, described in an earlier example. Figure 23–2 shows how fission may take place.

What Is a Chain Reaction?

The splitting of the U^{235} nucleus just described is remarkable for another reason. While a single neutron striking and entering the nucleus will cause the atom to split apart, two or three new neutrons are set free in the reaction that occurs. *More neutrons are set free in the fission process than are required to start it.*

To illustrate what this may mean,

suppose that each atom of U^{235} that splits sets free two useful neutrons. Then when the first U^{235} nucleus captures a neutron and splits, it will free two neutrons. Suppose each of these two neutrons is promptly captured by another U^{235} nucleus. In splitting, each of these two nuclei will set free two new neutrons, making four free neutrons in all. After one more step there will be eight free neutrons and with each successive step the number of free neutrons will double. The number of nuclei undergoing fission (splitting) will likewise double with each step. Any reaction that sustains itself and proceeds at a faster and faster rate is called a *chain reaction*. A chain reaction needs some impulse to set it off. It will then proceed on its own, involving more and more atoms as it goes. The splitting of the U^{235} atom suggested the possibility of a chain reaction which might result in splitting all of the U^{235} atoms in a piece of uranium and release enormous amounts of heat and gamma rays. This possibility was known to scientists long before it became a reality.

The Atomic Bomb

Scientists were aware of the possibility of setting off a chain reaction with U^{235} before our country entered World War II in December, 1941. The fission process had been observed with only a small number of atoms under laboratory conditions. The urgency of approaching war and the possibility of using atomic energy as a superexplosive in military weapons spurred on the search for ways to release and control atomic energy on a large scale. Even before our country was actively involved in the war, steps had been taken to organize and direct this research work. By August, 1942, the possibilities of producing an atomic bomb had become clear enough that the top-secret Manhattan Engineering Project was set up under Army control to coordinate all atomic research and development work. Eventually this mammoth project brought together the largest civilian army of trained scientists, mathematicians, engineers, and technicians ever assembled. Thousands of privately operated industrial plants and

Fig. 23–3. If the amount of U-235 in a mass of uranium is increased by artificial means, on the average the neutrons thrown out by fission of one nucleus score more than one hit against other "explosive" nuclei. Then a chain reaction builds up with explosive violence.

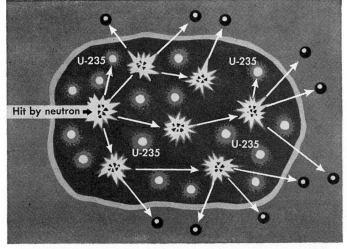

factories were associated with the project in supplying the necessary machinery and materials. After some 3 years of intensive work and the expenditure of 2 billion dollars, the first experimental bomb was ready. This test bomb was set off in the desert near Alamogordo, New Mexico, on the morning of July 16, 1945, under conditions of great secrecy. The bomb exploded according to plan and theories became realities.

In the course of World War II one atomic bomb was dropped from an airplane on the Japanese city of Hiroshima and a second one on the city of Nagasaki. In both cities large areas were completely destroyed with great loss of life. Radioactive fission products scattered by the explosion of the bombs contaminated other areas of the cities and produced delayed injuries and death.

CONTROLLING ATOMIC ENERGY

You have no doubt heard of an atomic pile and know that it is a device for obtaining energy on a large scale from the nuclei of atoms. The first successful pile was set up under the squash courts in Stagg Stadium at the University of Chicago. It began operation on December 2, 1942, and generated energy in the form of heat at a maximum rate of about 200 watts.

The general principle of a pile or *reactor*, as one is often called, is not difficult to understand. Fast neutrons produced by fission are not readily captured by another U^{235} nucleus until they are slowed down. U^{238} nuclei can capture neutrons most readily when the neutrons have speeds corresponding to about 25 electron-volts; U^{235} nuclei capture most readily neutrons whose speeds are much slower than this. To keep

the reaction in a pile going, it is therefore necessary to slow down the fast neutrons produced by fission. This is done by means of a *moderator*. Pure carbon (graphite) is a good moderator, and so is *heavy water*.

For a carbon pile, the atomic fuel is uranium metal, which is encased in small metal tubes inserted in holes in the graphite blocks from which the pile is built. A few neutrons introduced into the pile cause the first U^{235} nuclei to fission. Most of the fast neutrons produced by fission of the U^{235} nuclei escape from a fuel tube into the graphite moderator. The pile is so designed that by the time these neutrons arrive at another piece of uranium they have been slowed down so much that they are easily captured by the U^{235} nuclei in this piece, but are too slow for capture by the U^{238} nuclei. Therefore, there are more slow neutrons to be captured by U^{235} nuclei and produce new fissions.

If the supply of slow neutrons is great enough, the action within the pile may become an uncontrollable chain reaction and proceed with explosive violence. So the supply of neutrons within the pile has to be regulated. *Control rods* of cadmium or boron steel are used for this purpose. Both cadmium and boron are good absorbers of neutrons. The control rods are automatically pushed in and out of holes in the pile. When the rods are pushed farther in, more neutrons are absorbed and fewer are available for causing fission of U^{235} atoms. This slows down the reaction. When it is desired to increase the rate of reaction, the control rods are pulled farther out of the pile.

Heat is developed in the pile by the fission process. A cooling system is usually required to avoid excessive temperatures. The heat removed from the pile may be used to generate steam to drive engines or turbines.

Critical Mass

A single graphite block with a piece of uranium inside will not operate as a pile because too many of the fission neutrons escape from the surface of the block without causing other fissions. Two such carbon blocks together would have a better chance of operating, because some of the neutrons escaping from the first block could enter the second block and become available for capture by the U^{235} nuclei there. An atomic pile has to exceed a certain critical size to operate. The principle is something like that involved in burning logs in a fireplace. One log alone may not keep the fire going but two or three logs placed together will usually burn until they are reduced to ashes.

There is a *critical mass* for U^{235}. If the mass of a lump of this metal is below this *critical value*, the lump cannot maintain a chain reaction and explode. It is probable that the uranium in an atomic bomb is divided into separate pieces, each less than the critical mass. To set off the bomb, these masses might be driven together forcefully so that they act like a single mass greater than the critical mass. A chain reaction could then proceed with the speed of an explosion.

Artificial Chemical Elements

The chief use of some atomic piles or reactors is not to obtain energy from the nuclei of atoms, but rather to produce more fissionable material. If neutrons are not too slow they can be captured quite readily by the nuclei of U^{238} atoms. These are the more abundant kind of uranium atoms, constituting more than 99 percent of the atoms in ordinary uranium metal. When a U^{238} atom captures a neutron it does not split as U^{235} does, but becomes another isotope of uranium, U^{239}. This isotope is radioactive with a half-life of only 23 min. It disintegrates by emitting a beta particle and changes into an isotope of a new element, neptunium, or $_{93}N^{239}$. This neptunium atom is also radioactive with a half-life of about 2.3 days. In disintegrating, it in turn emits a beta particle and gamma rays, changing into another new element, plutonium, or $_{94}Pu^{239}$. This plutonium atom is quite

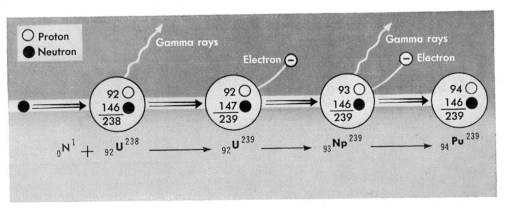

Fig. 23–4. How neptunium and plutonium atoms are formed from uranium-238. Plutonium is considered a stable element, although in time it releases an alpha particle and becomes uranium-235.

stable; while it is radioactive, its half-life is about 24,000 years.

Plutonium is a very important synthetic or artificial element because when its nucleus captures a neutron, it, too, will separate, splitting into two heavy fragments and giving out large amounts of energy. At the present time Pu^{239}, U^{235}, and a rarer isotope of uranium, U^{233}, are the chief atoms known to be easily fissionable. These are the atoms capable of maintaining an explosive chain reaction and the principal atoms from which nuclear energy can be obtained.

Plutonium can be made in a pile from the very abundant isotope of uranium, U^{238}. Since plutonium is a different chemical element from uranium, the two can be separated by chemical means. This makes it easier to obtain pure plutonium than pure uranium, U^{235}, which is very difficult to separate from U^{238} since they are chemically alike.

Other Products of a Reactor

Some atomic reactors are used chiefly for producing radioactive isotopes of the more familiar chemical elements. Almost every one of the chemical elements has one or more short-life isotopes that can be produced artificially in a pile. There is no chemical difference between active and inactive isotopes of the same element. Both enter into the same reactions and form identical compounds. An active isotope retains its radioactive property even after it has joined with other atoms to form a compound. If an atom of radioactive sodium, $_{11}Na^{24}$, joins with an atom of chlorine to form the compound sodium chloride (ordinary table salt), the salt will be radioactive. When any radioactive atom disintegrates, the particles and rays it emits can be detected by a sensitive Geiger counter nearby. This effect provides a way of tracing the paths taken by atoms and of locating atoms that have entered into or deposited on other material. In a way, this radioactive property is a *tag* by which a group of radioactive atoms may be identified.

The use of radioactive atoms as "tracers" is quite extensive in medical research, physiology, biology, and agriculture, where scientists are studying the motion of the blood and other fluids through living tissues. Physicists, chemists, and engineers are using "tagged" atoms in studying such problems as fuels and engine wear. Radioactive isotopes are replacing radium in the treatment of a number of diseases.

Cosmic Rays

Cosmic rays come into our atmosphere constantly day and night from all directions of outer space. The few ions always present in the air are caused by cosmic rays. These rays have been the subject of extensive study. Primary cosmic rays are generally believed to be very high-speed protons (billions of electron-volts) and possibly electrons. These are natural atomic missiles on a large scale. When these missiles strike atoms of air in the upper atmosphere, they break up these atoms and give rise to secondary cosmic rays. These secondary rays are very energetic alpha and beta particles and penetrating gamma rays, as well as other fragments of the smashed atoms. Photographic plates, Geiger counters, and cloud chambers are used to detect and record these rays.

The origin of cosmic rays is not known for certain. Some scientists believe they may come from the sun; others hold the view that cosmic rays come from interstellar space deep in the heavens beyond our solar system.

RADIOACTIVE PHOSPHORUS — P32
FOR STUDY OF PHOSPHATE FERTILIZER UPTAKE

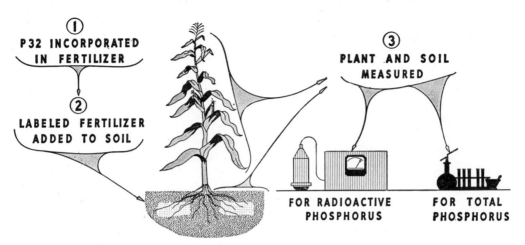

① P32 INCORPORATED IN FERTILIZER

② LABELED FERTILIZER ADDED TO SOIL

③ PLANT AND SOIL MEASURED

FOR RADIOACTIVE PHOSPHORUS

FOR TOTAL PHOSPHORUS

SHOWS:

1- FIXATION OF PHOSPHORUS BY SOIL
2- PHOSPHORUS UPTAKE BY PLANT
3- PROPER TYPE AND PLACEMENT OF FERTILIZER
4- EFFICIENCY OF FERTILIZER

Radioactive phosphorus atoms may be added to commercial fertilizer placed in the ground near the cornstalk. The amount of this fertilizer taken up by the stalk can then be measured by means of a Geiger counter held near the stalk. This illustrates the tracer technique used in many fields of scientific research. (*Isotopes Division, U.S. Atomic Energy Commission, Oak Ridge, Tenn.*)

Radioactivity in Biology

Sources of high-energy atomic particles and gamma rays have to be surrounded by a good absorbing shield, such as thick lead walls or heavy concrete masonry (or even water) to protect those who work nearby. As with X-rays, the early workers with radioactive materials did not know the danger to which they were exposed. Both Becquerel and Marie Curie are said to have received superficial burns from contact with the material with which they worked.

As previously stated, *any form of energy that can produce ionization can injure or kill living tissue,* if the exposure is great enough. You have seen that alpha and beta particles, neutrons, and gamma rays can all produce ionization in gases and liquids that absorb them. This is why radioactivity is dangerous and why radioactive materials must be handled with great care.

The dosage or exposure depends both on the intensity of the radiation and the length of time a person is exposed to it. The immediate effect of a large overdosage is often nausea and "radiation

Film badges worn by workers in radioactive areas. The films are developed and the total amount of radiation to which the wearer has been exposed is determined from the degree of blackening of the film. (*Tracerlab, Inc.*)

sickness." Like those of X-rays, the effects of radiation on the body are cumulative. The effect of a second exposure may add to that of an earlier exposure unless there is sufficient time between exposures for the body to recover. In some cases the effects of exposure to radiation may be delayed and may not be noticed for days after the exposure. Some biological effects attributed to extreme overexposure to radiation are: loss of hair, destruction of bones, decrease in number of white blood cells, cancer, and mutation (change in the inherited characteristics of the offspring).

Power from Atoms

An atomic reactor converts nuclear energy chiefly into heat. To use this energy for mechanical work, this heat may be used to produce steam, which in turn may operate a steam engine or a turbine. Experimental power reactors are in operation and others are under construction. These units are massive

556

and expensive. Heavy walls are required to shield the reactor for the safety of the persons operating it. Disposal of the radioactive waste products of the reactor presents another difficult problem. Nuclear power plants are difficult to devise for driving planes, ships, trains, and automobiles. Considerable progress has been made in this direction, however, and it seems possible that means of using nuclear power in some everyday applications may eventually be developed.

The cost of uranium-235 is estimated at $10,000 to $25,000 per pound. One pound of this fuel contains as much available energy as 2,000 tons of coal. This would make the cost of uranium fuel equivalent to that of coal at $10 to $25 a ton.

The production and processing of uranium in the United States are under the direct control of the Atomic Energy Commission. The amounts of U^{235} and Pu^{239} actually produced and available have not been disclosed.

The H-bomb

In recent years the efforts of a large group of scientific workers have been directed toward the development and production of a nuclear *fusion* type of bomb. In this bomb isotopes of hydrogen would be induced to react and *fuse* to form helium and release enormous amounts of energy in the form of heat and radioactivity, as discussed on p. 548. This hydrogen fusion bomb is commonly called a thermonuclear or H-bomb.

Several thermonuclear reactions between hydrogen isotopes are believed to be possible. All require high temperature and high pressure to start, and all release larger amounts of energy than are usually obtained from nuclear *fission* reactions in which nuclei split apart. One possible thermonuclear reaction would start with deuterons, $_1H^2$ (nuclei of deuterium atoms) and tritons, $_1H^3$ (nuclei of tritium atoms). If a triton and a deuteron interact, they may possibly produce an alpha particle (helium nucleus), a neutron, and a large amount of energy, as indicated in this equation:

$$_1H^3 + _1H^2 \rightarrow _2He^4 + _0n^1 + \text{energy}$$

These hydrogen isotopes might be enclosed within an ordinary fission-type atomic bomb, which, when detonated, might furnish the high temperature and pressure necessary to start the nuclear fusion reaction of the hydrogen isotopes. A bomb of this type could be many times more powerful than the fission bomb alone. Since there is no critical mass for the hydrogen isotopes, an H-bomb could probably be made as large or as small as desired without danger of a chain reaction setting it off. However, size of possible H-bombs may be limited by means of transportation.

The first atomic submarine engine, contained in a land-based submarine hull shown here, was generating power when this picture was taken inside the main building at the Submarine Reactor Test Station, in Idaho. The large sea tank is about 50 ft in diameter and almost 40 ft high. The submarine hull passes through the tank so that the reactor compartment is located within the tank and completely submerged in water. This Mark I power plant was the pilot plant for the Mark II reactor, which was installed in the U.S.S. "Nautilus," the first atomic power-driven submarine. Both the Mark I and the Mark II plants were built by the Westinghouse Electric Corporation, under contract with the Atomic Energy Commission. Installation of both plants in the submarine hulls was done by the Electric Boat Division of General Dynamics Corporation, builder of the "Nautilus." (*Westinghouse Electric Corporation*)

Application of Nuclear Power

Every great scientific discovery and its development have given rise to social, economic, and sometimes political problems. The discovery of a new and almost unlimited source of power within atoms has created problems for which the solution may be vital to the welfare of our civilization. Our potential sources of physical power are more vast than ever before. *How will this power be used?*

It can be used in bombs and other weapons to spread destruction and death, and perhaps make whole areas uninhabitable for many years. It can be used to spread destruction faster and more effectively than any other physical power known. This new form of energy could lead to the destruction of our present civilization.

On the other hand, there are possibilities of harnessing the energy from the nuclei of tiny atoms to advance medical knowledge; to assist experimental work in agriculture which may make food more abundant; to take over much of the work of the world now done by our diminishing supplies of coal and oil; and thus to make the world a better and more pleasant place in which to live.

Some of you may become atomic scientists or engage in occupations utilizing nuclear energy. You may play important roles in this drama of nuclear power. As citizens of our country all of you may have a voice in deciding how this new source of power will be used.

▶Do You Know?

1. Why could isotopes not be discovered by chemical separation methods?
2. What radioactive isotopes are most commonly used in hospitals for treatment of patients?
3. What special precautions are taken to protect workers who handle radioactive materials in hospitals, laboratories, and industries?
4. When coal burns, carbon atoms of the coal unite with oxygen atoms of the air to form carbon dioxide gas molecules. Heat energy is released by this chemical reaction. In what respect does this reaction differ from an atomic fission, which also releases heat?
5. What is meant by a hydrogen bomb?

HIGHLIGHTS

Atomic missiles useful for bombarding the nuclei of atoms are *electrons, protons, deuterons, alpha particles,* and *neutrons.*

The *cyclotron* is used to speed up atomic missiles.

In *nuclear fission,* mass disappears and energy appears according to Einstein's equation
$$E = m \times c^2$$

In *nuclear fusion* of light atoms into heavier ones, mass also disappears and energy appears.

A *chain reaction* may occur when a heavy atom such as uranium-235 undergoes fission.

Neptunium and *plutonium* are synthetic chemical elements produced in an atomic pile.

An *atomic pile* or *reactor* may be used for obtaining heat energy from atomic fuel.

Radioactive isotopes are used as tracers in research work, in medicine, and other sciences.

THINGS TO DO

1. List as many practical uses as you can find for radioactive isotopes made in nuclear reactors or by other means. Consult your local or school library.

2. Find out what is meant by a breeder reactor. What new fissionable material is produced in this type of reactor? Why does this process give promise of much more complete use of uranium than is possible in the ordinary type of reactor? Consult your local or school library.

3. Find out what progress has been made to date in the development of practical power plants to utilize the energy from nuclear reactions. Are any such power plants in actual operation? Consult your local or school library.

4. Look up information on any practical nuclear power plants which are being developed for use on airplanes, ships, submarines, or for industrial power applications of the future.

Index

NUCLEAR REACTOR

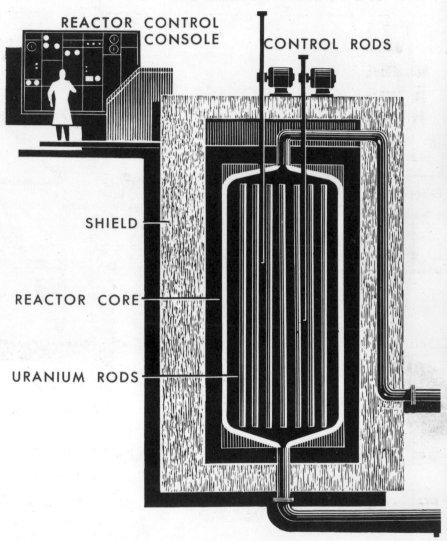

REACTOR CONTROL CONSOLE

CONTROL RODS

SHIELD

REACTOR CORE

URANIUM RODS

Heat produced by the atomic fission process in the advanced type reactor, left, would be absorbed by a liquid metal passing through the reactor core. The liquid metal then is piped to a water boiler, lower center, where steam is produced. The steam would drive a turbine generator, center, producing electricity.

North American Aviation, Inc.